ANALOG AND
DIGITAL FILTERS:
DESIGN AND REALIZATION

**PRENTICE-HALL SERIES IN ELECTRICAL
AND COMPUTER ENGINEERING**

Leon O. Chua, Editor

Chua and Lin, COMPUTER-AIDED ANALYSIS OF ELECTRONIC CIRCUITS:
ALGORITHMS AND COMPUTATIONAL TECHNIQUES
Lam, ANALOG AND DIGITAL FILTERS: DESIGN AND REALIZATION

ANALOG AND DIGITAL FILTERS: DESIGN AND REALIZATION

HARRY Y-F. LAM

Bell Telephone Laboratories, Inc.
Formerly with University of California, Berkeley

PRENTICE-HALL, INC., *Englewood Cliffs, New Jersey* 07632

Library of Congress Cataloging in Publication Data

Lam, Harry Y-F. (date)
Analog and digital filters.

(Prentice-Hall series in electrical and computer engineering)
Includes bibliographical references and index.
1. Electric filters. I. Title.
TK7872.F5L26   621.3815'32   78-6434
ISBN 0-13-032755-7

© 1979 by Prentice-Hall, Inc., Englewood Cliffs, N.J. 07632

Printed in the United States of America

10   9   8   7   6

PRENTICE-HALL INTERNATIONAL, INC., *London*
PRENTICE-HALL OF AUSTRALIA PTY. LIMITED, *Sydney*
PRENTICE-HALL OF CANADA, LTD., *Toronto*
PRENTICE-HALL OF INDIA PRIVATE LIMITED, *New Delhi*
PRENTICE-HALL OF JAPAN, INC., *Tokyo*
PRENTICE-HALL OF SOUTHEAST ASIA PTE. LTD., *Singapore*
WHITEHALL BOOKS LIMITED, *Wellington, New Zealand*

To my parents   *Lam, Kwai-Choi and Pak-Kam*

To my wife   *Alice*

CONTENTS

11 INTRODUCTION TO DIGITAL FILTERS   462

linear

12 DESIGN OF DIGITAL FILTERS   518

Theoretical   Approach

13 REALIZATION OF DIGITAL FILTERS   581

Practical   Approach

PREFACE

The basic concept of a filter was originally introduced by G. Campbell and K. Wagner independently in 1915 in relation with their work on transmission lines and vibrating systems. Since then, the development of filter knowledge and filter technologies has been and is still expanding. Today, filters have permeated the electronic technology so much that it is difficult to think of any moderately complex system or device that does not employ a filter in one form or another.

This book is a result of a junior/senior filter design course organized and taught by the author at the University of California, Berkeley. The course was developed with two purposes in mind. One is to give students some of the basic knowledge and the tools of filter design, with the modest aim that students will be able to do some simple (analog and digital) filter design work after completion of the course. The other purpose is to provide students with a solid background for more advanced courses in analog and digital filters. The prerequisite of the course is the two-quarter course sequence on the book *Basic Circuit Theory*, by C. A. Desoer and E. S. Kuh.

The basic approach of this book is practical. The treatment is simple and yet brings out the substance of the subject matter. Intuitive (and theoretically sound) arguments are used to explain the theory with extensive examples to illustrate the design techniques and procedures. The book leads the students step-by-step from the elementary to the fairly advanced topics. When the level of the material is beyond that assumed, the author gives references to relevant literature. As a result, the book should serve equally well as a text for a filter design course for junior/senior students and as a guide on filters to the practicing engineers who desire a good solid introduction to the field. It is the intention of the author that the book may be readily understood by a reader who has had a first course (or two courses) in circuit theory.

The book is closely coordinated to give students and readers a maximum amount of exposure to the many subject matters in the field. In Chapters 1 through 4, the author develops the fundamentals of analog filter design. Chapter 2 covers the building blocks of both passive and active filters. Chapter 3 introduces the properties of network functions. The implications of Hilbert transform, the concept of minimum phase functions, and the various procedures to construct network functions are discussed. Chapter 4 deals with Hurwitz polynomials and positive real functions, which form a mathematical foundation for passive networks.

In Chapters 5 through 7, the author considers the problem of passive circuit realizations. With the concept of positive real functions established in Chapter 4, the author examines the properties associated with RC and LC driving-point functions in Chapters 5 and 6. Based on these properties, realization techniques for RC and LC driving-point functions are derived. Chapter 7 applies these techniques to realize various classes of transfer functions. In particular, RC, LC, and Darlington ladder circuits are developed to synthesize transfer functions of low-pass, bandpass, and high-pass types; lattice circuits are used to realize all-pass transfer functions.

Chapter 8 examines the problem of finding appropriate transfer functions. The magnitude-selective filters of Butterworth and Chebyshev and the group delay Bessel filters are discussed in great detail. Supplementary graphs and tables as design aids are also included. Chapter 9 introduces the concept of sensitivity. Chapter 10 deals with active filters. Two basic approaches are considered. The direct approach involves the realization of passive RC 1-ports and 2-ports. The indirect approach is concerned primarily with second-order active-filter realizations. Both single-amplifier and multiple-amplifier techniques are considered. The advantages and disadvantages of each technique are discussed. Chapter 10 also examines the effect of nonideal operational amplifiers on circuit performance. Finally, a class of active circuits containing only operational amplifiers and resistors (called active R circuits) is introduced. This class of circuits is shown to be versatile in high-frequency applications.

Digital filters are discussed in Chapters 11 through 13. Chapter 11 presents the background material for digital filters including z-transforms, inverse z-transofrms, discrete Fourier transforms, frequency responses, sampling theorems, and the building blocks for digital filters. Chapter 12 develops techniques to obtain appropriate digital transfer functions. (A good understanding of Chapter 8 is required here.) The impulse invariance method and the bilinear transformation method are examined in detail. Chapter 13 deals with the realization of digital filters. A technique to eliminate delay-free loops is also presented.

A full set of problems, designed to enhance and to extend the presentation, is included at the end of each chapter. Most of these problems have been class-tested to ensure that their levels of difficulty and their degrees of complexity are proper for the students. To avoid assigning the same problems over successive years, every exercise contains problems having similar parts that differ only in their numerical parameters and in other trivial details.

The author would like to thank Professors J.D. McPherson of University of Wisconsin, Milwaukee, and K.A. Stromsmoe of University of Alberta for reading the complete final manuscript of this book. He also would like to acknowledge the contributions of the many students who took the course in 1974–1976; their enthusiastic class participation and feedback are invaluable information for the revisions and improvements made on the earlier versions. It is the pleasure of the author to express his appreciation to Professors L.O. Chua, C.A. Desoer, and E.S. Kuh of University of California, Berkeley, and Messrs. F.J. Witt, C.F. Kurth, and R.P. Snicer of Bell Telephone Laboratories, North Andover, Massachusetts, for their encouragement, constructive criticism, and moral support. Thanks are also due to the Department of Electrical Engineering and Computer Science of University of California, Berkeley, for providing a wonderful environment under which the work on this book was substantially completed.

Finally, the author would like to express his gratitude and appreciation to his wife Alice, who copied the first two versions of the manuscript (for students' use) and who maintained peace and quiet in their home.

HARRY Y-F. LAM

ANALOG AND
DIGITAL FILTERS:
DESIGN AND REALIZATION

1

INTRODUCTION

In the most general sense, a "filter" is a device or a system that alters in a prescribed way the input that passes through it. In essence, a filter converts inputs into outputs in such a fashion that certain desirable features of the inputs are retained in the outputs while undesirable features are suppressed. There are many kinds of filters; only a few examples are given here. In automobiles, the oil filter removes unwanted particles that are suspended in the oil passing through the filter; the air filter passes air but prevents dirt and dust from reaching the carburetor. Colored glass may be used as an optical filter to absorb light of certain wavelengths, thus altering the light that reaches the sensitized film in a camera.

An electrical filter is designed to separate and pass a desired signal from a mixture of desired and undesired signals. Typical examples of complex electrical filters are televisions and radios. More specifically, when a television is turned to a particular channel, say Channel 2, it will pass those signals (audio and visual) transmitted by Channel 2 and block out all other signals. On a smaller scale, filters are basic electronic components in many communication systems such as the telephone, television, radio, radar, and sonar. Electrical filters can also be found in power conversion circuits and power systems in general. In fact, electrical filters permeate modern technology so much that it is difficult to think of any moderately complex electronic device that does not employ a filter in one form or another.

Electrical filters may be classified in a number of ways. *Analog* filters are used to process analog or continuous-time signals; *digital* filters are used to process digital signals (discrete-time signals with quantized magnitude

1

levels).[1] Analog filters may be classified as *lumped* or *distributed* depending on the frequency ranges for which they are designed.[2] Finally, analog filters may also be classified as *passive* or *active* depending on the type of elements used in their realizations.

In more abstract terms, a filter is a system characterized by a set of *input–output* pairs or *excitation–response* pairs, as shown in Fig. 1-1, where

$$y(t) = \int_0^\infty h(t - \tau)\, x(\tau)\, d\tau \tag{1-1}$$

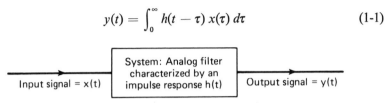

Fig. 1-1 A filter is a system with a set of prescribed input–output properties.

In writing (1-1), we assume that the single-input–single-output analog filter under consideration is *causal, linear, lumped,* and *time-invariant* and that $h(t)$ is the *impulse response* of the filter. The Laplace transform of (1-1) gives

$$Y(s) = H(s)X(s) \tag{1-2}$$

where $Y(s)$, $H(s)$, and $X(s)$ are respectively the Laplace transforms of $y(t)$, $h(t)$, and $x(t)$. Here, the filter is characterized by $H(s)$, the transfer function (or the frequency response function when $s = j\omega$) of the filter.[3] Because either s or $j\omega$ is a complex variable, $H(s)$ or $H(j\omega)$ is a complex quantity. That is, $H(j\omega)$ has a *real part* $\text{Re}\,[H(j\omega)]$ and an *imaginary part* $\text{Im}\,[H(j\omega)]$, and

$$H(j\omega) = \text{Re}\,[H(j\omega)] + j\,\text{Im}\,[H(j\omega)] \tag{1-3}$$

In terms of polar representation, we can write

$$H(j\omega) = |H(j\omega)|\, e^{j\underline{/H(j\omega)}} \tag{1-4}$$

where $|H(j\omega)|$ and $\underline{/H(j\omega)}$ denote respectively the *magnitude* and the *phase lead angle* of $H(j\omega)$, with

$$|H(j\omega)|^2 = \{\text{Re}\,[H(j\omega)]\}^2 + \{\text{Im}\,[H(j\omega)]\}^2$$
$$= H(j\omega)H(-j\omega) \tag{1-5}$$

$$\underline{/H(j\omega)} = \tan^{-1}\frac{\text{Im}\,[H(j\omega)]}{\text{Re}\,[H(j\omega)]} \tag{1-6}$$

---

[1] We discuss digital filters in Chapter 11. In the following discussion, we deal with analog filters and continuous-time systems only.

[2] In this book, we consider lumped filters only.

[3] In sinusoidal steady-state analysis, we let $s = j\omega$.

$$\text{Re}\,[H(j\omega)] = |H(j\omega)|\cos\underline{/H(j\omega)} \tag{1-7}$$

$$\text{Im}\,[H(j\omega)] = |H(j\omega)|\sin\underline{/H(j\omega)} \tag{1-8}$$

Note that the last equality of (1-5) holds because all coefficients of $H(s)$ are assumed to be real.

1-1 MAGNITUDE FUNCTION

As mentioned previously, the general purpose of an electrical filter is to separate and pass a desired signal from a mixture of desired and undesired signals. In the case of a radio receiver, the signal going into the receiver is a mixture of electrical noise and signals from all the radio stations in the area including the desired station. By tuning the radio receiver to a particular frequency setting, we filter out "all" the signals from the undesired stations and pass the signal transmitted by the desired station. Because of the limitations of causal systems, we can neither build a receiver that will pass one particular frequency, ω_p, and reject all other frequencies, nor can we build a broadcasting station that will broadcast at ω_p exactly. Consequently, we build a filter that will pass signals within an interval of frequencies $(\omega_{p_1}, \omega_{p_2})$ containing ω_p and reject all others, where the words "pass" and "reject" are used in a relative sense rather than in an absolute sense.

From (1-2), we have

$$|Y(j\omega)| = |H(j\omega)||X(j\omega)| \tag{1-9}$$

$$\underline{/Y(j\omega)} = \underline{/H(j\omega)} + \underline{/X(j\omega)} \tag{1-10}$$

Equation (1-9) says that the magnitude of the output signal is the product of the magnitudes of the input signal and the frequency response function of the filter. This means that if a filter has a magnitude function $|H(j\omega)|$ equal to *zero* (or approximately equal to zero) for a certain frequency range, say between ω_{s_1} and ω_{s_2}, then the output signal will have a zero (or an approximately zero) magnitude if the frequency of the input signal is within this frequency band of $(\omega_{s_1}, \omega_{s_2})$. Thus, the interval $(\omega_{s_1}, \omega_{s_2})$ is called the *stopband* of the filter. Similarly, if the magnitude function $|H(j\omega)|$ is greater than or equal to some number close to *one* within the frequency band $(\omega_{p_1}, \omega_{p_2})$, then $(\omega_{p_1}, \omega_{p_2})$ is called the *passband* of the filter.[4] This name is given because if the input frequency is within $(\omega_{p_1}, \omega_{p_2})$, then the output signal is an enhanced or at worst a slightly attenuated version of the input signal. In addition, we define a *transitional band* as a band of frequencies between a passband and a stopband. A specification on the magnitude of the frequency

---

[4]The *one* here may be interpreted as a *unit* normalized with respect to a magnitude reference.

response function of a filter may include specifications on passbands and stopbands as well as transitional bands.

Based on (1-9), we can define the following five basic types of frequency selective filters:

1. *Low-Pass* filter—A filter whose passband is from 0 to some frequency ω_p and whose stopband extends from some frequency ω_s to infinity, where $\omega_p < \omega_s$.
2. *High-Pass* filter—A filter whose passband is from some frequency ω_p to infinity and whose stop band is from 0 to ω_s, where $\omega_s < \omega_p$.
3. *Bandpass* filter—A filter whose passband is from some frequency ω_{p_1} to some other frequency ω_{p_2} and whose stopbands are from 0 to ω_{s_1} and from ω_{s_2} to ∞, where $\omega_{s_1} < \omega_{p_1} < \omega_{p_2} < \omega_{s_2}$.
4. *Band-Reject* filter—A filter whose passbands are from 0 to ω_{p_1} and from ω_{p_2} to ∞ and whose stopband is from ω_{s_1} to ω_{s_2}, where $\omega_{p_1} < \omega_{s_1} < \omega_{s_2} < \omega_{p_2}$.
5. *All-Pass* filter—A filter whose magnitude is 1 for all frequencies (i.e., whose passband is from 0 to ∞). This type of filter is used mainly for phase compensation and phase shifting purposes.

These five basic types of frequency selective filters are illustrated in Fig. 1-2. Of course, there are filters that do not belong to any one of these five

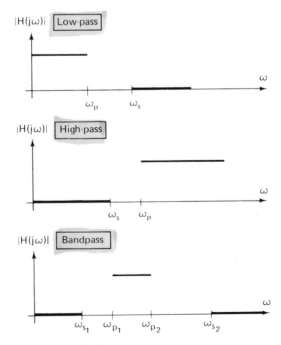

Fig. 1-2   Five basic types of frequency-selective filters.

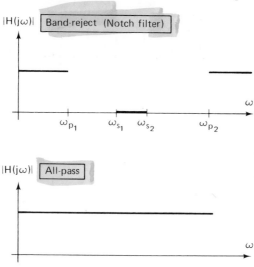

Fig. 1-2 (Continued)

types. In most cases of interest, the magnitude specifications of filters will fall into one of these five basic categories or a combination of these five types. A case in point is a filter whose magnitude specification is given in Fig. 1-3(a). This filter can be considered a combination of a low-pass and four bandpass filters, as shown in Fig. 1-3(b).

To illustrate some uses of some of these filters, let us consider the following two examples:

1. In transmitting a low-frequency signal $X_0(t)$, such as a voice signal, over a distance, it is imperative to modulate this low-frequency signal with a high-frequency signal carrier before transmitting. There are a number of ways to modulate a signal. Figure 1-4 is a schematic diagram of a double sideband amplitude modulation. At the receiver, the transmitted signal $X_1(t)$ goes through a mixer where the transmitted signal is multiplied by a signal at the modulating frequency. In order to recover the desired low-frequency signal $X_0(t)$, the output signal of the mixer $X_2(t)$ is passed through a low-pass filter with a passband containing $[0, \omega_L]$ and a stopband containing the frequencies from $(2\omega_H - \omega_L)$ to infinity.

2. In long distance communication, a line carries many signals simultaneously. This is accomplished by employing frequency multiplexing— each of the low-frequency input signals are frequency translated to a different center frequency, as shown in Fig. 1-5(a), where ω_i is the center frequency of the ith low-frequency signal. At the receiving end, the transmitted signal is fed through a band of parallel bandpass filters to corresponding message receivers, as shown in Figure 1-5(b).

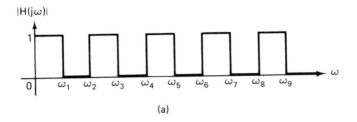

(a)

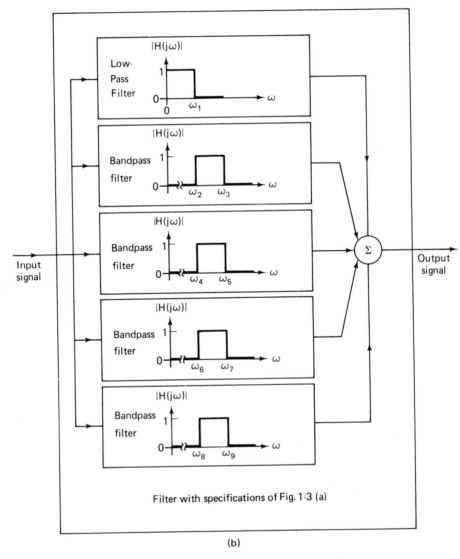

Filter with specifications of Fig. 1-3 (a)

(b)

Fig. 1-3 An example of a decomposable filter.

6

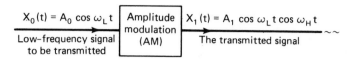

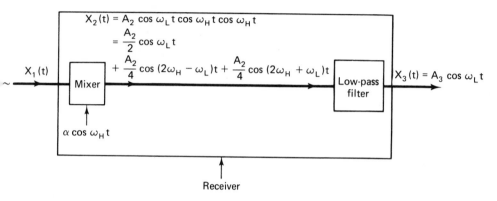

Fig. 1-4 A schematic diagram of a double sideband amplitude modulation.

Of course, there are cases in which none of the five basic types of filters is adequate. A specific case in point is as follows:

Consider a transatlantic coaxial submarine cable that is approximately 2000 miles long. The frequency band utilized is from 20 KHz to 164 KHz.[5] This band is divided into 36 telephone channels, each with a bandwidth of 4 KHz. Because of copper and electric loss in the cable, the signals are attenuated. For the highest-frequency channel, the cable loss over the 2000-mile distance is approximately 3200 dB.[6] For the lowest-frequency channel, the loss over the same distance is approximately 1100 dB. In other words, if we assume the input signal has a 1-volt amplitude level, then at the end of the 2000-mile cable, the highest channel will have a voltage amplitude level of 10^{-160} volts, and the lowest channel's signal level will be at 10^{-55} volts. Clearly, amplification is needed. As a consequence, amplifying repeaters are located at 40-mile intervals along the cable. This means that each amplifier must supply a gain of 22 dB to the lowest channel but 64 dB to the highest

---

[5]To cut down on costs for long distance communications, it is desirable to carry as many channels per line as possible. But because signal amplitude losses are higher at higher frequencies, there is a limit on the number of channels a line can carry. For the same reason, even though the frequency variable ω can take on any value between 0 and ∞, there is a *limited* band (assigned to each station by FCC) that can be used for radio and television broadcastings. Beyond a certain frequency limit, signal transmission is highly impractical.

[6]Magnitude loss in dB $\triangleq -20 \log |H(j\omega)| = -10 \log |H(j\omega)|^2$. Magnitude gain in dB $\triangleq 20 \log |H(j\omega)| = 10 \log |H(j\omega)|^2$.

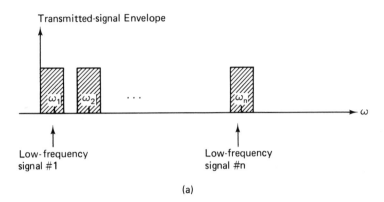

(a)

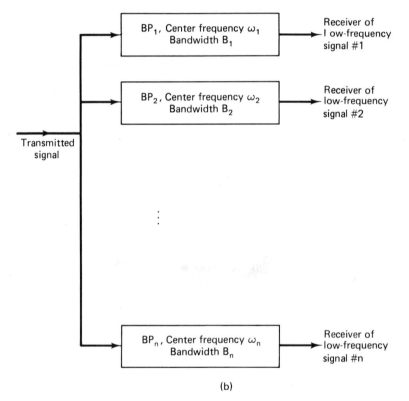

(b)

Fig. 1-5 A schematic diagram for frequency multiplexing.

channel and somewhere in between to the intermediate channels. Each amplifier will have a frequency response curve similar to the one shown in Figure 1-6.

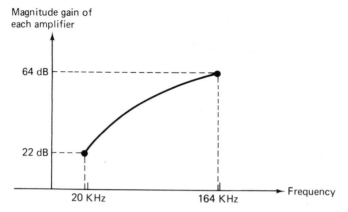

Magnitude gain of
each amplifier

Fig. 1-6   An example of a magnitude filter that is not a linear combination of the five basic types of frequency selective filters.

1-2   PHASE AND GROUP DELAY FUNCTIONS

So far, we have only considered the magnitude portion of the frequency response function of a filter; let us now examine the other portion that characterizes a filter, namely, its *phase angle* $\phi(\omega)$, or equivalently, its *group delay* function $\tau(\omega)$ defined by[7]

$$\phi(\omega) \triangleq -\underline{/H(j\omega)} \tag{1-11}$$

$$\tau(\omega) \triangleq \frac{d}{d\omega}\phi(\omega) = -\frac{d}{d\omega}\underline{/H(j\omega)} \tag{1-12}$$

To understand the physical implication of the phase angle or group delay function of a filter, let us study the following two cases:

Consider first a filter with a specification

$$\begin{aligned} H_1(j\omega) &= 1 \quad \text{for} \quad -\omega_c \le \omega \le \omega_c \\ &= 0 \quad \text{otherwise} \end{aligned} \tag{1-13}$$

that is, a filter with a zero phase angle and consequently zero group delay for all ω. The impulse response is given by

$$\begin{aligned} h_1(t) &= \frac{1}{2\pi}\int_{-\infty}^{\infty} H_1(j\omega)\,e^{j\omega t}\,d\omega = \frac{1}{2\pi}\int_{-\omega_c}^{\omega_c} e^{j\omega t}\,d\omega \\ &= \frac{1}{\pi t}\frac{1}{2j}[\exp(j\omega_c t) - \exp(-j\omega_c t)] \\ &= \frac{1}{\pi t}\sin\omega_c t = \frac{\omega_c}{\pi}\frac{\sin\omega_c t}{\omega_c t} \end{aligned} \tag{1-14}$$

when $H(j\omega)=1$

---

[7]In general, by phase angle, we mean the *phase lag* angle $\phi(\omega)$. $\underline{/H(j\omega)}$ is called the *phase lead* angle.

Now consider the second filter characterized by

$$H_2(j\omega) = 1 \exp\left[-j\frac{k\pi\omega}{2\omega_c}\right] \quad \text{for} \quad -\omega_c \leq \omega \leq \omega_c \tag{1-15}$$

$$= 0 \qquad\qquad\qquad \text{otherwise}$$

This filter differs from the last one just by the phase lag angle in the passband. The impulse response is given by

$$h_2(t) = \frac{\omega_c}{\pi} \frac{\sin\left(\omega_c t - \frac{k\pi}{2}\right)}{\omega_c t - \frac{k\pi}{2}} \tag{1-16}$$

Comparing (1-14) and (1-16), we see that the latter filter has a time lag of $(k\pi)/(2\omega_c)$ from the former one, as indicated in Figure 1-7. Notice that the group delay of the second filter,

$$\tau(\omega) = \frac{d}{d\omega}\left(\frac{k\pi\omega}{2\omega_c}\right) = \frac{k\pi}{2\omega_c} = T_d \tag{1-17}$$

is equal to the time delay in its impulse response.

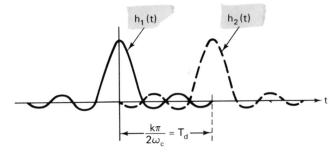

Fig. 1-7 An example illustrating the effect of group delay.

A comparison of the impulse responses of these two filters indicates that there is a direct relationship between the group delay of the filter [equivalently, the phase lag angle], and the time delay of its impulse response. In fact, (1-17) holds in all cases.

To be more precise, let us consider a filter characterized by a transfer function

$$H(s) = Ke^{-st_o} \tag{1-18}$$

Hence, the group delay function of the filter is

$$\tau(\omega) = -\frac{d}{d\omega}(-\omega t_o) = t_o \tag{1-19}$$

If we excite this filter with an input

$$x(t) = u(t - T_o) \tag{1-20}$$

where $u(t)$ represents the unit step function, then the output $y(t)$ will be given by

$$y(t) = Ku[t - (t_o + T_o)] \tag{1-21}$$

This implies that the group delay of a filter is essentially equal to $t_{out} - t_{in}$, where t_{in} is the time when the input attains its steady-state value, and t_{out} is the time when the output settles down to its steady-state condition.

If determination of the time when the signal enters the filter is of great importance in applications such as radar systems, the filters involved in the processing of returning signals are required to have a phase angle as linear as possible or, equivalently, a group delay function as close to a constant as possible. Note that a small deviation from a linear phase angle will distort the impulse response in many ways and hence introduce error in time estimation of the arriving signals.

Speech processing is another area in which linear phase filters find applications. Consider the case when a speech signal is passing through a filter having a phase characteristic shown in Figure 1-8. In this case, the high-frequency components of the speech signal will come through the filter before the low-frequency components. Consequently, the output will be a highly distorted version of the input. Clearly, this is undesirable in many speech-processing applications.

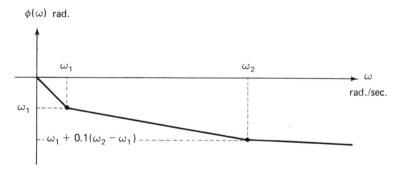

Fig. 1-8   An example illustrating the effect of a nonlinear phase filter.

It is well known that lumped analog filters can not have a perfect linear phase over the entire ω-axis.[8] Hence, when a linear phase filter is required, one should determine the frequency range of application and then design a filter having a linear phase characteristic over the frequency band of interest.

---

[8]Finite-impulse response digital filters can be designed to have a linear phase characteristic over *all* frequencies.

1-3 DESIGN PROCEDURE

Once the amplitude and the phase angle or group delay of a filter are specified, the filter is completely characterized. A design procedure such as the one shown in Fig. 1-9 can be used to realize a practical filter to meet the prescribed signal-processing requirements.

In Fig. 1-9, Step 1 contains the specifications of the desired filters. It may contain amplitude specifications on passbands and stopbands, transition bandwidths, phase angle or group delay specifications, and other desirable features such as input impedance level, output impedance level, signal level, size, weight, and cost. Step 2 specifies the task of finding an appropriate

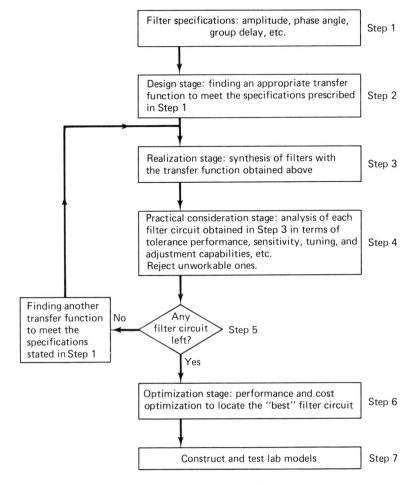

Fig. 1-9 A design procedure.

transfer function to meet the filter specifications as prescribed in Step 1. The choice will be influenced by the frequency range of operation, sensitivity of the zeros and poles, impedance levels, and so forth. Step 3 deals with the circuit realizations of the transfer function obtained in Step 2. Because no electrical components are ideal, the filters obtained in Step 3 will have to go through tolerance studies to determine their validity in practice, as indicated in Step 4. If none of the circuits obtained in Step 3 is satisfactory, then we may return to Step 2, or we may lower our standard of performance and start Step 4 over. If there are circuits left after Step 4, then a cost and performance optimization procedure will be used to determine the "best" circuit, as shown in Step 6. Once that is done, a real laboratory model can be built and tested to serve as a prototype for further investigation.

In this book, we consider primarily the tasks invoved in Steps 2, 3, and 4.

REFERENCES AND FURTHER READING

[1]   KUH, E. S., and PEDERSON, D. O. *Principles of Circuit Synthesis*. New York: McGraw-Hill, 1959.

[2]   WEINBERG, L. *Network Analysis and Synthesis*. Huntington, N.Y.: R. E. Krieger, 1975.

[3]   HUMPHREYS, D. S. *The Analysis, Design, and Synthesis of Electrical Filters*. Englewood Cliffs, N.J.: Prentice-Hall, Inc., 1970.

[4]   TEMES, G. C., and MITRA, S. K. *Modern Filter Theory and Design*. New York: Wiley-Interscience, 1973.

[5]   STOVER, W. A. *Circuit Design for Audio, AM/FM and TV*. New York: McGraw-Hill, 1967.

PROBLEMS

1-1. For each of the following $H(s)$, find the corresponding Re $[H(j\omega)]$, Im $[H(j\omega)]$, $|H(j\omega)|$, $\underline{/H(j\omega)}$, $\phi(\omega)$, and $\tau(\omega)$.

(a) $H(s) = \dfrac{1}{s+1}$

(b) $H(s) = \dfrac{s}{s+1}$

(c) $H(s) = \dfrac{1}{s^2+s+1}$

(d) $H(s) = \dfrac{s}{s^2+s+1}$

(e) $H(s) = \dfrac{s^2}{s^2+s+1}$

(f) $H(s) = \dfrac{3}{s^2 + 3s + 3}$

(g) $H(s) = \dfrac{3s}{s^2 + 3s + 3}$

(h) $H(s) = \dfrac{s^2}{s^2 + 3s + 3}$

(i) $H(s) = \dfrac{1}{s^2 + \sqrt{2}\,s + 1}$

(j) $H(s) = \dfrac{\sqrt{2}\,s}{s^2 + \sqrt{2}\,s + 1}$

(k) $H(s) = \dfrac{s^2}{s^2 + \sqrt{2}s + 1}$

1-2. Sketch the magnitude functions of the following $H(s)$.

(a) $H(s) = \dfrac{1}{s + 1}$

(b) $H(s) = \dfrac{s}{s + 1}$

(c) $H(s) = \dfrac{1}{s^2 + s + 1}$

(d) $H(s) = \dfrac{s}{s^2 + s + 1}$

(e) $H(s) = \dfrac{s^2}{s^2 + s + 1}$

1-3. Sketch the phase and group delay functions of the following $H(s)$.

(a) $H(s) = \dfrac{1}{s + 1}$

(b) $H(s) = \dfrac{s}{s + 1}$

(c) $H(s) = \dfrac{1}{s^2 + 3s + 3}$

(d) $H(s) = \dfrac{s}{s^2 + \sqrt{2}\,s + 1}$

(e) $H(s) = \dfrac{s^2}{s^2 + s + 1}$

1-4. Show that the following statements are true.

(a) $\text{Re}\,[H(j\omega)] = \text{Re}\,[H(-j\omega)]$

(b) $\text{Im}\,[H(j\omega)] = -\text{Im}\,[H(-j\omega)]$

(c) $|H(j\omega)| = |H(-j\omega)|$

(d) $\underline{/H(j\omega)} = -\underline{/H(-j\omega)}$

(e) $\phi(\omega) = -\phi(-\omega)$

(f) $\tau(\omega) = \tau(-\omega)$

1-5. Consider the system shown in Fig. 1-4. If the magnitude function of the low-pass filter is given by

(a) Fig. P1-5(a)

(b) Fig. P1-5(b)

(c) Fig. P1-5(c)

find the corresponding $x_3(t)$.

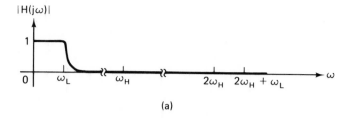

(a)

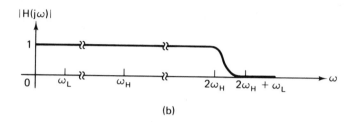

(b)

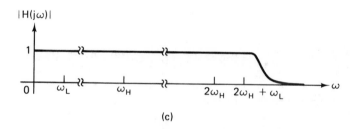

(c)

Fig. P1-5

1-6. For the circuit shown in Fig. P1-6, find the steady-state solutions $v_1(t)$ and $v_2(t)$ when

(a) $v_s(t) = \cos 10^3 t$

(b) $v_s(t) = \cos 10^6 t$

(c) Based on the results of (a) and (b), what type of filter is V_1/V_s? V_2/V_s?

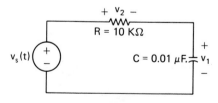

Fig. P1-6

1-7. For the circuit shown in Fig. P1-7, find the steady-state solutions $v_1(t)$, $v_2(t)$, and $v_3(t)$ when

(a) $v_s(t) = \cos 100t$

(b) $v_s(t) = \cos 10^5 t$

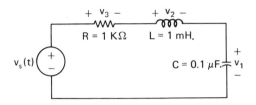

Fig. P1-7

(c) $v_s(t) = \cos 10^8 t$

(d) Based on the results of (a), (b), and (c), what type of filter is V_1/V_s? V_2/V_s? V_3/V_s?

(e) Find the transfer functions

$$H_i(s) \triangleq \frac{V_i}{V_s}$$

where $i = 1, 2, 3$.

(f) Sketch the magnitude functions $|H_i(j\omega)|$ for $i = 1, 2, 3$.

(g) Sketch the phase functions $\phi_i(\omega)$ of $H_i(s)$ for $i = 1, 2, 3$.

1-8. Consider a filter F whose frequency characteristics are shown in Fig. P1-8.

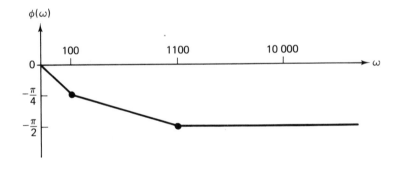

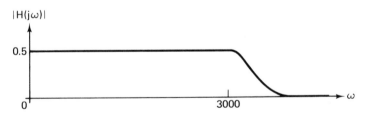

Fig. P1-8

If the input $x(t)$ to the filter F is given by

$$x(t) = \cos 60t + 10 \cos 600t + \cos 3000t$$

find the steady-state output $y(t)$.

2

BUILDING BLOCKS

A *port*, as shown in Fig. 2-1(a), is a pair of terminals with the condition that the instantaneous current entering one terminal will always equal the instantaneous current leaving the other terminal of the port. That is, $i_{in}(t) = i_{out}(t)$ for all t. The reference directions of a 1-port and a 2-port are shown in Figs. 2-1(b) and (c), respectively. Note that a three-terminal device may be considered as a 2-port, as shown in Figs. 2-1(d) and (e) but not conversely.

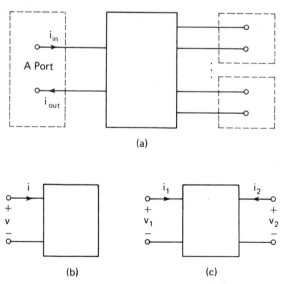

Fig. 2-1   (a) A port. (b) A 1-port. (c) A 2-port.

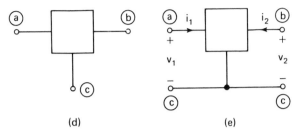

(d)   (e)

Fig. 2-1 (d) A 3-terminal element. (e) A 3-terminal element considered as a 2-port.

2-1 REPRESENTATION

In this book, we consider only *linear, lumped,* and *time-invariant* elements. In addition, we assume that all 1-port and 2-port devices contain no internal independent sources and that all initial conditions are zero. Hence, a 1-port element may be represented by $V = ZI$, where Z is called the *impedance* of the 1-port, or by $I = YV$, where Y is called the *admittance* of the 1-port.[1] Clearly, $Y = 1/Z$, and $Z = 1/Y$. In the 2-port case, the matter of representation becomes more complicated. There are essentially six basic representations for *regular* 2-ports.[2] They are:

(a) *Impedance* Representation

$$\begin{bmatrix} V_1 \\ V_2 \end{bmatrix} = \begin{bmatrix} z_{11} & z_{12} \\ z_{21} & z_{22} \end{bmatrix} \begin{bmatrix} I_1 \\ I_2 \end{bmatrix} \quad \text{or} \quad \mathbf{V} = \mathbf{ZI} \qquad (2\text{-}1)$$

---

[1]There are some 1-port elements that can not be represented by $V = ZI$ or $I = YV$. An example of such an element is a nullator, shown in Fig. 2-2(a), which is characterized by $V = 0$ and $I = 0$.

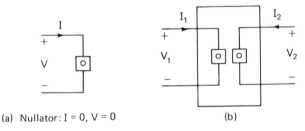

(a) Nullator: $I = 0$, $V = 0$ (b)

Fig. 2-2 (a) An example of a nonregular 1-port. (b) An example of a nonregular 2-port.

[2]There are degenerate cases in which a 2-port can not be represented by a 2×2 matrix relating the terminal variables V_1, V_2, I_1, and I_2. A case in point is a 2-port containing two nullators, as shown in Fig. 2-2(b). This 2 port is characterized by four equations: $V_1 = 0$, $V_2 = 0$, $I_1 = 0$, and $I_2 = 0$.

(b) *Admittance* Representation

$$\begin{bmatrix} I_1 \\ I_2 \end{bmatrix} = \begin{bmatrix} y_{11} & y_{12} \\ y_{21} & y_{22} \end{bmatrix} \begin{bmatrix} V_1 \\ V_2 \end{bmatrix} \quad \text{or} \quad \mathbf{I} = \mathbf{YV} \tag{2-2}$$

(c) and **(d)** *Hybrid* Representations

$$\begin{bmatrix} V_1 \\ I_2 \end{bmatrix} = \begin{bmatrix} h_{11} & h_{12} \\ h_{21} & h_{22} \end{bmatrix} \begin{bmatrix} I_1 \\ V_2 \end{bmatrix} = \mathbf{H} \begin{bmatrix} I_1 \\ V_2 \end{bmatrix} \tag{2-3}$$

and

$$\begin{bmatrix} I_1 \\ V_2 \end{bmatrix} = \begin{bmatrix} \hat{h}_{11} & \hat{h}_{12} \\ \hat{h}_{21} & \hat{h}_{22} \end{bmatrix} \begin{bmatrix} V_1 \\ I_2 \end{bmatrix} = \hat{\mathbf{H}} \begin{bmatrix} V_1 \\ I_2 \end{bmatrix} \tag{2-4}$$

(e) and **(f)** *Transmission* or *Chain* Representations

$$\begin{bmatrix} V_1 \\ I_1 \end{bmatrix} = \begin{bmatrix} a & b \\ c & d \end{bmatrix} \begin{bmatrix} V_2 \\ -I_2 \end{bmatrix} = \mathbf{C} \begin{bmatrix} V_2 \\ -I_2 \end{bmatrix} \tag{2-5}$$

and

$$\begin{bmatrix} V_2 \\ -I_2 \end{bmatrix} = \begin{bmatrix} \alpha & \beta \\ \gamma & \delta \end{bmatrix} \begin{bmatrix} V_1 \\ I_1 \end{bmatrix} = \hat{\mathbf{C}} \begin{bmatrix} V_1 \\ I_1 \end{bmatrix} \tag{2-6}$$

Clearly, $\mathbf{Z} = \mathbf{Y}^{-1}$, $\mathbf{Y} = \mathbf{Z}^{-1}$, $\mathbf{H} = \hat{\mathbf{H}}^{-1}$, $\hat{\mathbf{H}} = \mathbf{H}^{-1}$, $\mathbf{C} = \hat{\mathbf{C}}^{-1}$, and $\hat{\mathbf{C}} = \mathbf{C}^{-1}$.

A 2-port is said to be *reciprocal* if $z_{12} = z_{21}$ or $y_{12} = y_{21}$. All 1-ports are reciprocal elements by definition. A multiport resulting from an interconnection of reciprocal elements is reciprocal.

For 3-port devices there are more variations in their representations. Because we consider primarily 1-port and 2-port devices with the sole exception of operational amplifiers (which are, strictly speaking, 3-port devices), we do not consider the problem of representations of 3-port elements.

2-2 CIRCUIT COMPONENTS

Because the elements involved are linear, lumped, and time-invariant, the filters constructed as a result of an interconnection of these elements are called *linear, lumped*, and *time-invariant filters*. (For convenience, we henceforth omit the adjectives "linear," "lumped," and "time-invariant" when describing an element or circuit.) The components used to build this type of filters can be classified into two broad categories: basic building blocks and secondary building blocks. This classification is based on the observation that every element in the secondary building-block category can be realized by interconnecting elements in the basic building-block category. Clearly, secondary building blocks are not fundamental; they are, however, useful as a conceptual tool.

2-2-1. Basic Building Blocks

In this category, we have

1. *Resistors*. A resistor, shown in Fig. 2-3(a), is characterized by a relation $V = RI$ or $I = GV$, where $G = 1/R$.

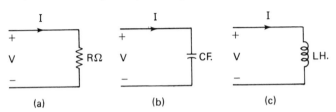

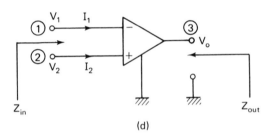

Fig. 2-3 Basic building blocks. (a) A resistor. (b) A capacitor. (c) An inductor. (d) An operational amplifier.

2. *Capacitors*. A capacitor, shown in Fig. 2-3(b), is characterized by a relation $I = sCV$ or $V = (1/sC)\,I$.
3. *Inductors*. An inductor, shown in Fig. 2-3(c), is characterized by a relation $V = sLI$ or $I = (1/sL)\,V$.
4. *Operational Amplifiers* (Op. Amp.). An operational amplifier, shown in Fig. 2-3(d), is characterized by
   (a) input impedance $Z_{in} = \infty$
   (b) output impedance $Z_{out} = 0$
   (c) $V_o = A(V_2 - V_1)$ with $A \to \infty$

where V_1, V_2, and V_o are the voltages between node 1 and ground, node 2 and ground, and node 3 and ground, respectively. This 3-port device can be represented by

$$\begin{bmatrix} I_1 \\ I_2 \\ V_o \end{bmatrix} = \begin{bmatrix} 0 & 0 & 0 \\ 0 & 0 & 0 \\ -A & A & 0 \end{bmatrix} \begin{bmatrix} V_1 \\ V_2 \\ I_o \end{bmatrix} \tag{2-7}$$

where $A \to \infty$. Normally, the op. amp. connection to ground is not shown but is understood to be present.

Before we proceed further, it should be emphasized that these basic building blocks are ideal elements only; they are of paper and pencil type and not of the real physical world type. In general, the electrical performance of a real physical element can be *modeled* to a sufficient degree of accuracy by a combination of these ideal elements. For example, an actual inductor, in most cases, can be adequately modeled by a series combination of an ideal resistor and an ideal inductor. In fact, the performances of many components do not deviate significantly from their ideal characteristics, particularly when they are designed to function within their specified operating ranges. Another point to note is that a physical op. amp. can have characteristics closely described by the ideal ones specified previously, providing it is properly biased, phase compensated, and accurately offsetted, and if it is operated in the *low-frequency* ranges with its output voltage level within $\pm E$ volts, where E is generally a few volts, depending on the power supplies.

To provide some short cuts in the calculations of circuits with op. amps., we recall that $I_1 = I_2 = 0$, meaning that no current will ever enter the input terminals of the op. amp. In addition, we invoke the principle of virtual short circuit, which states:

The Principle of Virtual Short Circuit:[3]   If the input terminals across Nodes 1 and 2 of an op. amp. are not connected directly across the terminals of an independent or controlled voltage source, then $V_1 = V_2$.

To see how this principle helps in computation, we analyze the circuit in Fig. 2-4 in two ways: once with and once without invoking the principle of virtual short circuit.

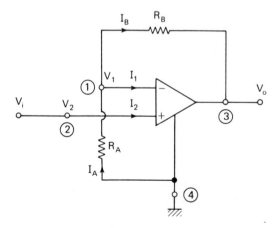

Fig. 2-4   An example illustrating the use of the principle of virtual short circuit.

---

[3]The principle of virtual short circuit is valid under the assumption that the op. amp. is operating in the *linear* mode.

Let us now find the relationship between V_o and V_i without invoking the principle of virtual short circuit. Because $I_1 = I_2 = 0$, a node equation at node 1 gives

$$I_A = I_B \tag{2-8}$$

A loop equation around nodes 3413 gives

$$R_B I_B + R_A I_A + V_o = 0 \tag{2-9}$$

Another loop equation around nodes 414 gives

$$V_1 + R_A I_A = 0 \tag{2-10}$$

In addition, op. amp. characteristics give

$$V_o = A(V_2 - V_1) \quad \text{with } A \to \infty \tag{2-11}$$

To find the relationship between $V_i = V_2$ and V_o, we try to eliminate all other variables in (2-8) through (2-11). Equations (2-8) and (2-10) imply that

$$I_A = I_B = -\frac{V_1}{R_A} \tag{2-12}$$

Substituting (2-12) into (2-9) and (2-11), we obtain

$$V_o = \frac{R_A + R_B}{R_A} V_1 = A(V_2 - V_1) \tag{2-13}$$

which can be written as

$$\left(A + \frac{R_A + R_B}{R_A}\right) V_1 = AV_2$$

or

$$V_1 = \frac{A}{A + [(R_A + R_B)/R_A]} V_2 \tag{2-14}$$

Substituting (2-14) into the first half of (2-13), we have

$$V_o = \frac{R_A + R_B}{R_A} \left(\frac{A}{A + [(R_A + R_B)/R_A]}\right) V_2$$

As $A \to \infty$, we obtain

$$V_o = \frac{R_A + R_B}{R_A} V_2$$

or

$$\frac{V_o}{V_i} = \frac{R_A + R_B}{R_A} \tag{2-15}$$

By applying the principle of virtual short circuit and doing the computation from scratch, we see that the computation is simpler:

$$V_1 = V_2 \implies -R_A I_A = V_i \quad \text{or} \quad I_A = -\frac{V_i}{R_A} \tag{2-16}$$

A loop equation around nodes 3413 and a node equation at node 1 give

$$R_B I_B + R_A I_A + V_o = 0 \tag{2-17}$$

$$I_A = I_B \tag{2-18}$$

Using (2-16) and (2-18), (2-17) becomes

$$V_o = -(R_A + R_B)I_A = \frac{R_A + R_B}{R_A}V_i \qquad (2\text{-}19)$$

which is the result we obtained in (2-15) after a lengthy computation and a limiting process.

We consider operational amplifiers more extensively later in conjunction with active filter synthesis in Chapter 10.

2-2-2. Secondary Building Blocks

As integrated circuit technology advances, there are more and more elements in this category. We restrict our study to the following eight elements.

1. *Controlled Sources.*

(a) A voltage-controlled voltage source (VCVS), shown in Fig. 2-5(a), is characterized by a relation $V_B = kV_A$. Two realizations of a VCVS are given in Figs. 2-5(b) and (c).

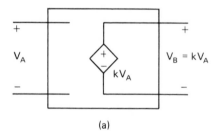

(a)

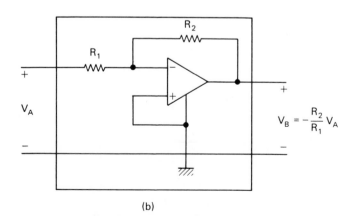

(b)

Fig. 2-5 Voltage-controlled voltage source. (a) Symbol of a VCVS. (b) An inverting VCVS.

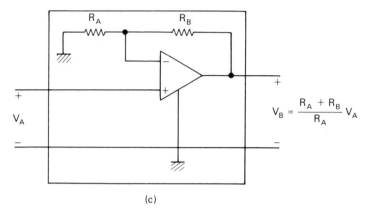

(c)

Fig. 2-5   (c) A noninverting VCVS.

(b) A voltage-controlled current source (VCIS), shown in Fig. 2-6(a), is characterized by a relation $I_B = g_c V_A$. Two realizations of VCIS are given in Figs. 2-6(b) and (c). In Fig. 2-6(b), a capacitor is usually used

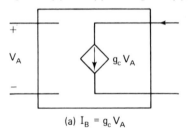

(a) $I_B = g_c V_A$

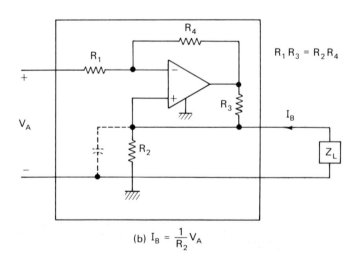

(b) $I_B = \dfrac{1}{R_2} V_A$

Fig. 2-6   Voltage-controlled current source. (a) Symbol for a VCIS. (b) A ground-load VCIS.

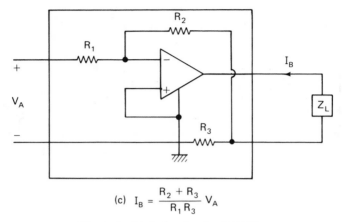

$$(c) \quad I_B = \frac{R_2 + R_3}{R_1 R_3} V_A$$

Fig. 2-6   (c) A floating-load VCIS.

to speed up the transient response. Also, the resistors are adjusted so that $R_1 R_3 = R_2 R_4$ to produce, besides other effects, a high internal impedance, and hence the circuit will function more closely as a true current source. Normally, R_1 and R_2 are large to draw small currents, and R_3 and R_4 are small to reduce voltage drops across them.

(c) A current-controlled voltage source (ICVS), shown in Fig. 2-7(a), is characterized by a relation $V_B = r_c I_A$. Due to the difficulty of sensing currents, a small resistance is inserted into the branch carrying the controlling current I_A to produce a voltage drop V_A, as shown in Fig. 2-7(b). The problem of realizing an ICVS is then reduced to the problem of realizing a VCVS.

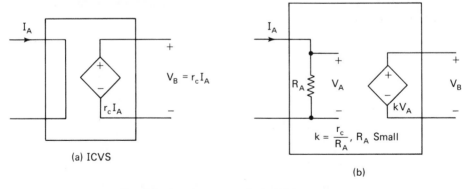

(a) ICVS

(b)

Fig. 2-7   Current-controlled voltage source.

(d) A current-controlled current source (ICIS), shown in Fig. 2-8(a), is characterized by a relation $I_B = k I_A$. The ICIS is also realized in an approximate fashion as that of ICVS, as shown in Fig. 2-8(b).

Note that all four types of controlled sources are nonreciprocal 2-port ele-

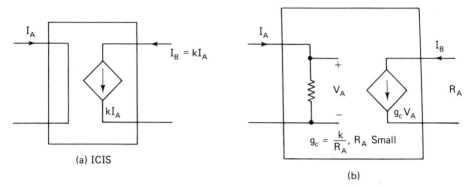

Fig. 2-8   Current-controlled current source.

ments. Usually, the left half or the controlling side of a controlled source is not explicitly shown in circuit diagrams.

2. Gyrators. A gyrator, shown in Fig. 2-9(a), is a 2-port device. It is characterized by the following admittance representation:

$$\begin{bmatrix} I_1 \\ I_2 \end{bmatrix} = \begin{bmatrix} 0 & g_1 \\ -g_2 & 0 \end{bmatrix} \begin{bmatrix} V_1 \\ V_2 \end{bmatrix} \tag{2-20}$$

Based on (2-20), a gyrator can be realized by two VCIS, as shown in Fig. 2-9(b). A realization of a gyrator with $g_1 = g_2$ using op. amps. is given in Fig. 2-9(c). In most cases of practical interests, we have $g_1 = g_2 = g$, and Fig. 2-9(a) is simplified to Fig. 2-9(d).

To show that Fig. 2-9(c) is a gyrator, we use the principle of virtual short circuit, which gives

$$I_C = \frac{V_1}{R} \tag{2-21}$$

Writing loop equations around 32G3, 31G3, G543G, 6G346, and 6G56 give

$$V_D = 2RI_C = 2V_1 \tag{2-22}$$

$$V_D = -RI_B + V_1 \quad \Longrightarrow \quad -I_B = \frac{V_1}{R} \tag{2-23}$$

$$-V_2 - RI_D + V_D = 0 \quad \Longrightarrow \quad I_D = \frac{-V_2 + 2V_1}{R} \tag{2-24}$$

$$V_E - V_D + 2I_D R = 0 \quad \Longrightarrow \quad V_E + 2I_D R = 2V_1 \tag{2-25}$$

$$V_E - V_2 + RI_F = 0 \tag{2-26}$$

Substituting (2-24) and (2-26) into (2-25), we obtain

$$V_2 - RI_F - 2V_2 + 4V_1 = 2V_1 \quad \Longrightarrow \quad I_F = \frac{2V_1 - V_2}{R} \tag{2-27}$$

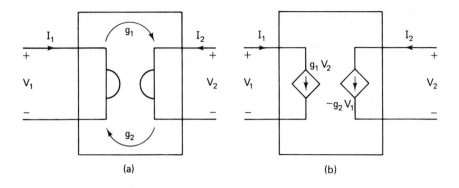

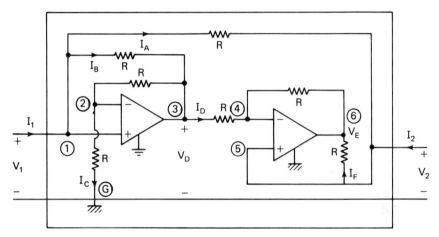

(c) Circuit realization of a gyrator with $|g_1|=|g_2|=\dfrac{1}{R}$

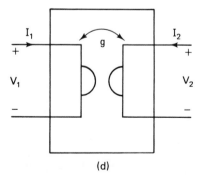

(d)

Fig. 2-9 Gyrators. (a) Symbol for a gyrator. (b) A gyrator realized by two VCIS. (c) A gyrator realized by op. amps. (d) Symbol for a gyrator with a gyration conductance g.

Between nodes 1 and 5, we have

$$I_A = \frac{V_1 - V_2}{R} \tag{2-28}$$

With the aid of (2-23), (2-27), and (2-28), the KCL equations at nodes 1 and 5 give

$$I_1 = I_A + I_B = \frac{V_1}{R} - \frac{V_2}{R} - \frac{V_1}{R} = -\frac{V_2}{R} \tag{2-29}$$

$$I_2 = -I_A + I_F = -\frac{V_1}{R} + \frac{V_2}{R} + \frac{2V_1}{R} - \frac{V_2}{R} = \frac{V_1}{R} \tag{2-30}$$

That is

$$\begin{bmatrix} I_1 \\ I_2 \end{bmatrix} = \begin{bmatrix} 0 & -\dfrac{1}{R} \\ \dfrac{1}{R} & 0 \end{bmatrix} \begin{bmatrix} V_1 \\ V_2 \end{bmatrix} \tag{2-31}$$

which is a gyrator with $g = -1/R$.

One important use of gyrators in the domain of active filters, as elsewhere, is in the realization of inductors. The circuit shown in Fig. 2-10(a) is a schematic realization of an inductor. The computation is given by

the capacitor equation: $I_2 = -sCV_2$ $\tag{2-32}$

the gyrator equations: $I_1 = gV_2$ and $I_2 = -gV_1$ $\tag{2-33}$

Combining these two equations, we obtain

$$-gV_1 = I_2 = -sCV_2 = -sC\left(\frac{1}{g}\right)I_1 \implies Z_{\text{in}} = \frac{V_1}{I_1} = s\left(\frac{C}{g^2}\right) \tag{2-34}$$

which is equivalent to an inductor with an inductance of C/g^2 Henries, as shown in Fig. 2-10(b).

Because gyrators are grounded,[4] Fig. 2-10(a) can realize grounded inductors only (i.e., one terminal of the synthetic inductor is connected to ground). A typical realization of a floating inductor (i.e., both terminals of the synthetic inductor are not connected directly to ground) is given in Fig. 2-10(c). The analysis is as follows:

the first gyrator equation: $I_1 = gV$ and $\hat{I}_1 = -gV_1$ $\tag{2-35}$

where $V = \hat{V}_1 = \hat{V}_2$,

the second gyrator equation: $\hat{I}_2 = gV_2$ and $I_2 = -gV$ $\tag{2-36}$

the capacitor equation: $-\hat{I}_1 + (-\hat{I}_2) = sCV$ $\tag{2-37}$

The first half of (2-35) and the second half of (2-36) give the result

$$I_1 = -I_2 \tag{2-38}$$

---

[4]In all existing circuit realizations of 2-port gyrators, the "lower" terminals of both ports are grounded. Figure 2-9(c) is a case in point.

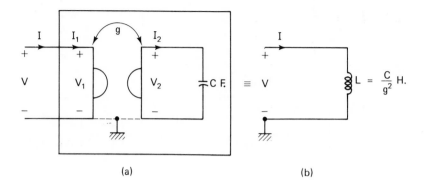

(a)   (b)

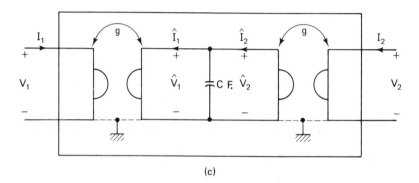

(c)

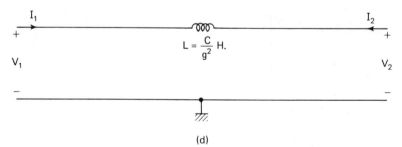

(d)

Fig. 2-10 Realizations of inductors by gyrator–capacitor combinations. (a) and (b) A synthetic grounded inductor. (c) and (d) A synthetic floating inductor.

Substituting (2-35) and (2-36) into (2-37), we obtain

$$gV_1 - gV_2 = sCV = sC\left(\frac{1}{g}\right)I_1 \implies V_1 - V_2 = s\left(\frac{C}{g^2}\right)I_1 \quad (2\text{-}39)$$

Together (2-38) and (2-39) describe a floating inductor with inductance C/g^2 Henries, as shown in Fig. 2-10(d).

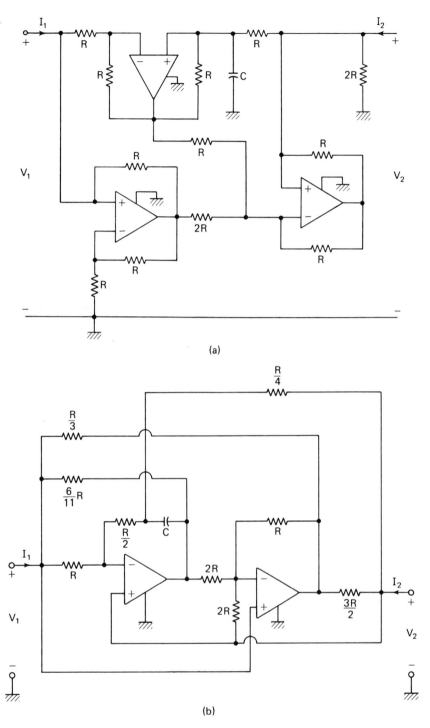

Fig. 2-11 Realizations of floating inductors (a) with 3 op. amps.; (b) and (c) with 2 op. amps.

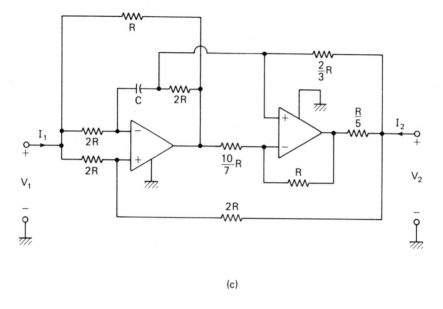

(c)

Fig. 2-11   (Continued)

A floating inductor as realized in Fig. 2-10(c) requires altogether four op. amps. Circuit realizations of floating inductors with less than four op. amps. are shown in Figs. 2-11(a) [3 op. amps.] and Figs. 2-11(b) and (c) [2 op. amps.].[5]

3. *Negative Impedance Converter (NIC)*.[6] An NIC, shown in Fig. 2-12(a), is a 2-port device characterized by a transmission matrix[7]

$$\begin{bmatrix} V_1 \\ I_1 \end{bmatrix} = \begin{bmatrix} 1 & 0 \\ 0 & -k \end{bmatrix} \begin{bmatrix} V_2 \\ -I_2 \end{bmatrix} \tag{2-40}$$

where k is a positive constant.

A simple realization of an NIC with one op. amp. is given in Fig. 2-12(b).

---

[5]See References [10] and [11].

[6]It is called a negative immittance converter in the literature.

[7]To be precise, (2-40) describes a current-inversion negative-impedance converter, or INIC. A voltage-inversion negative-impedance converter, or VNIC, is characterized by

$$\begin{bmatrix} V_1 \\ I_1 \end{bmatrix} = \begin{bmatrix} -k & 0 \\ 0 & 1 \end{bmatrix} \begin{bmatrix} V_2 \\ -I_2 \end{bmatrix}$$

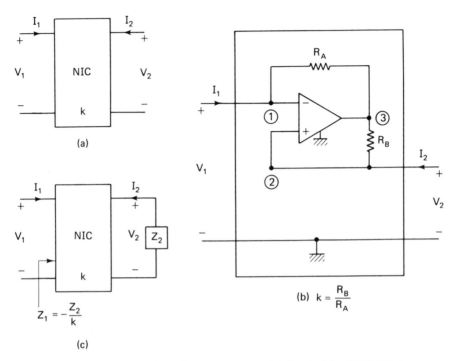

Fig. 2-12 Negative impedance converter. (a) Symbol for NIC. (b) A realization of an NIC with one operational amplifier. (c) An example illustrating a typical use of an NIC.

To see that Fig. 2-12(b) is characterized by (2-40), we apply the principle of virtual short circuit and obtain

$$V_1 = V_2 \tag{2-41}$$

Furthermore, a loop equation around 31G23 gives

$$-R_a I_1 + V_1 - V_2 + R_b I_2 = 0 \implies I_1 = \frac{R_b}{R_a} I_2 \tag{2-42}$$

Clearly, we can put (2-41) and (2-42) in the form of (2-40).

The reason we call the circuit in Fig. 2-12(a) a *negative impedance converter* is that if we connect an impedance Z_2 across port 2, as shown in Fig. 2-12(c), then the input impedance Z_1 is given by

$$Z_1 = -\frac{Z_2}{k} \tag{2-43}$$

That is, the input impedance is the negative of the load impedance scaled by a constant $1/k$.

4. *Generalized Impedance Converter (GIC)*.[8] A generalized impedance converter, shown in Fig. 2-13(a) is a 2-port device capable of making the input impedance of one of its two ports the product of the impedance terminating its remaining port and some internal impedances. It is characterized by a chain matrix

$$\begin{bmatrix} V_1 \\ I_1 \end{bmatrix} = \begin{bmatrix} k & 0 \\ 0 & \dfrac{1}{f(s)} \end{bmatrix} \begin{bmatrix} V_2 \\ -I_2 \end{bmatrix} \tag{2-44}$$

where $f(s)$ is called the *impedance transformation function* and k is usually normalized to unity. A circuit realization of a GIC with

$$k = 1 \quad \text{and} \quad f(s) = \frac{Z_2 Z_4}{Z_3 Z_5} \tag{2-45}$$

is shown in Fig. 2-13(b). In particular, if we let $Z_2 = R_2$, $Z_3 = R_3$, $Z_4 = R_4$, and $Z_5 = 1/sC_5$, then the 2-port is characterized by

$$\begin{bmatrix} V_1 \\ I_1 \end{bmatrix} = \begin{bmatrix} 1 & 0 \\ 0 & \dfrac{R_3}{R_2 R_4 C_5 s} \end{bmatrix} \begin{bmatrix} V_2 \\ -I_2 \end{bmatrix} \tag{2-46}$$

Observe that if we now terminate port 2 with a resistor R_6, as shown in Fig. 2-13(c), we obtain a driving-point impedance function

$$Z_{in} \triangleq \frac{V_1}{I_1} = \frac{R_2 R_4 R_6 C_5}{R_3} s \tag{2-47}$$

This means that the resulting 1-port is equivalent to a grounded inductor with $R_2 R_4 R_6 C_5 / R_3$ Henries.

5. *Frequency-Dependent Negative Resistor (FDNR)*. An FDNR is a 1-port device with an impedance $1/(s^2 D)$, where D is a positive constant and has the unit Farad squared, or F^2. Under sinusoidal steady-state operations, the impedance $Z(s)$ of an FDNR becomes

$$Z(j\omega) = -\frac{1}{\omega^2 D} \tag{2-48}$$

which is equivalent to a resistor whose negative resistance depends on the operating frequency. This is the reason for its lengthy name.

An FDNR has the circuit symbol shown in Fig. 2-14(a). A circuit realization of an FDNR can be obtained by terminating port 1 of the GIC of (2-45) with a capacitor, as shown in Fig. 2-14(b). The driving-point impedance of

---

[8]It is called a generalized immittance converter in the literature, because it applies to admittances as well as impedances.

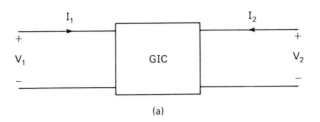

(a)

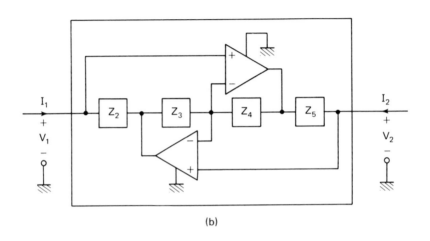

(b)

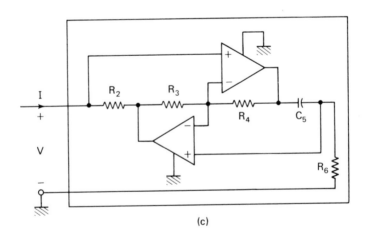

(c)

Fig. 2-13 Generalized impedance converter. (a) Symbol for GIC. (b) A circuit realization of an GIC with $k = 1$ and $f(s) = (Z_2 Z_4)/(Z_3 Z_5)$. (c) A grounded inductor with $L = R_2 R_4 R_6 C_5 / R_3$ Henries.

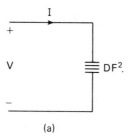

(a)

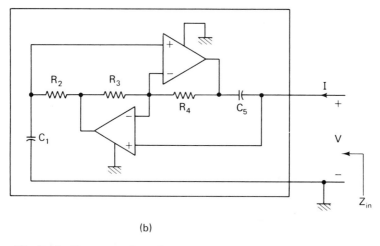

(b)

Fig. 2-14 Frequency-dependent negative resistor. (a) Symbol for FDNR. (b) A circuit realization of a FDNR.

the resulting 1-port is given by

$$Z_{in} = \frac{1}{s^2(R_2 R_4 C_1 C_5 / R_3)} \tag{2-49}$$

It is known that inductors are extremely difficult to fabricate in integrated circuits. At this time, grounded inductors can be designed by gyrator–capacitor pairs without too much problem, but floating inductors realized actively (i.e., via gyrators, op. amps., and NICs) are extremely unstable, sensitive, and not very practical. One way to avoid inductors in circuits is by a variable impedance scaling mechanism, with the scaling factor being $1/s$. This method is as follows: given a voltage- or current-ratio transfer function, we design a circuit to meet the required transfer function with RLC elements. Then, every inductor of L Henries is replaced by a $L\,\Omega$ resistor [i.e., its branch impedance is scaled from sL to $(1/s)sL = L$]; every resistor of $R\,\Omega$ is replaced by a $1/R$ Farad capacitor [i.e., its branch impedance is scaled from R to $(1/s)R$]; and every capacitor of C Farads is replaced by an FDNR with an impedance of

$1/(s^2 C)$ [i.e., its branch impedance is scaled from $1/sC$ to $(1/s)(1/sC)$]. By completing this process, we arrived at a new circuit without inductors. Moreover, both the original circuit and the variable-frequency-scaled circuit have the same voltage or current ratio transfer function.

6. Summer. A summer is a multiterminal device with the output an algebraically weighted sum of the inputs. A simple summer circuit is shown in Fig. 2-15; all the voltages indicated are node to datum voltages.

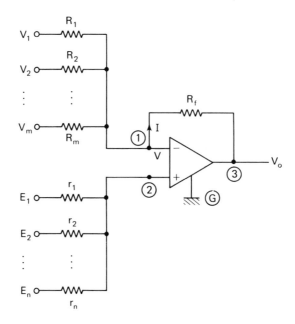

$$V_o = \sum_{i=1}^{n} \frac{1 + R_f G}{r_i g} E_i - \sum_{i=1}^{m} \frac{R_f}{R_i} V_i \quad \text{Where} \quad G = \sum_{i=1}^{n} \frac{1}{R_i} \quad \text{and} \quad g = \sum_{i=1}^{n} \frac{1}{r_i}$$

Fig. 2-15 A summer circuit.

To see that Fig. 2-15 is a summing circuit, let us write two KCL equations at nodes 1 and 2 and a KVL equation around the loop 3G213 as follows:

$$\sum_{k=1}^{m} \frac{V_k - V}{R_k} = I \tag{2-50}$$

$$\sum_{k=1}^{n} \frac{E_k - V}{r_k} = 0 \tag{2-51}$$

$$V_o - V + R_f I = 0 \tag{2-52}$$

Setting

$$g = \sum_{k=1}^{n} \frac{1}{r_k} \quad \text{and} \quad G = \sum_{k=1}^{m} \frac{1}{R_k} \tag{2-53}$$

we can write (2-51) and (2-50) as

$$\sum_{k=1}^{n} \frac{E_k}{r_k} = \sum_{k=1}^{n} \frac{V}{r_k} = gV \implies V = \sum_{k=1}^{n} \frac{E_k}{gr_k} \tag{2-54}$$

$$\sum_{k=1}^{m} \frac{V_k}{R_k} = I + \sum_{k=1}^{m} \frac{V}{R_k} = I + GV \implies I = \sum_{k=1}^{m} \frac{V_k}{R_k} - GV \tag{2-55}$$

Substituting (2-54) into (2-55), we obtain

$$I = \sum_{k=1}^{m} \frac{V_k}{R_k} - \sum_{k=1}^{n} \frac{G}{gr_k} E_k \tag{2-56}$$

Finally, using (2-54) and (2-56), we can write (2-52) as

$$\begin{aligned}
V_o &= V - R_f I \\
&= \sum_{k=1}^{n} \frac{E_k}{gr_k} + \sum_{k=1}^{n} \frac{R_f G}{gr_k} E_k - \sum_{k=1}^{m} \frac{R_f}{R_k} V_k \\
&= \sum_{k=1}^{n} \frac{1 + R_f G}{gr_k} E_k - \sum_{k=1}^{m} \frac{R_f}{R_k} V_k
\end{aligned} \tag{2-57}$$

If $E_n = 0$ in Fig. 2-15 (i.e., if the resistor r_n is connected to ground, which is usually the case), then

$$V_o = \sum_{k=1}^{n-1} \frac{1 + R_f G}{r_k g} E_k - \sum_{k=1}^{m} \frac{R_f}{R_k} V_k \tag{2-58}$$

where G and g are given as before by (2-53). Specifically, the circuit in Fig. 2-16 gives

$$V_o = -\frac{R_f}{R_1} V_1 - \frac{R_f}{R_2} V_2 + \frac{1 + GR_f}{gr_1} E_1 \tag{2-59}$$

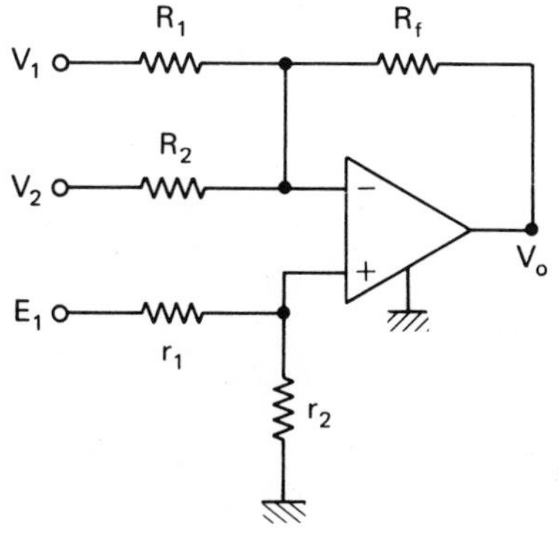

Fig. 2-16 A summer circuit.

where

$$g = \frac{1}{r_1} + \frac{1}{r_2} \quad \text{and} \quad G = \frac{1}{R_1} + \frac{1}{R_2} \tag{2-60}$$

7. Integrator. A circuit realization of an integrator with an op. amp. is shown in Fig. 2-17, where

$$V_o = -\frac{1}{sCR}V_{in} \tag{2-61}$$

If $RC = 1$, then $V_o = -(1/s)V_{in}$, which is an inverting integrator.

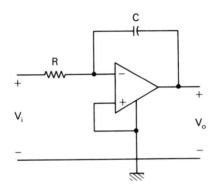

Fig. 2-17 An inverting integrator.

8. Differentiator. A circuit realization of a differentiator with an op. amp. is given in Fig. 2-18, where

$$V_o = -sCRV_{in} \tag{2-62}$$

If $RC = 1$, then $V_o = -sV_{in}$, which is an inverting differentiator.

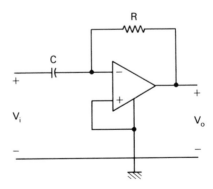

Fig. 2-18 An inverting differentiator.

REFERENCES AND FURTHER READING

[1] DESOER, C. A., and KUH, E. S. *Basic Circuit Theory*. New York: McGraw-Hill, 1969.

[2] GRAEME, J. G., TOBEY, G. E., and HUELSMAN, L. P. *Operational Amplifiers: Design and Application*, New York: McGraw-Hill, 1971.

[3] SMITH, J. I. *Modern Operational Circuit Design*, New York: Wiley-Interscience, 1971.

[4] WAIT, J. V., HUELSMAN, L. P., and KORN, G. A. *Introduction to Operational Amplifier Theory and Application*, New York: McGraw-Hill, 1975.

[5] ROBERGE, J. K. *Operational Amplifiers: Theory and Practice*, New York: Wiley, 1975.

[6] STOUT, D. F., and KAUFMAN, M. *Handbook of Operational Amplifier Circuit Design*, New York: McGraw-Hill, 1976.

[7] SU, K. L. *Active Network Synthesis*, New York: McGraw-Hill, 1965.

[8] MITRA, S. K. *Analysis and Synthesis of Linear Active Networks*, New York: Wiley, 1968.

[9] MITRA, S. K. *Active Inductorless Filters*, New York: IEEE Press, 1971.

[10] DEBOO, G. J. "Application of a Gyrator Type Circuit to Realize Ungrounded Inductors." *IEEE Trans. Circuit Theory* CT-14 (May 1967); 101–2.

[11] THE, L. Q., and YANAGISAWA, T. "Some New Lossless Floating Inductance Circuits." *Proc. IEEE* 65 (1977); 1071–2.

PROBLEMS

2-1. An FET has a small signal circuit model shown in Fig. P2-1, where $r_{gs} \simeq 10^{11} \ \Omega$, $g_{fs} \simeq 10^{-3}$ mhos, and $r_{ds} \simeq 300 \ \text{K}\Omega$. Find the admittance, the impedance, and a hybrid representation of the FET small-signal circuit model.

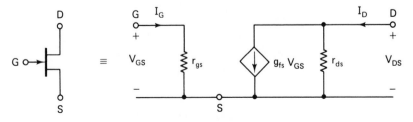

Fig. P2-1

2-2. A small signal equivalent circuit of a transistor is shown in Fig. P2-2, where $C_c = 200$ PF., $C_e = 20$ PF., $r_e = 25\ \Omega$, $r_b = 120\ \Omega$, $r_c = 1.25\ M\Omega$, and $\alpha = 0.98$. Find the admittance, the impedance, and a hybrid representation of the transistor equivalent circuit.

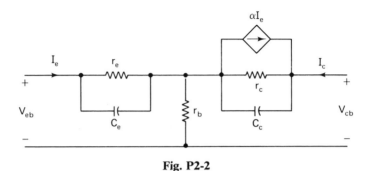

Fig. P2-2

2-3. (a) Find the impedance and the admittance representations of the symmetric lattice 2-port network N shown in Fig. P2-3.

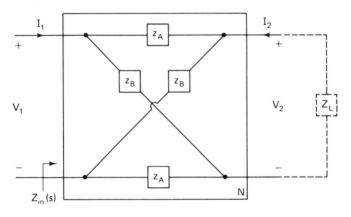

Fig. P2-3

(b) If port 2 of N is terminated with a load impedance Z_L, find the driving-point impedance function $Z_{in}(s)$.

2-4. Consider the circuit shown in Fig. P2-4, where the 2-port network N_1 has an impedance representation

$$V_1 = z_{11}I_1 + z_{12}I_2$$
$$V_2 = z_{21}I_1 + z_{22}I_2$$

Find the driving-point impedance function $Z(s)$.

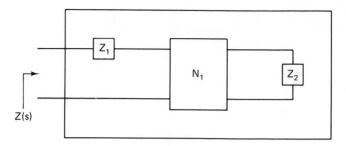

Fig. P2-4

2-5. Consider the circuit shown in Fig. P2-5, where the 2-port network N_2 has an admittance representation

$$I_1 = y_{11}V_1 + y_{12}V_2$$
$$I_2 = y_{21}V_1 + y_{22}V_2$$

Find the driving-point admittance function $Y(s)$.

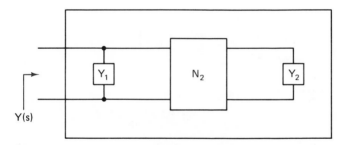

Fig. P2-5

2-6. Given the transmission matrix of a 2-port network N in Fig. P2-6(a) as

$$\begin{bmatrix} V_2 \\ -I_2 \end{bmatrix} = \begin{bmatrix} A & B \\ C & D \end{bmatrix} \begin{bmatrix} V_1 \\ I_1 \end{bmatrix}$$

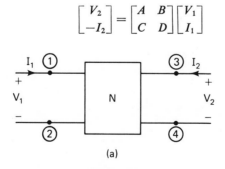

(a)

Fig. P2-6(a)

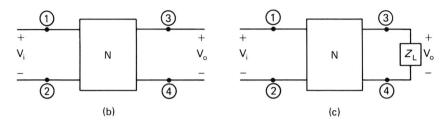

(b)   (c)

Fig. P2-6(b), (c)

Find the transfer functions V_o/V_i of the circuits shown in Fig. P2-6(b) and (c).

2-7. Find the transmission matrix of the circuit shown in Fig. P2-7.

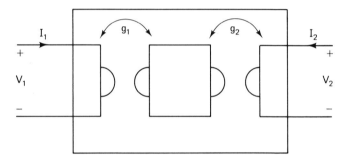

Fig. P2-7

2-8. **(a)** Find the transmission matrix of the circuit shown in Fig. P2-8.
(b) Find the transfer function $H(s) = V_2/V_1$.

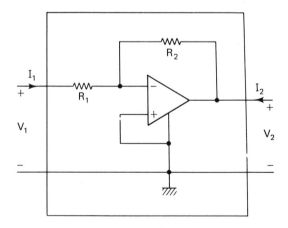

Fig. P2-8

2-9. Find the transfer functions of the three circuits shown in Fig. P2-9.

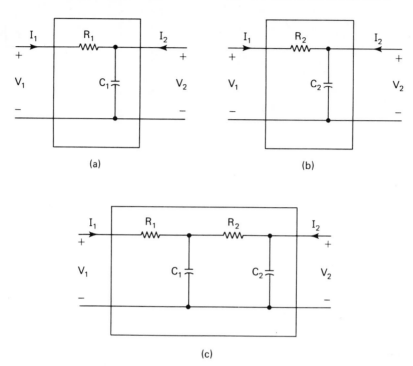

(a)

(b)

(c)

Fig. P2-9

2-10. Find the transfer functions of the three circuits shown in Fig. P2-10.

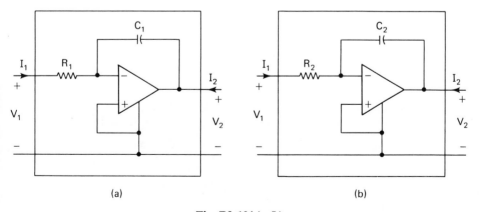

(a)

(b)

Fig. P2-10(a), (b)

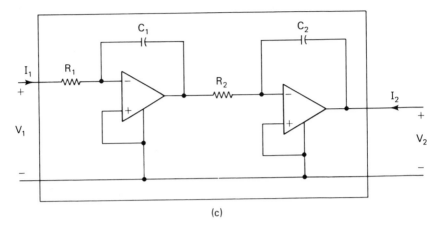

(c)

Fig. P2-10(c)

2-11. Find a hybrid representation of the 2-port network shown in Fig. P2-11.

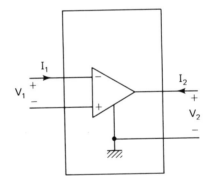

Fig. P2-11

2-12. **(a)** Verify that Fig. 2-5(b) is an inverting VCVS.

(b) Verify that Fig. 2-5(c) is a noninverting VCVS.

(c) The circuit shown in Fig. P2-12 is a noninverting VCVS, where the input voltage is not necessarily grounded. Find the voltage gain of the circuit.

2-13. **(a)** Show that the circuit in Fig. 2-6(b) is a VCIS with a grounded load Z_L.

(b) Show that the circuit in Fig. 2-6(c) is a VCIS with a floating load Z_L.

2-14. Show that the circuits in Fig. 2-11 are floating inductors.

2-15. **(a)** Show that the circuit in Fig. 2-13(b) is characterized by a hybrid representation given by (2-44) and (2-45).

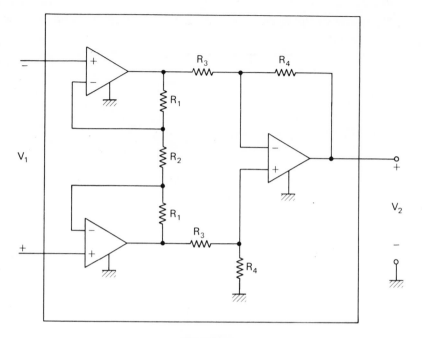

Fig. P2-12

(b) Show that the 1-port circuit in Fig. 2-13(c) is equivalent to a grounded inductor.

2-16. Show that the 1-port circuit in Fig. P2-16 is equivalent to an inductor.

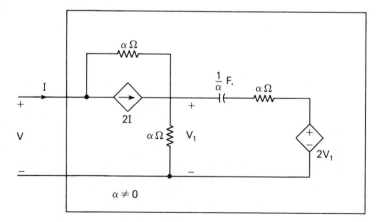

Fig. P2-16

2-17. Show that the 1-port circuit in Fig. P2-17 is equivalent to a grounded inductor.

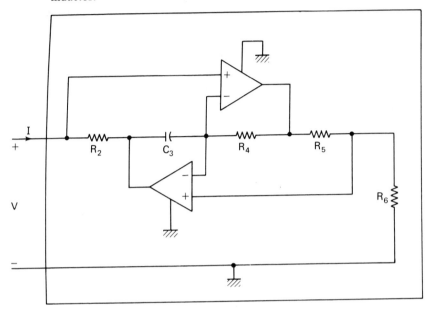

Fig. P2-17

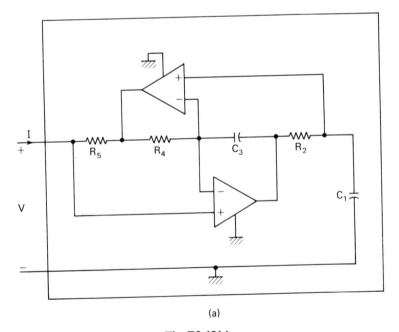

(a)

Fig. P2-18(a)

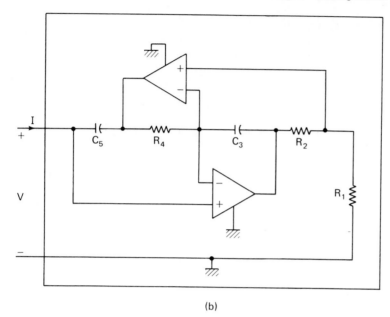

(b)

Fig. P2-18(b)

2-18. Show that the 1-port circuits in
    (a) Fig. 2-14.
    (b) Fig. P2-18(a)
    (c) Fig. P2-18(b)
    are grounded FDNRs.

2-19. Show that the circuit in Fig. P2-19 is a noninverting integrator.

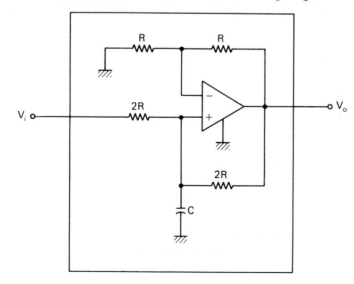

Fig. P2-19

2-20. Consider the circuit in Fig. P2-20.

   (a) Find the transfer function $H(s) = V_o/V_i$.

   (b) If $R_1C_1 = RC$, show that the circuit is a noninverting integrator.

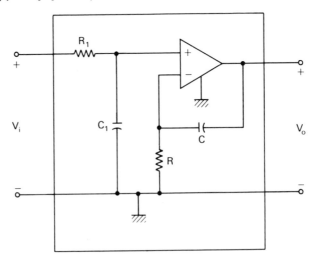

Fig. P2-20

2-21. Find the transfer functions V_o/V_i of the two circuits shown in Fig. P2-21.

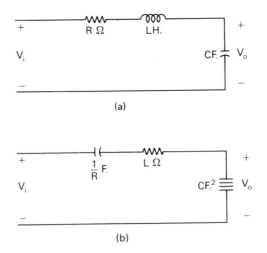

Fig. P2-21

2-22. Find the transfer functions V_o/V_i of the two circuits shown in Fig. P2-22. Note that these circuits realize a second-order Butterworth low pass filter.

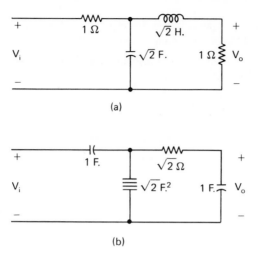

(a)

(b)

Fig. P2-22

2-23. Consider the two circuits in Fig. P2-23, where circuit (b) is obtained by an impedance scaling of each element in circuit (a) with a scaling factor of $1/s$.

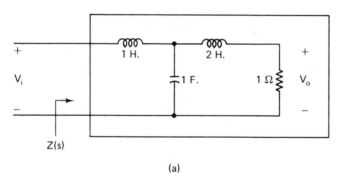

(a)

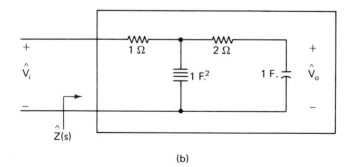

(b)

Fig. P2-23

(a) Find the transfer functions $H(s) = V_o/V_i$ and $\hat{H}(s) = \hat{V}_o/\hat{V}_i$.

(b) Find the driving-point impedance functions $Z(s)$ and $\hat{Z}(s)$.

2-24. By using summers, integrators and differentiators, design circuits in the form of Fig. P2-24 to obtain

(a) $V_o = 2V_1 + V_2 - V_3$

(b) $V_o = -V_1 - 3V_2 - V_3$

(c) $V_o = \dfrac{1}{s} V_1 - 2V_2 + sV_3$

(d) $V_o = \dfrac{1}{s} V_1 + sV_2 + V_2$

(e) $V_o = \dfrac{1}{s^2} V_1 + \dfrac{2}{s} V_1 + 3V_1 + 4sV_1 + 5sV_2$

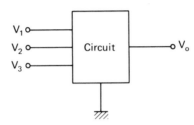

Fig. P2-24

2-25. Design circuits to simulate the following differential equations.

(a) $\dfrac{dy}{dt} = 4x(t)$

(b) $\dfrac{d^2y}{dt^2} + 2\dfrac{dy}{dt} + 2y = x(t) + \dfrac{dx}{dt}$

(c) $\dfrac{dy}{dt} + 3y(t) + \displaystyle\int_0^t y(\tau)\, d\tau = x(t)$

where $y(t)$ is the output and $x(t)$ is the input.

3

PROPERTIES
OF NETWORK FUNCTIONS

A network function is the Laplace transform of an impulse response. Its format is a ratio of two polynomials of the complex frequency s. Before we embark on our discussion of the properties of network functions, let us review some properties relating to polynomials of a complex variable s.

3-1 POLYNOMIALS OF A COMPLEX VARIABLE

A polynomial $p(s)$ is said to be *even* if it is a sum of even powers, and it is said to be *odd* if it is a sum of odd powers. For example, $p_1(s)$ and $p_2(s)$ are even polynomials, whereas $p_3(s)$ and $p_4(s)$ are odd polynomials, where

$$p_1(s) = as^6 + bs^2 + c$$
$$p_2(s) = ds^{20} + e$$
$$p_3(s) = fs^5 + gs^3 + hs$$
$$p_4(s) = ks^7 + ls^3$$

and $a, b, c, d, e, f, g, h, k$, and l are constants. Observe that if $M(s)$ is an even polynomial and $N(s)$ is an odd polynomial,[1] then

$$M(s) = M(-s) \qquad (3\text{-}1)$$
$$N(s) = -N(-s) \qquad (3\text{-}2)$$

---

[1]In this chapter, as well as in Chapters 4 through 8, $M(s)$ and $N(s)$, with or without subscripts, denote respectively an even and an odd polynomial or rational function.

Consider a general polynomial $p(s)$ given by

$$p(s) = a_0 + a_1 s + a_2 s^2 + a_3 s^3 + a_4 s^4 + a_5 s^5 + \dots$$

We can always write $p(s)$ as a sum of an even and an odd polynomial as

$$p(s) = (a_0 + a_2 s^2 + a_4 s^4 + \dots) + (a_1 s + a_3 s^3 + a_5 s^5 \dots)$$
$$\triangleq M(s) + N(s) \tag{3-3}$$

where $M(s) \triangleq a_0 + a_2 s^2 + a_4 s^4 + \dots$ and $N(s) \triangleq a_1 s + a_3 s^3 + a_5 s^5 + \dots$ are called, respectively, the *even and odd parts* of $p(s)$. In view of (3-1) and (3-2), we have

$$p(-s) = M(-s) + N(-s) = M(s) - N(s) \tag{3-4}$$

In this book, the coefficients of all polynomials under consideration are real. With this standing condition, we have the following properties for polynomials of a complex variable s:

1. Let $p(s)$ be a polynomial of s. Then

$$\overline{p(s)} = p(\bar{s}) \tag{3-5}$$

where $\bar{a}$ denotes the complex conjugate of a. For example, let

$$p(s) = a_2 s^2 + a_1 s + a_0$$

Then

$$\overline{p(s)} = \bar{a}_2 \bar{s}^2 + \bar{a}_1 \bar{s} + \bar{a}_0 = a_2 \bar{s}^2 + a_1 \bar{s} + a_0 = p(\bar{s})$$

2. If $M(s)$ is an even polynomial, then, by (3-1) and (3-5), we have

$$\overline{M(j\omega)} = M(\overline{j\omega}) = M(-j\omega) = M(j\omega) \tag{3-6}$$

where the first equality of (3-6) is due to (3-5), and the last equality of (3-6) is due to (3-1). In view of (3-6), $M(j\omega)$ is a *real* quantity for all ω.

3. If $N(s)$ is an odd polynomial, then, by (3-2) and (3-5), we have

$$\overline{N(j\omega)} = N(\overline{j\omega}) = N(-j\omega) = -N(j\omega) \tag{3-7}$$

Thus, $N(j\omega)$ is a *purely imaginary* quantity, and $N(j\omega)$ can be expressed as

$$N(j\omega) = jX(\omega) \tag{3-8}$$

where $X(\omega)$ is a real function of a real variable ω.

4. If s_k is a root of the polynomial $p(s)$, i.e.,

$$p(s_k) = M(s_k) + N(s_k) = 0$$

where $M(s)$ and $N(s)$ are, respectively, the even and odd parts of $p(s)$, then $(-s_k)$ is a root of the polynomial $p(-s) = M(s) - N(s)$. Clearly, the converse is also true. Hence, we have:

LEMMA 3-1. s_k is a root of $[M(s) + N(s)]$ if, and only if, $(-s_k)$ is a root of $[M(s) - N(s)]$, where $M(s)$ is an even polynomial and $N(s)$ is an odd polynomial.

5. The magnitude-squared function of $p(s) = M(s) + N(s)$, where $M(s)$ and $N(s)$ are the even and odd parts of $p(s)$, is given by

$$|p(j\omega)|^2 = p(s)p(-s)|_{s=j\omega}$$
$$= \{[M(s) + N(s)][M(s) - N(s)]\}|_{s=j\omega} \tag{3-9}$$
$$= [M^2(s) - N^2(s)]|_{s=j\omega} = M^2(j\omega) - N^2(j\omega)$$

Because $M(j\omega)$ is real and $N(j\omega)$ is purely imaginary, $M^2(j\omega)$ and $N^2(j\omega)$ are real, $M^2(j\omega) \geq 0$ and $N^2(j\omega) \leq 0$ for all ω. Consequently,

$$|p(j\omega)|^2 \geq 0 \quad \text{for all } \omega \tag{3-10}$$

In addition, we can conclude that $|p(j\omega)|^2$ is a polynomial of ω^2, or equivalently, $|p(j\omega)|^2$ is an even polynomial of the real variable ω. For example, let

$$p(s) = s^2 + \sqrt{2}s + 1$$

then

$$M(s) = s^2 + 1 \quad \text{and} \quad N(s) = \sqrt{2}s$$
$$M^2(s) - N^2(s) = s^4 + 2s^2 + 1 - 2s^2 = s^4 + 1$$
$$|p(j\omega)|^2 = [s^4 + 1]|_{s=j\omega} = 1 + \omega^4$$

6. The roots of $f(s) \triangleq [p(s)p(-s)] = M^2(s) - N^2(s)$ occur with *quadrantal symmetry*, meaning that:
   (a) Roots on the real axis of s-plane occur in pairs at σ_1 and $(-\sigma_1)$;
   (b) Roots on the imaginary axis of s-plane occur with even multiplicity and complex conjugate pairs [i.e., if $j\omega_1$ is a root of $f(s)$, then both $j\omega_1$ and $(-j\omega_1)$ are double, or quadruple, or . . ., roots of $f(s)$]; and
   (c) Complex roots occur in a quadruple manner [i.e., if $\sigma_1 + j\omega_1$ is a root of $p(s)p(-s)$, where $\sigma_1 \neq 0$ and $\omega_1 \neq 0$, then $\sigma_1 - j\omega_1$, $-(\sigma_1 + j\omega_1)$, and $-(\sigma_1 - j\omega_1)$ are also roots of $p(s)p(-s)$].

This root location property of $p(s)p(-s)$ is illustrated in Figure 3-1.

The quadrantal symmetry properties of the root locations of $p(s)$ $p(-s)$ can be proved by using Lemma 3-1. A simple case in point is given by

$$p(s) = (s^2 + 1)(s^2 + \sqrt{2}s + 1)(s + 1)$$

In this case, we have

$$p(s)p(-s) = (s^2 + 1)^2(s^4 + 1)(-s^2 + 1)$$

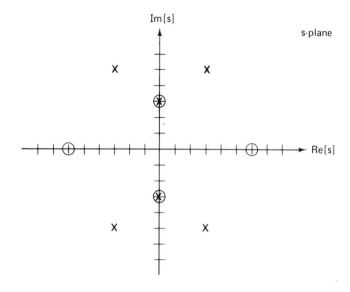

Legend: X = Complex roots in quadruples

◯ = Real roots in pairs

⊗ = Imaginary axis roots in conjugate pairs and with even multiplicities

Fig. 3-1 Roots of $f(s) \triangleq p(s)p(-s)$ are in quadrantal symmetry.

Thus, the roots of $p(s)p(-s)$ are

$$s_1 = 1, \quad s_2 = -1$$

$$s_3 = s_4 = j, \quad s_5 = s_6 = -j$$

$$s_7 = \frac{1}{\sqrt{2}} + j\frac{1}{\sqrt{2}}, \quad s_8 = \frac{1}{\sqrt{2}} - j\frac{1}{\sqrt{2}}$$

$$s_9 = -\frac{1}{\sqrt{2}} + j\frac{1}{\sqrt{2}}, \quad \text{and} \quad s_{10} = -\frac{1}{\sqrt{2}} - j\frac{1}{\sqrt{2}}$$

3-2 NETWORK FUNCTION

Let $F(s)$ be a network function that may be a driving-point (DP) imped-ance or admittance function of a 1-port element or that may be a transfer function between the input port and the output port of a 2-port network. Then $F(s)$ is a rational function of s with real coefficients and can be written as a ratio of two polynomials as follows:

transfer function

$$F(s) = \frac{A(s)}{B(s)} = \frac{\sum_{i=0}^{m} a_i s^i}{\sum_{i=0}^{n} b_i s^i} = \frac{M_1(s) + N_1(s)}{M_2(s) + N_2(s)} \tag{3-11}$$

where $A(s)$ and $B(s)$ are, respectively, the numerator and the denominator polynomials of $F(s)$; $M_1(s)$ and $N_1(s)$ are, respectively, the even and odd parts of $A(s)$; and $M_2(s)$ and $N_2(s)$ are, respectively, the even and odd parts of $B(s)$.

Multiplying (3-11) by $B(-s)/B(-s)$, we obtain

$$\begin{aligned} F(s) &= \frac{A(s)B(-s)}{B(s)B(-s)} = \frac{[M_1(s) + N_1(s)][M_2(s) - N_2(s)]}{M_2^2(s) - N_2^2(s)} \\ &= \frac{M_1(s)M_2(s) - N_1(s)N_2(s)}{M_2^2(s) - N_2^2(s)} + \frac{N_1(s)M_2(s) - N_2(s)M_1(s)}{M_2^2(s) - N_2^2(s)} \end{aligned} \tag{3-12}$$

Note that the first term of (3-12) is an even function,

$$\begin{aligned} M(s) &\triangleq \frac{M_1(s)M_2(s) - N_1(s)N_2(s)}{M_2^2(s) - N_2^2(s)} \\ &= \frac{M_1(-s)M_2(-s) - N_1(-s)N_2(-s)}{M_2^2(-s) - N_2^2(-s)} = M(-s) \end{aligned} \tag{3-13}$$

and the second term is an odd function,

$$\begin{aligned} N(s) &\triangleq \frac{N_1(s)M_2(s) - N_2(s)M_1(s)}{M_2^2(s) - N_2^2(s)} \\ &= \frac{-N_1(-s)M_2(-s) + N_2(-s)M_1(-s)}{M_2^2(-s) - N_2^2(-s)} = -N(-s) \end{aligned} \tag{3-14}$$

Henceforth, we call $M(s)$ and $N(s)$, respectively, the *even and odd parts* of the rational function $F(s)$ given by (3-11). Upon setting $s = j\omega$, (3-13) and (3-14) say that $M(j\omega)$ is real and $N(j\omega)$ is purely imaginary. Consequently

$$M(j\omega) = \text{Re}\,[F(j\omega)] \quad \text{and} \quad N(j\omega) = j\,\text{Im}\,[F(j\omega)] \tag{3-15}$$

Observe that (3-15) says that given the real {imaginary} part of $F(s)$, we can find the even {odd} part of $F(s)$, and vice versa.

3-2-1. Hilbert Transform

Relationships between the real and imaginary parts of a network function (which represents a causal system) may be expressed through the Hilbert transform as follows:

Suppose that a network function $F(s)$ is *analytic* in the closed right-half[2]

---

[2]Hereafter, we let RH {LH} s-plane to stand for the *right-half* {*left-half*} side of the s-plane.

side (including the imaginary axis) of the *s*-plane.[3] Let us write

$$F(j\omega) = R(\omega) + jX(\omega) \tag{3-16}$$

where $R(\omega)$ and $X(\omega)$ are, respectively, the real and the imaginary parts of $F(j\omega)$. If

$$\lim_{\omega \to \infty} F(j\omega) = R(\infty) = \text{a finite real constant} \tag{3-17}$$

then $R(\omega)$ and $X(\omega)$ are related by[4]

$$X(\omega) = -\frac{1}{\pi} \int_{-\infty}^{\infty} \frac{R(\zeta)}{\omega - \zeta} \, d\zeta \tag{3-18}$$

$$R(\omega) = \frac{1}{\pi} \int_{-\infty}^{\infty} \frac{X(\zeta)}{\omega - \zeta} \, d\zeta + R(\infty) \tag{3-19}$$

Note that there is a lack of symmetry between (3-18) and (3-19). This lack of symmetry is due to the fact that we are considering only network functions whose inverse Laplace transforms are *real* time functions. If we consider complex time functions, then there is a term $X(\infty)$ on the right-hand side of (3-18), and the two equations, namely (3-18) and (3-19), will be symmetric. On the other hand, if the impulse response $f(t)$, which is the inverse Laplace transform of $F(s)$, contains no impulse function at $t = 0$, then $R(\infty) = 0$ and (3-19) is simplified to[5]

$$R(\omega) = \frac{1}{\pi} \int_{-\infty}^{\infty} \frac{X(\zeta)}{\omega - \zeta} \, d\zeta \tag{3-19'}$$

The Hilbert transform says that if certain conditions are met (for causal, stable circuits, the required conditions are met), then:

1. If we are given the imaginary part $X(\omega)$, we can find the real part $R(\omega)$ via (3-19). From $R(\omega)$ and $X(\omega)$, we can form $F(j\omega)$. By analytic continuation (i.e., by replacing ω with s/j), we obtain $F(s)$.
2. If we are given the real part $R(\omega)$, (3-18) gives $X(\omega)$. Together we can again form $F(j\omega)$. Upon setting $\omega = s/j$, we obtain $F(s)$.

Example 3-1   Given the real part $R(\omega)$ to be

$$R(\omega) = \frac{\alpha}{\alpha^2 + \omega^2}$$

Find the associated network function $F(s)$.

---

[3]Because $F(s)$ is a rational function, "$F(s)$ is analytic in the closed RH *s*-plane" means that $F(s)$ has no poles—$F(s) \neq \infty$ for all s—in the RH *s*-plane. For the Hilbert transform to be applicable here, it is sufficient to require that the rational function $F(s)$ has no poles in the RH *s*-plane and that all imaginary axis poles of $F(s)$ are simple.

[4]There are many other equivalent expressions for Hilbert transforms. See Reference [4].

[5]Hereafter, we assume that $R(\infty) = 0$ and refer to both (3-19) and (3-19') as (3-19).

Solution: The imaginary part $X(\omega)$ is given by (3-18) as

$$X(\omega) = -\frac{1}{\pi} \int_{-\infty}^{\infty} \frac{\alpha}{(\alpha^2 + \zeta^2)(\omega - \zeta)} \, d\zeta = -\frac{\omega}{\alpha^2 + \omega^2}$$

Hence,

$$F(j\omega) = R(\omega) + jX(\omega)$$

$$= \frac{\alpha - j\omega}{\alpha^2 + \omega^2} = \frac{\alpha - j\omega}{\alpha^2 - (j\omega)^2} = \frac{1}{\alpha + j\omega}$$

that is

$$F(s) = \frac{1}{s + \alpha} \qquad \blacksquare$$

Note that, in general, the evaluations of the integrals in (3-18) and (3-19) are not easy and often require consultation with integration tables and with an area of mathematics called *distribution theory*.

If we now pay closer attention to (3-18) and (3-19), we see that both integrals are in the form of a convolution integral

$$f(\omega) = \int_{-\infty}^{\infty} g(\zeta) \, h(\omega - \zeta) \, d\zeta$$

$$\triangleq g(\omega) * h(\omega) \tag{3-20}$$

where $h(\omega) \triangleq \pm 1/(\pi\omega)$, and $g(\omega)$ is $R(\omega)$ in (3-18) and $X(\omega)$ in (3-19). Some savings in effort may result in evaluating (3-18) and (3-19) if we take advantage of the properties of convolution integrals. Some of these are:

1. Laplace transforms of $f(\omega)$ is given by the product of the Laplace transforms of $g(\omega)$ and $h(\omega)$. Note that in (3-18) and (3-19), the Laplace transforms will actually be performed on functions of ω rather than the usual time functions.
2. Equation (3-20) can also be written as

$$f(\omega) = \int_{-\infty}^{\infty} g(\omega - \zeta) \, h(\zeta) \, d\zeta$$

$$= g(\omega) * h(\omega) \tag{3-21}$$

3. $f(\omega) = g(\omega) * h(\omega)$

$$= [k\text{th derivative of } g(\omega)] * [k\text{th integral of } h(\omega)] \tag{3-22}$$

$$= [k\text{th integral of } g(\omega)] * [k\text{th derivative of } h(\omega)]$$

4. $\int_{-\infty}^{\omega} f(\omega') \, d\omega' = \left[\int_{-\infty}^{\omega} g(\omega') \, d\omega' \right] * h(\omega)$

$$= g(\omega) * \left[\int_{-\infty}^{\omega} h(\omega') \, d\omega' \right] \tag{3-23}$$

5. $\dfrac{d}{d\omega} f(\omega) = \left[\dfrac{d}{d\omega} g(\omega)\right] * h(\omega)$

$$= g(\omega) * \left[\dfrac{d}{d\omega} h(\omega)\right]$$

(3-24)

It has been shown that the Hilbert transform can be used to find the real part of a network function if the imaginary part is given or vice versa. Notice that the Hilbert transform is just a set of relationships between the real and the imaginary parts of a complex function that is analytic on the RH s-plane. If we write

$$F(j\omega) = e^{-\alpha(\omega)} e^{-j\phi(\omega)} = e^{-[\alpha(\omega) + j\phi(\omega)]}$$

(3-25)

then $\alpha(\omega) \triangleq -\ell n |F(j\omega)|$ is called the *attenuation or loss function* of the filter, and $\phi(\omega) \triangleq -\underline{/F(j\omega)}$ is called the *phase function* (to be precise: phase-lag function) of the filter. Taking logarithms of (3-25), we obtain

$$\gamma(j\omega) \triangleq -\ell n \, F(j\omega)$$

$$= -\ell n \, e^{-[\alpha(\omega) + j\phi(\omega)]}$$

(3-26)

$$= \alpha(\omega) + j\phi(\omega)$$

Observe that if $\gamma(s)$ is analytic on the RH s-plane, then $\alpha(\omega)$ and $\phi(\omega)$, being the real and the imaginary parts of $\gamma(j\omega)$, would be related by the Hilbert transform equations as:

$$\phi(\omega) = -\frac{1}{\pi} \int_{-\infty}^{\infty} \frac{\alpha(\zeta)}{\omega - \zeta} \, d\zeta$$

(3-27)

$$\alpha(\omega) = \frac{1}{\pi} \int_{-\infty}^{\infty} \frac{\phi(\zeta)}{\omega - \zeta} \, d\zeta$$

(3-28)

Example 3-2 Let the phase lag function of a desired filter be given by

$$\phi(\omega) = -\frac{k\pi}{2} \quad \text{for} \quad \omega \leq -\omega_c$$

$$= \frac{k\pi}{2} \frac{\omega}{\omega_c} \quad \text{for} \quad -\omega_c \leq \omega \leq \omega_c$$

(3-29)

$$= \frac{k\pi}{2} \quad \text{for} \quad \omega \geq \omega_c$$

as shown in Fig. 3-2(a). Find the associated attenuation or loss function $\alpha(\omega)$ of the desired filter.

Solution: Because $\tau(\omega) \triangleq d\phi(\omega)/d\omega$ [shown in Fig. 3-2(b)] has a simpler form than that of $\phi(\omega)$, we apply (3-24) to (3-28) and obtain

$$\frac{d\alpha(\omega)}{d\omega} = \frac{1}{\pi} \int_{-\infty}^{\infty} \frac{\dfrac{d}{d\zeta} \phi(\zeta)}{\omega - \zeta} \, d\zeta$$

(3-30)

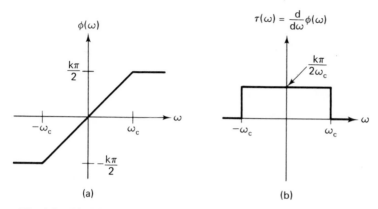

Fig. 3-2   (a) A linear phase filter. (b) A constant group delay filter.

Hence,

$$\frac{d\alpha(\omega)}{d\omega} = \frac{1}{\pi} \int_{-\omega_c}^{\omega_c} \frac{k\pi}{2\omega_c} \frac{1}{\omega - \zeta} \, d\zeta = \frac{k}{2\omega_c} \ell n \left| \frac{\omega - \omega_c}{\omega + \omega_c} \right| \tag{3-31}$$

Integrating (3-31), we obtain

$$\alpha(\omega) = \int_0^\omega \frac{k}{2\omega_c} \ell n \left| \frac{x - \omega_c}{x + \omega_c} \right| dx$$

$$= \frac{k}{2} \left[\ell n \left| \frac{\omega^2}{\omega_c^2} - 1 \right| - \frac{\omega}{\omega_c} \ell n \left| \frac{\frac{\omega}{\omega_c} - 1}{\frac{\omega}{\omega_c} + 1} \right| \right] \tag{3-32}$$

∎

The perfect constant group delay function of Fig. 3-2(b) within the interval $[-\omega_c, \omega_c]$ is of great interest in filter design. Hence, its associated attenuation function under the condition of minimum phase[6] is of great practical interest. However, it is difficult to see how (3-32) behaves except at extreme regions such as:

1. For $\omega \ll \omega_c$, by taking Taylor series of (3-32), we find[7]

$$\alpha(\omega) \simeq \frac{k}{2} \left[\frac{\omega}{\omega_c} \right]^2$$

2. When $\omega \to \infty$ i.e., for $\omega \gg \omega_c$, the approximation gives

$$\alpha(\omega) \simeq \frac{k}{2} \ell n \left[\frac{\omega}{\omega_c} \right]^2 + \frac{k}{2} \left(\frac{\omega}{\omega_c} \right) \frac{2\omega_c}{\omega + \omega_c}$$

$$\simeq \frac{k}{2} \ell n \left[\frac{\omega}{\omega_c} \right]^2 + k = k \ell n \left| \frac{\omega}{\omega_c} \right| + k$$

A sketch of $\alpha(\omega)$ is shown in Fig. 3-3.

---

[6] The concept of minimum phase is introduced later in this chapter.
[7] Note that $\ell n (1 + x) \simeq x$ when $|x| \ll 1$.

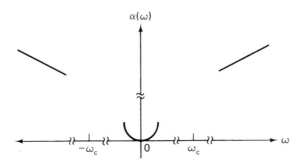

Fig. 3-3 The attenuation function associated with a constant group delay filter.

To apply the Hilbert transform to the phase and magnitude functions of a network function, we require $\gamma(s)$ to be analytic in the RH s-plane. Thus, we require not only that $F(s)$ be analytic in the RH s-plane but also its inverse $1/F(s)$. This is because $\gamma(s) = -\ell n\, F(s) = \ell n\, 1/F(s)$, and if $\gamma(s)$ is analytic, so is $-\gamma(s) = \ell n\, F(s)$. Hence, to apply (3-27) and (3-28), we have to make sure that both $F(s)$ and $1/F(s)$ are analytic in the RH s-plane, which means that no zero or pole of $F(s)$ is located in the RH s-plane.[8] This type of function is called *minimum phase.*

The reason for the name *minimum phase* is that if there are two network functions $F(s)$ and $\hat{F}(s)$ with the same magnitude function,

   (i) $|F(j\omega)| = |\hat{F}(j\omega)|$ for all ω such that
   (ii) $F(s)$ has one or more zeros in the RH s-plane, and
   (iii) $\hat{F}(s)$ has no zero in the RH s-plane,

then

$$\hat{\phi}(\omega) \leq \phi(\omega) \quad \text{for all } \omega \geq 0$$

where $\hat{\phi}(\omega) \triangleq -\underline{/\hat{F}(j\omega)}$ and $\phi(\omega) \triangleq -\underline{/F(j\omega)}$ are the phase functions of $\hat{F}(s)$ and $F(s)$, respectively. In other words, the network function $\hat{F}(s)$ that has no zero in the RH s-plane will have a smaller phase angle than that of the network function $F(s)$ that does have one or more zeros in the RH s-plane.

Even though system stability does not restrict the zero locations of a network function, most common filters are characterized by minimum phase functions. To be otherwise would require mutual couplings, multiple paths between the input and the output of the filter, or their combinations. All

---

[8]A point z_k $\{p_k\}$ is said to be a *zero* $\{pole\}$ of a network function $F(s)$ if $F(z_k) = 0$ $\{F(p_k) = \infty\}$. As a consequence of this definition, a zero $\{pole\}$ can either be a root of the numerator $\{denominator\}$ polynomial of $F(s)$ or be the point at infinity [i.e., $z_k = \infty$ $\{p_k = \infty\}$] if the degree of the numerator polynomial of $F(s)$ is less $\{greater\}$ than the degree of the denominator polynomial of $F(s)$.

of these are avoided in practice, because they tend to increase the complexity and sensitivity of the resulting filter network.

As illustrated in Examples 3-1 and 3-2, the evaluation of the integrals associated with the Hilbert transforms is extremely difficult in general. The strength of the Hilbert transform resides in what it says rather than what it does. The Hilbert transform states that if the real or the even part {the imaginary or the odd part} of a filter is specified to meet certain signal process-ing requirements, then the filter is specified completely. Similarly, if either the phase or the magnitude function of a minimum phase filter is prescribed along the imaginary axis of the *s*-plane, then the filter is completely charac-terized. In other words, a filter can be designed to meet either the phase or the magnitude specifications but not both in general. In this manner, the Hilbert transform spells out the theoretical limitations on filter performances.

3-2-2. Even and Odd Parts

Provided that $F(s)$ is analytic in the RH *s*-plane, the Hilbert transform gives a means to construct the whole function $F(s)$ if either its real or imagin-ary part along the imaginary axis of the *s*-plane is specified. If, in addition, $F(s)$ is of minimum phase, then the Hilbert transform states that we can find $F(s)$ if its magnitude or phase or group delay function is given. However, the difficulties of evaluating the associated Hilbert integrals reduce the practicality of the Hilbert transform to almost nothing. In this section, we describe alternative methods to construct the network function if either its real (even) part or its imaginary (odd) part is given. The other case involving magnitude and phase functions is discussed in the following section.

Recall that a network function $F(s)$ can be written as

$$F(s) = \frac{A(s)}{B(s)} = \frac{\sum\limits_{i=0}^{m} a_i s^i}{\sum\limits_{i=0}^{n} b_i s^i} = \frac{M_1(s) + N_1(s)}{M_2(s) + N_2(s)} = M(s) + N(s) \qquad (3\text{-}33)$$

where

$$M(s) = \frac{M_1(s)M_2(s) - N_1(s)N_2(s)}{M_2^2(s) - N_2^2(s)} \qquad (3\text{-}34)$$

and

$$N(s) = \frac{N_1(s)M_2(s) - N_2(s)M_1(s)}{M_2^2(s) - N_2^2(s)} \qquad (3\text{-}35)$$

Suppose that the even part $M(s)$ of the network function $F(s)$ is given as[9]

$$M(s) = \frac{C(s)}{D(s)} \qquad (3\text{-}36)$$

---

[9] If the real part $R(\omega)$ of $F(s)$ is given, then by (3-15), we can form $M(s)$ as $M(s) = R(s/j)$.

Without loss of generality, let us assume that $D(s)$ is an even polynomial with quadrantally symmetric roots.[10] Then

$$
\begin{aligned}
D(s) &= M_2^2(s) - N_2^2(s) \\
&= [M_2(s) + N_2(s)][M_2(s) - N_2(s)] \\
&= [M_2(s) + N_2(s)][M_2(-s) + N_2(-s)] \\
&= B(s)B(-s)
\end{aligned}
\tag{3-37}
$$

Hence, we can use the imaginary axis of the s-plane as a dividing boundary with either the LH or the RH poles assigned to $B(s)$ and the remaining half assigned to $B(-s)$.[11] Mathematically speaking, there is no preference as to which half should be assigned to $B(s)$. However, as engineers, we prefer to work with *stable* network functions (ones that contain no poles in the RH s-plane). Consequently, we assign the LH s-plane poles of $D(s)$ to $B(s)$, and the RH poles will automatically go to $B(-s)$. That is, we have used $D(s)$, the denominator of the given $M(s)$, to determine the denominator of the desired network function $F(s)$.

Knowing $B(s) = M_2(s) + N_2(s)$, a numerator polynomial $A(s) = \sum_{i=0}^{m} a_i s^i$ with a set of undetermined coefficients a_i, $i = 0, 1, 2, \ldots, m$, is assumed to form

$$
F(s) = \frac{\sum_{i=0}^{m} a_i s^i}{M_2(s) + N_2(s)}
\tag{3-38}
$$

By comparing the numerator of the even part of (3-38) and $C(s)$, the numerator of the given function $M(s)$, we obtain a system of simultaneous equations of $(m + 1)$ unknowns (involving the a_i's).[12] Solution of this system will give the values of the desired a_i's. Hence, $F(s)$ is completely determined.

---

[10]If the roots of the given $D(s)$ are not quadrantally symmetric, then we multiply both $C(s)$ and $D(s)$ of the given $M(s)$ by a polynomial $k(s)$ so that the resulting denominator, $\hat{D}(s) \triangleq k(s)D(s)$, has quadrantally symmetric roots. In this case, we consider the given function as

$$
M(s) = \frac{\hat{C}(s)}{\hat{D}(s)} \triangleq \frac{k(s)C(s)}{k(s)D(s)}.
$$

A simple (but not necessarily the best) choice of $k(s)$ is to let $k(s) \triangleq D(-s)$.

[11]If we use the imaginary axis of the s-plane as the dividing line, then what happens to the roots on the imaginary axis?

Because all imaginary axis roots, say s_k, of $D(s)$ must occur with even multiplicity, say $2l$, we can assign l roots at s_k to $B(s)$ and the remaining l roots at s_k to $B(-s)$. That is, the imaginary axis roots of $D(s)$ are divided such that half goes to $B(s)$ and the other half goes to $B(-s)$. Henceforth, the LH factors will include half of the imaginary axis roots as will the RH factors.

[12]Note that the system of equations arising in this procedure may contain $m + 1$ equations or less, depending on the situation. In any case, however, there exists *at least* one set of a_i's satisfying the foregoing system of equations.

Example 3-3 Given the even part $M(j\omega)$ of $F(s)$ to be

$$M(j\omega) = \frac{\omega^2}{\omega^6 + 1} \tag{3-39}$$

construct $F(s)$.

Solution: Because

$$M(j\omega) = \frac{\omega^2}{\omega^6 + 1} = \frac{-(j\omega)^2}{-(j\omega)^6 + 1}$$

we obtain

$$M(s) = \frac{-s^2}{-s^6 + 1} \triangleq \frac{C(s)}{D(s)} \tag{3-40}$$

Hence,

$$B(s)B(-s) = M_2^2(s) - N_2^2(s) = -s^6 + 1$$

$$= (-s + 1)(s^2 - s + 1)(s + 1)(s^2 + s + 1) \tag{3-41}$$

The factors that give the LH s-plane roots of $D(s)$ are $(s + 1)$ and $(s^2 + s + 1)$. Thus,

$$B(s) = M_2(s) + N_2(s) = (s + 1)(s^2 + s + 1)$$

$$= s^3 + 2s^2 + 2s + 1 \tag{3-42a}$$

$$M_2(s) = 2s^2 + 1 \tag{3-42b}$$

$$N_2(s) = s^3 + 2s \tag{3-42c}$$

From (3-34) and (3-40), the numerator of the even part of $F(s)$ is

$$M_1(s)M_2(s) - N_1(s)N_2(s) = -s^2 \triangleq C(s) \tag{3-43}$$

With $M_2(s)$ and $N_2(s)$ given by (3-42), we may choose $M_1(s)$ and $N_1(s)$ to be polynomials of degrees 2 and 1, respectively.[13] Hence, we can assume that

$$A(s) = \sum_{i=0}^{2} a_i s^i = a_0 + a_1 s + a_2 s^2$$

$$= M_1(s) + N_1(s) \tag{3-44}$$

That is, $M_1(s) = a_0 + a_2 s^2$, and $N_1(s) = a_1 s$. Consequently, (3-43) becomes

$$(a_2 s^2 + a_0)(2s^2 + 1) - (a_1 s)(s^3 + 2s) = -s^2$$

implying that

$$(2a_2 - a_1)s^4 + (2a_0 + a_2 - 2a_1)s^2 + a_0 = -s^2 \tag{3-45}$$

By equating coefficients of same powers on both sides of (3-45), we obtain the following system of equations:

$$a_0 = 0$$

$$2a_0 + a_2 - 2a_1 = -1 \tag{3-46}$$

$$2a_2 - a_1 = 0$$

---

[13]Under the constraints of (3-42), there are many choices of $A(s)$ that will satisfy (3-43). In this case, the simplest choice is when $A(s)$ is a second-degree polynomial. However, we may also let $A(s)$ be any polynomial of degree n, where $n > 0$ is an even integer.

As a general rule, the overall polynomial on the left side of (3-43) must have a degree at least as large as the degree of $C(s)$.

Solving (3-46) gives the solution

$$a_0 = 0, \quad a_1 = \tfrac{2}{3}, \quad \text{and} \quad a_2 = \tfrac{1}{3} \tag{3-47}$$

That is

$$F(s) = \frac{(2/3)s + (1/3)s^2}{s^3 + 2s^2 + 2s + 1} \qquad \blacksquare$$

If we are now given the odd part $N(s)$ of the network function $F(s)$, by using (3-35) instead of (3-34), we can construct a stable $F(s)$ in a manner similar to the previous case when $M(s)$ is given. We now summarize the construction procedure as follows:

CONSTRUCTION PROCEDURE 3-1

0. Let the given function be the odd {even} part $N(s)$ {$M(s)$} of $F(s)$ as

$$N(s)\{M(s)\} = \frac{C(s)}{D(s)}$$

where $D(s)$ is assumed to have quadrantally symmetric roots.

1. Find the roots of $M_2^2(s) - N_2^2(s)$ by factoring the polynomial $D(s)$.

2. Factors associated with LH s-plane roots of $D(s)$ are assigned to $B(s) = M_2(s) + N_2(s)$. Multiply all of these factors together to obtain

$$B(s) = \sum_{i=0}^{n} b_i s^i$$

Hence, we determine $M_2(s)$ and $N_2(s)$, the even and odd parts of $B(s)$, respectively.

3. Assume $A(s) = \sum_{i=0}^{m} a_i s^i$, where the a_i's are undetermined at this point. Form $M_1(s)$ and $N_1(s)$ based on this assumed $A(s)$. Note that the degree m is determined by comparing $C(s)$, the given numerator of $N(s)$ {$M(s)$}, with that of (3-35) {(3-34)}.

4. Form the polynomial $[N_1(s)M_2(s) - N_2(s)M_1(s)]$ {$[M_1(s)M_2(s) - N_1(s)N_2(s)]$}. Equate this resulting polynomial with $C(s)$. This will give rise to a set of k simultaneous equations in $(m + 1)$ unknowns, where $1 \leq k \leq m + 1$. The unknowns are the coefficients of $A(s)$.

5. Solve the system of equations obtained in Step 4 for a_i, $i = 0, 1, 2, \ldots, m$, and then form $F(s) = A(s)/B(s)$.

Example 3-4 Given the odd part $N(s)$ of $F(s)$ to be

$$N(j\omega) = \frac{-j\omega}{1 + \omega^6} \tag{3-48}$$

Find the desired network function $F(s)$.

Solution: From (3-48), we obtain

$$N(s) = \frac{-s}{1 - s^6} \triangleq \frac{C(s)}{D(s)} \tag{3-49}$$

That is

$$M_2^2(s) - N_2^2(s) = 1 - s^6 = D(s) \tag{3-50}$$

and

$$N_1(s)M_2(s) - N_2(s)M_1(s) = -s = C(s) \qquad (3\text{-}51)$$

We now follow the steps outlined in Construction Procedure 3-1:

1. $1 - s^6 = (-s + 1)(s^2 - s + 1)(s + 1)(s^2 + s + 1)$ (3-52a)
2. $B(s) = (s + 1)(s^2 + s + 1) = s^3 + 2s^2 + 2s + 1$ (3-52b)
   $M_2(s) = 2s^2 + 1$
   $N_2(s) = s^3 + 2s$ (3-52c)
3. To determine the lowest degree of the polynomial $A(s)$, let us consider the numerator equation of the odd part

$$N_1(s)M_2(s) - N_2(s)M_1(s) = -s \qquad (3\text{-}53)$$

Because $M_2(s)$ is of second degree and $N_2(s)$ of third, the simplest choice would be to assume the degree of $N_1(s)$ to be 1 and of $M_1(s)$ to be zero. (The next simplest choice would be to assume that $A(s)$ is a third-degree polynomial.) If we take the simplest route and assume $A(s)$ to be

$$A(s) = a_1 s + a_0 \qquad (3\text{-}54a)$$

then

$$M_1(s) = a_0 \qquad (3\text{-}54b)$$

$$N_1(s) = a_1 s \qquad (3\text{-}54c)$$

4. By substituting (3-52) and (3-54) into (3-53), we obtain

$$(a_1 s)(2s^2 + 1) - (s^3 + 2s)(a_0) = -s$$

or

$$(2a_1 - a_0)s^3 + (a_1 - 2a_0)s = -s \qquad (3\text{-}55)$$

Equating the coefficients of both sides of (3-55), we obtain a system of two equations in two unknowns as follows:

$$2a_1 - a_0 = 0$$

$$a_1 - 2a_0 = -1 \qquad (3\text{-}56)$$

5. Solving (3-56) yields

$$a_0 = \tfrac{2}{3} \quad \text{and} \quad a_1 = \tfrac{1}{3} \qquad (3\text{-}57)$$

Hence

$$A(s) = \tfrac{1}{3}(s + 2) \qquad (3\text{-}58)$$

and

$$F(s) = \frac{(1/3)(s + 2)}{s^3 + 2s^2 + 2s + 1} = \frac{s + 2}{3s^3 + 6s^2 + 6s + 3} \qquad (3\text{-}59)$$

∎

3-2-3. Phase and Magnitude Functions

The construction procedure presented in the previous section gives a method for obtaining $F(s)$ if either its odd part or its even part is given. In a sense, this is analogous to the Hilbert transform, which relates the real and the imaginary parts of $F(s)$. Because the Hilbert transform states also that if either its phase angle function or its loss function is given [provided, of course, that $F(s)$ is of minimum phase] then $F(s)$ is characterized completely, a natural question is: Given either the phase or the magnitude function, can a minimum phase network function $F(s)$ be constructed uniquely without resorting to the Hilbert integrals? The answers to both parts of this question are affirmative. However, the construction procedures for these two problems are quite different. We consider their solutions one by one.

Consider the network function of (3-33) through (3-35). With the aid of (3-15), we have

$$\phi(\omega) = -\tan^{-1} \frac{\text{Im}\,[F(j\omega)]}{\text{Re}\,[F(j\omega)]}$$

$$= -\tan^{-1} \frac{N(j\omega)}{jM(j\omega)}$$

$$= -\tan^{-1} \frac{N_1(j\omega)M_2(j\omega) - N_2(j\omega)M_1(j\omega)}{j[M_1(j\omega)M_2(j\omega) - N_1(j\omega)N_2(j\omega)]} \qquad (3\text{-}60)$$

$$\triangleq -\tan^{-1} \frac{\phi_o(s)}{j\phi_e(s)}\Bigg|_{s=j\omega}$$

where

$$\phi_o(s) \triangleq N_1(s)M_2(s) - N_2(s)M_1(s) \qquad (3\text{-}61)$$

and

$$\phi_e(s) \triangleq M_1(s)M_2(s) - N_1(s)N_2(s) \qquad (3\text{-}62)$$

Observe that $\phi_o(s)$ is an odd polynomial and that $\phi_e(s)$ is an even polynomial. If we sum $\phi_o(s)$ and $\phi_e(s)$ together, we obtain

$$p(s) = \phi_o(s) + \phi_e(s) = M_1(s)M_2(s) + N_1(s)M_2(s) - N_1(s)N_2(s) - N_2(s)M_1(s)$$

$$= [M_1(s) + N_1(s)][M_2(s) - N_2(s)] \qquad (3\text{-}63)$$

$$= A(s)B(-s) \qquad F(s) \rightarrow \text{has to be minimum phase}$$
$$\text{for a unique network funct.}$$

Equation (3-63) is the key to constructing $F(s)$. If we assume that $F(s)$ is of minimum phase, then all zeros and poles of $F(s)$ will be in the LH s-plane. That is,

$F(s)$ *has a minimum phase*

1. All roots of the polynomial $A(s)$ will be in the LH s-plane.
2. All roots of the polynomial $B(s)$ will be in the LH s-plane. By Lemma 3-1, all roots of the polynomial $B(-s)$ will be in the RH s-plane.

Hence, (3-63) suggests a procedure to construct $F(s)$ [provided $F(s)$ is minimum phase] as follows:

construction of $F(s)$ when $\phi(\omega)$ is given

CONSTRUCTION PROCEDURE 3-2
1. Let $p(s) \triangleq \phi_o(s) + \phi_e(s)$. Note that once $\phi(\omega)$ is given, $\phi_o(s)$ and $\phi_e(s)$ can be obtained.
2. Factor $p(s)$, or, equivalently, locate the roots of $p(s)$.

3. Factors associated with the LH s-plane roots of $p(s)$ are assigned to $A(s)$. Factors associated with the RH s-plane of $p(s)$ are assigned to $B(-s)$.

4. Find $B(s)$ simply by replacing s with $(-s)$ in the expression of $B(-s)$ found in Step 3.

5. Form $F(s) = A(s)/B(s)$.

This procedure will give rise to a minimum-phase network function $F(s)$ only. If we do not assign factors as indicated in Step 3, then some of the RH s-plane roots of $p(s)$ will be assigned to $A(s)$, and hence $F(s)$ will not be of minimum phase, and the construction procedure will not give rise to a *unique* $F(s)$.

Example 3-5 Construct $F(s)$ from the phase function

$$\phi(\omega) = -\tan^{-1} \frac{-\omega^5 + 5\omega^3 - 2\omega}{2\omega^4 - \omega^2 + 5} \tag{3-64}$$

Solution: By letting $\omega = s/j$, we obtain

$$\phi(\omega) = -\tan^{-1} \frac{-(j\omega)^5 - 5(j\omega)^3 - 2j\omega}{j[2(j\omega)^4 + (j\omega)^2 + 5]} \qquad \phi_o(s) \to odd$$

$$= -\tan^{-1} \left. \frac{-s^5 - 5s^3 - 2s}{j[2s^4 + s^2 + 5]} \right|_{s=j\omega} \overset{\triangle}{=} -\tan^{-1} \left. \frac{\phi_o(s)}{j\phi_e(s)} \right|_{s=j\omega}$$

$$\phi_e(s) \longleftarrow even$$

That is, $\phi_o(s) = -s^5 - 5s^3 - 2s$, and $\phi_e(s) = 2s^4 + s^2 + 5$. Let us now follow the procedure in Construction Procedure 3-2.

1. $p(s) = \phi_o(s) + \phi_e(s) = -s^5 + 2s^4 - 5s^3 + s^2 - 2s + 5$
2. $p(s) = (-s + 1)(s^2 + s + 1)(s^2 - 2s + 5)$
3. Assign $s^2 + s + 1$ to $A(s)$ and $(-s + 1)(s^2 - 2s + 5)$ to $B(-s)$. That is,

$$A(s) = s^2 + s + 1$$
$$B(-s) = (-s + 1)(s^2 - 2s + 5)$$

4. Hence,

$$B(s) = (s + 1)(s^2 + 2s + 5)$$
$$= s^3 + 3s^2 + 7s + 5$$

5. $F(s) = \dfrac{s^2 + s + 1}{s^3 + 3s^2 + 7s + 5}$ \hfill (3-65)

∎

Before we proceed to describe a procedure for constructing a minimum-phase network function $F(s)$ when the magnitude function $|F(j\omega)|$ is given, let us consider an important property of $|F(j\omega)|$. Because the coefficients of the rational function of $F(s)$ are real, we have

$$|F(j\omega)|^2 = F(j\omega)\overline{F(j\omega)} = F(j\omega)F(-j\omega)$$
$$= F(s)F(-s)|_{s=j\omega} \tag{3-66}$$

Let $F(s)$ be given by (3-33); then we can write

$$|F(j\omega)|^2 = \frac{A(s)}{B(s)}\frac{A(-s)}{B(-s)}\Big|_{s=j\omega} \tag{3-67}$$

This means that both the poles and zeros of $|F(j\omega)|^2|_{\omega=s/j} = F(s)F(-s)$ occur in quadruple symmetry. Hence, (3-67) provides us with a key to construct a minimum-phase network function $F(s)$.

Given $|F(j\omega)|$, a construction procedure to obtain $F(s)$ is given as follows:

CONSTRUCTION PROCEDURE 3-3

1. Form $|F(j\omega)|^2\Big|_{\omega=s/j} \triangleq \dfrac{C(s)}{D(s)}$ (3-68)

where $C(s)$ and $D(s)$ are, respectively, the numerator and the denominator of $|F(j\omega)|^2|_{\omega=s/j}$. Clearly, by (3-67),

$$C(s) = A(s)A(-s) \tag{3-69}$$

$$D(s) = B(s)B(-s) \tag{3-70}$$

2. Factor $C(s)$. Assign those factors associated with the LH s-plane zeros to $A(s)$.

3. Factor $D(s)$. Assign those factors associated with the LH s-plane poles to $B(s)$.

4. Form the minimum-phase network function

$$F(s) = \frac{A(s)}{B(s)}$$

where $A(s)$ and $B(s)$ are obtained in Steps 2 and 3, respectively.

Example 3-6   Given

$$|F(j\omega)|^2 = \frac{4+\omega^2}{1+\omega^6} \tag{3-71}$$

Find the minimum-phase network function $F(s)$.

Solution: Following the steps outlined in Construction Procedure 3-3, we have

1. $|F(j\omega)|^2\Big|_{\omega=s/j} = \dfrac{4-s^2}{1-s^6} \triangleq \dfrac{C(s)}{D(s)}$

$C(s) = 4 - s^2$ and $D(s) = 1 - s^6$

2. $C(s) = (2+s)(2-s)$ $\implies$ $A(s) = 2+s$

3. $D(s) = (s+1)(s^2+s+1)(1-s)(s^2-s+1)$

$B(s) = (s+1)(s^2+s+1)$

4. $F(s) = \dfrac{A(s)}{B(s)} = \dfrac{s+2}{(s+1)(s^2+s+1)}$ (3-72)

∎

Note that, as stated by the Hilbert transform, if either the odd part or the even part of $F(s)$ is given, we can find $F(s)$ provided $F(s)$ is analytic in the

RH s-plane [all poles of $F(s)$ are on the closed LH s-plane with the imaginary axis poles being simple]. If, however, either the magnitude or the phase function of $F(s)$ is given, we can construct a unique $F(s)$ only if $F(s)$ is of minimum phase [all the zeros and poles of $F(s)$ must occur on the closed LH s-plane with the imaginary axis poles and zeros being simple].

REFERENCES AND FURTHER READING

[1] WEINBERG, L. *Network Analysis and Synthesis*. Huntington, N.Y.: R. E. Krieger, 1975.

[2] HUMPHREYS, D. S. *The Analysis, Design, and Synthesis of Electrical Filters*. Englewood Cliffs, N.J.: Prentice-Hall, Inc., 1970.

[3] LEON, B. J., and WINTZ, P. A. *Basic Linear Networks for Electrical and Electronics Engineers*. New York: Holt, Rinehart and Winston, 1970.

[4] PAPOULIS, A. *The Fourier Integral and Its Applications*. New York: McGraw-Hill, 1962.

PROBLEMS

3-1. Find the even parts, the odd parts, and the magnitude-squared functions of the following polynomials.

(a) $p(s) = s^2 + 2s + 2$

(b) $p(s) = s^3 + 3s + 2$

(c) $p(s) = 4s^4 + 3s^3 + 2s^2 + s + 2$

(d) $p(s) = s^5 + 0.5s^3 + s$

(e) $p(s) = 6s^6 + \sqrt{2}s^2 + s$

3-2. Find the even parts and the odd parts of the following rational functions.

(a) $f(s) = \dfrac{1}{s+1}$

(b) $f(s) = \dfrac{2s}{s+1}$

(c) $f(s) = \dfrac{s}{s^2 + 2s + 2}$

(d) $f(s) = \dfrac{1}{s^2 + 2s + 2}$

(e) $f(s) = \dfrac{s^2}{s^2 + 2s + 2}$

(f) $f(s) = \dfrac{s+1}{s^2 + 2s + 2}$

(g) $f(s) = \dfrac{s^2 + 1}{s^2 + 2s + 2}$

(h) $f(s) = \dfrac{s^2 + s + 1}{s^2 + 2s + 2}$

(i) $f(s) = \dfrac{s}{s^2 + 1}$

(j) $f(s) = \dfrac{s^2 + 1}{s^3 + 3s}$

3-3. Suppose it is given that the roots of the polynomial

$$f(s) = s^4 + as^2 + b$$

occur with quadrantal symmetry. Hence, $f(s)$ can be expressed as

$$f(s) = p(s)p(-s)$$

where $p(s)$ is a second-order polynomial. Show that $p(s)$ is given by

$$p(s) = s^2 + a_0 s + b_0$$

where

$$b_0 = \sqrt{b} \quad \text{and} \quad a_0 = \sqrt{2b_0 - a}$$

and both a_0 and b_0 are real.

3-4. Find the roots of the following polynomials.

(a) $f(s) = s^4 + 1$
(b) $f(s) = s^4 - 2s^2 + 1$
(c) $f(s) = s^4 + 9s^2 + 25$
(d) $f(s) = s^4 + 5s^2 + 9$
(e) $f(s) = s^4 - 10s^2 + 9$
(f) $f(s) = s^6 - 1$
(g) $f(s) = s^6 + s^4 + 7s^2 - 9$
(h) $f(s) = s^6 - 3s^4 + 3s^2 - 1$
(i) $f(s) = s^6 - 3s^4 - 3s^2 - 4$
(j) $f(s) = s^6 - 7s^4 + 21s^2 - 36$
(k) $f(s) = s^6 - 2s^4 + s^2 - 36$

Hint: $s = -1$ is a root of (f), (g), and (h).
$s = -2$ is a root of (i), (j), and (k).
The roots occur with quadrantal symmetry.

3-5. For each real part $R(\omega)$ given in the following, find its associated rational function $F(s)$ such that $R(\omega) = \text{Re} \, [F(j\omega)]$.

(a) $R(\omega) = \dfrac{\omega^4}{1 + \omega^6}$

(b) $R(\omega) = \dfrac{4 - \omega^2}{\omega^4 - 3\omega^2 + 4}$

(c) $R(\omega) = \dfrac{4\omega^2 + 160}{\omega^2 + 16}$

(d) $R(\omega) = \dfrac{1 + \omega^2}{\omega^4 - \omega^2 + 1}$

(e) $R(\omega) = \dfrac{2\omega^2 - 1}{1 + \omega^6}$

(f) $R(\omega) = \dfrac{\omega^4 - 3\omega^2}{\omega^6 + 3\omega^4 + 3\omega^2 + 1}$

(g) $R(\omega) = \dfrac{-\omega^4 + 3\omega^2 + 6}{\omega^6 + 2\omega^4 + \omega^2 + 36}$

3-6. For each imaginary part $X(\omega)$ given in the following, find its associated rational function $F(s)$ such that $X(\omega) = \text{Im}\,[F(j\omega)]$.

(a) $X(\omega) = \dfrac{-\omega^3 + \omega}{\omega^4 - \omega^2 + 1}$

(b) $X(\omega) = \dfrac{-2\omega^3 + \omega}{\omega^4 - \omega^2 + 1}$

(c) $X(\omega) = \dfrac{-\omega^3}{\omega^4 - 3\omega^2 + 4}$

(d) $X(\omega) = \dfrac{3\omega^3 - \omega}{\omega^6 + 3\omega^4 + 3\omega^2 + 1}$

(e) $X(\omega) = \dfrac{-3\omega^3 - \omega}{\omega^6 + 2\omega^4 + \omega^2 + 36}$

(f) $X(\omega) = \dfrac{2\omega - \omega^3}{1 + \omega^6}$

3-7. Given the odd part $N(s)$ of a network function $F(s)$ as

$$N(s) = \frac{2s^3 + 22s}{s^4 + s^2 + 25}$$

(a) Find an $F(s)$ such that $F(\infty) = 1$.
(b) Find an $F(s)$ such that $F(0) = 1$.

Give reasons if it is not possible to find such an $F(s)$.

3-8. For each of the following phase functions $\phi(\omega)$, find its associated minimum phase function.

(a) $\phi(\omega) = -\tan^{-1} \dfrac{-\omega^3}{4 - \omega^2}$

(b) $\phi(\omega) = -\tan^{-1} \dfrac{2\omega^3 - \omega}{\omega^2 + 1}$

(c) $\phi(\omega) = -\tan^{-1} \dfrac{2\omega - \omega^3}{-1 + 2\omega^2}$

(d) $\phi(\omega) = -\tan^{-1} \dfrac{3\omega^3 - \omega}{\omega^4 - 3\omega^2}$

(e) $\phi(\omega) = -\tan^{-1} \dfrac{-3\omega^3 - \omega}{-\omega^4 + 3\omega^2 + 6}$

3-9. For each magnitude function given in the following, find its associated minimum phase function.

(a) $|H(j\omega)|^2 = \dfrac{\omega^4 - 5\omega^2 + 9}{\omega^4 + 10\omega^2 + 9}$

(b) $|H(j\omega)|^2 = \dfrac{1 + \omega^2}{\omega^6 - \omega^4 + 7\omega^2 + 9}$

(c) $|H(j\omega)|^2 = \dfrac{\omega^4 - 9\omega^2 + 25}{\omega^6 + 3\omega^4 - 3\omega^2 + 4}$

(d) $|H(j\omega)|^2 = \dfrac{\omega^4 + 10\omega^2 + 9}{\omega^6 + 7\omega^4 + 21\omega^2 + 36}$

(e) $|H(j\omega)|^2 = \dfrac{1 + \omega^6}{\omega^6 + 2\omega^4 + \omega^2 + 36}$

(f) $|H(j\omega)|^2 = \dfrac{\omega^4 + 2\omega^2 + 1}{\omega^8 - 5\omega^6 + 11\omega^4 - 11\omega^2 + 4}$

3-10. Write a computer program to implement

    (a) Construction Procedure 3-1.

    (b) Construction Procedure 3-2.

    (c) Construction Procedure 3-3.

4

POSITIVE REAL FUNCTIONS AND PASSIVITY

Let η be a 1-port element containing no internal independent sources. Assuming that all initial conditions inside η are zero, then η may be characterized by either $I(s) = Y(s)V(s)$ or $V(s) = Z(s)I(s)$, where $I(s)$ and $V(s)$ are, respectively, the Laplace transforms of the current entering and the voltage across the 1-port element; $Y(s)$ and $Z(s)$ are called, respectively, the *driving-point* (DP) *admittance* and *impedance functions* of the 1-port element. Basic to most synthesis with only positive-valued resistors, inductors, and capacitors[1] is the concept of *positive real* functions. It has been proven by Brune[2] that every driving-point function of a 1-port containing only passive elements is positive real. Conversely, every positive real function can be realized as a driving-point function of a network containing only passive elements such as positive RLC, ideal transformers, and coupled coils with symmetric and positive definite inductance matrices.[3]

A function $F(s)$ is said to be *positive real* (PR) if it satisfies the following two conditions:

1. $F(s)$ is real when s is real. — *very easy to check*
2. Re $[F(s)] \geq 0$ whenever Re $[s] \geq 0$. — *very difficult*

---

[1]Henceforth, unless explicitly specified otherwise, all resistances, inductances, and capacitances are assumed to be of positive values.

[2]See Reference [1].

[3]Passive resistors, inductors, and capacitors (RLC) are those with positive resistances, inductances, and capacitances, respectively.

An $n \times n$ symmetric matrix $\mathbf{A}$ is said to be *positive definite* if $\mathbf{x}^t\mathbf{A}\mathbf{x} > 0$ for all n-dimensional vector $\mathbf{x} \neq \mathbf{0}$.

The first condition may be checked rather easily by inspection, because it merely requires that all the coefficients of $F(s)$ be real. The second condition means that the complex function $F(\cdot)$ maps the right half (RH) and the imaginary axis of the s-plane into the RH and the imaginary axis of the F-plane, as shown in Fig. 4-1.

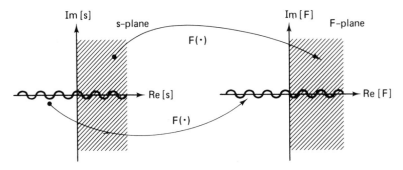

Fig. 4-1 Properties of PR functions.

With this background, we now consider a fundamental concept in passive circuit synthesis.

THEOREM 4-1   Let η be a 1-port network containing passive elements only. Then both the DP impedance and admittance functions of η are PR.

PROOF. To simplify our proof, we assume that η contains only passive resistors, inductors, and capacitors. The extension of this simplified proof to the general case is clear. In addition, we prove the theorem for the impedance function only. The admittance case may be proved in a *dual* manner.

Consider the circuit in Fig. 4-2, where the 1-port η contains only passive resistors, inductors, and capacitors. Tellegen's theorem states that

$$\sum_{k=1}^{b} V_k \bar{I}_k = 0 \tag{4-1}$$

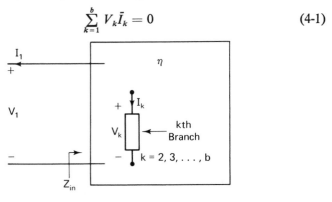

Fig. 4-2 A 1-port circuit containing $b - 1$ passive RLC elements.

where $\bar{I}_k$ is the complex conjugate of I_k, and we assume that η contains $b-1$ elements, namely from 2 to b. Clearly, (4-1) can be written as

$$-V_1\bar{I}_1 = \sum_{k=2}^{b} V_k\bar{I}_k = \sum_{\Re} V_k\bar{I}_k + \sum_{\mathfrak{C}} V_k\bar{I}_k + \sum_{\mathfrak{L}} V_k\bar{I}_k \qquad (4\text{-}2)$$

where $\sum_{\Re}$, $\sum_{\mathfrak{C}}$, and $\sum_{\mathfrak{L}}$ denote sums over all resistors, all capacitors, and all inductors, respectively. Let $Z_{\text{in}}(s)$ be the DP impedance of η, then

$$V_1 = -Z_{\text{in}}(s)I_1 \qquad (4\text{-}3\text{a})$$

In addition, if branch k is a resistor of R_k Ω, then

$$V_k = R_k I_k \qquad (4\text{-}3\text{b})$$

If branch k is a capacitor of C_k Farads, then

$$V_k = \frac{1}{sC_k}I_k \qquad (4\text{-}3\text{c})$$

Finally, if branch k is an inductor of L_k Henries, then

$$V_k = sL_k I_k \qquad (4\text{-}3\text{d})$$

Because η contains passive elements only, we have

$$R_k > 0, \quad L_k > 0, \quad \text{and} \quad C_k > 0 \qquad (4\text{-}4)$$

After substituting (4-3) into (4-2), we obtain

$$Z_{\text{in}}(s)|I_1|^2 = \sum_{\Re} R_k |I_k|^2 + \sum_{\mathfrak{C}} \frac{1}{sC_k}|I_k|^2 + \sum_{\mathfrak{L}} sL_k |I_k|^2$$

$$\Longrightarrow Z_{\text{in}}(s) = \sum_{\Re} R_k \frac{|I_k|^2}{|I_1|^2} + \frac{1}{s}\sum_{\mathfrak{C}} \frac{1}{C_k}\frac{|I_k|^2}{|I_1|^2} + s\sum_{\mathfrak{L}} L_k \frac{|I_k|^2}{|I_1|^2} \qquad (4\text{-}5)$$

Let $s = \sigma + j\omega$. Then (4-5) becomes

$$Z_{\text{in}}(s) = \sum_{\Re} R_k \frac{|I_k|^2}{|I_1|^2} + \frac{\sigma}{\sigma^2 + \omega^2}\sum_{\mathfrak{C}} \frac{1}{C_k}\frac{|I_k|^2}{|I_1|^2} + \sigma\sum_{\mathfrak{L}} L_k \frac{|I_k|^2}{|I_1|^2}$$

$$-j\frac{\omega}{\sigma^2 + \omega^2}\sum_{\mathfrak{C}} \frac{1}{C_k}\frac{|I_k|^2}{|I_1|^2} + j\omega\sum_{\mathfrak{L}} L_k \frac{|I_k|^2}{|I_1|^2} \qquad (4\text{-}6)$$

Hence, we have

$$\text{Re}\,[Z_{\text{in}}(s)] = \sum_{\Re} R_k \frac{|I_k|^2}{|I_1|^2} + \frac{\sigma}{\sigma^2 + \omega^2}\sum_{\mathfrak{C}} \frac{1}{C_k}\frac{|I_k|^2}{|I_1|^2} + \sigma\sum_{\mathfrak{L}} L_k \frac{|I_k|^2}{|I_1|^2} \qquad (4\text{-}7)$$

From (4-7), we can conclude that if $\sigma \geq 0$, then $\text{Re}\,[Z_{\text{in}}(s)] \geq 0$. That is

$$\text{Re}\,[Z_{\text{in}}(s)] \geq 0 \quad \text{whenever} \quad \text{Re}\,[s] \geq 0$$

From (4-6), if $\omega = 0$, then $Z_{\text{in}}(s)$ is real. Hence, we also can conclude that $Z_{\text{in}}(s)$ is real when s is real. Thus, $Z_{\text{in}}(s)$ is PR.   ∎

The converse to Theorem 4-1 has been shown to be true by Brune, and we simply state the result.[4]

---

[4]The proof of this theorem can be found in References [1] and [2].

THEOREM 4-2 Let $F(s)$ be a positive real function. Then $F(s)$ can be realized as a DP impedance or admittance function of a 1-port containing passive elements only.

In view of the previous two theorems, we can conclude:

COROLLARY 4-3 $F(s)$ is PR if, and only if, $1/F(s)$ is PR.

4-1 HURWITZ POLYNOMIAL

In general, it is very difficult to check condition 2 of a PR function. Hence, it is desirable to have alternate but equivalent conditions for checking the positive-realness of a function. One way to achieve this objective is through the concept of Hurwitz and modified Hurwitz polynomials.

A polynomial $p(s)$ is said to be *Hurwitz* if all the roots of $p(s)$ are located in the open left half (LH) s-plane (not including the imaginary axis); $p(s)$ is said to be *modified Hurwitz* if none of its roots are in the open RH s-plane and all imaginary axis roots are simple—with multiplicity equal to one.[5]

Based on the definitions stated in the preceding paragraph, we need to locate all the roots of a polynomial $p(s)$ before we can tell if $p(s)$ is a Hurwitz or a modified Hurwitz polynomial. It is known that finding all the roots of a polynomial is not an easy task. Consequently, direct applications of the definition of a Hurwitz or a modified Hurwitz polynomial are not desirable. In this section, we describe methods to determine if a polynomial is Hurwitz or modified Hurwitz (or neither) without finding its roots.

Let $p(s)$ be the polynomial in question. Assume first that $p(s)$ is neither an even nor an odd polynomial. To test whether such a polynomial $p(s)$ is indeed a Hurwitz polynomial, we may use the Hurwitz test, which applies the steps of Euclid's algorithm (in finding the greatest common factor) to the even and odd parts of $p(s)$ with some minor modifications. Specifically, we first decompose $p(s)$ into its even and odd parts, $M(s)$ and $N(s)$, respectively, as $p(s) = M(s) + N(s)$. Using $M(s)$ and $N(s)$ we form the test ratio $T(s)$, whose numerator has a higher degree than that of its denominator. Suppose that $p(s)$ is a polynomial of degree d. Then

$$T(s) = \frac{N(s)}{M(s)} \quad \text{if } d \text{ is an odd integer} \tag{4-8a}$$

and

$$T(s) = \frac{M(s)}{N(s)} \quad \text{if } d \text{ is an even integer} \tag{4-8b}$$

Next, we perform the *continued fraction expansion* about infinity on the test

---

[5]Clearly, a modified Hurwitz polynomial is not necessarily Hurwitz, but a Hurwitz polynomial is also a modified Hurwitz polynomial.

ratio $T(s)$, removing one pole at a time in the form of a quotient qs, resulting in

$$T(s) = q_1 s + \cfrac{1}{q_2 s + \cfrac{1}{q_3 s + \cfrac{1}{\begin{array}{c} \ddots \\ + \cfrac{1}{q_{\hat{d}} s} \end{array}}}} \tag{4-9}$$

where $q_i s$ is the ith quotient, and q_i is the associated coefficient.

If there is one or more quotients with negative coefficients, then $p(s)$ is neither a Hurwitz nor a modified Hurwitz polynomial. On the other hand, if there are d quotients ($\hat{d} = d$) and every quotient has a positive coefficient, then $p(s)$ is a Hurwitz polynomial. Finally, if the number of quotient $\hat{d}$ is less than d but every quotient has a positive coefficient, this means that there is a common factor $k(s)$ between $M(s)$ and $N(s)$. Hence, we can write $p(s)$ as

$$p(s) = k(s)[\hat{M}(s) + \hat{N}(s)] = k(s)\hat{p}(s) \tag{4-10}$$

where $M(s) = k(s)\hat{M}(s)$, $N(s) = k(s)\hat{N}(s)$, and $\hat{p}(s) = \hat{M}(s) + \hat{N}(s)$.

Because $k(s)$ is a common factor of both an even and an odd polynomial, $k(s)$ is either an odd or an even polynomial. Let us first consider the case when $k(s)$ is an even polynomial. In this case, we can write

$$k(s) = k(-s) \tag{4-11}$$

This implies that the roots of $k(s)$ will occur with symmetry about the origin—s_j is a root of $k(s)$ if and only if $-s_j$ is a root of $k(s)$. Observe that if s_j is not a purely imaginary number, then $k(s)$ will contain a RH s-plane root (because if s_j is in the LH s-plane, then $-s_j$ will be in the RH s-plane, and vice versa). Hence, $k(s)$ is at most a modified Hurwitz polynomial. This occurs only if all the roots of $k(s)$ are simple and purely imaginary—on the imaginary axis of the s-plane. Consequently, $p(s)$ can not be a Hurwitz polynomial.

Suppose now that $k(s)$ is an odd polynomial. Because an odd polynomial can be written as a product of s and an even polynomial, $k(s)$ is at most a modified Hurwitz polynomial. Hence, again, $p(s)$ can not be a Hurwitz polynomial.

Because all the $\hat{d}$ quotients of $T(s)$ have positive coefficients, the polynomial $\hat{p}(s)$ in (4-10) is Hurwitz. Thus, if $k(s)$ is a modified Hurwitz polynomial [i.e., if all the roots of $k(s)$ are simple and purely imaginary], then $p(s)$ is a modified Hurwitz polynomial.

A procedure to determine if $k(s)$ is a modified Hurwitz polynomial is described in the following in conjunction with the case when $p(s)$ is either an even or an odd polynomial.

Suppose now that $p(s)$ is either an even or an odd polynomial of degree d. Then $p(s)$ is a modified Hurwitz polynomial if and only if $p(s)$ has only simple and imaginary axis roots (including the origin).

To determine if $p(s)$ is a modified Hurwitz polynomial, we form a test ratio $\hat{T}(s)$ as

$$\hat{T}(s) = \frac{p(s)}{(d/ds)\,p(s)} = \frac{p(s)}{p'(s)} \qquad (4\text{-}12)$$

and perform the continued fraction expansion about infinity on $\hat{T}(s)$, as in (4-9). Then $p(s)$ is a modified Hurwitz polynomial if and only if there are d quotients in the expansion and each quotient has a positive coefficient.[6] The following examples illustrate these testing procedures.

Example 4-1   Determine if

$$p(s) = s^4 + 3s^3 + 5s^2 + 5s + 2 \qquad (4\text{-}13)$$

is a Hurwitz polynomial.

Solution: $p(s) = s^4 + 3s^3 + 5s^2 + 5s + 2$

$$= (s^4 + 5s^2 + 2) + (3s^3 + 5s)$$

$$= M(s) + N(s)$$

Because $d = 4$ is even, the test ratio is

$$T(s) \triangleq \frac{M(s)}{N(s)} = \frac{s^4 + 5s^2 + 2}{3s^3 + 5s} \qquad (4\text{-}14)$$

Clearly, at $s = \infty$, $T(s) = \infty$ [i.e., $T(s)$ has a pole at infinity]. Extracting this pole at infinity in the form of a quotient, we obtain

$$T(s) = \frac{1}{3}s + \frac{1}{T_1(s)} \qquad (4\text{-}15)$$

where $(1/3)s$ is the first quotient, $1/3$ is its coefficient, and

$$\frac{1}{T_1(s)} = T(s) - \frac{1}{3}s = \frac{(10/3)s^2 + 2}{3s^3 + 5s}$$

is the remainder. Hence,

$$T_1(s) = \frac{3s^3 + 5s}{(10/3)s^2 + 2} \qquad (4\text{-}16)$$

---

[6]In the case when $p(s)$ is either an even or an odd polynomial, if there is one or more negative coefficient in the continued fraction expansion of $\hat{T}(s)$, then $p(s)$ has a RH s-plane root; and if all coefficients are positive but there are only $\hat{d} < d$ quotients, then all roots of $p(s)$ are on the imaginary axis of the s-plane, but $p(s)$ has nonsimple or multiple roots. Either situation implies that $p(s)$ is not a modified Hurwitz polynomial.

Observe that $T_1(\infty) = \infty$. Thus, we can extract a pole from $T_1(s)$ in the form of a quotient as we did to $T(s)$. The result is to write $T_1(s)$ as

$$T_1(s) = \frac{9}{10}s + \frac{1}{T_2(s)} \tag{4-17}$$

where $(9/10)s$ is the second quotient, $9/10$ is its coefficient, and $1/T_2(s)$ is the second remainder. Substituting (4-17) into (4-11), we have

$$T(s) = \frac{1}{3}s + \frac{1}{(9/10)s + [1/T_2(s)]} \tag{4-18}$$

where

$$\frac{1}{T_2(s)} = T_1(s) - \frac{9}{10}s = \frac{(16/5)s}{(10/3)s^2 + 2}$$

or

$$T_2(s) = \frac{(10/3)s^2 + 2}{(16/5)s} \tag{4-19}$$

Clearly, $T_2(\infty) = \infty$. Removing the pole at infinity from $T_2(s)$, we obtain

$$T_2(s) = \frac{25}{24}s + \frac{1}{T_3(s)} \tag{4-20}$$

where $(25/24)s$ is the third quotient, $25/24$ is its coefficient, and

$$\frac{1}{T_3(s)} = T_2(s) - \frac{25}{24}s = \frac{2}{(16/5)s} = \frac{1}{(8/5)s} \tag{4-21}$$

is the third remainder. Substituting (4-20) and (4-21) into (4-18), we obtain the continued fraction expansion of $T(s)$ at $s = \infty$ as

$$T(s) = \frac{1}{3}s + \cfrac{1}{(9/10)s + \cfrac{1}{(25/24)s + \cfrac{1}{(8/5)s}}} \tag{4-22}$$

Because there are four quotients and their coefficients are positive (being 1/3, 9/10, 25/24, and 8/5), $p(s)$ is Hurwitz. ∎

The foregoing example gives a step-by-step procedure to obtain a continued fraction expansion of the test ratio $T(s)$. Though the process gives insight to what a continued fraction expansion really does, it is a cumbersome procedure. Fortunately, it is possible to obtain the continued fraction expansion of a rational function by a simpler means—a long division method. As an example, the continued fraction expansion of $T(s)$ of (4-12) at $s = \infty$ is given by

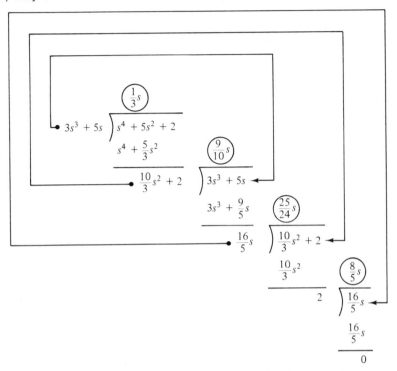

where the encircled quantities are the quotients. With these quotients, we can form (4-22) rather easily. In fact, we can determine whether a polynomial is Hurwitz or not by just checking the coefficients of the encircled quantities.

Example 4-2 Determine if the polynomial

$$p(s) = s^4 + s^3 + 6s^2 + 2s + 8 \qquad (4\text{-}23)$$

is a Hurwitz or a modified Hurwitz polynomial (or neither).

Solution: Because $p(s)$ is neither an even nor an odd polynomial, we write $p(s)$ as

$$p(s) = (s^4 + 6s^2 + 8) + (s^3 + 2s) \triangleq M(s) + N(s)$$

and form the test ratio

$$T(s) = \frac{M(s)}{N(s)} = \frac{s^4 + 6s^2 + 8}{s^3 + 2s} \qquad (4\text{-}24)$$

A continued fraction expansion of $T(s)$ at $s = \infty$ gives

$$T(s) = s + \frac{1}{(1/4)s} \qquad (4\text{-}25)$$

This implies that there is a common factor between $M(s) \triangleq s^4 + 6s^2 + 8$ and $N(s) \triangleq s^3 + 2s$. To find the greatest common factor (GCF) between $M(s)$ and $N(s)$ is trivial if we perform the continued fraction expansion by the long division method—the GCF is the divisor that leaves the remainder zero. For example, in this case, the long division process is given by

$$
\begin{array}{r}
s \\
s^3 + 2s \overline{)s^4 + 6s^2 + 8} \\
s^4 + 2s^2 \\
\hline
4s^2 + 8 \overline{)s^3 + 2s} \\
s^3 + 2s \\
\hline
0
\end{array} \quad \frac{1}{4}s
$$

Hence, $(4s^2 + 8)$ is the GCF between the even and odd parts of $p(s)$. That is, we can write $p(s)$ as

$$p(s) = (4s^2 + 8)[(s^2 + 4) + s] \triangleq k(s)\hat{p}(s)$$

Because all coefficients in (4-25) are positive, $\hat{p}(s) \triangleq s^2 + s + 4$ is Hurwitz. Hence, if $k(s) \triangleq 4s^2 + 8$ is modified Hurwitz, then $p(s)$ is also a modified Hurwitz polynomial.

To test if $k(s)$ is a modified Hurwitz polynomial, we form the test ratio

$$\hat{T}(s) = \frac{k(s)}{(d/ds)\,k(s)} = \frac{4s^2 + 8}{8s} \tag{4-26}$$

The continued fraction expansion of $\hat{T}(s)$ at $s = \infty$ is given by

$$\hat{T}(s) = \frac{1}{2}s + \frac{1}{s} \tag{4-27}$$

Because $k(s)$ is a second-degree polynomial and there are two quotients, both with positive coefficients, $k(s)$ is modified Hurwitz. Hence, $p(s)$ of (4-23) is a modified Hurwitz polynomial. ∎

Example 4-3 Determine if the polynomial

$$p(s) = s^6 + s^5 + 4s^4 + 2s^3 + 5s^2 + s + 2 \tag{4-28}$$

is Hurwitz or modified Hurwitz or neither.

Solution: Let us write $p(s)$ as

$$p(s) = (s^6 + 4s^4 + 5s^2 + 2) + (s^5 + 2s^3 + s)$$
$$\triangleq M(s) + N(s)$$

Hence, the test ratio $T(s)$ is given by

$$T(s) = \frac{s^6 + 4s^4 + 5s^2 + 2}{s^5 + 2s^3 + s}$$
$$= s + \frac{1}{(1/2)s} \tag{4-29}$$

This implies that the GCF, $k(s)$, between $M(s) \triangleq s^6 + 4s^4 + 5s^2 + 2$ and $N(s) = s^5 + 2s^3 + s$ is not a constant. In fact, $k(s)$ is given by

$$k(s) = 2s^4 + 4s^2 + 2 \tag{4-30}$$

To test if $k(s)$ is modified Hurwitz, we form the test ratio $\hat{T}(s)$ as

$$\hat{T}(s) = \frac{k(s)}{(d/ds)\,k(s)} = \frac{2s^4 + 4s^2 + 2}{8s^3 + 8s} \tag{4-31}$$

and perform the continued fraction expansion of $\hat{T}(s)$ at $s = \infty$ as

$$\hat{T}(s) = \frac{1}{4}s + \frac{1}{(1/4)s} \tag{4-32}$$

Because $k(s)$ is a fourth-degree polynomial and there are only two quotients in (4-32), $k(s)$ has multiple imaginary axis roots. Indeed $s = \pm j$ are double roots of $k(s)$. Hence, $p(s)$ of (4-28) is neither a Hurwitz nor a modified Hurwitz polynomial. ∎

Example 4-4 Determine if

$$p(s) = s^5 + 2s^3 + 2s \tag{4-33}$$

is a modified Hurwitz polynomial.

Solution: Because $p(s)$ is an odd polynomial, we form the test ratio

$$\hat{T}(s) = \frac{s^5 + 2s^3 + 2s}{5s^4 + 6s^2 + 2} \tag{4-34}$$

A (partial) continued fraction expansion of $\hat{T}(s)$ at $s = \infty$ gives

$$\hat{T}(s) = \frac{1}{5}s + \cfrac{1}{\frac{25}{4}s + \cfrac{1}{-\frac{1}{5}s + \cfrac{2s}{-4s^2 + 2}}} \tag{4-35}$$

Because the third quotient has a negative coefficient, we can terminate the expansion process and conclude that $p(s)$ of (4-33) is not a modified Hurwitz polynomial. Indeed, $p(s)$ has two RH s-plane roots. ∎

Example 4-5 Determine if

$$p(s) = s^6 + 6s^4 + 11s^2 + 6 \tag{4-36}$$

is a modified Hurwitz polynomial.

Solution: By (4-12), the test ratio is

$$\hat{T}(s) = \frac{s^6 + 6s^4 + 11s^2 + 6}{6s^5 + 24s^3 + 22s} \tag{4-37}$$

A continued fraction expansion of $\hat{T}(s)$ at $s = \infty$ gives

$$\hat{T}(s) = \frac{1}{6}s + \cfrac{1}{3s + \cfrac{1}{s + \cfrac{1}{\frac{3}{5}s + \cfrac{1}{\frac{25}{3}s + \cfrac{1}{\frac{1}{15}s}}}}} \tag{4-38}$$

Because there are six quotients and all of them have positive coefficients, $p(s)$ is a modified Hurwitz polynomial. ∎

The Hurwitz test is a fundamental tool in many disciplines, especially in stability studies of linear systems. Many necessary conditions have been found; conditions that a polynomial must satisfy in order to be a candidate for a Hurwitz polynomial. Two of these necessary conditions are:

1. No missing terms in the polynomial.   (4-39a)
2. Either all coefficients are positive or all are negative.   (4-39b)

For example, the polynomial $p_1(s) = s^3 + s + 2$ is not Hurwitz, because it has a missing term—the second-power term. The polynomial $p_2(s) = s^3 + s^2 - s + 1$ is not Hurwitz, because there are positive as well as negative coefficients present in the polynomial.

It should be emphasized here that the two conditions in (4-39) are necessary but not sufficient. For example, the polynomial

$$p_3(s) = s^4 + s^3 + 6s^2 + 26s + 20 \qquad (4\text{-}40)$$

satisfies both the necessary conditions of (4-39), but $p_3(s)$ of (4-40) is *not* a Hurwitz polynomial, because $p_3(s)$ has a pair of complex roots $1 \pm j3$ in the RH s-plane. In other words, if a polynomial $p(s)$ does not pass either one of the two tests in (4-39), then $p(s)$ is not Hurwitz. However, if $p(s)$ passes all these two conditions, it does not mean that $p(s)$ is Hurwitz. In that case, a Hurwitz test should be administered to $p(s)$ to determine its status. For simple cases, we know some sufficient conditions also. They are:

1. A first- or second-order polynomial with no missing terms and with all its coefficients being of the same sign is Hurwitz.   (4-41a)
2. A product of Hurwitz polynomials is Hurwitz.   (4-41b)

These two sufficient conditions can be used to advantage. For example, if a complicated polynomial can be factored into (or is in the form of) a product of first- and second-order polynomials as

$$p(s) = p_1(s)p_2(s)\ldots p_q(s) \qquad (4\text{-}42)$$

where each $p_i(s)$, $i = 1, 2, \ldots, q$, is either a first- or a second-degree polynomial, then the Hurwitz test of $p(s)$ is now reduced to checking the coefficients of each polynomial factor $p_i(s)$, where $i = 1, 2, \ldots, q$. If every factor $p_i(s)$, where $i = 1, 2, \ldots, q$, is Hurwitz, then $p(s)$ is Hurwitz. On the other hand, if one factor, say $p_k(s)$, is not a Hurwitz polynomial, then $p(s)$ is also not a Hurwitz polynomial.

Example 4-6   Determine if

$$p(s) = s^5 + 6s^4 + 16s^3 + 27s^2 + 22s + 12 \qquad (4\text{-}43)$$

is a Hurwitz polynomial.

Solution: Clearly $p(s)$ of (4-43) satisfies the conditions in (4-39). We can administer the Hurwitz test to determine if $p(s)$ is Hurwitz, or we can take advantage of the sufficient conditions of (4-41) by factoring $p(s)$ as follows:

$$p(s) = (s^2 + s + 1)(s^2 + 2s + 4)(s + 3) \qquad (4\text{-}44)$$

The first sufficient condition test says that every one of the three factors of $p(s)$ is Hurwitz, and the second sufficient condition test concludes that $p(s)$ is Hurwitz. ∎

Observe that products of Hurwitz and modified Hurwitz polynomials are not necessarily modified Hurwitz polynomials. A case in point is given as follows: Suppose that $p(s)$ is a product of a Hurwitz and two modified Hurwitz polynomials as

$$p(s) = (s^2 + s + 1)(s^3 + s)(s^2 + 1) \qquad (4\text{-}45)$$

Because $p(s)$ has double roots at $s = \pm j$, $p(s)$ is not a modified Hurwitz polynomial. However, a product of Hurwitz polynomials and a single modified Hurwitz polynomial is always a modified Hurwitz polynomial. Finally, we state a result that will be of use later.

THEOREM 4-4 Let $p(s) = M(s) + N(s)$ be a Hurwitz polynomial, where $M(s)$ and $N(s)$ are, respecitvely, the even and odd parts of $p(s)$, then the rational functions

$$F_1(s) \triangleq \frac{M(s)}{N(s)} \quad \text{and} \quad F_2(s) \triangleq \frac{N(s)}{M(s)} \qquad (4\text{-}46)$$

can be realized as driving-point impedance or admittance functions of 1-port networks containing inductors and capacitors only.

Conversely, the sum of the numerator and the denominator of a driving-point function of a lossless 1-port is a Hurwitz polynomial.

4-2 POSITIVE REAL (PR) FUNCTIONS

Recall that a positive real function $F(s)$ satisfies two conditions: the *real part*—$F(s)$ is real when s is real [which means that the coefficients of both the numerator and the denominator polynomials of $F(s)$ must be real]—and the *positive part*—Re $[F(s)] \geq 0$ whenever Re $[s] \geq 0$. In general, the positive part is difficult to check. In the following, we state some alternate but equivalent conditions.

THEOREM 4-5 $F(s) \triangleq A(s)/B(s)$ is PR if, and only if, it satisfies the following conditions:

1. $F(s)$ is real when s is real.
2. $B(s)$ is either a Hurwitz or a modified Hurwitz polynomial.

3. The imaginary axis poles of $F(s)$ are simple[7] and have real and positive residues.

4. $\mathrm{Re}\,[F(j\omega)] \geq 0$ for all ω. (4-47)

∎

Note that the *residue* of a function $F(s)$ at the simple pole s_k, denoted by ξ_k, is given by

$$\xi_k = [(s - s_k)F(s)]\Big|_{s=s_k} = \frac{A(s)}{(d/ds)\,B(s)}\Big|_{s=s_k} \quad \text{if } s_k \text{ is finite} \quad (4\text{-}48a)$$

$$\xi_k = \lim_{s\to\infty} \frac{1}{s} F(s) \quad \text{if } s_k = \infty \quad (4\text{-}48b)$$

where $A(s)$ and $B(s)$ are, respectively, the numerator and the denominator polynomials of $F(s)$. From (4-48), we observe that the residue of $F(s)$ at a real pole is real and the residues of $F(s)$ at a pair of complex conjugate poles are complex conjugates.

To illustrate the use of (4-48), let us consider the rational function

$$F(s) = \frac{4s + 2}{s^3 + 7s^2 + 17s + 15} = \frac{4s + 2}{(s + 3)(s + 2 + j)(s + 2 - j)} \quad (4\text{-}49)$$

Here, $F(s)$ has three simple poles, namely: $s_1 = -3$, $s_2 = -2 - j$, and $s_3 = -2 + j$. The residue of $F(s)$ at s_1 can be calculated in two ways, as indicated in (4-48), as

$$\xi_1 = [(s - s_1)F(s)]\Big|_{s=s_1} = \frac{4s_1 + 2}{(s_1 + 2 + j)(s_1 + 2 - j)}$$

$$= \frac{-12 + 2}{(-1 + j)(-1 - j)} = -\frac{10}{2} = -5$$

or

$$\xi_1 = \frac{4s + 2}{(d/ds)\,[s^3 + 7s^2 + 17s + 15]}\Big|_{s=s_1} = \frac{4s + 2}{3s^2 + 14s + 17}\Big|_{s=s_1=-3}$$

$$= \frac{-12 + 2}{27 - 42 + 17} = -\frac{10}{2} = -5 \quad (4\text{-}50a)$$

The residues of $F(s)$ at the poles s_2 and s_3 are given as follows:

$$\xi_2 = \frac{4s + 2}{(s + 3)(s + 2 - j)}\Big|_{s=s_2=-2-j} = \frac{3 + 2j}{1 + j} = \frac{5 - j}{2} \quad (4\text{-}50b)$$

$$\xi_3 = \frac{4s + 2}{(s + 3)(s + 2 + j)}\Big|_{s=s_3=-2+j} = \frac{5 + j}{2} \quad (4\text{-}50c)$$

---

[7]Imaginary axis poles of $F(s)$ include the pole at $s = \infty$ (if applicable). Because condition 2 of Theorem 4-5 already ensures that *finite* imaginary axis poles of $F(s)$ are simple, we need to be concerned only with the (possible) pole at infinity. If the degree of $A(s)$ is at most one degree larger than the degree of $B(s)$, then $F(s)$ has at most a simple pole at $s = \infty$.

Conditions 2 through 4 of Theorem 4-5 form a set of testing criteria for the positive condition of $F(s)$; i.e.,

$$\text{Re}\,[F(s)] \geq 0 \quad \text{whenever Re}\,[s] \geq 0 \qquad (4\text{-}51)$$

Unlike (4-51), condition 4 of Theorem 4-5 requires us to test Re $[F(s)]$ along the imaginary axis only. This, in general, is done by brute force or direct calculations. In complicated cases, a Sturm test[8] can be used to determine if condition 4 of Theorem 4-5 is satisfied.

In view of Corollary 4-3 (that the inverse of a PR function is another PR function) and of the conditions stated in Theorem 4-5, the following are some necessary conditions for $F(s) = A(s)/B(s)$ to be PR:

1. The difference between the polynomial degrees of $A(s)$ and $B(s)$ is at most one. (4-52a)
   (The reason is that the imaginary axis poles of a PR function must be simple, and poles at the origin and infinity are considered to be imaginary axis poles. Hence, poles at the origin and infinity have to be simple.)
2. The difference between the lowest powers of $A(s)$ and $B(s)$ is at most one. (4-52b)
   (Same reason as in condition 1.)
3. All coefficients of $A(s)$ and $B(s)$ are nonnegative.[9] (4-52c)
   (This is to ensure that both $A(s)$ and $B(s)$ are at least modified Hurwitz.)
4. No multiple imaginary axis poles or zeros. No RH s-plane poles or zeros. (4-52d)

Example 4-7

1. $F_1(s) = (s^4 + s^3 + s^2 + s + 1)/(2s + 7)$ is not PR, because the difference between the highest powers of $A(s)$ and $B(s)$ is more than one.
2. $F_2(s) = s^2/(2s + 7)$ is not PR, because the difference between the lowest powers of $A(s)$ and $B(s)$ is more than one.
3. $F_3(s) = (s^2 + 4s - 3)/(s^2 + 4s + 9)$ is not PR, because there is a negative coefficient in $A(s)$.
4. $F_4(s) = (s^2 + 4s + 3)/(-s^2 + 4s + 9)$ is not PR, because there is a negative coefficient in $B(s)$.
5. $F_5(s) = (s - 3)/(s + 4)$ is not PR because of a RH s-plane zero.
6. $F_6(s) = (s + 3)/(s - 4)$ is not PR, because there is a RH s-plane pole.
7. $F_7(s) = (s^3 + s^2 + s + 2)/(s^4 + 2s^2 + 1)$ and $F_8(s) = (s + 3)/s^2$ are not PR because of multiple poles on the imaginary axis.
8. $F_9(s) = [s^2(s + 1)]/(s^3 + 3s^2 + 2s + 1)$ is not PR because of multiple imaginary axis zeros. ∎

---

[8]See Reference [8] for details.

[9]Zero coefficients may be allowed in $A(s)$ and $B(s)$, because $A(s)$ and $B(s)$ may be modified Hurwitz polynomials, and yet $F(s)$ is PR. See $F_{10}(s)$ in Example 4-8.

The conditions listed in (4-52) are necessary but not sufficient. They are used to screen out obvious non-PR functions. To declare a rational function to be PR, we must apply Theorem 4-5 or its equivalences.

Example 4-8 Determine if the rational function

$$F_{10}(s) = \frac{s^2 + s + 2}{s^2 + 2} \tag{4-53}$$

is PR.

Solution: It can be shown easily that $F_{10}(s)$ passes all the necessary condition tests of (4-52). This means that $F_{10}(s)$ is a potential PR function. We now apply Theorem 4-5.

1. $F_{10}(s)$ is real when s is real.
2. The denominator $B(s)$ of $F_{10}(s)$ is modified Hurwitz, with the imaginary axis poles being at $s_1 = j\sqrt{2}$ and $s_2 = -j\sqrt{2}$. Both poles are simple.
3. Let ξ_k be the residue of $F_{10}(s)$ at the pole s_k. Then

$$\xi_1 = \frac{s^2 + s + 2}{s + j\sqrt{2}}\bigg|_{s=s_1=j\sqrt{2}} = \frac{1}{2}$$

and

$$\xi_2 = \frac{s^2 + s + 2}{s - j\sqrt{2}}\bigg|_{s=s_2=-j\sqrt{2}} = \frac{1}{2}$$

That is, both ξ_1 and ξ_2 are real and positive.

4. $\text{Re}\,[F_{10}(j\omega)] = \text{Re}\left[\frac{2 - \omega^2 + j\omega}{2 - \omega^2}\right]$

$$= \frac{2 - \omega^2}{2 - \omega^2} = 1 > 0 \quad \text{for all } \omega.$$

Because $F_{10}(s)$ satisfies the four conditions of Theorem 4-5, $F_{10}(s)$ is PR. ∎

Example 4-9 Determine if

$$F(s) = \frac{A(s)}{B(s)} = \frac{s^3 + 5s^2 + 7s + 4}{s^3 + 2s^2 + 6s + 5} \tag{4-54}$$

is a PR function.

$F(s) = F_1(s) + F_2(s)$

Solution: We follow the route taken by Example 4-8. If $F_1(s)$ & $F_2(s)$ are PR then $F(s)$ is PR.

0. $F(s)$ satisfies all the observation tests listed in (4-52) and therefore is a *candidate* for PRness.
1. All coefficients of $F(s)$ are real; hence, $F(s)$ is real when s is real.
2. The denominator polynomial of $F(s)$, $B(s) = s^3 + 2s^2 + 6s + 5$, is Hurwitz. This can be verified by the Hurwitz test performed on $B(s)$. Hence, all poles of $F(s)$ [or the roots of $B(s)$] are in the LH s-plane.
3. There are no imaginary axis poles.
4. From Chapter 3, we know that $\text{Re}\,[F(s)] = M(s) =$ the even part of $F(s)$. Hence, (3-34) implies

$$\text{Re}\,[F(j\omega)] = M(j\omega) = \frac{M_1(j\omega)M_2(j\omega) - N_1(j\omega)N_2(j\omega)}{M_2^2(j\omega) - N_2^2(j\omega)} \tag{4-55}$$

where $M_1(s)$ and $M_2(s)$ are the *even* parts of $A(s)$ and $B(s)$, respectively, and $N_1(s)$ and $N_2(s)$ are the *odd* parts of $A(s)$ and $B(s)$, respectively. Because $|B(j\omega)|^2 = M_2^2(j\omega) - N_2^2(j\omega) \geq 0$ for all ω, we conclude that Re $[F(j\omega)] \geq 0$ for all ω if, and only if,

$$M_1(j\omega)M_2(j\omega) - N_1(j\omega)N_2(j\omega) \geq 0 \quad \text{for all } \omega \qquad (4\text{-}56)$$

In this particular case, we have

$$M_1(s) = 5s^2 + 4, \quad N_1(s) = s^3 + 7s, \quad M_2(s) = 2s^2 + 5, \text{ and } N_2(s) = s^3 + 6s$$

Hence, (4-56) becomes

$$M_1(j\omega)M_2(j\omega) - N_1(j\omega)N_2(j\omega) = \omega^6 - 3\omega^4 + 9\omega^2 + 20$$

$$= \omega^2(\omega^2 - \tfrac{3}{2})^2 + [\tfrac{27}{4}\omega^2] + 20 \geq 0 \quad \text{for all } \omega$$

By (4-56), we conclude that

$$\text{Re } [F(j\omega)] \geq 0 \quad \text{for all } \omega$$

Hence, the four conditions of Theorem 4-5 are satisfied. This means that $F(s)$ is PR. ∎

As demonstrated in Examples 4-8 and 4-9, the affirmative PR tests are relatively easy for simple rational functions such as $F_{10}(s)$ of (4-53), but the PR tests are time-consuming for complicated functions such as $F(s)$ of (4-54). If it is possible to decompose a complicated rational function into sums of simpler functions, then we can use the following fact to advantage:

A sum of PR functions is a PR function. (4-57)

We now list a few more equivalent conditions for testing PR functions.

THEOREM 4-6 $F(s) = A(s)/B(s)$ is PR if, and only if,

1. $F(s)$ is real when s is real.
2. $p(s) \triangleq A(s) + B(s)$ is Hurwitz.
3. Re $[F(j\omega)] \geq 0$ for all ω. ∎

Note that, on many occasions, testing the conditions of Theorem 4-6 may be easier than testing those of Theorem 4-5.

THEOREM 4-7 $F(s)$ is PR if, and only if,

1. $F(s)$ is real when s is real.
2. $|\underline{/F(s)}| \leq |\underline{/s}|$ whenever $|\underline{/s}| < \pi/2$. ∎

THEOREM 4-8   Let $F(s) = A(s)/B(s)$ and

$$G(s) \triangleq \frac{F(s) - 1}{F(s) + 1} = \frac{A(s) - B(s)}{A(s) + B(s)} \qquad (4\text{-}58)$$

Then $F(s)$ is PR if, and only if,

1. $F(s)$ is real when s is real.
2. $|G(s)| \leq 1$ whenever Re $[s] \geq 0$.   ∎

THEOREM 4-9   Let $G(s)$ be defined by (4-58). Then $F(s)$ is PR if, and only if,

1. $F(s)$ is real when s is real.
2. $A(s) + B(s)$ is Hurwitz.
3. $|G(j\omega)| \leq 1$ for all ω.   ∎

4-3 PASSIVITY

To close this chapter, we consider very briefly the concept of passivity and its relationship with PR functions.

A 1-port network element is said to be *passive* if its terminal voltage $v(t)$ and current $i(t)$ satisfy the condition

$$\int_{t_0}^{t} v(\tau)\, i(\tau)\, d\tau + \mathcal{E}(t_0) \geq 0 \quad \text{for all } t \geq t_0 \tag{4-59}$$

where $\mathcal{E}(t_0)$ is the energy stored in the network at time t_0. A 1-port is said to be *initially relaxed* at t_0 if all initial conditions at t_0 are zero. Consequently, $\mathcal{E}(t_0) = 0$. Hence, an initially relaxed (we assume this to be the case from now on in our discussions on passivity) 1-port is passive if

$$\int_{t_0}^{t} v(\tau)\, i(\tau)\, d\tau \geq 0 \quad \text{for all } t \geq t_0 \tag{4-60}$$

Equation (4-60) simply means that the energy consumed by the 1-port is greater or equal to zero. A 1-port is said to be *active* if it is not passive.

In terms of frequency domain specifications, (4-60) implies that the driving-point (DP) function of the 1-port is PR.[10] That is, a 1-port is passive if, and only if, its DP functions are PR. Basic passive elements include RLC and ideal transformers. The DP function of a 1-port containing only RLC and ideal transformers is PR.[11] Note that ideal transformers and LC elements are *lossless* elements. They are special cases of passive elements. Note also that although gyrators are lossless if the gyration constants are equal, we exclude them from the foregoing passive-element list because gyrators are synthesized in this book by using operational amplifiers, which are

---

[10]See, for example, References [9] or [10].

[11]In this book, we do not use ideal transformers for circuit realizations.

active devices. Hence, the term *passive filter* denotes a filter containing RLC and ideal transformers only. Passive realization means only that passive elements are used in the process of synthesis and design. If only passive elements are used, the realizable DP functions are in the domain of PR functions.

REFERENCES AND FURTHER READING

[1] BRUNE, O. "Synthesis of a Finite Two-Terminal Network Whose Driving-Point Impedance Is a Prescribed Function of Frequency." *J. Math. Phys.* 10 (1931): 191–237.

[2] WEINBERG, L. *Network Analysis and Synthesis.* Huntington, N.Y.: R. E. Krieger, 1975.

[3] DESOER, C. A., and KUH, E. S. *Basic Circuit Theory.* New York: McGraw-Hill, 1969.

[4] HUMPHREYS, D. S. *The Analysis, Design, and Synthesis of Electrical Filters.* Englewood Cliffs, N.J.: Prentice-Hall, Inc., 1970.

[5] CHEN, C. T. *Introduction to Linear System Theory.* New York: Holt, Rinehart and Winston, 1970.

[6] ZADEH, L. A., and DESOER, C. A. *Linear System Theory.* New York: McGraw-Hill, 1963.

[7] ANDERSON, B. D. O., and VONGPANITLERD, S. *Network Analysis and Synthesis.* Englewood Cliffs, N.J.: Prentice-Hall, Inc., 1973.

[8] LAL, M., SINGH, H., and PANWAR, R. S. "Sturm Test Algorithm for Digital Computer." *IEEE Trans. Circuit and Systems* CAS-22 (1975): 62–63.

[9] KUH, E. S., and ROHRER, R. A. *Theory of Linear Active Networks.* San Francisco, CA.: Holden-Day, 1967.

[10] NEWCOMB, R. W. *Linear Multiport Synthesis.* New York: McGraw-Hill, 1966.

PROBLEMS

4-1. Determine which of the following polynomials are Hurwitz or modified Hurwitz.

(a) $p(s) = s^4 + 2s^3 + s^2 + 7s + 1$

(b) $p(s) = s^4 + s^3 + 3s^2 + s + 2$

(c) $p(s) = s^4 + 2s^3 + 5s^2 + 2s + 6$

(d) $p(s) = 3s^4 + 2s^3 + 3s^2 + 2s + 3$

(e) $p(s) = s^4 + 2s^3 + 3s^2 + 4s + 2$

(f) $p(s) = s^4 + 5s^3 + 11s^2 + 11s + 4$
(g) $p(s) = s^5 + s^4 + 4s^3 + 2s^2 + 2s + 1$
(h) $p(s) = 3s^5 + 5s^4 + 5s^3 + 5s^2 + 5s + 3$
(i) $p(s) = s^5 + s^4 + 3s^3 + 3s^2 + 2s + 2$
(j) $p(s) = s^5 + s^4 + 2s^3 + 2s^2 + s + 1$
(k) $p(s) = s^5 + 3s^3 + s$
(l) $p(s) = s^4 + s^2 + 1$
(m) $p(s) = s^5 + 5s^3 + 4s$
(n) $p(s) = s^6 + s^2 + 1$
(o) $p(s) = s^6 + s^4 + s^2 + 1$
(p) $p(s) = s^6 + 2s^4 + s^2 + 3$

4-2. Find the conditions under which an nth-degree polynomial is Hurwitz, where $n = 1, 2, 3$, and 4.

4-3. Consider the polynomial

$$p(s) = s^4 + 2s^3 + as^2 + 2s + 1$$

Find the range of values for a such that $p(s)$ is a Hurwitz polynomial.

4-4. Consider the polynomial

$$p(s) = s^3 + 2s^2 + as + 1$$

Find the range of values for a such that $p(s)$ is at least a modified Hurwitz polynomial.

4-5. Consider the polynomial

$$p(s) = s^3 + as^2 + bs + 1$$

Find the relationships between a and b such that

(a) $p(s)$ is a Hurwitz polynomial.
(b) $p(s)$ is at least a modified Hurwitz polynomial.

If a ranges between 1 and 2, find the range of b such that

(c) $p(s)$ is a Hurwitz polynomial.
(d) $p(s)$ is at least a modified Hurwitz polynomial.

4-6. Consider the following three rational functions

$$F_1(s) = \frac{(s + 1)^2}{(s^2 + 1)(s^2 + s + 1)}$$

$$F_2(s) = \frac{s^2 + s + 1}{(s^2 + 1)(s + 1)}$$

and

$$F_3(s) = \frac{s^2 + 1}{(s + 1)^2(s^2 + s + 1)}$$

Determine which of the following $F(s)$ are PR functions. Give your reasons.

(a) $F(s) = F_1(s) + F_2(s)$

(b) $F(s) = F_1(s) + F_2(s) - F_3(s)$

(c) $F(s) = \dfrac{F_1(s)}{F_2(s)}$

(d) $F(s) = \dfrac{F_1(s)}{F_3(s)}$

(e) $F(s) = F_1(s)F_2(s)$

(f) $F(s) = F_1(s)F_3(s)$

(g) $F(s) = F_2(s)F_3(s)$

(h) $F(s) = F_1(s)F_2(s)F_3(s)$

4-7. Determine which of the following functions are PR. Justify your answers.

(a) $F(s) = s$

(b) $F(s) = \dfrac{1}{s}$

(c) $F(s) = \dfrac{s + 2}{s + 1}$

(d) $F(s) = \dfrac{s + 4}{s^2 + s + 15}$

(e) $F(s) = \dfrac{s^2 + s + 4}{s + 5}$

(f) $F(s) = \dfrac{s^2 + 9}{s^3 + 4s}$

(g) $F(s) = \dfrac{s^3 + 9s}{s^2 + 4}$

(h) $F(s) = \dfrac{s^3 + 6s^2 + 2s + 1}{(s + 1)^2}$

(i) $F(s) = \dfrac{s^3 + 2s^2 + 3s + 1}{s^3 + 5s^2 + 11s + 10}$

(j) $F(s) = \dfrac{s^3 + 6s^2 + 2s + 1}{s^3 + 3s + 1}$

(k) $F(s) = \dfrac{(s + 2)^2(s + 1)}{s^4 + 6s^2 + 9}$

(l) $F(s) = \dfrac{s^4 + s^3 + 2s^2 + 5}{4s^2 + 2s + 1}$

(m) $F(s) = \dfrac{3s^3 + s}{s^4 + s^3 + 2s^2 + s + 5}$

(n) $F(s) = \dfrac{10s^4 + 8s^2 + 1}{4s^5 + 10s^3 + 4s}$

4-8. For each $F(s)$ given in the following, find the range of a such that $F(s)$ is a PR function.

(a) $F(s) = \dfrac{s^2 + as + 1}{s^2 + 3s + 2}$

(b) $F(s) = \dfrac{s^2 + as + 1}{s^2 + 2}$

(c) $F(s) = \dfrac{s^2 + as + 1}{s^3 + 2s}$

(d) $F(s) = \dfrac{s + 2}{s^2 + as + 1}$

(e) $F(s) = \dfrac{s^2 + 3s + a}{(s + 2)^2}$

(f) $F(s) = \dfrac{(s^2 + 2)(s + 1)}{as^2 + s + 2}$

(g) $F(s) = \dfrac{s^2 + 4s + 2a}{(s + 1)^2(s + 2)}$

(h) $F(s) = \dfrac{s}{s^2 + 3s + a}$

(i) $F(s) = \dfrac{s^2 + 2s + 1}{(s + 1)(s^2 + 3s + a)}$

(j) $F(s) = \dfrac{(s + 1)(s^2 + 1)}{(s^2 + 2s + a)(s^2 + as + 1)}$

4-9. Given the odd part $N(s)$ of a network function $F(s)$ as

$$N(s) = \frac{2s^3 + 22s}{s^4 + s^2 + 25}$$

(a) Find an $F(s)$ such that $F(s)$ is PR and $F(\infty) = 1$.
(b) Find an $F(s)$ such that $F(s)$ is PR and $F(0) = 1$.

4-10. Show that the 1-port networks in Fig. P4-10 are passive.

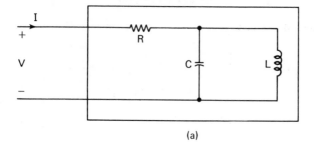

(a)

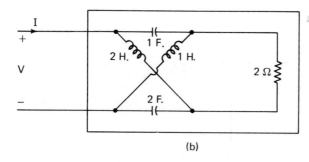

(b)

Fig. P4-10(a), (b)

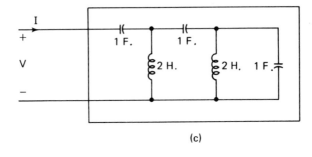

(c)

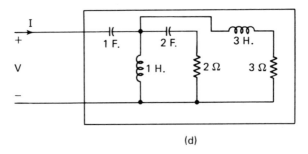

(d)

Fig. P4-10(c), (d)

4-11. Determine which of the 1-port networks in Fig. P4-11 are passive.

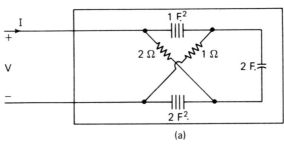

(a)

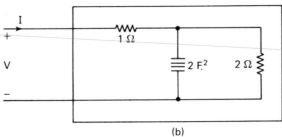

(b)

Fig. P4-11(a), (b)

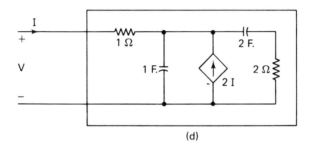

(c)

(d)

Fig. P4-11(c), (d)

4-12. (a) Find the driving-point impedance function of the 1-port network N in Fig. P4-12 to meet the following specifications:

   (i) If a unit step voltage is applied to N, the current $i(t)$ is given by $i(t) = b_1 + b_2 \exp(-4t)$.

   (ii) If a unit step current is applied to N, the voltage $v(t)$ is given by $v(t) = a_1 + a_2 \exp(-t)$.

   (iii) If a dc voltage of 4 volts is applied to N, the steady-state current is 3 Amps.

(b) Show that N can be realized by passive components.

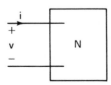

Fig. P4-12

4-13. Given the coefficients of a polynomial

$$p(s) = p_0 + p_1 s + p_2 s^2 + \ldots + p_n s^n$$

write a computer program to determine if $p(s)$ is a Hurwitz polynomial, a modified Hurwitz polynomial, or others.

4-14. Given the coefficients of two polynomials

$$A(s) = a_0 + a_1 s + a_2 s^2 + \ldots + a_m s^m$$

and

$$B(s) = b_0 + b_1 s + b_2 s^2 + \ldots + b_n s^n$$

write a computer program to determine if the rational function

$$F(s) = \frac{A(s)}{B(s)}$$

is a PR function.

5

PROPERTIES
AND REALIZATIONS
OF LOSSLESS
DRIVING-POINT FUNCTIONS

A circuit element is said to be *lossless* if it does not consume any *average* power. In the sinusoidal steady-state condition, the average power dissipated in an element is given by

$$P_{av} = \frac{1}{T} \int_0^T i(t)\, v(t)\, dt$$

$$= \frac{1}{2} V_m I_m \cos(\phi_v - \phi_i) \tag{5-1}$$

where $i(t) = I_m \cos(\omega t + \phi_i)$ and $v(t) = V_m \cos(\omega t + \phi_v)$ are, respectively, the current entering and the voltage across the element, and $T = 2\pi/\omega$. Because the absolute value of the difference between the phase angles of the voltage and the current waveforms of an inductor or a capacitor, $|\phi_v - \phi_i|$, is always 90°, it is clear that inductors and capacitors are lossless elements. In Sec. 5-1, we consider the properties of driving-point (DP) functions of 1-ports containing only lossless elements.[1] Together, these properties constitute the conditions of a DP function that is realizable with lossless elements. In Sec. 5-2, we consider some synthesis procedures for realizing lossless 1-port DP functions. It turns out that every lossless 1-port DP function can be realized by a 1-port containing only inductors and capacitors. Hence, hereafter, we call a lossless 1-port DP function a LC DP function and a 1-port containing only inductors and capacitors a LC 1-port.

---

[1] In addition to inductors and capacitors, lossless elements include ideal transformers, coupled coils, and gyrators.

5-1 PROPERTIES OF LOSSLESS DP FUNCTIONS

There are basically six important properties associated with a DP function of a lossless 1-port. Together, these six properties determine the general form of DP functions of lossless 1-ports.

PROPERTY 1. All the poles and zeros of a DP impedance or admittance function of a lossless 1-port occur on the imaginary axis of the s-plane.

PROOF. For simplicity, we assume that the lossless 1-port η contains only inductors and capacitors. The extension to include other lossless elements is straightforward but cumbersome.

It has been shown in Chapter 4 that the impedance function $Z_{\text{in}}(s)$ of a 1-port η containing only inductors and capacitors is given by

$$Z_{\text{in}}(s) = s \sum_{\mathcal{L}} L_k \frac{|I_k|^2}{|I_1|^2} + \frac{1}{s} \sum_{\mathcal{C}} \frac{1}{C_k} \frac{|I_k|^2}{|I_1|^2} \tag{5-2}$$

Note that (5-2) is obtained from (4-5) under the condition that η contains no resistors. From (5-2), we observe that the zeros of $Z_{\text{in}}(s)$ satisfy equations of the form

$$\alpha s + \frac{1}{s}\beta = 0$$

or

$$\alpha s^2 + \beta = 0 \tag{5-3a}$$

where

$$\alpha \triangleq \sum_{\mathcal{L}} L_k \frac{|I_k|^2}{|I_1|^2} \geq 0$$

and

$$\beta \triangleq \sum_{\mathcal{C}} \frac{1}{C_k} \frac{|I_k|^2}{|I_1|^2} \geq 0$$

Note that both α and β depend on the I_k's and I_1, which are functions of s. Hence, α and β depend on s. Because all solutions of (5-3a) must also satisfy the equation

$$s^2 = -\frac{\beta}{\alpha} < 0 \tag{5-3b}$$

we may still conclude from (5-3) that the zeros of $Z_{\text{in}}(s)$ are on the imaginary axis of the s-plane. In a dual manner we can also show that the driving-point admittance function $Y_{\text{in}}(s)$ of η is given by

$$Y_{\text{in}}(s) = s \sum_{\mathcal{C}} C_k \frac{|v_k|^2}{|v_1|^2} + \frac{1}{s} \sum_{\mathcal{L}} \frac{1}{L_k} \frac{|v_k|^2}{|v_1|^2} \tag{5-4}$$

Hence, the zeros of $Y_{\text{in}}(s)$ occur also on the imaginary axis of the s-plane.

Because

$$Y_{in}(s) = \frac{1}{Z_{in}(s)} \quad \text{and} \quad Z_{in}(s) = \frac{1}{Y_{in}(s)} \tag{5-5}$$

we conclude that all the poles and zeros of a driving-point impedance or admittance function of a lossless 1-port are on the imaginary axis of the s-plane. ∎

PROPERTY 2. Every DP impedance or admittance function of a lossless 1-port is an odd rational function.

PROOF. It is well known that in the sinusoidal steady-state condition, the average power consumed by a lossless 1-port η is given by

$$\text{Re}\,[Z(j\omega)]\,|I(j\omega)|^2 = \text{Re}\,[Y(j\omega)]\,|V(j\omega)|^2 = 0 \tag{5-6}$$

where Z and Y are, respectively, the DP impedance and admittance functions of η. Equation (5-6) means that the DP functions of every lossless 1-port η have one fundamental property;

$$\text{Re}\,[F_{LC}(j\omega)] = 0 \tag{5-7}$$

where $F_{LC}(s)$ denotes either the DP impedance or the admittance function of a lossless 1-port.[2] By (3-15) of Chapter 3, (5-7) implies that the even part of $F_{LC}(s)$ is *identically zero*. Consequently, $F_{LC}(s)$ is an odd rational function of s. Thus,

$$F_{LC}(s) = \frac{N(s)}{M(s)} \quad \text{or} \quad F_{LC}(s) = \frac{M(s)}{N(s)} \tag{5-8}$$

where $N(s)$ is an odd polynomial and $M(s)$ is an even polynomial. ∎

PROPERTY 3. Suppose that a DP function of a lossless 1-port is given by (5-8). Let d_N and d_M be the degrees of polynomials $N(s)$ and $M(s)$, respectively. Then

$$|d_N - d_M| = 1 \tag{5-9}$$

PROOF. Because a lossless 1-port is passive, $F_{LC}(s)$ is PR. A necessary condition for $F_{LC}(s)$ to be PR is that

$$|d_N - d_M| \le 1 \tag{5-10}$$

Since $N(s)$ is odd and $M(s)$ is even,

$$|d_N - d_M| = \text{an odd integer} \tag{5-11}$$

Clearly, (5-10) and (5-11) imply (5-9). ∎

---

[2]Hereafter, we let $F_{LC}(s)$ denote either the impedance or the admittance function of a lossless 1-port.

PROPERTY 4. All poles and zeros of $F_{LC}(s)$ are simple.

PROOF. By Property 1, all poles and zeros of $F_{LC}(s)$ are on the imaginary axis of the s-plane. Because $F_{LC}(s)$ is PR, all its imaginary axis poles and zeros are simple. Hence, the conclusion. ∎

Properties 1 and 2 imply that both the numerator and the denominator of $F_{LC}(s)$ are composed of factors in the form of $(s^2 + \omega_k^2)$ except, of course, for an s term either in the numerator or in the denominator of $F_{LC}(s)$. Hence, $F_{LC}(s)$ is in one of the following two forms:

$$F_{LC}(s) = \frac{k(s^2 + \omega_1^2)(s^2 + \omega_3^2)\ldots(s^2 + \omega_r^2)}{s(s^2 + \omega_2^2)(s^2 + \omega_4^2)\ldots(s^2 + \omega_q^2)} \tag{5-12a}$$

$$F_{LC}(s) = \frac{ks(s^2 + \omega_2^2)(s^2 + \omega_4^2)\ldots(s^2 + \omega_q^2)}{(s^2 + \omega_1^2)(s^2 + \omega_3^2)\ldots(s^2 + \omega_r^2)} \tag{5-12b}$$

where r is an odd interger and q is an even integer. Property 3 says that either

$$q = r + 1 \quad \text{or} \quad r = q + 1 \tag{5-13}$$

and Property 4 demands that

$$\omega_i \neq \omega_k \quad \text{whenever} \quad i \neq k = 1, 2, \ldots, r, q \quad \text{or} \quad q, r \tag{5-14}$$

From here on, we primarily develop the $F_{LC}(s)$ of (5-12a) only. The $F_{LC}(s)$ of (5-12b) may be developed in an analogous manner.

PROPERTY 5. Except at the poles of $F_{LC}(s)$, $F_{LC}(j\omega)/j$ is a monotonically increasing function of ω.

PROOF. Dividing (5-12a) by s and letting $p = s^2$, we obtain

$$\frac{F_{LC}(s)}{s} = \frac{k(p + \omega_1^2)(p + \omega_3^2)\ldots(p + \omega_r^2)}{p(p + \omega_2^2)(p + \omega_4^2)\ldots(p + \omega_q^2)} \tag{5-15}$$

A partial fraction expansion of (5-15) gives

$$\frac{F_{LC}(s)}{s} = k_\infty + \frac{k_0}{p} + \sum_{i=\text{even}}^{q} \frac{k_i}{p + \omega_i^2}$$

or

$$F_{LC}(s) = k_\infty s + \frac{k_0}{s} + \sum_{i=\text{even}}^{q} \frac{k_i s}{s^2 + \omega_i^2} \tag{5-16}$$

Note that the term k_∞ is present in (5-16) only if $r = q + 1$ is the case in (5-12a). To see the nature of the constants k_i, $i = 0, 2, 4, \ldots, q$ and ∞, let us write (5-16) as

$$F_{LC}(s) = k_\infty s + \frac{k_0}{s} + \sum_{i=\text{even}}^{q} \left[\frac{\alpha_i}{s + j\omega_i} + \frac{\bar{\alpha}_i}{s - j\omega_i} \right] \tag{5-17}$$

where $\bar{\alpha}_i$ denotes the complex conjugate of α_i.[3] Because lossless 1-ports are passive, $F_{LC}(s)$ is PR. Hence, the constants k_∞ [the residue of $F_{LC}(s)$ at the pole $s = \infty$], k_0 [the residue of $F_{LC}(s)$ at the pole $s = 0$], and α_i and $\bar{\alpha}_i$ [the residues of $F_{LC}(s)$ at the poles $-j\omega_i$ and $j\omega_i$] are positive and real.[4] Thus, $\alpha_i = \bar{\alpha}_i$ is positive and real. Equating (5-16) and (5-17), we obtain the relationship between k_i and α_i as

$$\frac{k_i s}{s^2 + \omega_i^2} = \frac{\alpha_i(s - j\omega_i) + \alpha_i(s + j\omega_i)}{s^2 + \omega_i^2} = \frac{2\alpha_i s}{s^2 + \omega_i^2}$$

or

$$k_i = 2\alpha_i \tag{5-18}$$

Each α_i is a real and positive constant; therefore, k_i is also a positive and real constant. Hence, we have

$$k_i = \text{real and positive} \tag{5-19}$$

where $i = 0, 2, 4, \ldots, q$ and ∞. Differentiating (5-16) with respect to s, we obtain

$$\frac{dF_{LC}(s)}{ds} = k_\infty - \frac{k_0}{s^2} + \sum_{i=\text{even}}^{q} \frac{k_i(\omega_i^2 - s^2)}{(s^2 + \omega_i^2)^2} \tag{5-20}$$

Letting $s = j\omega$, (5-20) gives

$$\frac{dF_{LC}(j\omega)}{dj\omega} = k_\infty + \frac{k_0}{\omega^2} + \sum_{i=\text{even}}^{q} \frac{k_i(\omega_i^2 + \omega^2)}{(\omega_i^2 - \omega^2)^2} \tag{5-21}$$

Except when ω is at a pole of $F_{LC}(s)$, each term on the left-hand side of (5-21) is positive for all ω. Therefore, we conclude that

$$\frac{dF_{LC}(j\omega)}{jd\omega} > 0 \tag{5-22}$$

for all ω except at the poles of $F_{LC}(s)$, and our conclusion follows. ∎

Some typical sketches of the function $F_{LC}(j\omega)/j$ versus ω are shown in Fig. 5-1, where the discontinuities occur at the poles of $F_{LC}(s)$. Notice that $s = 0$ is either a zero or a pole of $F_{LC}(s)$, and so is the point $s = \infty$. In view of Fig. 5-1 and the montonically increasing property of Property 5, it is clear that the zeros and poles of $F_{LC}(s)$ must interlace each other on the imaginary axis of the s-plane. Hence, we have

$$0 \leq \omega_1 \leq \omega_2 \leq \omega_3 \ldots \tag{5-23}$$

This is another important property of lossless DP function. For future reference, we note

---

[3]Recall that (4-48a) implies that the residues at a pair of complex conjugate poles are complex conjugates of each other.

[4]Strictly speaking, the constants k_∞ and k_0 are real and nonnegative. We say k_∞ and k_0 are real and positive, because whenever the terms $k_\infty s$ and k_0/s are present in (5-17), k_∞ and k_0 are real and positive.

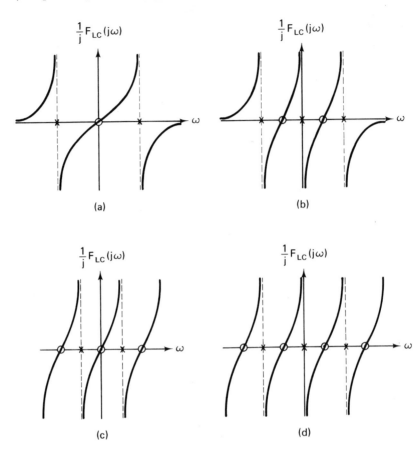

Legend: 0 = zero of $F_{LC}(s)$, and x = pole of $F_{LC}(s)$.

Fig. 5-1   Some typical plots of $(1/j)F_{LC}(j\omega)$ versus ω.

PROPERTY 6. The points $s = 0$ and $s = \infty$ are critical frequencies[5] of $F_{LC}(s)$. In addition, the poles and zeros of $F_{LC}(s)$ alternate with each other along the imaginary axis of the s-plane.   ∎

5-2   REALIZATION OF LOSSLESS DP FUNCTIONS

In this section we present four methods for realizing lossless DP functions. They are Foster's first and second forms and Cauer's first and second forms.

---

[5]A critical frequency of $F_{LC}(s)$ is either a pole or a zero of $F_{LC}(s)$.

$$F_{LC}(s) = \frac{K(s^2+\omega_1^2)(s^2+\omega_3^2)+\cdots(s^2+\omega_r^2)}{s(s^2+\omega_2^2)(s^2+\omega_4^2)+\cdots(s^2+\omega_8^2)}$$

$$= K_\infty s + \frac{k_0}{s} + \sum_{i=0,2,4}^{q} \frac{1}{\frac{s}{k_i} + \left(\frac{k_i}{\omega_i^2}\right)s}$$

5-2-1. Foster's Realization Methods

To consider the realization problem of general lossless DP functions, let us rewrite (5-16) as:

$$F_{LC}(s) = k_\infty s + \frac{k_0}{s} + \sum_{i=\text{even}}^{q} \frac{1}{\dfrac{s}{k_i} + \dfrac{1}{(k_i/\omega_i^2)s}} \qquad (5\text{-}24)$$

where all the k_i's and ω_i's are positive and real. If $F_{LC}(s)$ is a DP impedance function, then we can write

$$F_{LC}(s) = Z_{LC}(s) = L_\infty s + \frac{1}{C_0 s} + \sum_{i=\text{even}}^{q} \frac{1}{C_i s + (1/L_i s)} \qquad (5\text{-}25)$$

where

$$L_\infty = k_\infty, \quad C_0 = \frac{1}{k_0}, \quad C_i = \frac{1}{k_i}, \quad \text{and} \quad L_i = \frac{k_i}{\omega_i^2} \qquad (5\text{-}26)$$

A circuit realization of (5-25) is given by Fig. 5-2.[6] Equation (5-25) with (5-26) or Fig. 5-2 is called *Foster's first form*. Dually, if $F_{LC}(s)$ is a DP admittance function, then we can write (5-24) as

$$F_{LC}(s) = Y_{LC}(s) = C_\infty s + \frac{1}{L_0 s} + \sum_{i=\text{even}}^{q} \frac{1}{L_i s + (1/C_i s)} \qquad (5\text{-}27)$$

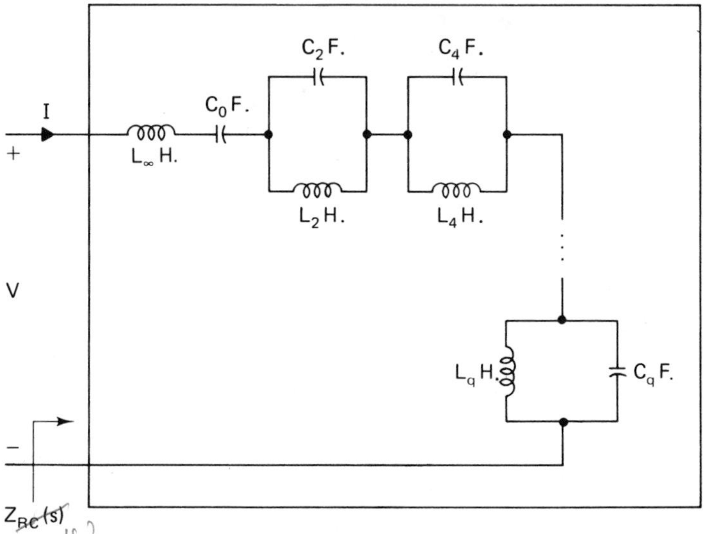

Fig. 5-2 Foster's first form.

[6]In all circuit diagrams in this book, the symbol, "$Z=$" {"$Y=$"} stands for "The DP impedance {admittance} function looking into the 1-port circuit from here is equal to."

where

$$C_\infty = k_\infty, \quad L_0 = \frac{1}{k_0}, \quad L_i = \frac{1}{k_i}, \quad \text{and} \quad C_i = \frac{k_i}{\omega_i^2} \qquad (5\text{-}28)$$

A circuit implementation of (5-27) is shown in Fig. 5-3. Equation (5-27) with (5-28) or Fig. 5-3 is called *Foster's second form.*

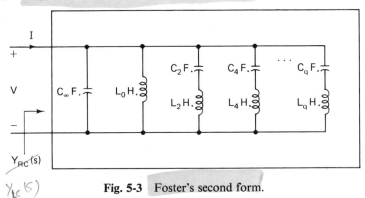

Fig. 5-3 Foster's second form.

Observe that Foster's first form deals only with DP *impedance* functions, and Foster's second form deals only with DP *admittance* functions. In view of these two Foster's forms, we can make the following conclusion:

THEOREM 5-1 All lossless DP functions can be realized by a 1-port containing only inductors and capacitors.

Example 5-1 Given the lossless impedance function

$$Z(s) = \frac{(s^2 + 1)(s^2 + 9)}{s(s^2 + 4)(s^2 + 16)} \qquad (5\text{-}29)$$

find circuit realizations of (5-29) via Foster's two methods.

Solution: Let us first check if $Z(s)$ satisfies all the properties of a LC DP function.[7] To start with, $Z(s)$ is an odd rational function with the denominator polynomial degree one larger than that of the numerator polynomial. $Z(s)$ has a pole at $s = 0$ and a zero at $s = \infty$. The zeros are at $\pm j1$, $\pm j3$, and ∞; the poles are at 0, $\pm j2$, and $\pm j4$, as shown in Fig. 5-4. Clearly, all poles and zeros are simple, and they alternate on the imaginary axis of the s-plane. To find the residues, we let $p = s^2$ and write

$$\frac{Z(s)}{s} = \frac{(s^2 + 1)(s^2 + 9)}{s^2(s^2 + 4)(s^2 + 16)} = \frac{(p + 1)(p + 9)}{p(p + 4)(p + 16)}$$

$$= \frac{p^2 + 10p + 9}{p(p + 4)(p + 16)} \qquad (5\text{-}30)$$

$$= \frac{A}{p} + \frac{B}{p + 4} + \frac{C}{p + 16} \triangleq \hat{Z}(p)$$

---

[7]We should check to make sure that the given DP function satisfies all properties of LC DP functions before we proceed to realize it with lossless elements. However, for obvious reasons, we do not perform these checks in later examples.

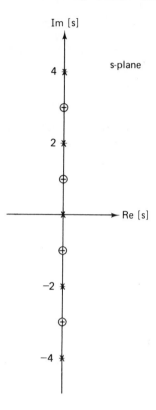

Legend: 0 = zeroes and x = poles

Fig. 5-4 Pole-zero diagram of $Z(s)$ of (5-29).

where A, B, and C are residues of $\hat{Z}(p)$ at the poles $p_1 = 0$, $p_2 = -4$, and $p_3 = -16$. By (4-48), we find

$$A = \frac{9}{64}, \quad B = \frac{5}{16}, \quad \text{and} \quad C = \frac{35}{64}$$

Therefore,

$$\frac{Z(s)}{s} = \frac{9/64}{s^2} + \frac{5/16}{s^2 + 4} + \frac{35/64}{s^2 + 16}$$

or

$$Z(s) = \frac{9/64}{s} + \frac{(5/16)s}{s^2 + 4} + \frac{(35/64)s}{s^2 + 16} \tag{5-31}$$

That is, all residues of $Z(s)$ are real and positive. Hence, $Z(s)$ satisfies all properties of a LC DP function[8]—$Z(s)$ can be realized by lossless elements alone.

---

[8]Property 5—$(1/j)\, z(j\omega)$ is a monotonically increasing function of ω, except at the poles of $Z(s)$—is satisfied, because the poles and zeros of $F_{LC}(s)$ alternate on the imaginary axis of the s-plane and both the points $s = 0$ and $s = \infty$ are critical frequencies.

For low freq operation — Inductors become bulky and frequently non-realizable

To realize $Z(s)$, let us write (5-31) as

$$Z(s) = \frac{1}{\frac{64}{9}s} + \frac{1}{\frac{16}{5}s + \frac{1}{\frac{5}{64}s}} + \frac{1}{\frac{64}{35}s + \frac{1}{\frac{35}{1024}s}} \tag{5-32}$$

The Foster's first-form realization of (5-29) or equivalently (5-32) is given by Fig. 5-5(a).

Another realization of $Z(s)$ of (5-29) can be obtained via Foster's second form. Because $Y(s) = 1/Z(s)$, we have

$$Y(s) = \frac{s(s^2 + 4)(s^2 + 16)}{(s^2 + 1)(s^2 + 9)}$$

$$\frac{Y(s)}{s} = 1 + \frac{45/8}{s^2 + 1} + \frac{35/8}{s^2 + 9}$$

Hence,

$$Y(s) = s + \frac{(45/8)s}{s^2 + 1} + \frac{(35/8)s}{s^2 + 9}$$

$$= s + \frac{1}{\frac{8}{45}s + \frac{1}{(45/8)s}} + \frac{1}{\frac{8}{35}s + \frac{1}{(35/72)s}} \tag{5-33}$$

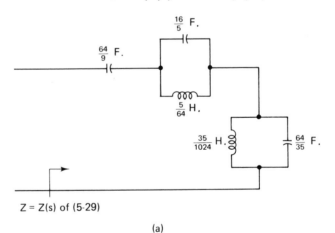

Z = Z(s) of (5-29)

(a)

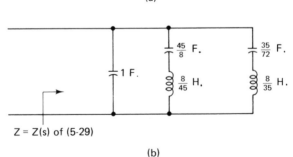

Z = Z(s) of (5-29)

(b)

Fig. 5-5 Realizations of $Z(s)$ of (5-29). (a) Foster's first form. (b) Foster's second form.

The Foster's second-form realization of $Z(s)$ of (5-29) via (5-33) is given in Fig. 5-5(b). Note that both Figs. 5-5(a) and (b) have the same DP impedance and admittance functions.

[handwritten margin notes: impedance, Admittance — First Form; Impedance, Admittance — Second Form; continued fraction expansion at $s = \infty$; continued fraction expansion at $s = 0$]*

5-2-2. Cauer's Realization Methods

The Foster forms are not the only possible circuit realizations of lossless DP functions. In general, if an impedance function $Z(s)$, or an admittance function $Y(s)$, is realizable, then there exist many and sometimes even an infinite number of possible circuit realizations. In this section, we consider Cauer's methods for realizing lossless DP functions.

5-2-2-1. Cauer's First Form
By Property 3, the degrees of the numerator and denominator polynomials of a lossless DP function differ by exactly 1. Hence, the point $s = \infty$ is either a pole or a zero of $F_{LC}(s)$. Without loss of generality, we can assume that $s = \infty$ is a pole of $F_{LC}(s)$—$F_{LC}(\infty) = \infty$, or the numerator degree of $F_{LC}(s)$ is one larger than the denominator degree. Let $p(s)$ be the polynomial that is the sum of both the numerator and denominator polynomials of $F_{LC}(s)$. By Theorem 4-4, $p(s)$ is Hurwitz. Hence, $F_{LC}(s)$, being the test ratio of $p(s)$ in the Hurwitz test, has a continued fraction expansion at $s = \infty$ as

$$F_{LC}(s) = k_1 s + \cfrac{1}{k_2 s + \cfrac{1}{k_3 s + \cfrac{\ddots}{\quad + \cfrac{1}{k_n s}}}} \tag{5-34}$$

[handwritten margin note: Driving point Impedance is a pole $s = \infty$ pole]*

where n is the degree of the numerator polynomial of $F_{LC}(s)$ and the coefficients $k_1, k_2, \ldots, k_n$ are real and positive constants. To examine these constants, we let $F_{LC_1}(s) = F_{LC}(s)$ and write

$$F_{LC_1}(s) = k_1 s + \frac{1}{F_{LC_2}(s)} \tag{5-35a}$$

where

$$k_1 = \lim_{s \to \infty} \frac{1}{s} F_{LC_1}(s) \tag{5-35b}$$

is the residue of $F_{LC_1}(s)$ at the pole $s = \infty$.[9] From (5-34), we observe that

$$F_{LC_1}(\infty) = \lim_{s \to \infty} k_1 s \tag{5-36}$$

---

[9] See (4-48b).

Hence, the remainder term of (5-35a) satisfies the equation

$$\frac{1}{F_{LC_2}(\infty)} = 0$$

or

$$F_{LC_2}(\infty) = \infty \tag{5-37}$$

Thus, we can perform this pole-extraction procedure on $F_{LC_2}(s)$ as

$$F_{LC_2}(s) = k_2 s + \frac{1}{F_{LC_3}(s)} \tag{5-38a}$$

where again

$$k_2 = \lim_{s \to \infty} \frac{1}{s} F_{LC_2}(s) \tag{5-38b}$$

is the residue of $F_{LC_2}(s)$ at the pole $s = \infty$. If we repeat the procedures of (5-35) and (5-38) as many times as necessary, then the constants k_i are residues of $F_{LC_i}(s)$ at the pole $s = \infty$, where $i = 1, 2, \dots, n$.

If $F_{LC}(s)$ has a zero at infinity rather than a pole as we have assumed in the foregoing, we let $F_{LC_1}(s) = 1/F_{LC}(s)$. Hence $F_{LC_1}(s)$ has a pole at infinity. Now the process of (5-34) or the repeated process of (5-35) through (5-38) can be performed as in the previous case. In this case, the resulting continued fraction expansion at infinity is given by

$$F_{LC}(s) = \frac{1}{F_{LC_1}(s)} = \cfrac{1}{k_1 s + \cfrac{1}{k_2 s + \cfrac{1}{k_3 s + \cfrac{}{} }}} \tag{5-39}$$

$$+ \frac{1}{k_n s}$$

where n is the degree of the denominator polynomial of $F_{LC}(s)$. In the following, we consider (5-34) only. Equation (5-39) is illustrated by an example.

If $F_{LC}(s) = Z_{LC}(s)$ is an impedance function, then (5-35) has a circuit interpretation shown in Fig. 5-6(a). Similarly, the action of (5-38) is shown in Fig. 5-6(b), and Fig. 5-6(c) shows the next step. On the other hand, if $F_{LC}(s) = Y_{LC}(s)$ is an admittance function, then the circuit interpretations of (5-35) and (5-38) are shown, respectively, in Figs. 5-7(a) and (b), and Fig. 5-7(c) shows the subsequent step. Note that in both Figs. 5-6 and 5-7, the expansion of $F_{LC}(s)$ about the point at $s = \infty$ gives rise to circuit realizations with *series inductors and shunt capacitors*. This is called *Cauer's first form*.

Example 5-2 Realize the DP impedance function

$$Z(s) = \frac{(s^2 + 1)(s^2 + 9)}{s(s^2 + 4)(s^2 + 16)} = \frac{s^4 + 10s^2 + 9}{s^5 + 20s^3 + 64s} \tag{5-40}$$

by Cauer's first form.

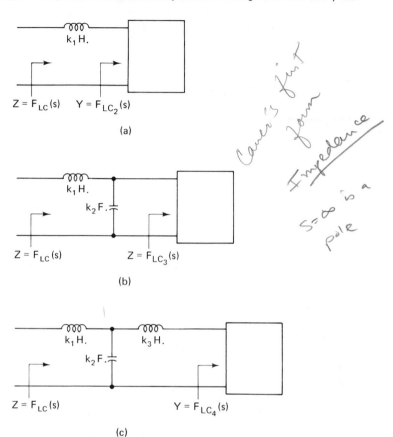

$Z = F_{LC}(s)$ $Y = F_{LC_2}(s)$

(a)

$Z = F_{LC}(s)$ $Z = F_{LC_3}(s)$

(b)

$Z = F_{LC}(s)$ $Y = F_{LC_4}(s)$

(c)

Fig. 5-6   Cauer's first-form realization procedure of a lossless DP impedance function $F_{LC}(s)$.

Solution: Because the denominator polynomial of $Z(s)$ is of higher degree, $Z(s)$ has a zero at $s = \infty$. Hence, we perform a continued fraction expansion at $s = \infty$ on the corresponding admittance function $Y(s)$ as[10]

$$Y(s) = \frac{1}{Z(s)} = \frac{s^5 + 20s^3 + 64s}{s^4 + 10s^2 + 9}$$

$$= s + \cfrac{1}{\cfrac{1}{10}s + \cfrac{1}{\cfrac{20}{9}s + \cfrac{1}{\cfrac{9}{70}s + \cfrac{1}{\cfrac{35}{9}s}}}} \qquad (5\text{-}41)$$

---

[10]Cauer's first form requires us to perform the continued fraction expansion at the point $s = \infty$ on the DP function whose numerator polynomial degree is larger than that of its denominator.

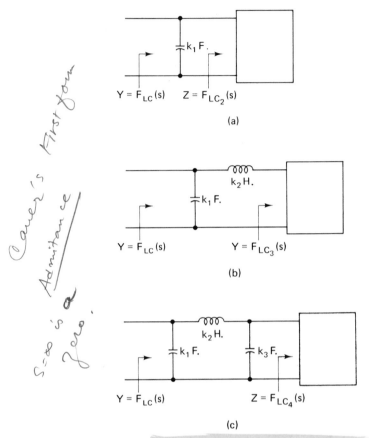

Fig. 5-7   Cauer's first-form realization procedure of a lossless DP admittance function $F_{LC}(s)$.

To realize the given impedance function $Z(s)$ of (5-40) is equivalent to realize the admittance function $Y(s)$ of (5-41). Because $Y(s)$ can be written as a sum of two terms as

$$Y(s) = s + \frac{1}{Z_2(s)} \tag{5-42}$$

where

$$Z_2(s) = \frac{1}{10}s + \cfrac{1}{\frac{20}{9}s + \cfrac{1}{\frac{9}{70}s + \cfrac{1}{\frac{35}{9}s}}} \tag{5-43}$$

we realize $Y(s)$ by connecting a 1-Farad capacitor in parallel with a 1-port that has a DP impedance function $Z_2(s)$ given by (5-43). Observe that $Z_2(s)$ in turn is the sum of two terms as

$$Z_2(s) = \frac{1}{10}s + \frac{1}{Y_3(s)} \tag{5-44}$$

where

$$Y_3(s) = \frac{20}{9}s + \cfrac{1}{\cfrac{9}{70}s + \cfrac{1}{\cfrac{35}{9}s}} \tag{5-45}$$

Hence, we can realize the DP impedance function $Z_2(s)$ by connecting an inductor with $1/10$ Henries in series with a 1-port characterized by a DP admittance function $Y_3(s)$ of (5-45). Clearly, we can repeat this process until we have completed the realization of $Y(s)$ of (5-41).

Figure 5-8 is a circuit realization of the DP impedance function $Z(s)$ of (5-40) via the procedure described in the previous paragraph. The DP functions of $Z_4(s)$ and $Y_5(s)$ in Fig. 5-8 are given by

$$Z_4(s) = \frac{9}{70}s + \frac{1}{(35/9)s} \tag{5-46a}$$

and

$$Y_5(s) = \frac{35}{9}s \tag{5-46b}$$

∎

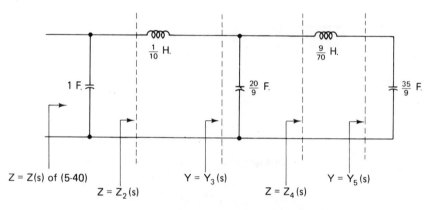

Fig. 5-8 Cauer's first-form realization of $Z(s)$ of (5-40).

5-2-2-2. Cauer's Second Form In the foregoing development of Cauer's first form, we expanded the DP function about the pole at $s = \infty$. We now consider the case when the lossless DP function is expanded at the pole $s = 0$.

Consider a lossless DP function $F_{LC}(s)$. Without loss of generality, let us assume, in view of (5-8), that the denominator is an odd polynomial and that the numerator is an even polynomial.[11] Then $F_{LC}(s)$ has a pole at $s = 0$. If we

---

[11]Note that if $F_{LC}(s)$ has an odd numerator polynomial and an even denominator polynomial, then we can work with $[F_{LC}(s)]^{-1}$ rather than $F_{LC}(s)$ itself. In this case, we let $F_{LC_1}(s) \triangleq [F_{LC}(s)]^{-1}$. The purpose is to work with a lossless DP function (either the impedance or the admittance function) that has an odd denominator polynomial, i.e., with a pole at $s = 0$.

let $F_{LC_1}(s) = F_{LC}(s)$ and extract the pole of $F_{LC_1}(s)$ at $s = 0$, we obtain

$$F_{LC_1}(s) = \frac{k_1}{s} + \frac{1}{F_{LC_2}(s)} \qquad (5\text{-}47a)$$

where

$$k_1 = sF_{LC_1}(s)|_{s=0} \qquad (5\text{-}47b)$$

is the residue of $F_{LC_1}(s)$ at the pole $s = 0$, and the remaining term $[F_{LC_2}(s)]^{-1}$ has a zero at $s = 0$. That is, $F_{LC_2}(s)$ has a pole at $s = 0$. Hence, we can repeat the foregoing procedure of extracting the pole of $F_{LC_2}(s)$ at $s = 0$. This process gives

$$F_{LC_2}(s) = \frac{k_2}{s} + \frac{1}{F_{LC_3}(s)} \qquad (5\text{-}48a)$$

where

$$k_2 = sF_{LC_2}(s)|_{s=0} \qquad (5\text{-}48b)$$

and $F_{LC_3}(s)$ again has a pole at $s = 0$. Substituting (5-48) into (5-47) leads to

$$F_{LC_1}(s) = \frac{k_1}{s} + \cfrac{1}{\cfrac{k_2}{s} + \cfrac{1}{F_{LC_3}(s)}} \qquad (5\text{-}49)$$

Repeating the process as many times as necessary, we finally obtain

$$F_{LC}(s) = F_{LC_1}(s) = \frac{k_1}{s} + \cfrac{1}{\cfrac{k_2}{s} + \cfrac{1}{\ddots}}$$

$$\qquad (5\text{-}50)$$

$$+ \cfrac{1}{\dfrac{k_n}{s}}$$

Cauer's second form Impedance

If $F_{LC}(s)$ is a lossless DP impedance function, then (5-47) and (5-48) are illustrated in Figs. 5-9(a) and (b), and Fig. 5-9(c) points out the third step in the process.

On the other hand, if $F_{LC}(s)$ is a DP admittance function, then the circuit interpretation of (5-47) and (5-48) are shown in Figs. 5-10(a) and (b), and Fig. 5-10(c) illustrates the action of the next step.

Equation (5-50) and Fig. 5-9 or Fig. 5-10 constitute Cauer's second form. Notice that in Cauer's second form, there are only two types of circuit elements, namely, *series capacitors* and *shunt inductors*. Because grounded inductors are more readily realizable by active circuits, as opposed to floating inductors, Cauer's second form is a more preferable form among the methods discussed, in realizing lossless DP functions when the desired resulting 1-port is grounded. However, as we see in later chapters, the method used to realize a certain DP function is often dictated by other factors. One of these factors is the transmission zero requirements of the associated transfer function.[12]

---

[12]See Chapter 7 for details.

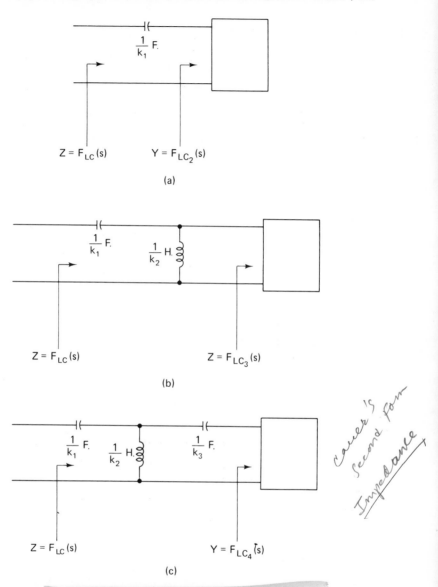

Fig. 5-9 Cauer's second-form realization procedure of a lossless DP impedance function $F_{LC}(s)$.

Observe that (5-50) is a continued fraction expansion of $F_{LC}(s)$. Each quotient is equal to infinity at the point $s = 0$; therefore this continued fraction expansion of $F_{LC}(s)$ is said to be performed at the point $s = 0$. Note also that we arrive at (5-50) through a series of divide-and-invert processes. Hence, we can obtain (5-50) through a long division process. With both the numerator and denominator polynomials of $F_{LC}(s)$ arranged in ascending

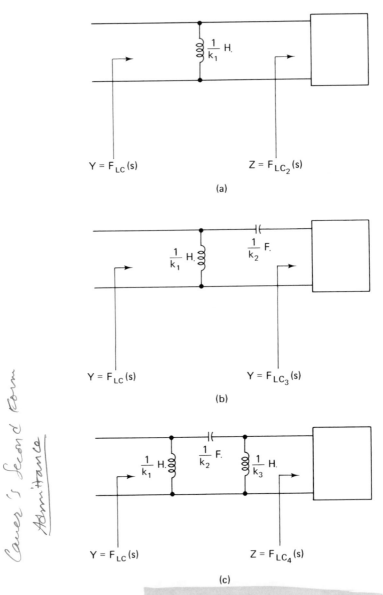

Fig. 5-10 Cauer's second-form realization procedure of a lossless DP admittance function $F_{LC}(s)$.

powers of s, we eliminate the lowest power term in each division. For example, the continued fraction expansion at $s = 0$ of

$$F(s) = \frac{9 + 10s^2 + s^4}{64s + 20s^3 + s^5} \tag{5-51}$$

can be obtained as follows:

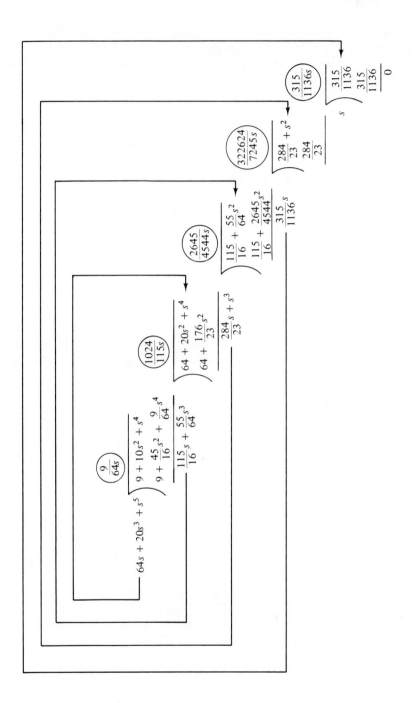

115

Note that in each inversion, we have divided both the numerator and the denominator by s. With these quotients (the encircled quantities in the long division), we can form the continued fraction expansion of $F(s)$ at $s = 0$ as

$$F(s) = \frac{0.1406}{s} + \cfrac{1}{\cfrac{8.904}{s} + \cfrac{1}{\cfrac{0.5821}{s} + \cfrac{1}{\cfrac{44.53}{s} + \cfrac{1}{\cfrac{0.2773}{s}}}}} \qquad (5\text{-}52)$$

Another method to obtain the continued fraction expansion at $s = 0$ can be seen by writing (5-50) as

$$F_{LC}(s) = k_1 p + \cfrac{1}{k_2 p + \cfrac{1}{k_3 p + \cfrac{}{\ddots + \cfrac{1}{k_n p}}}} \qquad (5\text{-}53)$$

where $p \triangleq s^{-1}$. Note that (5-34) and (5-53) are identical in form if we replace s by p. Hence, we can obtain the continued fraction expansion of a function $F(s)$ at the point $s = 0$ by using the following procedure:

1. Assume $F(s)$ is given by

$$F(s) = \frac{M(s)}{N(s)}$$

where $M(s)$ is an even polynomial of degree d_M and $N(s)$ is an odd polynomial of degree d_N. Let

$$d = \max\{d_N, d_M\}$$

2. Multiply both the numerator and the denominator of $F(s)$ by s^{-d}, and define

$$\hat{F}(p) = \frac{A(p)}{B(p)} \triangleq \frac{s^{-d}M(s)}{s^{-d}N(s)} = F(s) \qquad (5\text{-}54)$$

where $p \triangleq s^{-1}$.
3. Perform the continued fraction expansion at the point $p = \infty$ on the function $\hat{F}(p)$ as in (5-34).
4. Replace p in Step 3 by s^{-1}. The result is a continued fraction expansion of $F(s)$ at the point $s = 0$.

To illustrate this procedure, let us consider the function $F(s)$ of (5-51). To find the continued fraction expansion of $F(s)$ at the point $s = 0$, we perform the following steps:

1. Since $d_N = 5$ and $d_M = 4$, $d = 5$.

2. $\hat{F}(p) = \dfrac{s^{-5}[9 + 10s^2 + s^4]}{s^{-5}[64s + 20s^3 + s^5]} = \dfrac{9p^5 + 10p^3 + p}{64p^4 + 20p^2 + 1}$ (5-55)

3. The continued fraction expansion of $\hat{F}(p)$ at $p = \infty$ is given by

$$F(p) = 0.1406p + \cfrac{1}{8.904p + \cfrac{1}{0.5821p + \cfrac{1}{44.53p + \cfrac{1}{0.2773p}}}}$$ (5-56)

4. Replacing p by $1/s$, we obtain the continued fraction expansion at $s = 0$ of $F(s)$ as in (5-52).

Example 5-3 Realize $Z(s) = (64s + 20s^3 + s^5)/(9 + 10s^2 + s^4)$ by Cauer's second form.

Solution: To apply Cauer's second form, we consider[13]

$$Y_1(s) = \frac{1}{Z(s)} = \frac{9 + 10s^2 + s^4}{64s + 20s^3 + s^5}$$ (5-57)

The continued fraction expansion of $Y_1(s)$ at $s = 0$ is given by

$$Y_1(s) = \frac{0.1406}{s} + \cfrac{1}{\dfrac{8.904}{s} + \cfrac{1}{\dfrac{0.5821}{s} + \cfrac{1}{\dfrac{44.53}{s} + \cfrac{1}{\dfrac{0.2773}{s}}}}}$$ (5-58)

A circuit realization of (5-57) or equivalently (5-58) by using Cauer's second form is given in Fig. 5-11, where

$$Y_5(s) = \frac{0.2773}{s}$$

$$Z_4(s) = \frac{44.53}{s} + \frac{1}{Y_5(s)}$$ (5-59)

$$Y_3(s) = \frac{0.5821}{s} + \frac{1}{Z_4(s)}$$

and

$$Z_2(s) = \frac{8.904}{s} + \frac{1}{Y_3(s)}$$ ∎

To conclude this section, it should be pointed out that a realization of a lossless DP function can be started by any one of the aforementioned four forms, namely, the two Foster's forms and the two Cauer's forms. The initial form of realization can be terminated at any stage and the realization

---

[13]Recall that Cauer's second form requires us to consider the function whose denominator is an odd polynomial and whose numerator is an even polynomial.

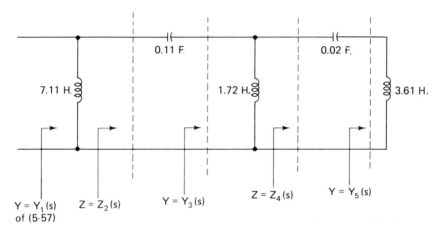

Fig. 5-11 Cauer's second-form realization of $Z(s)$ of Example 5-3.

continued by using another form. This changing of realization methods can be as frequent as one desires. In that case, the end result, of course, will not be a Cauer or a Foster form. However, the resulting circuit will still realize the given lossless DP function.

Example 5-4 Realize the DP admittance function

$$Y(s) = \frac{s^3 + 3s}{s^2 + 1} \qquad (5\text{-}60)$$

by first using Cauer's second form once and the remainder by using Cauer's first form.

Solution: To use Cauer's second form, we consider the DP function with an odd denominator polynomial. Hence, we consider the impedance function

$$Z(s) = \frac{s^2 + 1}{s^3 + 3s} \qquad (5\text{-}61)$$

rather than the given $Y(s)$. The first step of the continued fraction expansion of $Z(s)$ at $s = 0$ is given by

$$Z(s) = \frac{1}{3s} + \frac{(2/3)s}{s^2 + 3} \triangleq \frac{1}{3s} + Z_R(s) \qquad (5\text{-}62)$$

The circuit implementation of (5-62) is shown in Fig. 5-12(a). As instructed by the problem, we are going to realize

$$Z_R(s) = \frac{(2/3)s}{s^2 + 3} \qquad (5\text{-}63)$$

by Cauer's first form. Because Cauer's first form deals with the LC DP function with a higher numerator polynomial degree, we need to work with the admittance function

$$Y_R(s) = \frac{s^2 + 3}{(2/3)s} \qquad (5\text{-}64)$$

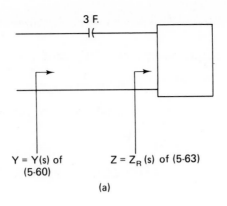

(a)

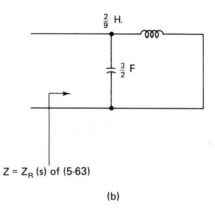

(b)

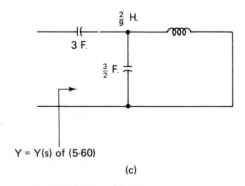

Fig. 5-12 Solution to Example 5-4.

The continued fraction expansion of $Y_R(s)$ at $s = \infty$ is given by

$$Y_R(s) = \frac{3}{2}s + \frac{1}{(2/9)s} \tag{5-65}$$

$Y_R(s)$ of (5-65) is realized in Fig. 5-12(b). Hence, the desired circuit realization of (5-60) is given in Fig. 5-12(c). ∎

5-3 CONCLUDING REMARKS

In this chapter, we have presented the basic properties of lossless DP functions. These properties form the realizability conditions of LC DP functions. A summary of these conditions follows.

REALIZABILITY CONDITIONS OF LC DP FUNCTIONS

1. All poles and zeros of $F_{LC}(s)$ are simple and on the imaginary axis of the s-plane.
2. Poles and zeros of $F_{LC}(s)$ alternate on the imaginary axis.
3. The points $s = 0$ and $s = \infty$ are critical frequencies.
4. $F_{LC}(s)$ is an odd rational function with degrees of numerator and denominator polynomials differing by exactly one.
5. All residues of $F_{LC}(s)$ are real and positive.

In this chapter, we have also presented four methods for realizing lossless DP functions. Foster's first form applies only to impedance functions, and Foster's second form deals only with admittance functions. Cauer's two forms can both be applied to either an impedance or an admittance function. Cauer's first form works with a DP function whose numerator polynomial is of higher degree than that of the denominator polynomial, and Cauer's second form works with a DP function whose denominator is an odd polynomial.

Foster's forms are relatively easier to implement, but Cauer's forms are more useful, particularly in the realization of transfer functions as discussed in Chapter 7. The circuit structure of Foster's first form consists of series connections of parallel LC branches, and that of Foster's second form consists of parallel connections of series LC branches. The circuit configuration of both Cauer's forms are *ladder* circuits. Cauer's first form consists of series inductors and shunt capacitors, creating transmission zeros[14] at $s = \infty$, and Cauer's second form consists of series capacitors and shunt inductors, creating transmission zeros at $s = 0$. The basic circuit configurations of both Foster's and Cauer's forms are summarized in Fig. 5-13.

---

[14]The concept of *transmission zero* is introduced in Chapter 7. Here it suffices to say that transmission zeros of circuit are zeros of a network function associated with the circuit.

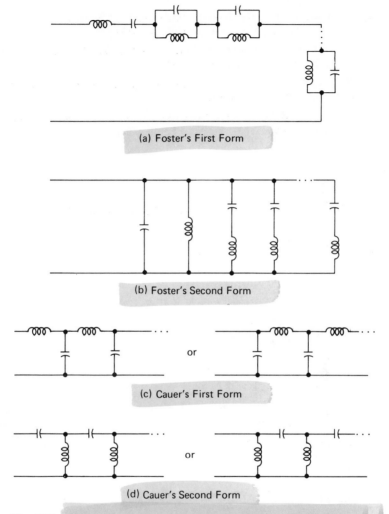

(a) Foster's First Form

(b) Foster's Second Form

(c) Cauer's First Form

(d) Cauer's Second Form

Fig. 5-13 Circuit structures of Foster's two forms and Cauer's two forms.

REFERENCES AND FURTHER READING

[1] DESOER, C. A., and KUH, E. S. *Basic Circuit Theory*. New York: McGraw-Hill, 1969.

[2] FOSTER, R. M. "A Reactance Theorem." *Bell Syst. Tech. J.* 3 (1924): 259–67.

[3] WEINBERG, L. *Network Analysis and Synthesis*. Huntington, N.Y.: R. E. Krieger, 1975.

[4] HUMPHREYS, D. S. *The Analysis, Design, and Synthesis of Electrical Filters.* Englewood Cliffs, N.J.: Prentice-Hall, Inc., 1970.

[5] PEIKARI, B. *Fundamentals of Network Analysis and Synthesis.* Englewood Cliffs, N.J.: Prentice-Hall, Inc., 1974.

[6] BUDAK, A. *Passive and Active Network Analysis and Synthesis.* Boston, MA.: Houghton Mifflin, 1974.

[7] ANDERSON, B. D. O., and VONGPANITLERD, S. *Network Analysis and Synthesis.* Englewood Cliffs, N.J.: Prentice-Hall, Inc., 1973.

PROBLEMS

5-1. Determine which of the following $F(s)$ are realizable as lossless DP functions. Justify your answers.

(a) $F(s) = \dfrac{s^4 + 5s^2 + 6}{s^4 + 3s^2 + 2}$

(b) $F(s) = \dfrac{s^3 + 5s}{s^4 + 3s^2 + 2}$

(c) $F(s) = \dfrac{s^3 + 1.5s}{s^4 + 3s^2 + 2}$

(d) $F(s) = \dfrac{s^3 + 1.5s}{s^4 + 2s^2 + 1}$

(e) $F(s) = \dfrac{s^3 + 1.5s}{s^2 + 1}$

(f) $F(s) = \dfrac{s^5 + 2s^3 + s}{s^4 + 3s^2 + 2}$

(g) $F(s) = \dfrac{s^5 + 3s^3 + 2s}{s^4 + 5.5s^2 + 6}$

(h) $F(s) = \dfrac{s^4 + 3s^2 + 2}{s^5 + 5.5s^3 + 6s}$

(i) $F(s) = \dfrac{s^4 + 3s^2 + 2}{s^5 + 5.5s^3 + 6}$

(j) $F(s) = \dfrac{s^4 + 3s^2 + 2}{s^6 + 2s^4 + 6s^2 + 3}$

5-2. Consider the 1-port network N shown in Fig. P5-2.

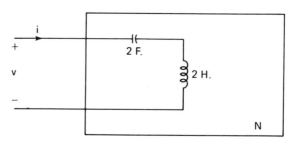

Fig. P5-2

(a) If $v(t) = A \cos \omega t$, find the steady-state response $i(t)$, and show that the average power dissipation is zero.

(b) Find the DP impedance function $Z(s)$ of N, and show that $Z(s)$ satisfies all the properties of a lossless DP function.

5-3. Consider the 1-port network N shown in Fig. P5-3.

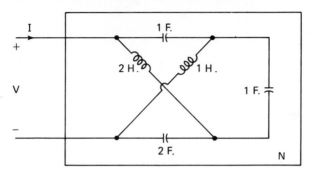

Fig. P5-3

(a) Find the DP impedance function $Z(s)$ of N.

(b) Show that $Z(s)$ satisfies all the properties of a lossless DP function.

(c) Realize $Z(s)$ by Foster's first form.

(d) Realize $Z(s)$ by Foster's second form.

(e) Realize $Z(s)$ by Cauer's first form.

(f) Realize $Z(s)$ by Cauer's second form.

Note: The DP impedance function of N is given by

$$Z(s) = \frac{10s^4 + 8s^2 + 1}{4s^5 + 10s^3 + 4s}$$

5-4. Repeat Problem 5-3 for the 1-port networks shown in Fig. P5-4.

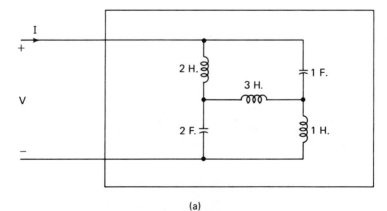

(a)

Fig. P5-4(a)

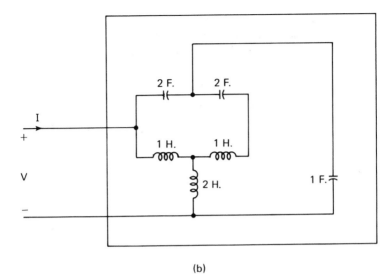

(b)

Fig. P5-4(b)

5-5. For each $F(s)$ given in the following, find the range of a such that $F(s)$ is realizable as a lossless DP function.

(a) $F(s) = \dfrac{s^3 + as}{s^4 + 3s^2 + 2}$

(b) $F(s) = \dfrac{s^5 + as^3 + 1.5s}{s^4 + 3s^2 + 2}$

(c) $F(s) = \dfrac{s^3 + 4s}{s^4 + as^2 + 2}$

(d) $F(s) = \dfrac{2.5s^4 + 2s^2 + a}{s^5 + 2.5s^3 + s}$

(e) $F(s) = \dfrac{2.5s^4 + as^2 + 0.25}{s^5 + 2.5s^3 + s}$

5-6. Realize the following DP impedance functions by two Foster's and two Cauer's forms. If a given $Z(s)$ is not realizable, state your reasons.

(a) $Z(s) = \dfrac{s(s^2 + 2)}{(s^2 + 1)}$

(b) $Z(s) = \dfrac{(s^2 + 3)}{s(s^2 + 4)}$

(c) $Z(s) = \dfrac{(s^2 + 1)(s^2 + 3)}{s(s^2 + 2)}$

(d) $Z(s) = \dfrac{s(s^2 + 2)(s^2 + 4)}{(s^2 + 1)(s^2 + 3)}$

(e) $Z(s) = \dfrac{(s^2 + 2)(s^2 + 4)}{s(s^2 + 1)(s^2 + 3)}$

5-7. Realize the following DP admittance functions by two Foster's forms and two Cauer's forms. If a given $Y(s)$ is not realizable, state your reasons.

(a) $Y(s) = \dfrac{s(s^2 + 2)}{(s^2 + 1)}$

(b) $Y(s) = \dfrac{s^2 + 3}{s(s^2 + 4)}$

(c) $Y(s) = \dfrac{(s^2 + 1)(s^2 + 3)}{s(s^2 + 2)}$

(d) $Y(s) = \dfrac{s(s^2 + 2)(s^2 + 4)}{(s^2 + 1)(s^2 + 3)}$

(e) $Y(s) = \dfrac{(s^2 + 2)(s^2 + 4)}{s(s^2 + 1)(s^2 + 3)}$

5-8. Realize the DP impedance function

$$Z(s) = \frac{(s^2 + 1)(s^2 + 4)}{s(s^2 + 3)(s^2 + 5)}$$

by the following procedures:

(a) Start with Cauer's first form (for two elements), and complete the realization with Cauer's second form.

(b) Start with Cauer's second form (for three elements), and complete the realization with Cauer's first form.

(c) Start with Cauer's first form (for one element); then switch to Cauer's second form (for one element), and complete the realization with Foster's first form.

5-9. (a) Realize the DP admittance function

$$Y(s) = \frac{4s^3 + 6s}{s^4 + 5s^2 + 4}$$

by Cauer's first form.

(b) Verify that the DP admittance function of the circuit obtained in (a) is indeed given by $Y(s)$.

5-10. (a) Realize the DP impedance function

$$Z(s) = \frac{4s^3 + 6s}{s^4 + 5s^2 + 4}$$

by Cauer's second form.

(b) Verify that the DP impedance function of the circuit obtained in (a) is indeed given by $Z(s)$.

5-11. Given the coefficients of the polynomials

$$A(s) = a_0 + a_1 s + a_2 s^2 + \ldots + a_m s^m$$

and

$$B(s) = b_0 + b_1 s + b_2 s^2 + \ldots + b_n s^n$$

write a computer program to determine if

$$F(s) = \frac{A(s)}{B(s)}$$

is realizable as a lossless DP function.

5-12. Given a lossless DP impedance {admittance} function $Z(s)$ $\{Y(s)\}$, write a computer program to realize $Z(s)$ $\{Y(s)\}$ by

(a) Foster's first form.

(b) Foster's second form.

(c) Cauer's first form.

(d) Cauer's second form.

6

PROPERTIES
AND REALIZATIONS
OF PASSIVE RC
DRIVING-POINT FUNCTIONS

For low-frequency operations, large inductance values are normally required leading to discrete inductors that are heavy, lossy, bulky, and costly. In addition, true integrated circuit inductors are still not possible. Synthetic inductors, such as those produced by gyrator–capacitor combinations, still present practical problems. With these constraints, the feasible physical circuits are simply passive and active RC circuits.[1]

It is shown in this chapter that both the poles and zeros of a passive RC 1-port impedance or admittance function are on the negative real axis of the s-plane.[2] This means that the poles of a transfer function of a passive RC 2-port must be on the negative real axis of the s-plane. Fortunately, with the inclusion of active devices, such as operational amplifiers and VCVS, complex s-plane poles can be obtained. Hence, in theory, an active RC network appears to be capable of performing all the filtering functions of its passive RLC counterparts. However, component tolerances and parameter sensitivities, particularly those associated with an active device, often border on or exceed the practical limits of realizability at high frequencies. On the other hand, in low-frequency applications for which parameter variations are not as critical, active RC devices are the dominant forms of realization. As we see later, the realization of DP functions by resistors and capacitors is of fundamental importance to the design of RC active circuits.

---

[1]Passive RC circuits are circuits containing resistors and capacitors only. Active RC circuits contain active devices in addition to resistors and capacitors.

[2]In this book, the negative real axis of the s-plane includes the origin $s = 0$ and the point $s = \infty$.

In this chapter, we examine the basic properties and realization methods of a driving-point function realizable by resistors and capacitors only. This class of DP functions is called RC DP functions.

6-1 PROPERTIES OF RC DP IMPEDANCE
FUNCTIONS

Properties and realization techniques of RC DP functions are most readily established by making parallel comparisons with those of LC DP functions. Although this is not the most rigorous procedure, it does lead to accurate results and provide additional insight into the properties of two-element type impedance and admittance functions.

In Chapter 5, it has been shown that every lossless LC 1-port impedance function can be described by (5-25), which is repeated here for convenience

$$Z_{LC}(s) = L_\infty s + \frac{1}{C_0 s} + \sum_{i=1}^{n} \frac{1}{C_i s + (1/L_i s)} \tag{6-1}$$

This means that every LC 1-port admits an equivalent 1-port circuit in the form of Fig. 5-2.

Given an RC 1-port η_{RC}, let η_{LC} be the 1-port circuit obtained by replacing each resistor of $R_k \Omega$ in η_{RC} with an inductor of $R_k H$. In view of the comments of the previous paragraph, η_{LC} admits an equivalent 1-port circuit $\hat{\eta}_{LC}$ in the form of Fig. 5-2. If we now obtain a 1-port circuit $\hat{\eta}_{RC}$ by replacing each inductor of $L_k H$ in $\hat{\eta}_{LC}$ by a resistor of $L_k \Omega$, then clearly, $\hat{\eta}_{RC}$ is equivalent to η_{RC}, just as $\hat{\eta}_{LC}$ is equivalent to η_{LC}.

The DP impedance of $\hat{\eta}_{LC}$ is given by (6-1), and $\hat{\eta}_{RC}$ is obtained by replacing each impedance branch of sL_k in $\hat{\eta}_{LC}$ with an impedance of $R_k = L_k$; therefore, the DP impedance function of $\hat{\eta}_{RC}$ is given by

$$Z_{RC}(s) = R_\infty + \frac{1}{C_0 s} + \sum_{i=1}^{n} \frac{1}{C_i s + (1/R_i)} \tag{6-2}$$

Letting

$$\sigma_i = \frac{1}{R_i C_i}, \quad k_i = \frac{1}{C_i}, \quad k_\infty = R_\infty, \quad \text{and} \quad k_0 = \frac{1}{C_0} \tag{6-3}$$

(6-2) becomes

$$Z_{RC}(s) = k_\infty + \frac{k_0}{s} + \sum_{i=1}^{n} \frac{k_i}{s + \sigma_i} \tag{6-4}$$

where σ_i and k_i, for $i = 1, 2, \ldots, n$; k_0; and k_∞ are positive and real. Because η_{RC} and $\hat{\eta}_{RC}$ are equivalent 1-ports, the DP impedance function of η_{RC} is clearly given by (6-4) also. Hence, we conclude that the impedance function of every RC 1-port can be written in the form of (6-4).

With the preliminary work completed, we now discuss some general properties of RC 1-port impedance functions.

PROPERTY ZRC1   All poles and zeros of an RC 1-port impedance function occur on the negative real axis of the s-plane.

PROOF. From (4-5), the DP impedance function of an RC 1-port satisfies the following equation

$$Z_{in}(s) = \sum_{\Re} R_k \frac{|I_k|^2}{|I_1|^2} + \frac{1}{s} \sum_{\mathfrak{C}} \frac{1}{C_k} \frac{|I_k|^2}{|I_1|^2} \tag{6-5}$$

In turn, (6-5) says that the zeros of $Z_{in}(s)$ must satisfy equations of the form

$$\alpha s + \beta = 0 \tag{6-6}$$

where

$$\alpha \triangleq \sum_{\Re} R_k \frac{|I_k|^2}{|I_1|^2} \geq 0$$

and

$$\beta \triangleq \sum_{\mathfrak{C}} \frac{1}{C_k} \frac{|I_k|^2}{|I_1|^2} \geq 0$$

Even though both α and β are functions of s, based on (6-6), we may still conclude that the zeros of an RC 1-port impedance function are on the negative real axis of the s-plane. In a *dual* manner, we may conclude that the zeros of an RC 1-port admittance function must be on the negative real axis of the s-plane also. Hence, both the zeros and poles of an RC 1-port DP function are on the negative real axis of the s-plane.   ∎

Based on the general form of an RC DP impedance function, $Z_{RC}(s)$ of (6-4), we make the following observations:

PROPERTY ZRC2   The residues of $Z_{RC}(s)$ are real and positive.

PROOF. From (6-4), the residues of $Z_{RC}(s)$ are the constants k_i; where $i = 0, 1, 2, \ldots, n$; and ∞. These residues are real and positive as indicated by (6-3).[3]   ∎

PROPERTY ZRC3 $Z_{RC}(s)$ can not have a pole at $s = \infty$. In addition,[4]

$$Z_{RC}(\infty) < Z_{RC}(0) \tag{6-7}$$

PROOF. From (6-4), $Z_{RC}(\infty) = k_\infty$, which is a finite nonnegative number. Hence $s = \infty$ can not be a pole of $Z_{RC}(s)$. Also, from (6-4)

$$Z_{RC}(0) = k_\infty + \frac{k_0}{0} + \sum_{i=1}^{n} \frac{k_i}{\sigma_i} \tag{6-8}$$

If $k_0 \neq 0$, then $Z_{RC}(s)$ has a pole at $s = 0$, and $Z_{RC}(0) = \infty$. If $k_0 = 0$, then

---

[3]The constants k_0 and k_∞ are real and positive whenever they appear in (6-4). Strictly speaking, k_0 and k_∞ are real and nonnegative constants.

[4]Note that $Z_{RC}(-\infty) = Z_{RC}(\infty)$.

the point $s = 0$ is not a pole of $Z_{RC}(s)$. In this case, we have

$$Z_{RC}(0) = k_\infty + \sum_{i=1}^{n} \frac{k_i}{\sigma_i} = Z_{RC}(\infty) + \sum_{i=1}^{n} \frac{k_i}{\sigma_i} > Z_{RC}(\infty) \qquad (6\text{-}9)$$

This completes the proof of Property ZRC3. ∎

PROPERTY ZRC4 $Z_{RC}(s)$ is a monotonically decreasing function along the real axis of the s-plane, except at the poles of $Z_{RC}(s)$.

PROOF. Differentiating (6-4) with respect to s, we obtain

$$\frac{dZ_{RC}(s)}{ds} = -\frac{k_0}{s^2} - \sum_{i=1}^{n} \frac{k_i}{(s + \sigma_i)^2} \qquad (6\text{-}10)$$

Setting $s = \sigma$, (6-10) becomes

$$\frac{dZ_{RC}(\sigma)}{d\sigma} = -\frac{k_0}{\sigma^2} - \sum_{i=1}^{n} \frac{k_i}{(\sigma + \sigma_i)^2} \qquad (6\text{-}11)$$

Because the k_i's are positive and real as concluded by Property ZRC2,

$$\frac{dZ_{RC}(\sigma)}{d\sigma} < 0 \qquad (6\text{-}12)$$

for all σ, except when $\sigma = -\sigma_i$ which are the poles of $Z_{RC}(s)$. ∎

Some typical sketches of $Z_{RC}(\sigma)$ versus σ are shown in Fig. 6-1. As a consequence of Property ZRC4, we have the following two properties:

PROPERTY ZRC5 All poles and zeros of $Z_{RC}(s)$ are simple, and they interlace each other along the negative real axis of the s-plane. The critical point closest to the origin must be a pole (it may occur right at the origin), and the one closest to $s = \infty$ is zero (again, it may occur at $s = \infty$). Including the point $s = \infty$, the number of poles of $Z_{RC}(s)$ equals the number of zeros of $Z_{RC}(s)$. (See Fig. 6-1.) ∎

PROPERTY ZRC6 If $s = \infty$ is not a zero of $Z_{RC}(s)$, then $Z_{RC}(s)$ can be written as

$$Z_{RC}(s) = \frac{k_\infty(s + \hat{\sigma}_2)(s + \hat{\sigma}_4)\ldots(s + \hat{\sigma}_r)}{(s + \hat{\sigma}_1)(s + \hat{\sigma}_3)\ldots(s + \hat{\sigma}_{r-1})} \qquad (6\text{-}13)$$

where

$$0 \leq \hat{\sigma}_1 < \hat{\sigma}_2 < \hat{\sigma}_3 \ldots < \hat{\sigma}_r \qquad (6\text{-}14)$$

and r is an even integer. On the other hand, if $s = \infty$ is a zero of $Z_{RC}(s)$, then $Z_{RC}(s)$ is given by

$$Z_{RC}(s) = \frac{k(s + \hat{\sigma}_2)(s + \hat{\sigma}_4)\ldots(s + \hat{\sigma}_r)}{(s + \hat{\sigma}_1)(s + \hat{\sigma}_3)\ldots(s + \hat{\sigma}_{r+1})} \qquad (6\text{-}15)$$

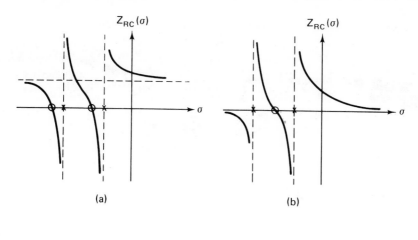

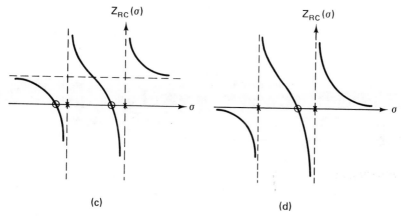

Legend: 0 = zero and x = pole

Fig. 6-1 Typical plots of $Z_{RC}(\sigma)$ versus σ. (a) and (c) $s = \infty$ is not a zero of $Z_{RC}(s)$. (b) and (d) $s = \infty$ is a zero of $Z_{RC}(s)$. (a) and (b) $s = 0$ is not a pole of $Z_{RC}(s)$. (c) and (d) $s = 0$ is a pole of $Z_{RC}(s)$.

where r is an even integer, and

$$0 \leq \hat{\sigma}_1 < \hat{\sigma}_2 < \ldots < \hat{\sigma}_{r+1} \qquad (6\text{-}16)$$

∎

Note that (6-13) simply says that there are as many finite poles as there are finite zeros.[5] Hence, the degrees of the numerator polynomial and the

---

[5]A point s_k is said to be a *finite pole* {*zero*} of a rational function $F(s)$ if s_k is a pole {zero} of $F(s)$ and $|s_k| \neq \infty$.

denominator polynomial are the same. In (6-15), the degree of the denominator polynomial is one greater than that of the numerator polynomial, implying that there are more finite poles than finite zeros. If $Z_{RC}(s)$ is given as a ratio of two polynomials as $Z_{RC}(s) = A(s)/B(s)$, where $A(s)$ and $B(s)$ are polynomials of degrees d_A and d_B, respectively, then Property ZRC6 implies that

$$d_B - 1 \leq d_A \leq d_B \qquad (6\text{-}17)$$

Properties ZRC5 and ZRC6 play a very important part in RC active filter design in Chapter 10.

PROPERTY ZRC7 $\mathrm{Re}[Z_{RC}(j\omega)]$ decreases monotonically as $|\omega|$ increases.

PROOF. From (6-4), the real part of $Z_{RC}(j\omega)$ is given by

$$\mathrm{Re}[Z_{RC}(j\omega)] = k_\infty + \sum_{i=1}^{n} \frac{k_i \sigma_i}{\omega^2 + \sigma_i^2} \qquad (6\text{-}18)$$

As $|\omega|$ increases, the second term on the right-hand side of (6-18) decreases, and the first term remains constant. Hence, our conclusion follows. ∎

Property ZRC7 means that $\mathrm{Re}[Z_{RC}(j\omega)]$ attains its minimum value at $\omega = \infty$. From (6-4), $Z_{RC}(j\infty) = Z_{RC}(\infty)$ is a real quantity. Hence, we have

$$Z_{RC}(\infty) = \mathrm{Re}[Z_{RC}(\infty)] \leq \mathrm{Re}[Z_{RC}(j\omega)] \quad \text{for all } \omega \qquad (6\text{-}19)$$

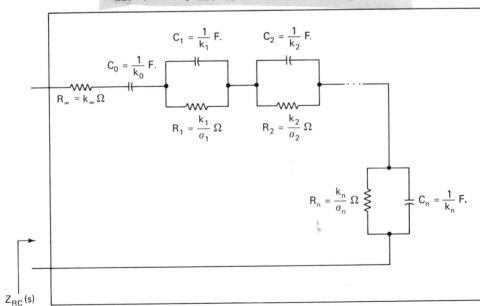

$Z_{RC}(s)$

Fig. 6-2   Circuit structure of Foster's first form.

Equation (6-19) is very useful in RC DP 1-port synthesis, particularly with Cauer's first form. It turns out that $Z_{RC}(\infty)$ is the largest positive constant that can be extracted from $Z_{RC}(s)$, and yet the remainder impedance function $Z_{RC}^r(s) \triangleq Z_{RC}(s) - Z_{RC}(\infty)$ is a PR function having all properties of an RC DP impedance function.[6] This fact is utilized in Cauer's first-form realization of RC DP functions.

A circuit realization of (6-2) via the partial fraction expansion of (6-4) and (6-3) is given in Fig. 6-2, which is called *Foster's first form*. Notice that the circuit in Fig. 6-2 is the same as that in Fig. 5-2, except that the inductors are replaced by resistors with appropriate values.

6-2 PROPERTIES OF RC DP ADMITTANCE FUNCTIONS

Based on (5-27) rather than (5-25), we can show that the DP admittance function of an RC 1-port has the following general form

$$Y_{RC}(s) = C_\infty s + \frac{1}{R_0} + \sum_{i=1}^{n} \frac{1}{R_i + (1/C_i s)} \qquad (6\text{-}20)$$

If we let

$$k_0 = \frac{1}{R_0}, \quad k_i = \frac{1}{R_i}, \quad k_\infty = C_\infty, \quad \text{and} \quad \sigma_i = \frac{1}{R_i C_i} \qquad (6\text{-}21)$$

then (6-20) can be written as

$$Y_{RC}(s) = k_\infty s + k_0 + \sum_{i=1}^{n} \frac{k_i s}{s + \sigma_i} \qquad (6\text{-}22)$$

where k_i and σ_i, for $i = 1, 2, \ldots, n$; k_0; and k_∞ are positive and real. In view of the format of the RC DP admittance function $Y_{RC}(s)$ of (6-20) to (6-22), we can state the following:[7]

PROPERTY YRC1 All poles and zeros of $Y_{RC}(s)$ are on the negative real axis of the s-plane. ∎

PROPERTY YRC2 The residues of $Y_{RC}(s)$ at the finite negative real poles are real and negative. The residue of $Y_{RC}(s)$ at the pole $s = \infty$ is positive and real.[8]

---

[6]See References [1] and [2] for details.

[7]If a property of $Y_{RC}(s)$ can be proved by a dual development, parallel with that of $Z_{RC}(s)$, we simply state that property.

[8]Whenever the term $k_\infty s \{k_0\}$ appears in (6-22), $k_\infty \{k_0\}$ is a real and positive constant.

PROOF. From (6-22), the residue of $Y_{RC}(s)$ at $s = \infty$ is given by

$$\xi_\infty = \lim_{s \to \infty} \frac{1}{s} Y_{RC}(s) = k_\infty \tag{6-23}$$

By (6-21), ξ_∞ is positive and real.

The residue of $Y_{RC}(s)$ at a finite negative real pole $s = -\sigma_j$ is given by

$$\xi_j = (s + \sigma_j) Y_{RC}(s) \Big|_{s = -\sigma_j} \tag{6-24}$$

Substituting (6-22) into (6-24), we obtain

$$\xi_j = k_j s \Big|_{s = -\sigma_j} = -k_j \sigma_j \tag{6-25}$$

From (6-21) and (6-25), ξ_j is negative and real. ∎

PROPERTY YRC3 $Y_{RC}(s)$ can not have a pole at $s = 0$. In addition,

$$Y_{RC}(0) \leq Y_{RC}(\infty) = |Y_{RC}(-\infty)| \tag{6-26}$$

Note that $Y_{RC}(s)$ may have a pole at $s = \infty$ and/or a zero at $s = 0$. ∎

PROPERTY YRC4 $Y_{RC}(s)$ is a monotonically increasing function along the real axis of the s-plane, except at the poles of $Y_{RC}(s)$.

PROOF. Differentiating (6-22), we obtain

$$\frac{dY_{RC}(\sigma)}{d\sigma} = k_\infty + \sum_{i=1}^{n} \frac{k_i \sigma_i}{(\sigma + \sigma_i)^2} \tag{6-27}$$

By (6-21) and (6-27),

$$\frac{dY_{RC}(\sigma)}{d\sigma} > 0 \tag{6-28}$$

for all σ except at the poles of $Y_{RC}(s)$. ∎

Some typical sketches of $Y_{RC}(\sigma)$ versus σ are given by Fig. 6-3.

PROPERTY YRC5 All poles and zeros of $Y_{RC}(s)$ are simple, and they interlace each other along the negative real axis of the s-plane. The critical point closest to the origin must be a zero (it may occur at the origin), and the one closest to infinity is a pole ($s = \infty$ may be a pole). Including the point $s = \infty$, the number of poles of $Y_{RC}(s)$ equals the number of zeros of $Y_{RC}(s)$. (See Fig. 6-3.) ∎

PROPERTY YRC6 If $s = \infty$ is not a pole of $Y_{RC}(s)$, then $Y_{RC}(s)$ can be written as:

$$Y_{RC}(s) = \frac{k_\infty (s + \hat{\sigma}_1)(s + \hat{\sigma}_3) \ldots (s + \hat{\sigma}_r)}{(s + \hat{\sigma}_2)(s + \hat{\sigma}_4) \ldots (s + \hat{\sigma}_{r+1})} \tag{6-29}$$

where r is an odd integer, and

$$0 \leq \hat{\sigma}_1 < \hat{\sigma}_2 < \ldots < \hat{\sigma}_{r+1} \tag{6-30}$$

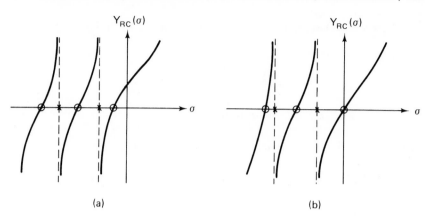

(a)   (b)

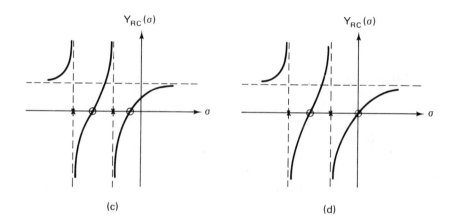

(c)   (d)

Legend: x = poles and 0 = zeros

Fig. 6-3   Typical plots of $Y_{RC}(\sigma)$ versus σ. (a) and (c) $s = 0$ is not a zero of $Y_{RC}(s)$. (b) and (d) $s = 0$ is a zero of $Y_{RC}(s)$. (a) and (b) $s = \infty$ is a pole of $Y_{RC}(s)$. (c) and (d) $s = \infty$ is not a pole of $Y_{RC}(s)$.

In this case, both the numerator and the denominator polynomials of $Y_{RC}(s)$ have the same degree. On the other hand, if $s = \infty$ is a pole of $Y_{RC}(s)$, then $Y_{RC}(s)$ can be written as:

$$Y_{RC}(s) = \frac{k(s + \hat{\sigma}_1)(s + \hat{\sigma}_3)\dots(s + \hat{\sigma}_r)}{(s + \hat{\sigma}_2)(s + \hat{\sigma}_4)\dots(s + \hat{\sigma}_{r-1})} \qquad (6\text{-}31)$$

where r is an odd integer, and

$$0 \leq \hat{\sigma}_1 < \hat{\sigma}_2 < \dots < \hat{\sigma}_r \qquad (6\text{-}32)$$

Equation (6-31) says that the numerator polynomial of $Y_{RC}(s)$ is of a greater degree than that of the denominator polynomial.   ∎

PROPERTY YRC7 Re $[Y_{RC}(j\omega)/j\omega]$ decreases as $|\omega|$ increases.

PROOF. From (6-22)

$$\frac{Y_{RC}(s)}{s} = k_\infty + \frac{k_0}{s} + \sum_{i=1}^{n} \frac{k_i}{s + \sigma_i} \tag{6-33}$$

Notice that $Y_{RC}(s)/s$ is in the form of an RC DP impedance function of (6-4). Hence, by Property ZRC7 of DP impedance functions of RC 1-ports, we conclude that Re $[Y_{RC}(j\omega)/j\omega]$ decreases as $|\omega|$ increases. ∎

PROPERTY YRC8 Re $[Y_{RC}(j\omega)]$ is a monotonically increasing function of $|\omega|$. In addition

$$Y_{RC}(0) \leq \text{Re } [Y_{RC}(j\omega)] \quad \text{for all } \omega \tag{6-34}$$

PROOF. From (6-22), we obtain

$$\text{Re } [Y_{RC}(j\omega)] = k_0 + \sum_{i=1}^{n} \text{Re}\left[\frac{k_i j\omega}{i\omega + \sigma_i}\right]$$

$$= k_0 + \sum_{i=1}^{n} \frac{k_i \omega^2}{\sigma_i^2 + \omega^2} \tag{6-35}$$

Clearly, Re $[Y_{RC}(0)] = k_0$ is the minimum value of Re $[Y_{RC}(j\omega)]$, because the second term on the right-hand side of (6-35) is positive for all $\omega \neq 0$.

It can be shown from (6-35) that Re $[Y_{RC}(j\omega)]$ is a monotonically increasing function of $|\omega|$. A sketch of Re $[Y_{RC}(j\omega)]$ versus ω is shown in Fig. 6-4, where

$$A = \text{Re } [Y_{RC}(\infty)] = k_0 + \sum_{i=1}^{n} k_i \geq k_0 = Y_{RC}(0) \tag{6-36}$$

∎

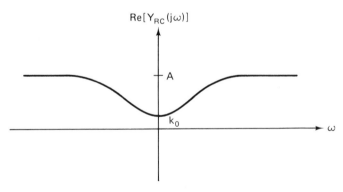

Fig. 6-4 A typical plot of Re $[Y_{RC}(j\omega)]$ versus ω.

It turns out that $Y_{RC}(0)$ is the largest constant that can be extracted from $Y_{RC}(s)$ such that the remainder function $Y'_{RC}(s) \triangleq Y_{RC}(s) - Y_{RC}(0)$ is still a

PR function having all properties of an RC DP admittance function. This fact forms the basic foundation for Cauer's second-form realization of RC DP functions.

A circuit realization of (6-22) or equivalently (6-20) with (6-21) is given in Fig. 6-5, which is called *Foster's second form.*

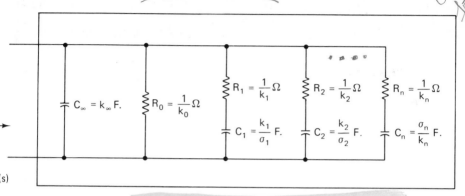

Fig. 6-5   Circuit structure of Foster's second form.

6-3   EXAMPLE OF FOSTER'S REALIZATION METHODS

Example 6-1   Realize

$$Z_{RC}(s) = \frac{(s + 1)(s + 3)}{s(s + 2)(s + 4)} \tag{6-37}$$

by Foster's two forms.

Solution: It can be shown that the impedance function of (6-37) satisfies all the properties of a passive RC DP impedance function. Hence, passive RC circuit realizations are possible.

A partial fraction expansion of (6-37) leads to

$$Z_{RC}(s) = \frac{A}{s} + \frac{B}{s + 2} + \frac{C}{s + 4} \tag{6-38}$$

where A, B, and C are the residues of $Z_{RC}(s)$ at the poles $s_1 = 0$, $s_2 = -2$, and $s_3 = -4$, respectively. Hence,

$$A = sZ_{RC}(s)\Big|_{s=0} = \frac{3}{8}$$

$$B = (s + 2)Z_{RC}(s)\Big|_{s=-2} = \frac{1}{4}$$

$$C = (s + 4)Z_{RC}(s)\Big|_{s=-4} = \frac{3}{8}$$

and (6-38) becomes

$$Z_{RC}(s) = \frac{3/8}{s} + \frac{1/4}{s+2} + \frac{3/8}{s+4} \tag{6-39}$$

Writing (6-39) in the form of (6-2) gives

$$Z_{RC}(s) = \frac{1}{(8/3)s} + \frac{1}{4s+8} + \frac{1}{(8/3)s+(32/3)} \tag{6-40}$$

A circuit realization of (6-37) or equivalently (6-40) is given in Fig. 6-6(a).

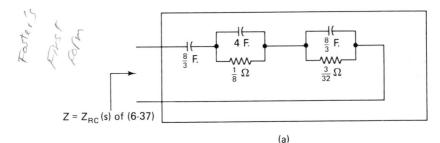

(a)

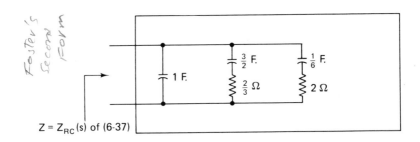

(b)

Fig. 6-6 Circuit realizations of the RC DP impedance function of (6-37) via (a) Foster's first form, and (b) Foster's second form.

To realize (6-37) by Foster's second form, we consider

$$Y_{RC}(s) = \frac{1}{Z_{RC}(s)} = \frac{s(s+2)(s+4)}{(s+1)(s+3)} \tag{6-41}$$

Taking the partial fraction expansion of $Y_{RC}(s)/s$, we obtain

$$\frac{Y_{RC}(s)}{s} = \frac{(s+2)(s+4)}{(s+1)(s+3)} = \frac{s^2+6s+8}{s^2+4s+3} = 1 + \frac{2s+5}{(s+1)(s+3)}$$

$$= 1 + \frac{D}{s+1} + \frac{E}{s+3} \tag{6-42}$$

where

$$D = (s+1)\frac{2s+5}{(s+1)(s+3)}\bigg|_{s=-1} = \frac{3}{2}$$

and

$$E = (s + 3)\frac{2s + 5}{(s + 1)(s + 3)}\Big|_{s=-3} = \frac{1}{2}$$

Hence, (6-42) becomes

$$\frac{Y_{RC}(s)}{s} = 1 + \frac{3/2}{s + 1} + \frac{1/2}{s + 3}$$

or

$$Y_{RC}(s) = s + \frac{(3/2)s}{s + 1} + \frac{(1/2)s}{s + 3}$$

$$= s + \frac{1}{\dfrac{2}{3} + \dfrac{2}{3s}} + \frac{1}{2 + \dfrac{6}{s}} \qquad (6\text{-}43)$$

A circuit realization of (6-37) via Foster's second form of (6-43) is given by Fig. 6-6(b). ∎

6-4   CAUER'S REALIZATION METHODS

As is in the case of LC 1-ports, Foster's two forms are not the only methods available to synthesize RC DP impedance or admittance functions. In this section, we consider two additional methods: Cauer's two forms. Cauer's first form is based on the following two pieces of information:

1a $s = \infty$ may be a pole of $Y_{RC}(s)$.
1b. $Z_{RC}(\infty) \leq \text{Re} [Z_{RC}(j\omega)]$ for all ω.

As a consequence of 1b, the remainder impedance function $Z_{RC}^r(s) \triangleq Z_{RC}(s) - Z_{RC}(\infty)$ is still an RC DP impedance function. In addition, $Z_{RC}^r(\infty) = 0$. Hence, $Y_{RC}^r(s)$ has a pole at $s = \infty$. In a similar manner, Cauer's second form depends on the following two facts:

2a. $s = 0$ may be a pole of $Z_{RC}(s)$.
2b. $Y_{RC}(0) \leq \text{Re} [Y_{RC}(j\omega)]$ for all ω.

Consequently, the remainder admittance function $\hat{Y}_{RC}^r(s) \triangleq Y_{RC}(s) - Y_{RC}(0)$ is still a PR function having all properties of a DP admittance function of an RC 1-port. Furthermore, $\hat{Y}_{RC}^r(0) = 0$. Hence, $\hat{Z}_{RC}^r(s)$ has a pole at $s = 0$.

6-4-1.   Cauer's First Form

Cauer's first form examines alternatively $Z_{RC}(s)$ and $Y_{RC}(s)$ at the point $s = \infty$. Let us first consider $Y_{RC}(s)$ at $s = \infty$. There are two possibilities: Either $Y_{RC}(\infty)$ is finite, or $s = \infty$ is a pole of $Y_{RC}(s)$. Assume first that $s = \infty$ is a pole of $Y_{RC}(s)$. Then the pole can be removed in the form of a *shunt capacitor.* Mathematically speaking, this is equivalent to writing $Y_{RC}(s)$ as

$$Y_{RC}(s) = C_0 s + Y_1(s) \qquad (6\text{-}44a)$$

where

$$C_0 = \frac{1}{s} Y_{RC}(s) \Big|_{s=\infty} \qquad (6\text{-}44b)$$

is the residue of $Y_{RC}(s)$ at the pole $s = \infty$, and the remainder function

$$Y_1(s) = Y_{RC}(s) - C_0 s \qquad (6\text{-}44c)$$

is also an RC DP admittance function with $Y_1(\infty)$ being a finite quantity. Because $Y_{RC}(s)$ is written as a sum of two terms as in (6-44), we can realize $Y_{RC}(s)$ by connecting a (shunt) capacitor in parallel with an RC 1-port characterized by the DP admittance function of $Y_1(s)$, as shown in Fig. 6-7(a). Clearly, $Y_1(s)$ is simpler than $Y_{RC}(s)$. To realize $Y_1(s)$, we consider the other possibility for $Y_{RC}(s)$—$s = \infty$ is not a pole of $Y_{RC}(s)$. In this case, let us invert $Y_{RC}(s)$ to obtain $Z_{RC}(s)$. Based on condition 1b or Property ZRC7 of $Z_{RC}(s)$, we can remove $Z_{RC}(\infty)$ from $Z_{RC}(s)$, which corresponds to a *series resistor*, and still leave an RC DP impedance function. In equation form, this corre-

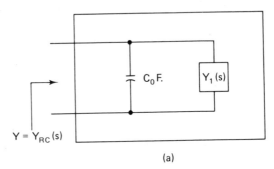

$Y = Y_{RC}(s)$

(a)

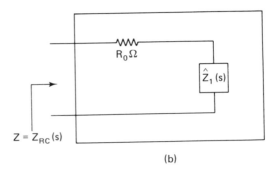

$Z = Z_{RC}(s)$

(b)

Fig. 6-7 Basic realization procedure for Cauer's first form (a) when $s = \infty$ is a pole of $Y_{RC}(s)$, and (b) when $s = \infty$ is not a pole of $Y_{RC}(s)$.

sponds to writing $Z_{RC}(s)$ as

$$Z_{RC}(s) = R_0 + \hat{Z}_1(s) \tag{6-45a}$$

where

$$R_0 = Z_{RC}(\infty) \tag{6-45b}$$

and the remainder function $\hat{Z}_1(s)$ is an RC DP impedance function. Because $Z_{RC}(s)$ is written as a sum of two terms, as in (6-45), we can realize $Z_{RC}(s)$ by connecting a (series) resistor in series with an RC 1-port characterized by a DP impedance function of $\hat{Z}_1(s)$. This is illustrated in Fig. 6-7(b). From (6-45), we obtain

$$\hat{Z}_1(\infty) = 0 \tag{6-46}$$

Hence, $s = \infty$ is a pole of $\hat{Y}_1(s)$. To realize $\hat{Y}_1(s)$, we return to the previous case when $s = \infty$ is a pole of an RC DP admittance function. This process can be repeated, and we arrive at the first Cauer's form shown in Fig. 6-8.

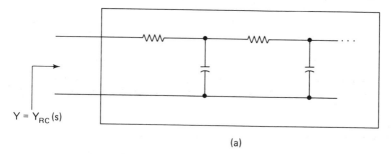

(a)

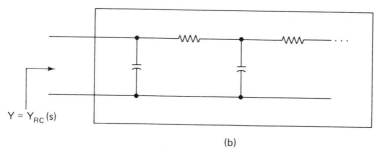

(b)

Fig. 6-8 Circuit structure of Cauer's first form (a) when $s = \infty$ is not a pole of $Y_{RC}(s)$ and (b) when $s = \infty$ is a pole of $Y_{RC}(s)$.

To see the effect of removing R_0 from $Z_{RC}(s)$ as indicated in (6-45) and Fig. 6-7(b), let us consider a typical plot of $Z_{RC}(\sigma)$ versus σ when $Z_{RC}(\infty) \neq 0$, as shown in Fig. 6-9. To subtract a constant $R_0 = Z_{RC}(\infty)$ from $Z_{RC}(s)$ is equivalent to raising the horizontal axis up by a height of R_0, as indicated by the dotted horizontal axis line in Fig. 6-9. Observe that the pole locations remain unchanged, poles and zeros still interlace with each other even though

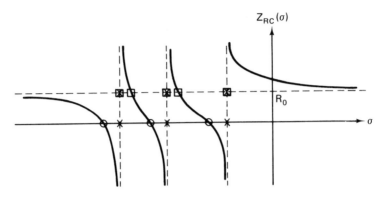

Legend: x = pole, and 0 = zero of $Z_{RC}(s)$.
⊠ = pole, and □ = zero of the remainder DP impedance
function, $Z'_{RC}(s) \triangleq Z_{RC}(s) - Z_{RC}(\infty)$.

Fig. 6-9 A typical plot of $Z_{RC}(\sigma)$ versus σ.

the zero positions have been changed, and most important of all, a new zero
is created at $s = \infty$. This means that the remainder DP impedance function
has a zero at $s = \infty$; its associated DP admittance function has a pole at
$s = \infty$.

Example 6-2 Realize the following RC 1-port DP impedance function

$$Z(s) = \frac{s^2 + 4s + 3}{s^3 + 6s^2 + 8s} = \frac{(s+1)(s+3)}{s(s+2)(s+4)} \qquad (6-47)$$

by Cauer's first form.

Solution: Because the given impedance function has a zero at $s = \infty$, its
admittance function

$$Y(s) = \frac{s^3 + 6s^2 + 8s}{s^2 + 4s + 3} \qquad (6-48)$$

has a pole at $s = \infty$. The residue of this pole is given by

$$\xi_0 \triangleq \frac{1}{s} Y(s)\Big|_{s=\infty} = 1$$

Removing this pole from $Y(s)$, we write (6-48) as

$$Y(s) = \xi_0 s + Y_1(s) = s + Y_1(s) \qquad (6-49)$$

where $Y_1(s)$ is the remainder function given by

$$Y_1(s) = Y(s) - s = \frac{2s^2 + 5s}{s^2 + 4s + 3}$$

The circuit interpretation of this step is shown in Fig. 6-10(a). Because $Y_1(\infty)$ is
finite, we invert $Y_1(s)$ to obtain

$$Z_1(s) = \frac{s^2 + 4s + 3}{2s^2 + 5s} \qquad (6-50)$$

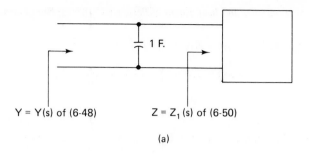

Y = Y(s) of (6-48)   Z = Z₁ (s) of (6-50)

(a)

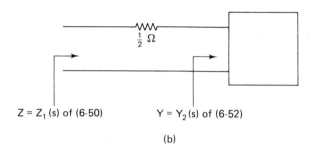

Z = Z₁ (s) of (6-50)   Y = Y₂ (s) of (6-52)

(b)

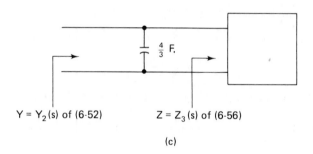

Y = Y₂ (s) of (6-52)   Z = Z₃ (s) of (6-56)

(c)

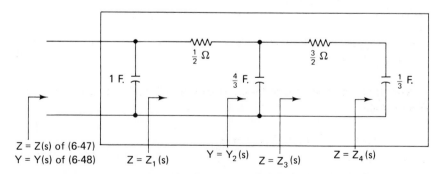

Z = Z(s) of (6-47)
Y = Y(s) of (6-48)   Z = Z₁ (s)   Y = Y₂ (s)   Z = Z₃ (s)   Z = Z₄ (s)

Fig. 6-10 Cauer's first-form realization of the RC DP impedance function of (6-47).

We now proceed to remove $Z_1(\infty) = 1/2$ from $Z_1(s)$ as

$$Z_2(s) = Z_1(s) - Z_1(\infty) = Z_1(s) - \frac{1}{2}$$

$$= \frac{(3/2)s + 3}{2s^2 + 5s} \tag{6-51}$$

This step is illustrated in Fig. 6-10(b). Clearly, $Z_2(\infty) = 0$. Hence, we consider

$$Y_2(s) = \frac{2s^2 + 5s}{(3/2)s + 3} \tag{6-52}$$

$Y_2(s)$ has a pole at $s = \infty$. Extracting this pole requires us to find the residue ξ_2 of $Y_2(s)$ at the pole $s = \infty$, and

$$\xi_2 = \frac{1}{s} Y_2(s)\Big|_{s=\infty} = \frac{4}{3} \tag{6-53}$$

Hence, we can write

$$Y_2(s) = \frac{4}{3} s + Y_3(s) \tag{6-54}$$

where

$$Y_3(s) = Y_2(s) - \frac{4}{3} s = \frac{2s}{3s + 6} \tag{6-55}$$

This step is shown in Fig. 6-10(c). Because $Y_3(\infty)$ is finite, we consider

$$Z_3(s) = \frac{3s + 6}{2s} \tag{6-56}$$

Extracting a series resistor of $Z_3(\infty) = 3/2 \ \Omega$ from $Z_3(s)$, we write

$$Z_3(s) = \frac{3}{2} + Z_4(s) \tag{6-57}$$

where the remainder function

$$Z_4(s) = Z_3(s) - \frac{3}{2} = \frac{3}{s} = \frac{1}{(1/3)s} \tag{6-58}$$

is just a capacitor of 1/3 F. The whole process of this realization is summarized in Fig. 6-10(d). ∎

Note that with the help of (6-58), (6-56), (6-52), and (6-50), we can write $Y(s)$ of (6-48) as

$$Y(s) = s + Y_1(s) = s + \frac{1}{Z_1(s)}$$

$$= s + \frac{1}{\dfrac{1}{2} + Z_2(s)} = s + \frac{1}{\dfrac{1}{2} + \dfrac{1}{Y_2(s)}}$$

$$= s + \cfrac{1}{\cfrac{1}{2} + \cfrac{1}{\cfrac{4}{3}s + Y_3(s)}} = s + \cfrac{1}{\cfrac{1}{2} + \cfrac{1}{\cfrac{4}{3}s + \cfrac{1}{Z_3(s)}}}$$

$$= s + \cfrac{1}{\cfrac{1}{2} + \cfrac{1}{\cfrac{4}{3}s + \cfrac{1}{\cfrac{3}{2} + Z_4(s)}}}$$

$$= s + \cfrac{1}{\cfrac{1}{2} + \cfrac{1}{\cfrac{4}{3}s + \cfrac{1}{\cfrac{3}{2} + \cfrac{1}{\cfrac{1}{3}s}}}} \qquad (6\text{-}59)$$

Observe that (6-59) is in the form of a continued fraction expansion. Hence, we can derive (6-59) by the divide-and-invert process about the point $s = \infty$. This requires us to eliminate the highest power term in each division. For example, the quotients of the continued fraction expansion at $s = \infty$ of $Y(s)$ of (6-48) via the divide-and-invert process is given by the encircled quantities in the following:

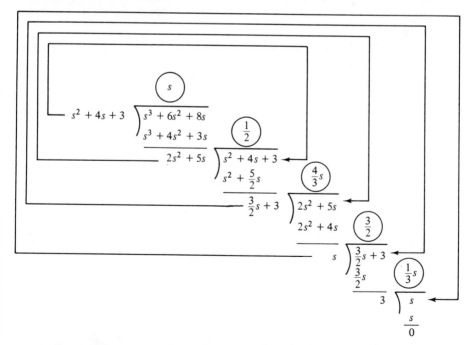

Hence, we obtain the continued fraction expansion of $Y(s)$, as is in (6-59).

6-4-2. Cauer's Second Form

If we now examine alternatively $Y_{RC}(s)$ and $Z_{RC}(s)$ at the point $s = 0$ instead of at $s = \infty$, we would obtain Cauer's second form. In this case, we consider the DP impedance function $Z_{RC}(s)$. If $s = 0$ is a pole of $Z_{RC}(s)$, we remove the pole in the form of a *series capacitor*. This is equivalent to expressing $Z_{RC}(s)$ as

$$Z_{RC}(s) = \frac{k_0}{s} + Z_1(s) \qquad (6\text{-}60a)$$

where

$$k_0 = sZ_{RC}(s)\Big|_{s=0} \qquad (6\text{-}60b)$$

is the residue of $Z_{RC}(s)$ at the pole $s = 0$ and $Z_1(s)$ is the remainder impedance function. As is in the case of Cauer's first form, $Z_1(s)$ satisfies all properties of an RC DP impedance function. In addition, $Z_1(0)$ is finite—$s = 0$ is not a pole of $Z_1(s)$. Because $Z_{RC}(s)$ is expressed as a sum of two terms, as in (6-60), we can realize $Z_{RC}(s)$ by connecting a (series) capacitor in series with an RC 1-port characterized by the DP impedance function of $Z_1(s)$, as shown in Fig. 6-11(a). Hence, the problem of realizing $Z_{RC}(s)$ is reduced to realizing a simpler RC DP impedance function $Z_1(s)$. To realize $Z_1(s)$, we consider the case when $s = 0$ is not a pole of $Z_{RC}(s)$. In this case, let us first obtain $Y_{RC}(s)$ by inverting $Z_{RC}(s)$. By condition 2b or Property YRC8 of RC DP admittance functions, we can remove $Y_{RC}(0)$ in the form of a *shunt resistor* and still leave a PR remainder function that is also an RC DP admittance function. This means that we write $Y_{RC}(s)$ as

$$Y_{RC}(s) = g_0 + \hat{Y}_1(s) \qquad (6\text{-}61a)$$

where

$$g_0 = Y_{RC}(0) \qquad (6\text{-}61b)$$

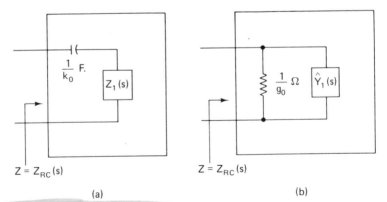

$$Z = Z_{RC}(s) \qquad\qquad\qquad Z = Z_{RC}(s)$$

(a) (b)

Fig. 6-11 Basic realization procedure of Cauer's second form (a) when $s = 0$ is a pole of $Z_{RC}(s)$, and (b) when $s = 0$ is not a pole of $Z_{RC}(s)$.

146

and $\hat{Y}_1(s)$ is the remainder RC DP admittance function. In view of (6-61), we can realize $Y_{RC}(s)$ by connecting a (shunt) resistor in parallel with $\hat{Y}_1(s)$. This step is illustrated in Fig. 6-11(b). Note that (6-61) implies that

$$\hat{Y}_1(0) = 0 \qquad (6\text{-}62)$$

Hence, $s = 0$ is a pole of the corresponding RC DP impedance function $\hat{Z}_1(s)$. This means that we can repeat the process of removing series capacitors and shunt resistors until the realization circuit is completed, as shown in Fig. 6-12.

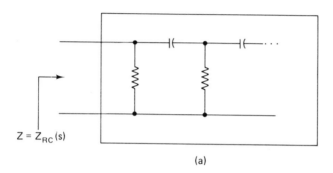

(a)

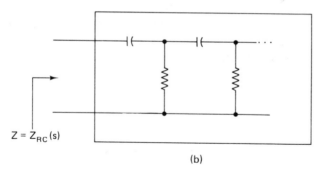

(b)

Fig. 6-12 Circuit structure of Cauer's second form (a) when $s = 0$ is not a pole of $Z_{RC}(s)$, and (b) when $s = 0$ is a pole of $Z_{RC}(s)$.

Example 6-3 Realize the RC DP impedance function

$$Z(s) = \frac{3 + 4s + s^2}{8s + 6s^2 + s^3} \qquad (6\text{-}63)$$

by Cauer's second form.

Solution: Because $Z(s)$ has a pole at $s = 0$, we remove this pole by first finding its residue ζ_0 as

$$\zeta_0 = sZ(s)\Big|_{s=0} = \frac{3}{8}$$

and then write $Z(s)$ as

$$Z(s) = \frac{3}{8s} + Z_1(s) \tag{6-64}$$

where

$$Z_1(s) = Z(s) - \frac{3}{8s} = \frac{(7/4) + (5/8)s}{8 + 6s + s^2} \tag{6-65}$$

is the remainder function. Note that $Z_1(s)$ is PR and satisfies all the conditions of an RC DP impedance function. The step of (6-64) is shown in Fig. 6-13(a).

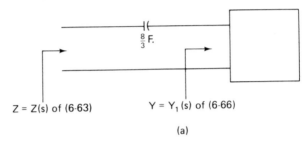

Z = Z(s) of (6-63)   Y = Y₁ (s) of (6-66)

(a)

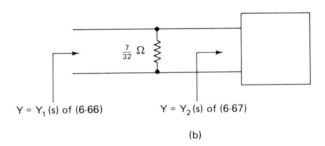

Y = Y₁ (s) of (6-66)   Y = Y₂ (s) of (6-67)

(b)

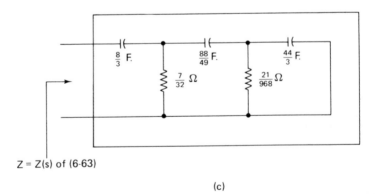

Z = Z(s) of (6-63)

(c)

Fig. 6-13 Cauer's second-form realization of the RC DP impedance function of (6-63).

Because $Z_1(0)$ is finite, we consider

$$Y_1(s) = \frac{8 + 6s + s^2}{(7/4) + (5/8)s} \tag{6-66}$$

Removing the constant $Y_1(0)$ from $Y_1(s)$ in the form of a shunt resistor, we obtain the remainder function $Y_2(s)$ as

$$Y_2(s) = Y_1(s) - Y_1(0) = Y_1(s) - \frac{32}{7}$$
$$= \frac{(22/7)s + s^2}{(7/4) + (5/8)s} \tag{6-67}$$

This step is illustrated in Fig. 6-13(b). Repeating the foregoing procedure, we express

$$Z_2(s) = \frac{(7/4) + (5/8)s}{(22/7)s + s^2}$$

as

$$Z_2(s) = \frac{49}{88s} + Z_3(s) \tag{6-68}$$

where 49/88 is the residue of $Z_2(s)$ at the pole $s = 0$ and

$$Z_3(s) = Z_2(s) - \frac{49}{88s} = \frac{3/44}{(22/7) + s} \tag{6-69}$$

This gives

$$Y_3(s) = \frac{(22/7) + s}{3/44} = Y_3(0) + Y_4(s) = \frac{968}{21} + Y_4(s) \tag{6-70}$$

where

$$Y_4(s) = Y_3(s) - \frac{968}{21} = \frac{44s}{3}$$

or

$$Z_4(s) = \frac{1}{(44/3)s} \tag{6-71}$$

A circuit realization of (6-63) via Cauer's second form, as developed here, is shown in Fig. 6-13(c). ∎

Note that by substituting (6-71) into (6-70), then into (6-68), then into (6-67), and finally into (6-64), we obtain

$$Z(s) = \frac{3}{8s} + \cfrac{1}{\dfrac{32}{7} + \cfrac{1}{\dfrac{49}{88s} + \cfrac{1}{\dfrac{968}{21} + \cfrac{1}{\dfrac{3}{44s}}}}} \tag{6-72}$$

We can also obtain (6-72) by a long division method with both the divisor and dividend polynomials arranged in ascending powers of s as

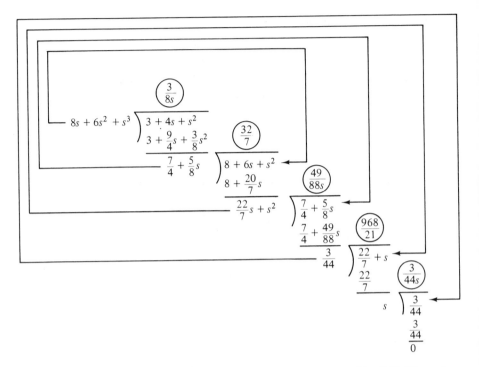

Note that (6-72) is the continued fraction expansion of $Z(s)$ of (6-63) at the point $s = 0$.

As is in the LC case, realization of RC DP functions does not require us to use a particular method throughout the whole process. We can switch from one form of realization to another form of realization at any stage and as often as we desire. In other words, we can realize an RC DP impedance or admittance function via a combination of Foster's and Cauer's forms.

Example 6-4   Realize the RC DP impedance function

$$Z(s) = \frac{(s + 1)(s + 3)(s + 5)}{s(s + 2)(s + 4)(s + 6)} \tag{6-73}$$

by the following procedure:

1. Use Cauer's first form to extract two capacitors.
2. Use Cauer's second form to extract one capacitor.
3. The remainder function is realized by Foster's second form.

Solution: Cauer's first form requires us to examine the admittance function

$$Y(s) = \frac{s(s + 2)(s + 4)(s + 6)}{(s + 1)(s + 3)(s + 5)} \tag{6-74}$$

at the point $s = \infty$. Because $Y(\infty) = \infty$, we perform a partial continued fraction expansion of $Y(s)$ at $s = \infty$ as

$$Y(s) = \frac{s^4 + 12s^3 + 44s^2 + 48s}{s^3 + 9s^2 + 23s + 15}$$

$$= s + \cfrac{1}{\cfrac{1}{3} + \cfrac{1}{\cfrac{3}{2}s + Y_1(s)}} \qquad (6\text{-}75)$$

where

$$Y_1(s) = \frac{3s^2 + (21/2)s}{2s^2 + 12s + 15} \qquad (6\text{-}76)$$

This step is implemented in Fig. 6-14(a). Next, we use Cauer's second form to

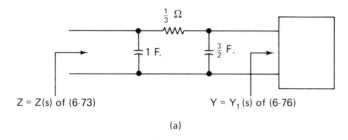

(a)

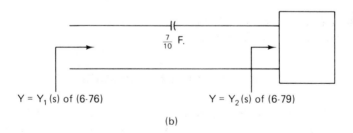

(b)

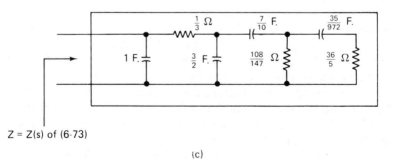

(c)

Fig. 6-14 A circuit realization of the RC DP impedance function of (6-73).

partially realize $Y_1(s)$. This requires us to examine

$$Z_1(s) = \frac{1}{Y_1(s)} = \frac{15 + 12s + 2s^2}{(21/2)s + 3s^2} \tag{6-77}$$

at the point $s = 0$. Because $s = 0$ is a pole of $Z_1(s)$, we perform a partial continued fraction expansion of $Z_1(s)$ at $s = 0$ as

$$Z_1(s) = \frac{10}{7s} + \frac{1}{Y_2(s)} \tag{6-78}$$

where

$$Y_2(s) = \frac{3s + (21/2)}{2s + (54/7)} \tag{6-79}$$

This step is illustrated in Fig. 6-14(b). As instructed by the problem, we must realize $Y_2(s)$ by Foster's second form. To do that, we perform a partial fraction expansion of

$$\frac{Y_2(s)}{s} = \frac{3s + (21/2)}{s[2s + (54/7)]} \tag{6-80}$$

and obtain

$$\frac{Y_2(s)}{s} = \frac{147/108}{s} + \frac{5/36}{s + (27/7)}$$

or

$$Y_2(s) = \frac{147}{108} + \frac{1}{\dfrac{36}{5} + \dfrac{972}{35s}} \tag{6-81}$$

A circuit realization of (6-73) as required by the problem—via (6-75), (6-78), and (6-81)—is shown in Fig. 6-14(c).   ∎

6-5   CONCLUDING REMARKS

In this chapter, we have presented the basic properties of RC DP functions. These properties are summarized in Table 6-1. The general formats of RC DP impedance and admittance functions are different, as indicated by (6-4) and (6-20); therefore, the basic properties of RC DP admittance and impedance functions are different also. Observe that together rows 2, 3, and 6 of $Z_{RC}(s)\{Y_{RC}(s)\}$ in Table 6-1 form the realizability conditions of RC DP impedance {admittance} functions. Other sufficient realizability conditions can be formed by rows 1 and 6 or by row 5 of Table 6-1.

We have also presented four methods to realize RC DP functions. Foster's first form deals with DP impedance functions; Foster's second form deals with admittance functions. However, either one of Cauer's two forms can be applied to both impedance and admittance functions.

To summarize the realization procedures, Foster's forms involve *partial fraction expansion*, and Cauer's forms involve *continued fraction expansion*.

TABLE 6-1 Properties of RC DP Functions

	$Z_{RC}(s)$	$Y_{RC}(s)$
1.	$Z_{RC}(s) = R_\infty + \dfrac{1}{C_0 s} + \sum \dfrac{1}{C_i s + \dfrac{1}{R_i}}$ $= k_\infty + \dfrac{k_0}{s} + \sum \dfrac{k_i}{s + \sigma_i}$	$Y_{RC}(s) = C_\infty s + \dfrac{1}{R_0} + \sum \dfrac{1}{R_i + \dfrac{1}{C_i s}}$ $= k_\infty s + k_0 + \sum \dfrac{k_i s}{s + \sigma_i}$
2.	All poles and zeros are simple, negative, and real.	All poles and zeros are simple, negative, and real.
3.	Poles and zero alternate. Critical frequency closest to the origin is a pole and closest to infinity is a zero.	Poles and zeros alternate. Critical frequency closest to the origin is a zero and closest to infinity is a pole.
4.	If $Z_{RC}(s) = A(s)/B(s)$, then degree of $A(s) \leq$ degree of $B(s)$. Less if $s = \infty$ is a zero and equal if $s = \infty$ is not a zero.	If $Y_{RC}(s) = A(s)/B(s)$, then degree of $A(s) \geq$ degree of $B(s)$. Greater if $s = \infty$ is a pole and equal if $s = \infty$ is not a pole.
5.	$Z_{RC}(s) = \dfrac{(s + \sigma_2)(s + \sigma_4)\dots}{(s + \sigma_1)(s + \sigma_3)\dots}$ $0 \leq \sigma_1 < \sigma_2 < \sigma_3 < \sigma_4 \dots$	$Y_{RC}(s) = \dfrac{(s + \sigma_1)(s + \sigma_3)\dots}{(s + \sigma_2)(s + \sigma_4)\dots}$ $0 \leq \sigma_1 < \sigma_2 < \sigma_3 < \sigma_4 \dots$
6.	All residues are positive and real.	Residue at the infinity pole is positive and real. Residues at finite poles are negative and real.
7.	$Z_{RC}(s)$ can not have a pole at $s = \infty$. If $Z_{RC}(\infty) \neq 0$, then $Z_{RC}(\infty)$ is the largest constant that one can extract while the remainder $[Z_{RC}(s) - Z_{RC}(\infty)]$ is still an RC DP impedance function.	$Y_{RC}(s)$ can not have a pole at $s = 0$. If $Y_{RC}(0) \neq 0$, then $Y_{RC}(0)$ is the largest constant that one can extract while the remainder $[Y_{RC}(s) - Y_{RC}(0)]$ is still an RC DP admittance function.
8.	$Z_{RC}(\sigma)$ is monotonically decreasing except at the poles.	$Y_{RC}(\sigma)$ is monotonically increasing except at the poles.

Cauer's first form utilizes a continued fraction expansion at the point $s = \infty$. If $Y_{RC}(\infty) = \infty$, then Cauer's first form works with $Y_{RC}(s)$. If $Y_{RC}(\infty) \neq \infty$, then Cauer's first form works with $Z_{RC}(s) = 1/Y_{RC}(s)$. Cauer's second form requires a continued fraction expansion at the point $s = 0$. If $Z_{RC}(0) = \infty$, then Cauer's second form works with $Z_{RC}(s)$. If $Z_{RC}(0) \neq \infty$, then Cauer's second form works with $Y_{RC}(s) = 1/Z_{RC}(s)$.

The circuit structure of Foster's and Cauer's forms are summarized in Fig. 6-15. Note that Cauer's first form consists of series resistors and shunt capacitors producing transmission zeros at $s = \infty$ and that Cauer's second form contains series capacitors and shunt resistors creating transmission zeros at $s = 0$.

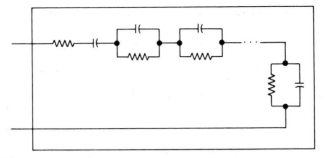

(a)   Foster's First Form

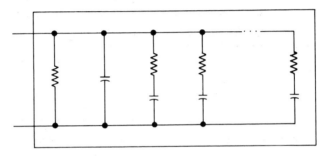

(b)   Foster's Second Form

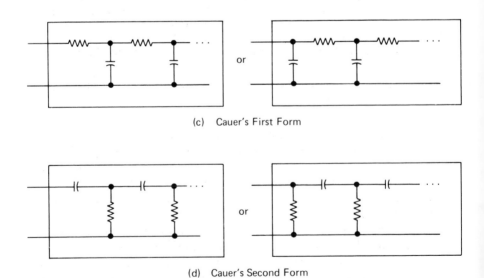

(c)   Cauer's First Form

or

(d)   Cauer's Second Form

Fig. 6-15   Basic circuit structures of Foster's and Cauer's forms.

To conclude this chapter, we would like to point out that the RC DP function realization methods are identical to those of LC DP function realizations. The only difference is that the former case uses resistors and the latter case uses inductors.

REFERENCES AND FURTHER READING

[1] WEINBERG, L. *Network Analysis and Synthesis.* Huntington, N.Y.: R. E. Krieger, 1975.

[2] HUMPHREYS, D. S. *The Analysis, Design, and Synthesis of Electrical Filters.* Englewood Cliffs, N.J.: Prentice-Hall, Inc., 1970.

[3] PEIKARI, B. *Fundamentals of Network Analysis and Synthesis.* Englewood Cliffs, N.J.: Prentice-Hall, Inc., 1974.

[4] BUDAK, A. *Passive and Active Network Analysis and Synthesis.* Boston, MA.: Houghton Mifflin, 1974.

PROBLEMS

6-1. Determine which of the following $Z(s)$ are realizable as RC DP impedance functions:

(a) $Z(s) = \dfrac{s^2 + 7s + 12}{s^2 + 3s + 2}$

(b) $Z(s) = \dfrac{s^2 + 5s}{s^2 + 3s + 2}$

(c) $Z(s) = \dfrac{s + 5}{s^2 + 3s + 2}$

(d) $Z(s) = \dfrac{s + 1.5}{s^2 + 2s + 1}$

(e) $Z(s) = \dfrac{s^2 + 3s + 2}{s + 1.5}$

(f) $Z(s) = \dfrac{s^2 + 7s + 12}{s^3 + 3s^2 + 3s + 1}$

(g) $Z(s) = \dfrac{s^2 + 4s + 3.75}{s^3 + 6s^2 + 11s + 6}$

(h) $Z(s) = \dfrac{s^3 + 8s^2 + 17s + 10}{s^3 + 11.5s^2 + 39s + 36}$

(i) $Z(s) = \dfrac{s^2 + 3s + 2}{s^3 + 6s^2 + 8.75s + 3}$

(j) $Z(s) = \dfrac{s^3 + 6s^2 + 8.75s + 3}{s^2 + 3s + 2}$

6-2. Determine which of the following $Y(s)$ are realizable as RC DP admittance functions:

(a) $Y(s) = \dfrac{s^2 + 7s + 12}{s^2 + 3s + 2}$

(b) $Y(s) = \dfrac{s^2 + 5s}{s^2 + 3s + 2}$

(c) $Y(s) = \dfrac{s^2 + 3s + 2}{s + 5}$

(d) $Y(s) = \dfrac{s^2 + 3s + 1}{s + 1.5}$

(e) $Y(s) = \dfrac{s + 1.5}{s^2 + 2s + 1}$

(f) $Y(s) = \dfrac{s^2 + 7s + 12}{s^3 + 3s^2 + 3s + 1}$

(g) $Y(s) = \dfrac{s^3 + 6s^2 + 11s + 6}{s^2 + 4s + 3.75}$

(h) $Y(s) = \dfrac{s^3 + 8s^2 + 17s + 10}{s^3 + 11.5s^2 + 39s + 36}$

(i) $Y(s) = \dfrac{s^2 + 3s + 2}{s^3 + 6s^2 + 8.75s + 3}$

(j) $Y(s) = \dfrac{s^3 + 6s^2 + 8.75s + 3}{s^2 + 3s + 2}$

6-3. Consider the 1-port network N shown in Fig. P6-3.

(a) Show that the DP impedance function of N satisfies all the properties of an RC DP impedance function.

(b) Show that the DP admittance function of N satisfies all the properties of an RC DP admittance function.

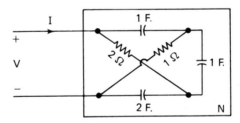

Fig. P6-3

6-4. Consider the 1-port network N shown in Fig. P6-4.

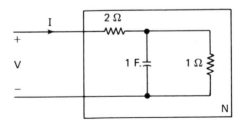

Fig. P6-4

(a) Find the DP impedance function $Z(s)$ of N.
(b) Show that $Z(s)$ satisfies all the properties of an RC DP impedance function.
(c) Show that the DP admittance function $Y(s)$ of N satisfies all the properties of an RC DP admittance function.
(d) Realize either $Y(s)$ or $Z(s)$ by Foster's two forms.
(e) Realize either $Y(s)$ or $Z(s)$ by Cauer's two forms.

6-5. Repeat Problem 6-4 for the 1-port networks shown in Fig. P6-5.

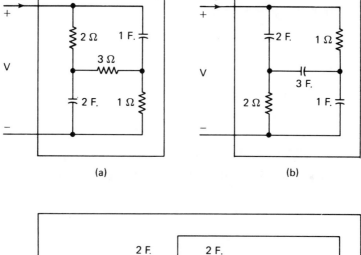

(a)   (b)

(c)

Fig. P6-5

6-6. For each $Z(s)$ given in the following, find the range of a such that $Z(s)$ is realizable as an RC DP impedance function:

(a) $Z(s) = \dfrac{s + a}{s^2 + 3s + 2}$

(b) $Z(s) = \dfrac{s^2 + 4s + a}{s^2 + 3s + 2}$

(c) $Z(s) = \dfrac{s^2 + as + 3}{s^2 + 3s + 2}$

(d) $Z(s) = \dfrac{s^2 + 5s + 6}{s^2 + as + 2}$

(e) $Z(s) = \dfrac{s^2 + 5s + 6}{s^2 + 3s + a}$

(f) $Z(s) = \dfrac{s^2 + 3s + a}{s^3 + 5s^2 + 6s}$

6-7. For each $Y(s)$ given in the following, find the range of a such that $Y(s)$ is realizable as an RC DP admittance function:

(a) $Y(s) = \dfrac{s^2 + 5s + a}{s^2 + 7s + 10}$

(b) $Y(s) = \dfrac{s^2 + as + 4}{s^2 + 7s + 10}$

(c) $Y(s) = \dfrac{s^2 + 10s + 16}{s^2 + as + 20}$

(d) $Y(s) = \dfrac{s^2 + 10s + 16}{s^2 + 12s + a}$

(e) $Y(s) = \dfrac{s^3 + 7.5s^2 + as + 5}{s^2 + 5s + 4}$

(f) $Y(s) = \dfrac{s^2 + as^2 + 13.5s + 5}{s^2 + 5s + 4}$

6-8. Realize the following RC DP admittance functions by Foster's two forms and Cauer's two forms:

(a) $Y(s) = \dfrac{(s + 1)(s + 3)}{s + 2}$

(b) $Y(s) = \dfrac{s(s + 2)}{(s + 1)(s + 3)}$

(c) $Y(s) = \dfrac{(s + 1)(s + 5)}{(s + 4)(s + 6)}$

(d) $Y(s) = \dfrac{s(s + 4)(s + 6)}{(s + 1)(s + 5)}$

(e) $Y(s) = \dfrac{(s + 1)(s + 5)(s + 10)}{(s + 2)(s + 6)(s + 12)}$

6-9. For each RC DP admittance function in Problem 6-8, let us define $\hat{Z}(s) \triangleq Y(s)/s$. Show that $\hat{Z}(s)$ satisfies all properties of an RC DP impedance function. In addition, realize $\hat{Z}(s)$ as an RC DP impedance function by Foster's two forms and Cauer's two forms.

6-10. Realize the DP impedance function

$$Z(s) = \frac{(s + 2)(s + 4)}{(s + 1)(s + 3)(s + 5)}$$

by using the following procedures:

(a) Start with Cauer's first form (for two capacitors), and complete the realization with Cauer's second form.

(b) Start with Cauer's second form (for two capacitors), and complete the realization with Cauer's first form.

(c) Start with Cauer's first form (for one capacitor); then switch to Cauer's second form (for one capacitor), and complete the realization with Foster's second form.

6-11. (a) Realize the RC DP impedance function

$$Z(s) = \frac{s+2}{(s+1)(s+5)}$$

by Cauer's first form.

(b) Verify that the 1-port network obtained in (a) has a DP impedance function given by $Z(s)$.

(c) Realize $Z(s)$ by Cauer's second form.

(d) Verify that the 1-port network obtained in (c) has a DP impedance function given by $Z(s)$.

6-12. Find an RLC circuit realization for each of the following DP impedance functions:

(a) $Z(s) = \dfrac{(s^2 + 4)(s^2 + 6)}{s(s^2 + 5)} + \dfrac{s+3}{(s+1)(s+5)}$

(b) $Z(s) = \dfrac{s+2}{(s+1)(s+4)} + \dfrac{s(s^2+2)}{(s^2+1)(s^2+4)}$

(c) $Z(s) = \dfrac{s(s^2+4)}{(s^2+3)(s^2+6)} + \dfrac{(s+2)(s+5)}{s(s+4)}$

(d) $Z(s) = \dfrac{(s+2)(s+4)}{s(s+3)} + \dfrac{(s^2+3)(s^2+6)}{s(s^2+4)}$

(e) $Z(s) = \dfrac{s(s^2+3)(s^2+6)}{(s^2+1)(s^2+5)} + \dfrac{(s+3)(s+6)}{(s+1)(s+5)}$

6-13. Find an RLC circuit realization for each of the following DP admittance functions:

(a) $Y(s) = \dfrac{(s^2+1)(s^2+5)}{s(s^2+3)} + \dfrac{(s+1)(s+5)}{(s+3)}$

(b) $Y(s) = \dfrac{s(s^2+5)}{(s^2+4)(s^2+6)} + \dfrac{(s+1)(s+4)}{s+2}$

(c) $Y(s) = \dfrac{s(s^2+4)}{(s^2+3)(s^2+6)} + \dfrac{s(s+4)}{(s+2)(s+5)}$

(d) $Y(s) = \dfrac{s(s+3)}{(s+2)(s+4)} + \dfrac{(s^2+3)(s^2+6)}{s(s^2+4)}$

(e) $Y(s) = \dfrac{(s+1)(s+3)}{(s+2)(s+4)} + \dfrac{(s^2+1)(s^2+3)}{s(s^2+2)(s^2+4)}$

(f) $Y(s) = \dfrac{3s^4 + 9s^3 + 24s^2 + 28s}{(s+1)(s+2)(s^2+4)}$

6-14. Find the conditions under which the product of two RC DP impedance {admittance} functions is an RC DP impedance {admittance} function.

6-15. There is a theorem that says: Let $A(s)$ be an arbitrary polynomial of degree n_A and $B(s)$ be another arbitrary polynomial of degree n_B having only distinct negative real roots. Then $F(s) = A(s)/B(s)$ can be written as

$$F(s) = \frac{A(s)}{B(s)} = Z_{RC}^{(1)}(s) - Z_{RC}^{(2)}(s) \quad \text{if } n_A \leq n_B$$

$$= Y_{RC}^{(1)}(s) - Y_{RC}^{(2)}(s) \quad \text{if } n_A \leq n_B + 1$$

where $Z_{RC}^{(1)}$ and $Z_{RC}^{(2)}$ are RC DP impedance functions and $Y_{RC}^{(1)}$ and $Y_{RC}^{(2)}$ are RC DP admittance functions.

For example, the impedance function

$$Z(s) = \frac{4s + 1}{s^2 + 5s + 4}$$

can be expressed as

$$Z(s) = \frac{5}{s + 4} - \frac{1}{s + 1}$$

Hence

$$Z_{RC}^{(1)}(s) = \frac{5}{s + 4} \quad \text{and} \quad Z_{RC}^{(2)}(s) = \frac{1}{s + 1}$$

In a similar manner, the admittance function

$$Y(s) = \frac{s(4s + 1)}{s^2 + 5s + 4}$$

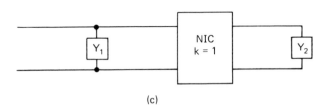

(a)

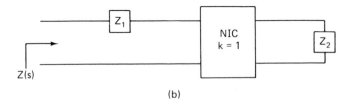

(b)

(c)

Fig. P6-15

can be expressed as

$$\frac{Y(s)}{s} = \frac{5}{s+4} - \frac{1}{s+1}$$

or

$$Y(s) = \frac{5s}{s+4} - \frac{s}{s+1}$$

Hence,

$$Y_{RC}^{(1)} = \frac{5s}{s+4} \quad \text{and} \quad Y_{RC}^{(2)} = \frac{s}{s+1}$$

(a) Consider the circuit in Fig. P6-15(a), where the NIC 2-port is characterized by (2-40) with $k = 1$. Find $Z_{in}(s)$.

(b) Find the DP impedance function $Z(s)$ of the circuit shown in Fig. P6-15(b).

(c) Realize the DP impedance function

$$Z(s) = \frac{s^4 + 4s^3 + 7s^2 + 22s + 24}{s(s+1)(s+2)(s+3)(s+4)}$$

in the form of Fig. P6-15(b).

(d) Find the DP admittance function $Y(s)$ of the circuit shown in Fig. P6-15(c).

(e) Realize the DP admittance function

$$Y(s) = \frac{s^4 + 4s^3 + 7s^2 + 22s + 24}{(s+1)(s+2)(s+3)(s+4)}$$

in the form of Fig. P6-15(c).

6-16. Define $\pm RC$ circuits as circuits containing positive and negative resistances and positive capacitances. Based on (6-2) and (6-20), find the properties of:

(a) DP impedance functions of $\pm RC$ 1-ports.

(b) DP admittance functions of $\pm RC$ 1-ports.

6-17. Given the coefficients of the polynomials:

$$A(s) = a_0 + a_1 s + a_2 s^2 + \ldots + a_m s^m$$
$$B(s) = b_0 + b_1 s + b_2 s^2 + \ldots + b_n s^n$$

write a computer program to determine if the function

$$F(s) = \frac{A(s)}{B(s)}$$

is realizable as

(a) an RC DP impedance function.

(b) an RC DP admittance function.

6-18. Given an RC DP impedance function $Z(s)$ {admittance function $Y(s)$}, write a computer program to realize $Z(s)$ {$Y(s)$} by:

(a) Foster's first form,

(b) Foster's second form,

(c) Cauer's first form, and

(d) Cauer's second form.

7

PASSIVE REALIZATION
OF TRANSFER FUNCTIONS

Through the years, engineers have devised many techniques for realizing various types of transfer functions with passive elements only. We consider some of these techniques, particularly techniques that reduce the problem of realizing a transfer function to that of realizing a DP function. These techniques are simple, and yet they have been proven to be very useful and are applicable to a very large class of practical problems.

In this chapter, we consider three basic circuit structures. They are the ladder circuits, the lattice circuits, and the Darlington circuits. In Sec. 7-1, we discuss the basic properties and realization methods of both RC and LC ladder circuits. We show that RC {LC} ladder circuits can realize only those transfer functions with simple poles and with all poles and zeros on the negative real {the imaginary} axis of the s-plane.[1] Lattice networks are examined in Sec. 7-2 in conjunction with all - pass transfer functions. Finally, in Sec. 7-3, we consider the Darlington circuits. Although the realization procedures are more involved than the previous two circuit structures, Darlington circuits can be used to realize a much larger class of transfer functions.

Before we proceed, it should be pointed out that common to all passive synthesis techniques—by using passive elements only—a transfer function can be realized up to a constant multiple only. For example, if the desired transfer function is $H(s)$, then a circuit with a transfer function $\hat{H}(s) = \alpha H(s)$,

---

[1]Recall that the negative real {the imaginary} axis of the s-plane includes the origin $s = 0$ and the point at infinity $s = \infty$.

where α is a nonzero constant, is a realization of the desired transfer function.[2]

7-1 LADDER NETWORKS

In this section, we consider RC and LC ladder networks. A typical ladder network has the structure shown in Fig. 7-1.

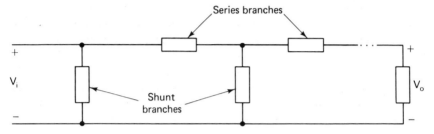

Fig. 7-1 Ladder circuit structure.

An important concept associated with ladder networks is the *transmission zeros*. A transmission zero is a complex frequency s_k such that $H(s_k) = 0$, where $H(s)$ is the transfer function of the network. In ladder networks, there are two sources of transmission zeros; they are the complex frequencies where

1. The impedance function of a series branch is infinite, and
2. The impedance function of a shunt branch is zero.

In the first case, a series branch becomes an open circuit. Hence, no signal will pass through toward the output. In the second case, a shunt branch becomes a short circuit. Thus, all current will flow through that short circuit shunt branch, leaving no current flowing toward the output. In both cases, no current will arrive at the output end. Hence, the (steady-state) output will be zero if the input is at the transmission zero frequencies.[3]

7-1-1. RC Ladder Networks

A ladder network is said to be an RC ladder if it contains only resistors and capacitors. Because the poles and zeros of an RC DP impedance function are on the negative real axis of the s-plane, the transmission zeros of

---

[2]Unless explicitly stated otherwise, all transfer functions in this book are voltage-ratio transfer functions.

[3]See Reference [1] for more details on transmission zeros.

an RC ladder network (being the poles of RC impedance functions of the series branches, and the zeros of RC impedance functions of the shunt branches) will be restricted to the negative real axis of the *s*-plane. Furthermore, if each branch of an RC ladder network contains only one element (either a resistor or a capacitor), then the transmission zeros can occur only at two points: $s = 0$ and $s = \infty$. This is because each series capacitor can produce a transmission zero at $s = 0$, and each shunt capacitor can produce a transmission zero at $s = \infty$. Recall that Cauer's first form consists of shunt capacitors and series resistors. Thus, Cauer's first form realization of RC DP functions produces transmission zeros at $s = \infty$. On the other hand, Cauer's second form contains shunt resistors and series capacitors thereby producing transmission zeros at $s = 0$.

Another important property associated with RC ladder networks is that the poles of the transfer functions are also restricted to the negative real axis of the *s*-plane. To see this, let us consider the RC 2-port in Fig. 7-2. Suppose that the 2-port is characterized by an impedance representation

$$\begin{bmatrix} V_1 \\ V_2 \end{bmatrix} = \begin{bmatrix} z_{11} & z_{21} \\ z_{21} & z_{22} \end{bmatrix} \begin{bmatrix} I_1 \\ I_2 \end{bmatrix} \tag{7-1}$$

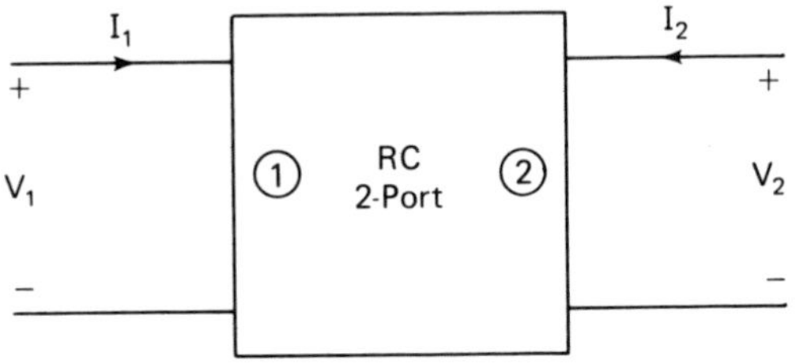

Fig. 7-2 An RC 2-port.

Then the voltage-ratio transfer function $H(s)$ is given by

$$H(s) = \frac{V_2}{V_1}\bigg|_{I_2=0} = \frac{z_{21}}{z_{11}} \tag{7-2}$$

Let

$$z_{11}(s) = \frac{n_{11}(s)}{d_{11}(s)} \tag{7-3a}$$

and

$$z_{21}(s) = \frac{n_{21}(s)}{d_{21}(s)} \tag{7-3b}$$

where $n_{11}(s)$, $d_{11}(s)$, $n_{21}(s)$, and $d_{21}(s)$ are polynomials of s. Then (7-2) becomes

$$H(s) = \frac{n_{21}(s)\, d_{11}(s)}{d_{21}(s)\, n_{11}(s)} \tag{7-4}$$

A condition for a 2-port to be passive is that $z_{21}(s)$ can not have any pole that is not contained in both $z_{11}(s)$ and $z_{22}(s)$. Because the RC 2-port in Fig. 7-2 is passive, $d_{11}(s)$ contains all the factors of $d_{21}(s)$. With this in mind, (7-4) says that the poles of $H(s)$ are actually the zeros of $z_{11}(s)$. Because $z_{11}(s)$ is the DP impedance function looking into the RC 2-port from port ①, the zeros of $z_{11}(s)$ are simple, real, and negative. Hence, the poles of $H(s)$ are also simple, real, and negative. In summary, we have the following theorem:

THEOREM 7-1 The transmission zeros and the poles of transfer functions of RC ladder networks are real and negative, and the poles are simple. In addition, if each branch of an RC ladder network contains either a capacitor or a resistor, then the transmission zeros of the circuit can occur only at the points $s = 0$ and $s = \infty$. In this case, the transfer function is given by

$$H(s) = \frac{ks^m}{s^n + b_{n-1}s^{n-1} + \ldots + b_0} = \frac{ks^m}{B(s)} \qquad (7\text{-}5)$$

where $0 \leq m \leq n$ and $B(s)$ is an nth-degree polynomial with simple negative real roots.[4] ∎

Observe that as $s \to 0$, if $m \neq 0$, then (7-5) gives

$$\lim_{s \to 0} H(s) \simeq \lim_{s \to 0} \frac{k}{b_0} s^m \qquad (7\text{-}6a)$$

That is, $H(s)$ goes to zero at the rate of s^m as $s \to 0$. On the other hand, as $s \to \infty$, if $n \neq m$, then (7-5) gives

$$\lim_{s \to \infty} H(s) \simeq \lim_{s \to \infty} \frac{ks^m}{s^n} = \lim_{s \to \infty} \frac{k}{s^{(n-m)}} \qquad (7\text{-}6b)$$

This indicates that $H(s)$ goes to zero at the rate of $1/s^{(n-m)}$ as $s \to \infty$. Hence, the transfer function of (7-5) has m transmission zeros at $s = 0$ and $(n - m)$ transmission zeros at $s = \infty$.

In this section, we consider realization methods for three classes of RC transfer functions—the three possible cases of (7-5)—as follows:

Case 1. $m = 0$: all transmission zeros are at $s = \infty$.
Case 2. $m = n$: all transmission zeros are at $s = 0$.
Case 3. $0 < m < n$: m transmission zeros are at $s = 0$, and $(n - m)$ transmission zeros are at $s = \infty$.

All these methods are based on the assumption that $z_{11}(s)$ and $z_{21}(s)$ of the 2-port impedance representation of the resulting RC ladder circuit have

---

[4] By negative real roots, we mean to include the origin also. That is, $B(s)$ may have a simple root at $s = 0$.

identical denominators. That is,[5]

$$d_{11}(s) = d_{21}(s) \tag{7-7}$$

Substituting (7-7) into (7-4), we obtain

$$H(s) = \frac{n_{21}(s)}{n_{11}(s)} \tag{7-8}$$

Note that (7-8) says that the denominator of $H(s)$ is the numerator of the RC DP impedance function $z_{11}(s)$. Comparing (7-5) and (7-8), we obtain

$$n_{11}(s) = B(s) \tag{7-9a}$$

and

$$n_{21}(s) = ks^m \tag{7-9b}$$

---

[5] All realization methods introduced in this chapter yield circuits satisfying the condition of (7-7). Note that (7-7) means that there are no *private poles* in the RC 2-port. (See Reference [3] for details with regard to private poles.)

Examples where private poles may exist are shown in Fig. 7-3. In Fig. 7-3(a), if there is no pole cancellation between $Z_A \{Z_B\}$ and N_1, then the poles of $Z_A \{Z_B\}$ will appear as poles of $z_{11}(s) \{z_{22}(s)\}$ but not as poles of $z_{21}(s)$. In the same manner, the poles of $Y_C(s) \{Y_D(s)\}$ will appear as poles of $y_{11}(s) \{y_{22}(s)\}$ but not as poles of $y_{12}(s)$ provided there is no pole cancellation between $Y_C \{Y_D\}$ and N_2 in Fig. 7-3(b).

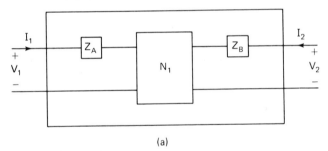

(a)

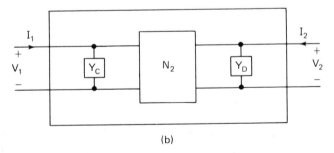

(b)

Fig. 7-3 Circuit configurations where private poles may exist.

That is, to realize the transfer function of (7-5), we need to realize an appropriately chosen RC DP impedance function $z_{11}(s)$ satisfying (7-9a) with a proper method to produce the prescribed transmission zeros as indicated by (7-5) and (7-9b).

The DP function $z_{11}(s)$ is chosen to satisfy (7-9) and the properties of RC impedance functions given in Chapter 6.[6] This is achieved simply by choosing $z_{11}(s)$ to have the following properties:

$$H(s) = \frac{z_{21}}{z_{11}}$$

$$z_{11} = \frac{a_i(s)}{b_i(s)}$$

$$B(s) = a_{ii}(s)$$

RC1. The numerator of $z_{11}(s)$ is given by $B(s)$—the zeros of $z_{11}(s)$ are the poles of $H(s)$.

RC2. The poles of $z_{11}(s)$ are simple, real, negative, and alternating with the given roots of $B(s)$ such that the critical frequency of $z_{11}(s)$ nearest the origin is a pole and the one nearest $s = \infty$ is a zero.

RC3. The degree of the denominator polynomial of $z_{11}(s)$ is set to be n.[7]

Assuming that an appropriate RC DP impedance function of $z_{11}(s)$ has been chosen, the next step is to realize this $z_{11}(s)$ with a proper procedure to yield the prescribed transmission zero requirements.

CASE 1: The first case is when all the transmission zeros of the RC transfer function are at $s = \infty$. In this case, the transfer function is given by (7-5) with $m = 0$ and is repeated here as

$$H(s) = \frac{k}{s^n + b_{n-1}s^{n-1} + \ldots + b_0} \triangleq \frac{k}{B(s)} \qquad (7\text{-}10)$$

where $B(s)$ has simple negative real roots. Recall that Cauer's first form realization of RC DP impedance functions produces transmission zeros at $s = \infty$. Hence, the realization of the transfer function of (7-10) is achieved by realizing the chosen $z_{11}(s)$ by Cauer's first form, which involves a continued fraction expansion of $z_{11}(s)$ at $s = \infty$.

---

[6]In order for $z_{11}(s)$ to satisfy all properties of an RC DP impedance function, $B(s)$ can not have a root at $s = 0$. In Section 7-1-3, we will introduce a dual technique to overcome this difficulty.

[7]Recall that one of the properties of an RC DP impedance function is that its denominator polynomial degree is equal to or one greater than the degree of its numerator polynomial. To choose the denominator degree of $z_{11}(s)$ to be $(n + 1)$ rather than n, we need $(n + 1)$ rather than n dynamic elements in the resulting realization circuit. Since this additional complexity does not yield any apparent return, we have no reason to complicate our problem. Hence, we simply set the denominator degree of $z_{11}(s)$ to be n. In addition, in the case when all transmission zeros are at $s = \infty$, condition RC3 insures that the first element in the Cauer's first form realization of $z_{11}(s)$ will always be a series resistor and hence no redundant shunt capacitor can ever occur.

Example 7-1 Synthesize the transfer function

$$H(s) = \frac{V_o}{V_i} = \frac{k}{(s+2)(s+4)} = \frac{k}{s^2 + 6s + 8} \tag{7-11}$$

Solution: From (7-2), we know that

$$H(s) = \frac{z_{21}(s)}{z_{11}(s)} = \frac{k}{(s+2)(s+4)} \tag{7-12}$$

Based on (7-12), there are many choices of $z_{11}(s)$. The restrictions are that the zeros of $z_{11}(s)$ are at $s = -2$ and $s = -4$, and that $z_{11}(s)$ satisfies all properties of an RC DP impedance function with a second-order denominator polynomial. A simple choice is to let

$$z_{11}(s) = \frac{(s+2)(s+4)}{(s+1)(s+3)} \tag{7-13}$$

Clearly, the $z_{11}(s)$ of (7-13) satisfies all requirements as specified by conditions RC1, RC2, and RC3. From (7-12) and (7-13), we identify

$$z_{21}(s) = \frac{k}{(s+1)(s+3)} \tag{7-14}$$

To realize the transfer function of (7-11), it is necessary to realize the DP impedance function of (7-13) and make sure that the transmission zeros of the resulting RC ladder circuit are all at $s = \infty$, as dictated by (7-11). This can be done in one step by using Cauer's first form to realize $z_{11}(s)$ of (7-13). Noting that the continued fraction expansion of $z_{11}(s)$ at $s = \infty$ is given by

$$\begin{aligned}
z_{11}(s) &= \frac{s^2 + 6s + 8}{s^2 + 4s + 3} \\
&= 1 + \cfrac{1}{\frac{1}{2}s + \cfrac{1}{\frac{4}{3} + \cfrac{1}{\frac{3}{2}s + \cfrac{1}{\frac{1}{3}}}}}
\end{aligned} \tag{7-15}$$

a circuit realization of $z_{11}(s)$ via (7-15) is given in Fig. 7-4, where the output

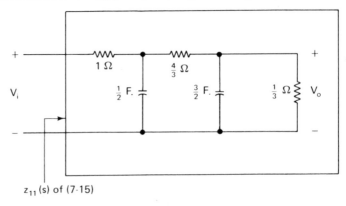

$z_{11}(s)$ of (7-15)

Fig. 7-4 A circuit realization of $H(s)$ of (7-12).

voltage is taken across the last element in the realization process.[8] The transmission zeros of the circuit in Fig. 7-4 are all at $s = \infty$, where the shunt impedances are zero. Hence, the circuit in Fig. 7-4 realizes $z_{11}(s)$ of (7-13), $z_{21}(s)$ of (7-14), and the transfer function of (7-11), *simultaneously*. To see that this is the case, it is sufficient to show that when $V_i = 1$, V_o is given by

$$V_o = \frac{k}{(s+2)(s+4)} = \frac{k}{s^2 + 6s + 8} = H(s) \tag{7-16}$$

When $V_i = 1$,[9] we can redraw the circuit in Fig. 7-4 as shown in Fig. 7-5. The

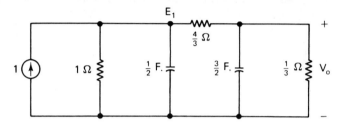

Fig. 7-5 An equivalent circuit of Fig. 7-4 when $V_i = 1$.

nodal equations are

$$\begin{bmatrix} 1 + \dfrac{1}{2}s + \dfrac{3}{4} & -\dfrac{3}{4} \\[2mm] -\dfrac{3}{4} & \dfrac{3}{4} + 3 + \dfrac{3}{2}s \end{bmatrix} \begin{bmatrix} E_1 \\[2mm] V_o \end{bmatrix} = \begin{bmatrix} 1 \\[2mm] 0 \end{bmatrix} \tag{7-17}$$

Cramer's rule says that

$$V_o = \frac{\det \begin{bmatrix} \dfrac{7}{4} + \dfrac{1}{2}s & 1 \\[2mm] -\dfrac{3}{4} & 0 \end{bmatrix}}{\det \begin{bmatrix} \dfrac{7}{4} + \dfrac{1}{2}s & -\dfrac{3}{4} \\[2mm] -\dfrac{3}{4} & \dfrac{15}{4} + \dfrac{3}{2}s \end{bmatrix}} = \frac{\dfrac{3}{4}}{\left(\dfrac{7}{4} + \dfrac{1}{2}s\right)\left(\dfrac{15}{4} + \dfrac{3}{2}s\right) - \dfrac{9}{16}}$$

$$= \frac{\dfrac{3}{4}}{\dfrac{3}{4}s^2 + \dfrac{18}{4}s + \dfrac{24}{4}} = \frac{1}{s^2 + 6s + 8} = \frac{1}{(s+2)(s+4)} \tag{7-18}$$

∎

---

[8]If a transfer function is realized by any one of the ladder circuit structure techniques, then the output voltage is always across the last element in the realization process. This applies to both Sections 7-1-1 and 7-1-2.

[9]Observe that, in the present context, $V_i = 1$ is an expression in the frequency (Laplace transformed) domain. In the time domain, this is equivalent to letting $v_i(t)$ be a unit impulse function.

CASE 2: The second case that we discuss in the RC ladder realization of voltage ratio transfer function is when all transmission zeros of the transfer function are at $s = 0$. In this case, the transfer functions are of the form

$$H(s) = \frac{V_o}{V_i} \triangleq \frac{ks^n}{s^n + b_{n-1}s^{n-1} + \ldots + b_0} \triangleq \frac{ks^n}{B(s)} \tag{7-19}$$

where the roots of $B(s)$ are simple, negative, and real. Because Cauer's second form yields networks made up of shunt resistive branches and series capacitive branches producing transmission zeros at the point $s = 0$ only, we use Cauer's second form to realize the chosen $z_{11}(s)$ and the transfer function of (7-19) simultaneously.

Example 7-2 Realize

$$H(s) = \frac{V_o}{V_i} = \frac{ks^2}{(s+2)(s+4)} \tag{7-20}$$

Solution: As is in the case of Example 7-1, a simple choice of $z_{11}(s)$ to satisfy conditions RC1, RC2, and RC3 is

$$z_{11}(s) = \frac{(s+2)(s+4)}{(s+1)(s+3)} \tag{7-21}$$

Hence, we can identify

$$z_{21}(s) = \frac{ks^2}{(s+1)(s+3)} \tag{7-22}$$

To realize $z_{11}(s)$ of (7-21) and $z_{21}(s)$ of (7-22) simultaneously to give rise to the prescribed transfer function of (7-20), where all transmission zeros are at $s = 0$, we use Cauer's second form to realize $z_{11}(s)$. This involves a continued fraction expansion of $z_{11}(s)$ at $s = 0$:

$$z_{11}(s) = \frac{8 + 6s + s^2}{3 + 4s + s^2}$$

$$= \cfrac{1}{\dfrac{3}{8} + \cfrac{1}{\dfrac{32}{7s} + \cfrac{1}{\dfrac{49}{88} + \cfrac{1}{\dfrac{968}{21s} + \cfrac{1}{\dfrac{3}{44}}}}}} \tag{7-23}$$

A circuit realization of the transfer function of (7-20) is given in Fig. 7-6, which is also a Cauer's second form realization of the $z_{11}(s)$ of (7-21).

To see that the circuit in Fig. 7-6 realizes the transfer function of (7-20), we let $V_i = 1$ and compute V_o. Our conclusion will be valid if

$$V_o = H(s) = \frac{ks^2}{s^2 + 6s + 8}$$

With $V_i = 1$, we redraw the circuit in Fig. 7-6 as in Fig. 7-7. The nodal equation

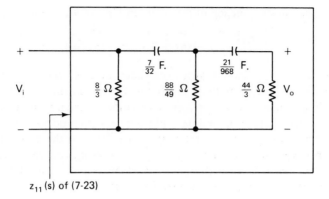

$z_{11}(s)$ of (7-23)

Fig. 7-6 A circuit realization of $H(s)$ of (7-20).

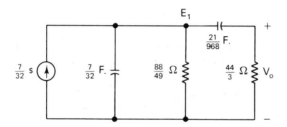

Fig. 7-7 An equivalent circuit of Fig. 7-6 when $V_i = 1$.

is given by

$$
\begin{bmatrix}
\dfrac{7s}{32} + \dfrac{21s}{968} + \dfrac{49}{88} & -\dfrac{21s}{968} \\[3mm]
-\dfrac{21s}{968} & \dfrac{21s}{968} + \dfrac{3}{44}
\end{bmatrix}
\begin{bmatrix}
E_1 \\[3mm]
V_o
\end{bmatrix}
=
\begin{bmatrix}
\dfrac{7}{32}s \\[3mm]
0
\end{bmatrix}
$$

By Cramer's rule, we obtain

$$
V_o = \frac{\dfrac{21s}{968}\dfrac{7s}{32}}{\left(\dfrac{931s}{3972} + \dfrac{49}{88}\right)\left(\dfrac{21s}{968} + \dfrac{3}{44}\right) - \left(\dfrac{21s}{968}\right)^2}
$$

$$
= \frac{\dfrac{147}{968 \times 32}s^2}{\dfrac{17787}{3748096}s^2 + \dfrac{4851}{170368}s + \dfrac{147}{3872}}
$$

$$
= \frac{17787s^2}{17787s^2 + 106722s + 142296}
$$

$$
= \frac{s^2}{s^2 + 6s + 8}
$$

Hence, the transfer function of the circuit in Fig. 7-6 is given by

$$H(s) = \frac{s^2}{s^2 + 6s + 8} = \frac{s^2}{(s + 2)(s + 4)}$$ ∎

CASE 3: The last case that we consider in this section is when the transmission zeros occur both at $s = 0$ and $s = \infty$. In this case, the chosen RC DP impedance function $z_{11}(s)$ is expanded partially in a continued fraction expansion at $s = 0$, and partially at $s = \infty$ to produce the prescribed transmission zeros. We may start with either form of the expansion. The first expansion is stopped when the required transmission zeros have been obtained. The remainder function is then expanded in another Cauer form. To see how this works, let us consider Example 7-3.

Example 7-3 Realize the voltage-ratio transfer function

$$H(s) \triangleq \frac{V_o}{V_i} = \frac{ks}{(s + 2)(s + 4)} \tag{7-24}$$

Solution: The transfer function of (7-24) has a transmission zero at $s = \infty$ and another transmission zero at $s = 0$. To start the realization procedure, let us choose $z_{11}(s)$ as

$$z_{11}(s) = \frac{(s + 2)(s + 4)}{(s + 1)(s + 3)} \tag{7-25}$$

and, hence,

$$z_{21}(s) = \frac{ks}{(s + 1)(s + 3)} \tag{7-26}$$

We note here that $z_{11}(s)$ of (7-25) is the same function as those in Examples 7-1 and 7-2 but that $z_{21}(s)$ is different. Hence, neither one of the Cauer's two forms will realize (7-24). As proposed, we use a combination of these two forms. Let us first expand $z_{11}(s)$ of (7-25) at $s = \infty$ to extract the transmission zero at $s = \infty$. Because there is only one transmission zero at $s = \infty$, we stop this continued fraction expansion at $s = \infty$ *as soon as* we have extracted a shunt capacitor. This involves writing $z_{11}(s)$ as

$$z_{11}(s) = \frac{s^2 + 6s + 8}{s^2 + 4s + 3} = 1 + \cfrac{1}{\cfrac{1}{2}s + \cfrac{(3/2)s + 3}{2s + 5}} = 1 + \cfrac{1}{\cfrac{1}{2}s + y_R(s)} \tag{7-27}$$

This process is illustrated in Fig. 7-8(a). The remainder admittance function

$$y_R(s) \triangleq \frac{(3/2)s + 3}{2s + 5} = \frac{3 + (3/2)s}{5 + 2s} \tag{7-28}$$

is then expanded by Cauer's second form:

$$y_R(s) = \frac{3}{5} + \cfrac{1}{\cfrac{50}{3s} + \cfrac{1}{\cfrac{3}{20}}} \tag{7-29}$$

Hence, a circuit realization of $z_{11}(s)$ of (7-25) and $z_{21}(s)$ of (7-26), simultaneously, to produce $H(s)$ of (7-24) via (7-27) to (7-29) is shown in Fig. 7-8(b).

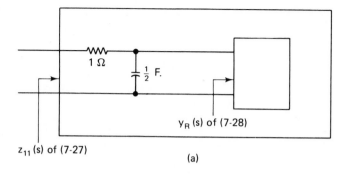

z_{11} (s) of (7-27)

(a)

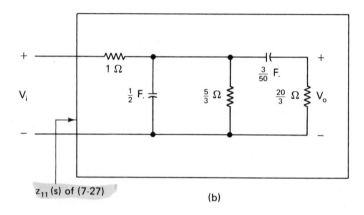

z_{11} (s) of (7-27)

(b)

Fig. 7-8 A circuit realization of $H(s)$ of (7-24). (a) An intermediate step. (b) Final circuit realization.

If we do not stop the Cauer's first-form expansion of $z_{11}(s)$ of (7-25) as soon
as we have extracted the required number of capacitors and instead stop just
before the next shunt capacitor is extracted, then $z_{11}(s)$ is written as

$$z_{11}(s) = \frac{s^2 + 6s + 8}{s^2 + 4s + 3} = 1 + \cfrac{1}{\frac{1}{2}s + \cfrac{1}{\frac{4}{3} + \cfrac{1}{\frac{3}{2}s + 3}}} \tag{7-30}$$

where the remainder admittance function

$$y_R(s) \triangleq \frac{3}{2}s + 3 \tag{7-31}$$

is then expanded at $s = 0$:

$$y_R(s) = 3 + \frac{1}{(2/3s)} \tag{7-32}$$

A circuit implementation of this procedure is given by Fig. 7-9.

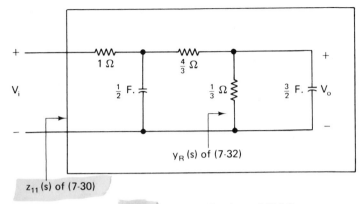

Fig. 7-9 Not a circuit realization of (7-24).

A simple analysis of the circuit in Fig. 7-9 shows that the transfer function of the circuit is given by[10]

$$\frac{V_o}{V_i} = \frac{1}{s^2 + 6s + 8}$$

which is not the desired transfer function of (7-24). Hence, it is mandatory to *stop the first realization process as soon as the required number of capacitors have been extracted.*

Another realization of the transfer function of (7-24) is accomplished by expanding $z_{11}(s)$ of (7-25) at $s = 0$ first. The expansion is stopped as soon as a series capacitor is extracted—a transmission zero is produced at $s = 0$. The remainder function is then expanded at $s = \infty$. To implement this procedure, we expand $z_{11}(s)$:

$$z_{11}(s) = \frac{s^2 + 6s + 8}{s^2 + 4s + 3} = \cfrac{1}{\cfrac{3}{8} + \cfrac{1}{\cfrac{32}{7s} + \cfrac{s + \cfrac{22}{7}}{\cfrac{5}{8}s + \cfrac{7}{4}}}} \qquad (7\text{-}33)$$

and the remainder impedance function z_R is written as

$$z_R(s) = \frac{s + (22/7)}{\cfrac{5}{8}s + \cfrac{7}{4}} = \frac{8}{5} + \cfrac{1}{\cfrac{175}{96}s + \cfrac{1}{\cfrac{48}{245}}} \qquad (7\text{-}34)$$

A circuit realization of (7-25) and (7-26) simultaneously to produce $H(s)$ of (7-24) via (7-33) and (7-34) is given by Fig. 7-10.

A simple analysis yields that the transfer function of the circuit in Fig. 7-10 is given by

---

[10]See Example 7-1.

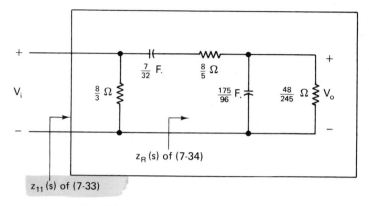

Fig. 7-10   A circuit realization of (7-24).

$$H(s) = \frac{(12/35)s}{s^2 + 6s + 8}$$

Hence, Fig. 7-10 indeed presents a circuit realization of (7-24).   ∎

From Examples 7-1 through 7-3, we observe that even though the chosen $z_{11}(s)$ are the same, different DP realization methods will yield different $z_{21}(s)$ and consequently different $H(s)$. We note also that given the two impedance matrix parameters, $z_{21}(s)$ and $z_{11}(s)$ of an RC 2-port, the procedures presented in this section can be used to realize the prescribed 2-port.

7-1-2. LC Ladder Networks

Following the pattern of reasoning as presented in the preceding section for the case of RC ladder networks, we have the following theorem for LC ladder networks:

THEOREM 7-2   The transmission zeros and the poles of the transfer functions of LC ladder networks are all on the imaginary axis of the s-plane, and the poles are simple. In addition, if each branch of the LC ladder network contains only one element (either an inductor or a capacitor), then the transmission zeros are restricted to the points $s = 0$ and $s = \infty$. In this case, the transfer function is in the form of

$$H(s) = \frac{ks^m}{s^n + b_{n-1}s^{n-1} + \ldots + b_0} \triangleq \frac{ks^m}{B(s)} \tag{7-35}$$

where $B(s)$ is an nth-degree polynomial with simple and imaginary axis roots[11] and $0 \leq m \leq n$. However, in this case, both m and n are even integers, implying that the transfer function $H(s)$ of (7-35) is an even rational function

---

[11]Recall that the imaginary axis includes the points $s = 0$ and $s = \infty$.

[i.e., both the numerator and the denominator of $H(s)$ are even polynomials].[12]

To see that $H(s)$ is an even rational function, let us consider the LC 2-port circuit shown in Fig. 7-11. Suppose that the LC 2-port has an impedance representation

$$\begin{bmatrix} V_1 \\ V_2 \end{bmatrix} = \begin{bmatrix} z_{11} & z_{12} \\ z_{21} & z_{22} \end{bmatrix} \begin{bmatrix} I_1 \\ I_2 \end{bmatrix} \tag{7-36}$$

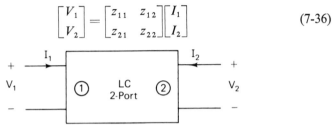

Fig. 7-11 An LC 2-port.

where $z_{12}(s) = z_{21}(s)$.[13] Then it can be shown that all the z-parameters, namely $z_{11}, z_{12} = z_{21}$, and z_{22} are odd rational functions.[14] Because the transfer function

$$H(s) = \frac{V_o}{V_i}\bigg|_{I_2=0} = \frac{z_{21}}{z_{11}} \tag{7-37}$$

is a ratio of two odd rational functions, $H(s)$ is an even rational function.

As is in the case of RC ladder circuits, realization of the LC transfer function of (7-35) is accomplished by realizing a suitably chosen LC DP impedance function, $z_{11}(s)$, with an appropriate Cauer form or a combination of Cauer's two forms. Specifically, the chosen impedance function

$$z_{11}(s) = \frac{B(s)}{D(s)} \tag{7-38}$$

must satisfy the following two conditions:

LC1. The roots of $D(s)$ are simple, purely imaginary, and alternating with the roots of $B(s)$ such that $z_{11}(s)$ satisfies all the properties of an LC DP impedance function as given in Chapter 5.

LC2. $D(s)$ is an odd polynomial with degree $n_D = n - 1$. This ensures

---

[12]What is really required is that $H(s)$ is an even rational function. This implies that either both m and n are even integers or they both are odd integers. Because $B(s)$ has only purely imaginary roots, $B(s)$ is either an even or an odd polynomial. So if m is odd, then $B(s)$ is an odd polynomial and the cancellation of the term s from both the numerator ks^m and the denominator $B(s)$ of $H(s)$ will reduce $H(s)$ to $H(s) = ks^{m-1}/B_R(s)$, where $B_R(s) \triangleq B(s)/s$ is an even polynomial and $(m-1)$ is an even integer. Hence, in this section, we deal with the case when m is an even integer and $B(s)$ is an even polynomial.

[13]This is because the LC 2-port, like the RC 2-port in the preceding section, is reciprocal.

[14]See Sec. 7-3 for details.

that the appropriate Cauer's forms or their combination will work with the impedance function of $z_{11}(s)$.[15]

At this point, we divide (7-35) into three cases.

CASE 1: $m = 0$. In this case, all transmission zeros are at $s = \infty$. Cauer's first form is used to realize $z_{11}(s)$. The reason is that the structure of Cauer's first form involves series inductances and shunt capacitances, both of which give rise to transmission zeros at $s = \infty$. Hence, Cauer's first form will atuomatically realize $z_{11}(s)$ and the associated $z_{21}(s)$, simultaneously, to produce a transfer function of (7-35) with $m = 0$.

CASE 2: $m = n$. In this case, all transmission zeros are at $s = 0$; hence, Cauer's second form should be used. Cauer's second form contains series capacitance and shunt inductance branches that produce transmission zeros at $s = 0$. Hence, Cauer's second form will realize $z_{11}(s)$ and its associated $z_{21}(s)$ to produce a transfer function of (7-35) with $m = n$.

CASE 3: $0 < m < n$. In this case, transmission zeros occur both at $s = 0$ and $s = \infty$. We need to use a combination of Cauer's two forms to do the realization. We can first use Cauer's first {second} form to extract $n - m$ {m} elements from $z_{11}(s)$ and the remainder LC DP function is realized by Cauer's second {first} form.

Example 7-4   Realize

$$H(s) = \frac{V_o}{V_i} = \frac{k}{(s^2 + 1)(s^2 + 9)} \triangleq \frac{k}{B(s)} \tag{7-39}$$

Solution: Let us choose

$$z_{11}(s) = \frac{(s^2 + 1)(s^2 + 9)}{s(s^2 + 4)} = \frac{s^4 + 10s^2 + 9}{s^3 + 4s} \tag{7-40}$$

By (7-37), we have

$$z_{21}(s) = \frac{k}{s(s^2 + 4)} \tag{7-41}$$

---

[15]This is true for the following two reasons:
1. Cauer's first form works with the LC DP function whose numerator polynomial is of a higher degree than that of its denominator polynomial. Because $D(s)$ is of degree $n_D < n$, Cauer's first form will work with $z_{11}(s)$ rather than the $1/z_{11}(s)$.
2. Cauer's second form works with the LC DP function whose denominator is an odd polynomial. Because $D(s)$ is an odd polynomial, Cauer's second form will work with the DP impedance function $z_{11}(s)$.

However, the main reason for setting the degree of $D(s)$ to $(n - 1)$ is not really to ensure that the realization will work with $z_{11}(s)$ but for economy. If we let $n_D = n + 1$, then we need $(n + 1)$ elements to realize $z_{11}(s)$. In the present case—$n_D = n - 1$—we need only n elements to realize $z_{11}(s)$.

Because all transmission zeros are at $s = \infty$, we use Cauer's first form to do the realization. Mathematically speaking, this involves a partial fraction expansion of $z_{11}(s)$ at the point $s = \infty$:

$$z_{11}(s) = s + \cfrac{1}{\cfrac{1}{6}s + \cfrac{1}{\cfrac{12}{5}s + \cfrac{1}{\cfrac{5}{18}s}}} \qquad (7\text{-}42)$$

A circuit realization of $z_{11}(s)$ of (7-40) and $z_{21}(s)$ of (7-41), simultaneously, to produce $H(s)$ of (7-39) via (7-42) is shown in Fig. 7-12.

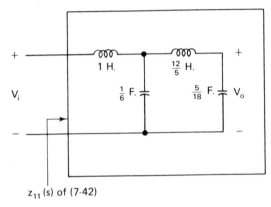

$z_{11}(s)$ of (7-42)

Fig. 7-12   A circuit realization of $H(s)$ of (7-39).

An analysis of the circuit in Fig. 7-12 shows that the voltage-ratio transfer function is given by

$$H(s) = \frac{V_o}{V_i} = \frac{9}{(s^2 + 1)(s^2 + 3)}$$

Hence, Fig. 7-12 is indeed a circuit realization of the transfer function of (7-39).

∎

Example 7-5   Realize the voltage-ratio transfer function

$$H(s) = \frac{V_o}{V_i} = \frac{ks^4}{(s^2 + 1)(s^2 + 9)} \qquad (7\text{-}43)$$

Solution: Let us choose

$$z_{11}(s) = \frac{(s^2 + 1)(s^2 + 9)}{s(s^2 + 4)} \qquad (7\text{-}44)$$

This $z_{11}(s)$ satisfies all the properties of LC DP impedance functions. By (7-37),

$$z_{21}(s) = \frac{ks^4}{s(s^2 + 4)} \qquad (7\text{-}45)$$

Because all transmission zeros are at $s = 0$, we use Cauer's second form to realize $z_{11}(s)$. This involves a continued fraction expansion of $z_{11}(s)$ at $s = 0$:

$$z_{11}(s) = \frac{s^4 + 10s^2 + 9}{s^3 + 4s}$$

$$= \frac{9}{4s} + \cfrac{1}{\cfrac{16}{31s} + \cfrac{1}{\cfrac{961}{60s} + \cfrac{1}{\cfrac{15}{31s}}}} \qquad (7\text{-}46)$$

A circuit realization of the transfer function $H(s)$ of (7-43), obtained by realizing the LC DP impedance function $z_{11}(s)$ of (7-46) with Cauer's second form, is shown in Fig. 7-13. ∎

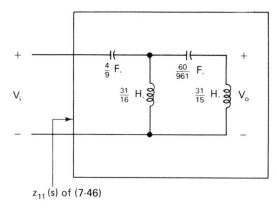

$z_{11}(s)$ of (7-46)

Fig. 7-13   A circuit realization of $H(s)$ of (7-43).

Example 7-6   Realize

$$H(s) = \frac{V_o}{V_i} = \frac{ks^2}{(s^2 + 1)(s^2 + 9)} \qquad (7\text{-}47)$$

Solution: A simple choice for $z_{11}(s)$ is given by

$$z_{11}(s) = \frac{(s^2 + 1)(s^2 + 9)}{s(s^2 + 4)} \qquad (7\text{-}48)$$

In this case, we have

$$z_{21}(s) = \frac{ks}{s^2 + 4} \qquad (7\text{-}49)$$

The transfer function of (7-47) has two transmission zeros at $s = 0$ and another two transmission zeros at $s = \infty$. To realize these transmission zeros and $z_{11}(s)$ simultaneously, we can use Cauer's first form to extract two elements from $z_{11}(s)$ producing two transmission zeros at $s = \infty$, and the remainder function is then realized by Cauer's second form, producing another two transmission zeros at $s = 0$. This involves the following expansion of $z_{11}(s)$:

$$z_{11}(s) = \frac{s^4 + 10s^2 + 9}{s^3 + 4s}$$

$$= s + \cfrac{1}{\cfrac{1}{6}s + \cfrac{(5/2)s}{6s^2 + 9}} \triangleq s + \cfrac{1}{\cfrac{1}{6}s + y_R(s)} \qquad (7\text{-}50)$$

where the remainder admittance function $y_R(s)$ is expanded by Cauer's second form:

$$z_R(s) = \frac{1}{y_R(s)} = \frac{6s^2 + 9}{(5/2)s} = \frac{9 + 6s^2}{(5/2)s}$$

$$= \frac{18}{5s} + \frac{1}{(5/12s)}$$

(7-51)

A circuit implementation of this procedure is shown in Fig. 7-14(a).

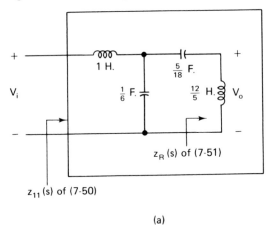

$z_{11}(s)$ of (7-50)

(a)

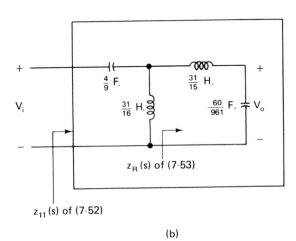

$z_{11}(s)$ of (7-52)

(b)

Fig. 7-14 Two circuit realizations of $H(s)$ of (7-47).

On the other hand, we can realize $z_{11}(s)$ by first using Cauer's second form to extract two elements from $z_{11}(s)$ to produce two transmission zeros at $s = 0$ and then realizing the remainder by Cauer's first form. This involves the expansion of $z_{11}(s)$:

$$z_{11}(s) = \frac{9 + 10s^2 + s^4}{4s + s^3}$$

$$= \frac{9}{4s} + \frac{1}{\dfrac{16}{31s} + \dfrac{(15/31)s}{s^2 + (31/4)}} \triangleq \frac{9}{4s} + \frac{1}{\dfrac{16}{31s} + y_R(s)} \tag{7-52}$$

where the remainder function

$$z_R(s) = \frac{1}{y_R(s)} = \frac{s^2 + (31/4)}{(15/31)s} \tag{7-53}$$

is expanded at $s = \infty$:

$$z_R(s) = \frac{31}{15}s + \frac{1}{(60/961)s} \tag{7-54}$$

A circuit realization of (7-47) via (7-52) and (7-54) is shown in Fig. 7-14(b). ▌

7-1-3. Alternative Considerations

In the preceding two sections, we considered the realization of transfer functions of RC and LC ladder networks via the 2-port impedance representations. In this section, we examine the problem of transfer-function realization through the admittance representation.

Suppose that the RC {LC} 2-port shown in Fig. 7-15 has an admittance representation

$$\begin{bmatrix} I_1 \\ I_2 \end{bmatrix} = \begin{bmatrix} y_{11} & y_{12} \\ y_{21} & y_{22} \end{bmatrix} \begin{bmatrix} V_1 \\ V_2 \end{bmatrix} \tag{7-55}$$

where $y_{12} = y_{21}$. Then the voltage-ratio transfer function is given by the second equation of (7-55), with $I_2 = 0$ as[16]

$$H(s) = \frac{V_2}{V_1}\bigg|_{I_2=0} = -\frac{y_{21}(s)}{y_{22}(s)} \tag{7-56}$$

Observe that (7-56) is similar to that of (7-2), with y_{22} and $-y_{21}$ replacing

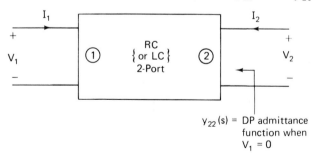

$y_{22}(s)$ = DP admittance
function when
$V_1 = 0$

Fig. 7-15   An RC·{LC} 2-port.

---

[16]Using the relationships between the impedance and the admittance representations of a reciprocal 2-port (see Reference [1]), it can be shown that $-(y_{21}/y_{22}) = (z_{21}/z_{11})$.

z_{11} and z_{21}, respectively. Hence, the realization of a given transfer function satisfying the RC {LC} ladder-circuit structure requirements of Theorem 7-1 {Theorem 7-2} can be obtained by a proper realization of an appropriately chosen RC {LC} DP admittance function $y_{22}(s)$.

Let the prescribed transfer function be given by

$$H(s) = \frac{ks^m}{B(s)} \tag{7-57}$$

where $B(s)$ is an nth-degree polynomial with simple and negative real {imaginary} axis roots. Then $y_{22}(s)$ is given by

$$y_{22}(s) = \frac{B(s)}{D(s)} \tag{7-58}$$

where $D(s)$ is chosen such that $y_{22}(s)$ satisfies all conditions of an RC {LC} DP admittance function as presented in Chapter 6 {Chapter 5}. For simplicity and economy, let us choose n_D, the degree of the polynomial $D(s)$, to be[17]

$$n_D = n - 1 \tag{7-59}$$

Substituting (7-57) and (7-58) into (7-56), we obtain

$$y_{21}(s) = -\frac{ks^m}{D(s)} \tag{7-60}$$

To realize $H(s)$ of (7-57), we need to realize $y_{22}(s)$ of (7-58) and $y_{21}(s)$ of (7-60), simultaneously, to meet the transmission zero requirements of $H(s)$. This means that:

1. If $m = 0$, the case when all transmission zeros are at $s = \infty$, we use Cauer's first form to realize $y_{22}(s)$.
2. If $m = n$, the case when all transmission zeros are at $s = 0$, we use Cauer's second form to realize $y_{22}(s)$.
3. If $0 < m < n$, we realize m transmission zeros at $s = 0$ by Cauer's second form and $(n - m)$ transmission zeros at $s = \infty$ by Cauer's first form.

Example 7-7 Realize the voltage-ratio transfer function

$$H(s) = \frac{k}{(s + 2)(s + 4)} \tag{7-61}$$

Solution: Let us choose $y_{22}(s)$ to be

$$y_{22}(s) = \frac{(s + 2)(s + 4)}{(s + 3)} \tag{7-62}$$

---

[17]Observe that (7-59) and RC3 of Section 7-1-1 are different because RC DP impedance and admittance functions have different properties. On the contrary, (7-59) and LC2 are identical, because LC DP impedance and admittance functions have identical properties.

Clearly, $y_{22}(s)$ satisfies all properties of an RC DP admittance function and

$$y_{21}(s) = -\frac{k}{s+3} \tag{7-63}$$

Because all transmission zeros of the transfer function are located at $s = \infty$, we use Cauer's first form to realize $y_{22}(s)$. This involves a continued fraction expansion of $y_{22}(s)$ at $s = \infty$:

$$y_{22}(s) = \frac{s^2 + 6s + 8}{s + 3}$$

$$= s + \cfrac{1}{\cfrac{1}{3} + \cfrac{1}{9s + \cfrac{1}{1/24}}} \tag{7-64}$$

Figure 7-16 contains a Cauer's first-form realization of $y_{22}(s)$ of (7-64). With the output being the voltage across port ② and the input across port ①, Fig. 7-16 also provides a circuit realization of the transfer function of (7-61). Indeed, a simple analysis of the circuit in Fig. 7-16 yields the voltage-ratio transfer function

$$H(s) = \frac{V_o}{V_i} = \frac{8}{(s+2)(s+4)} \qquad \blacksquare$$

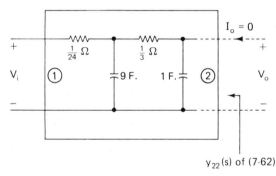

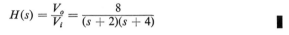

Fig. 7-16   A circuit realization of $H(s)$ of (7-61).

Example 7-8   Realize

$$H(s) = \frac{ks}{(s+2)(s+4)} \tag{7-65}$$

Solution: Let

$$y_{22}(s) = \frac{(s+2)(s+4)}{(s+3)} \tag{7-66}$$

By (7-60),

$$y_{21}(s) = \frac{ks}{s+3}$$

Because there is a transmission zero at $s = \infty$ and another transmission zero at $s = 0$, we use a combination of Cauer's forms to realize $y_{22}(s)$. First we use Cauer's first form to realize a transmission zero at $s = \infty$. This involves a partial continued fraction expansion of $y_{22}(s)$ at $s = \infty$:

$$y_{22}(s) = s + \frac{3s + 8}{s + 3} \triangleq s + y_R(s) \tag{7-67}$$

Notice that as soon as we have extracted the necessary number of capacitors to provide the required transmission zeros, we should stop the process. The remainder admittance function $y_R(s)$ is to be realized by Cauer's second form. Because

$$z_R(0) = \frac{1}{y_R(0)} \neq \infty \tag{7-68}$$

we perform a continued fraction expansion at $s = 0$ on $y_R(s)$:

$$y_R(s) = \frac{8 + 3s}{3 + s} = \frac{8}{3} + \cfrac{1}{\cfrac{9}{s} + \cfrac{1}{1/3}} \tag{7-69}$$

A circuit realization of $y_{22}(s)$ of (7-66) via (7-67) and (7-69) is shown in Fig. 7-17.

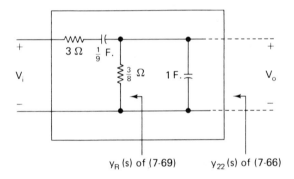

$$y_R(s) \text{ of } (7\text{-}69) \qquad\qquad y_{22}(s) \text{ of } (7\text{-}66)$$

Fig. 7-17 A circuit realization of (7-65).

With the usual labeling of input and output voltages, Fig. 7-17 provides a circuit realization of $H(s)$ of (7-65). Indeed, the voltage-ratio transfer function of the circuit in Fig. 7-17 is given by

$$H(s) = \frac{V_o}{V_i} = \frac{(1/3)s}{(s + 2)(s + 4)} \qquad\blacksquare$$

Example 7-9 Realize

$$H(s) = \frac{ks^2}{(s^2 + 2)(s^2 + 4)} \tag{7-70}$$

Solution: Let

$$y_{22}(s) = \frac{(s^2 + 2)(s^2 + 4)}{s(s^2 + 3)} \tag{7-71}$$

Then

$$y_{21}(s) = -\frac{ks}{s^2 + 3} \tag{7-72}$$

Because there are two transmission zeros at $s = 0$ and two at $s = \infty$, we need to use a combination of Cauer's forms. First we use Cauer's first form to realize the two transmission zeros at $s = \infty$. This involves a partial continued fraction expansion of $y_{22}(s)$ at $s = \infty$:

$$y_{22}(s) = s + \cfrac{1}{\cfrac{1}{3}s + \cfrac{1}{\cfrac{3s^2 + 8}{(1/3)s}}} \triangleq s + \cfrac{1}{\cfrac{1}{3}s + \cfrac{1}{y_R(s)}} \tag{7-73}$$

To produce the remaining two transmission zeros at $s = 0$, we realize $y_R(s)$ by Cauer's second form:

$$y_R(s) = \frac{8 + 3s^2}{(1/3)s} = \frac{24}{s} + \frac{1}{(1/9s)} \tag{7-74}$$

A circuit realization of $H(s)$ of (7-70) based on the realization of $y_{22}(s)$ by a combination of Cauer's forms, as indicated by (7-73) and (7-74), is shown in Fig. 7-18. ∎

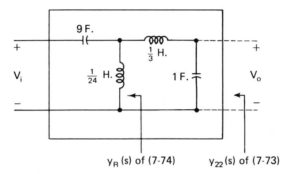

Fig. 7-18 A circuit realization of $H(s)$ of (7-70).

Example 7-10 Realize

$$H(s) = \frac{ks^4}{(s^2 + 2)(s^2 + 4)} \tag{7-75}$$

Solution: Let

$$y_{22}(s) = \frac{(s^2 + 2)(s^2 + 4)}{s(s^2 + 3)} \tag{7-76}$$

Then

$$y_{21}(s) = \frac{ks^3}{s^2 + 3} \tag{7-77}$$

Because all transmission zeros are at $s = 0$, we realize $y_{22}(s)$ by Cauer's second form:

$$y_{22}(s) = \frac{8 + 6s^2 + s^4}{3s + s^3}$$

$$= \frac{8}{3s} + \cfrac{1}{\cfrac{9}{10s} + \cfrac{1}{\cfrac{100}{3s} + \cfrac{1}{\cfrac{1}{10s}}}} \tag{7-78}$$

A circuit realization of $H(s)$ of (7-75) based on (7-78) is shown in Fig. 7-19. ∎

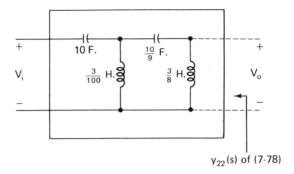

$y_{22}(s)$ of (7-78)

Fig. 7-19 A circuit realization of $H(s)$ of (7-75).

7-2 LATTICE NETWORKS

A lattice network has an interconnection structure as shown in Fig. 7-20(a). If there is no restriction on the elements contained by the z_i's, where $i = 1, 2, 3$, and 4, then a lattice structure can be used to realize almost all transfer functions. In this section, we consider a special class of lattice networks, as shown in Fig. 7-20(b), where

$$z_a = z_1 = z_4 \quad \text{and} \quad z_b = z_2 = z_3 \qquad (7-79)$$

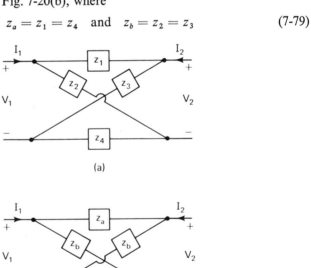

(a)

(b)

Fig. 7-20 (a) A general lattice network. (b) A symmetric lattice network.

The circuit structure in Fig. 7-20(b) is known as the *symmetric lattice* network.

A simple analysis of the symmetric lattice network yields a 2-port impedance representation

$$V_1 = \frac{z_a + z_b}{2}I_1 + \frac{z_b - z_a}{2}I_2 \qquad (7\text{-}80)$$

and

$$V_2 = \frac{z_b - z_a}{2}I_1 + \frac{z_a + z_b}{2}I_2 \qquad (7\text{-}81)$$

If a symmetric lattice is used to synthesize a voltage-ratio transfer function, then

$$H(s) = \frac{V_2}{V_1}\bigg|_{I_2=0} = \frac{z_b - z_a}{z_b + z_a} \qquad (7\text{-}82)$$

Equation (7-82) indicates a way to realize *all-pass* transfer functions.

An all-pass network is characterized by a transfer function of the form

$$H(s) = \frac{p(-s)}{p(s)} \qquad (7\text{-}83)$$

where $p(s)$ is a Hurwitz polynomial. By writing

$$p(s) = m(s) + n(s) \qquad (7\text{-}84)$$

where $m(s)$ and $n(s)$ are the even and odd parts of $p(s)$, respectively, (7-83) becomes

$$H(s) = \frac{m(s) - n(s)}{m(s) + n(s)} = \frac{\dfrac{m(s)}{n(s)} - 1}{\dfrac{m(s)}{n(s)} + 1} \qquad (7\text{-}85a)$$

$$= \frac{1 - \dfrac{n(s)}{m(s)}}{1 + \dfrac{n(s)}{m(s)}} \qquad (7\text{-}85b)$$

Because $p(s)$ is Hurwitz, Theorem 4-4 says that both $m(s)/n(s)$ and $n(s)/m(s)$ can be realized as an LC DP impedance function. Comparing (7-85a) {(7-85b)} with (7-82), we can conclude that it is always possible to realize an all-pass voltage-ratio transfer function by a symmetric lattice network of Fig. 7-20(b) with $z_b = m(s)/n(s)$ $\{z_a = n(s)/m(s)\}$ being an LC 1-port impedance function and z_a $\{z_b\}$ simply being a $1\,\Omega$ resistor. Hence, the problem of realizing an all-pass transfer function is now reduced to the problem of realizing an LC DP impedance function.

Example 7-11 Realize

$$H(s) = \frac{V_o}{V_i} = \frac{s^2 - s + 1}{s^2 + s + 1} \qquad (7\text{-}86)$$

Solution: $H(s)$ of (7-86) can be written as

$$\frac{(s^2+1)-s}{(s^2+1)+s} \Rightarrow \qquad H(s) = \frac{\dfrac{s^2+1}{s} - 1}{\dfrac{s^2+1}{s} + 1} = \frac{z_b - z_a}{z_b + z_a} \qquad (7\text{-}87)$$

A comparison of the terms in (7-82) and (7-87) yields

$$z_b = \frac{s^2+1}{s} = s + \frac{1}{s} \qquad (7\text{-}88\text{a})$$

and

$$z_a = 1 \qquad (7\text{-}88\text{b})$$

A circuit realization of the transfer function of (7-86) is now reduced to the realization of the LC DP impedance function of $z_b(s)$ of (7-88a). The final result is shown in Fig. 7-21(a).

Another realization of (7-86) is possible if we write $H(s)$ as

$$H(s) = \frac{1 - \dfrac{s}{s^2+1}}{1 + \dfrac{s}{s^2+1}} \qquad (7\text{-}89)$$

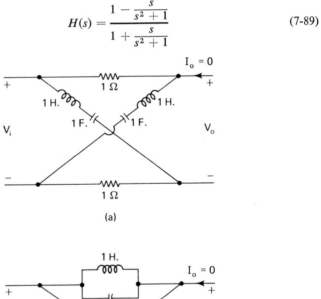

(a)

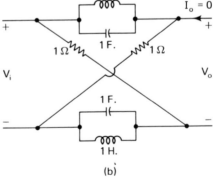

(b)

Fig. 7-21   Two circuit realizations of the all-pass function of (7-86).

Comparing (7-89) with (7-82), we obtain

$$z_a = \frac{s}{s^2 + 1} = \frac{1}{s + \dfrac{1}{s}} \quad \text{and} \quad z_b = 1 \tag{7-90}$$

A circuit implementation of (7-90) is given by Fig. 7-21(b). ∎

7-3 DARLINGTON METHODS

Darlington solved the general problem of realizing a transfer function by means of a lossless 2-port network terminated in resistances.[18] All circuits in the forms of those shown in Fig. 7-22 are called *Darlington networks*.

In this section we do not discuss the Darlington synthesis method per se, but we do discuss some simplified Darlington procedures for a restricted but frequently encountered class of transfer functions. Before we proceed to

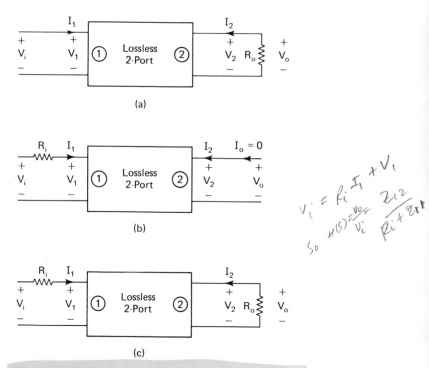

(a)

(b)

(c)

Fig. 7-22 Darlington circuit structures (a) Lossless 2-port terminated by a load resistor. (b) Lossless 2-port terminated by a source resistor. (c) Lossless 2-port terminated by a source resistor and a load resistor.

[18]See References [4] and [5].

present the special cases of Darlington synthesis methods, let us consider some important properties of z-parameters and y-parameters of lossless 2-ports, and of the resulting voltage-ratio transfer functions.

Let the lossless 2-port in Fig. 7-22 be represented by an impedance representation

$$\begin{bmatrix} V_1 \\ V_2 \end{bmatrix} = \begin{bmatrix} z_{11} & z_{12} \\ z_{21} & z_{22} \end{bmatrix} \begin{bmatrix} I_1 \\ I_2 \end{bmatrix} \tag{7-91a}$$

or an admittance representation

$$\begin{bmatrix} I_1 \\ I_2 \end{bmatrix} = \begin{bmatrix} y_{11} & y_{12} \\ y_{21} & y_{22} \end{bmatrix} \begin{bmatrix} V_1 \\ V_2 \end{bmatrix} \tag{7-91b}$$

where $z_{12} = z_{21}$ and $y_{12} = y_{21}$. Because z_{11} and z_{22} $\{y_{11}$ and $y_{22}\}$ are DP impedance {admittance} functions of LC 1-ports, they are odd rational functions with simple and alternating poles and zeros on the imaginary axis of the s-plane. The lossless 2-port is passive. Hence, the *residue matrix* of the 2-port at the pole p_j, given by ξ^j as

$$\xi^j = \begin{bmatrix} \xi_{11}^j & \xi_{12}^j \\ \xi_{21}^j & \xi_{22}^j \end{bmatrix} \tag{7-92}$$

is real and positive semidefinite, where

$$\xi_{ik}^j = \text{residue of } z_{ik} \ \{y_{ik}\} \text{ at the pole } p_j \qquad i, k = 1, 2$$

and a pole of the 2-port is a pole of any one of the four z-parameters $\{y$-parameters$\}$. If p_j is a pole of z_{12} $\{y_{12}\}$ but not of z_{11} or z_{22} $\{y_{11}$ or $y_{22}\}$, then ξ_{11}^j or ξ_{22}^j is zero, and ξ_j of (7-92) is not a positive semidefinite matrix. Hence, we conclude that all poles of z_{12} $\{y_{12}\}$ are poles of z_{11} and z_{22} $\{y_{11}$ and $y_{22}\}$.[19] This means that a partial fraction expansion of z_{12} $\{y_{12}\}$ will have the same form as that of z_{11} or z_{22} $\{y_{11}$ or $y_{22}\}$:

$$z_{12}\{y_{12}\} = \frac{\xi_{12}^{(0)}}{s} + \xi_{12}^{(\infty)}s + \sum_{i=1}^{n} \frac{\xi_{12}^{(i)}s}{s^2 + \omega_i^2} \tag{7-93}$$

Therefore z_{12} $\{y_{12}\}$, just like z_{11} or z_{22} $\{y_{11}$ or $y_{22}\}$, is an odd rational function; that is,

$$z_{12}(s) = \frac{m(s)}{n(s)} \quad \text{or} \quad \frac{n(s)}{m(s)} \tag{7-94a}$$

$$\left\{ y_{12}(s) = \frac{m(s)}{n(s)} \quad \text{or} \quad \frac{n(s)}{m(s)} \right\} \tag{7-94b}$$

where $m(s)$ and $n(s)$ are, respectively, an even and an odd polynomial.

Next, let us consider the transfer functions of Fig. 7-22. For Fig. 7-22(a), the admittance representation of the lossless 2-port and the equation

$$V_2 = -R_o I_2 \tag{7-95}$$

---

[19]Note that not all poles of z_{11} or z_{22} $\{y_{11}$ or $y_{22}\}$ are poles of z_{12} $\{y_{12}\}$.

give

$$H(s) \triangleq \frac{V_o}{V_i} = \frac{-y_{12}}{\dfrac{1}{R_o} + y_{22}} \qquad (7\text{-}96)$$

For Fig. 7-22(b), with $I_2 = 0$, the impedance representation of the lossless 2-port and the equation

$$V_i = R_i I_1 + V_1 \qquad (7\text{-}97)$$

lead to

$$H(s) \triangleq \frac{V_o}{V_i} = \frac{z_{12}}{R_i + z_{11}} \qquad = \frac{c(s)}{k + D(s)} \qquad (7\text{-}98)$$

Finally, for Fig. 7-22(c), we have

$$R_i = 1\,\Omega \quad z_{12}$$

$$H(s) = \frac{z_{12}}{1 + z_{11}}$$

$$H(s) \triangleq \frac{V_o}{V_i} = \frac{-y_{12}}{\dfrac{1}{R_o} + y_{22}} \quad \frac{1}{R_i\left[y_{11} - \dfrac{y_{12}^2}{\dfrac{1}{R_o} + y_{22}} \right] + 1} \qquad (7\text{-}99)$$

Given a transfer function $H(s)$, let us suppose that we can find an appropriate polynomial $P(s)$ such that

$$H(s) = \frac{A(s)}{B(s)} = \frac{A(s)/P(s)}{B(s)/P(s)} = \frac{C(s)}{k + D(s)} \qquad (7\text{-}100)$$

where k is a constant and $C(s)$ and $D(s)$ are odd rational functions. If Fig. 7-22(a) is used, we can identify y_{12} and y_{22} easily by comparing (7-96) and (7-100). In this case, the problem is reduced to the realization of y_{12} and y_{22} simultaneously. Methods for a simultaneous realization of y_{12} and y_{22} have been discussed in Section 7-1-3. If Fig. 7-22(b) is used, we can identify z_{12} and z_{11} by comparing (7-98) and (7-100). Again, realization of (7-100) is reduced to the simultaneous realization of $z_{11}(s)$ and $z_{12}(s)$, which has been presented in Section 7-1-2. This identification process works nicely for Figs. 7-22(a) and (b). However, for Fig. 7-22(c), the situation is quite different, as one can see by comparing (7-99) and (7-100). Hence, we will discuss separately the single termination cases of Figs. 7-22(a) and (b) and the double termination case of Fig. 7-22(c).

7-3-1. Lossless Network with Single Termination

For convenience, we let R_o of Fig. 7-22(a) and R_i of Fig. 7-22(b) be 1 Ω. If we need a different value for R_o or R_i, we can perform an impedance scaling (discussed in Chapter 8) on the resulting network.[20] Under this convenient simplification, (7-96) and (7-98) are similar to each other, with z_{12} and z_{11} corresponding to $-y_{12}$ and y_{22}. We first discuss the case of Fig.

---

[20]Note that the voltage-ratio transfer functions of the impedance scaled network and the original network are identical.

7-22(a) and (7-96) in detail and then outline the synthesis procedure for the case of Fig. 7-22(b) and (7-98).

With $R_o = 1 \, \Omega$, (7-96) becomes

$$H(s) = \frac{V_o}{V_i} = \frac{-y_{12}}{1 + y_{22}} \tag{7-101}$$

Because y_{12} and y_{22} are odd rational functions having the same denominator, let us write

$$y_{12}(s) = \frac{n_{12}(s)}{d_{22}(s)} \quad \text{and} \quad y_{22}(s) = \frac{n_{22}(s)}{d_{22}(s)} \tag{7-102}$$

where $n_{12}(s)$ and $n_{22}(s)$ are odd polynomials if $d_{22}(s)$ is an even polynomial, and where $n_{12}(s)$ and $n_{22}(s)$ are even polynomials if $d_{22}(s)$ is an odd polynomial. Substituting (7-102) into (7-101), we obtain

$$H(s) \triangleq \frac{A(s)}{B(s)} = -\frac{n_{12}(s)}{n_{22}(s) + d_{22}(s)} \tag{7-103}$$

From (7-103), we observe that $A(s)$ is the numerator of y_{12} and hence is either an odd or an even polynomial. In addition, $B(s)$ is the sum of the numerator and the denominator polynomials of an LC DP admittance function $y_{22}(s)$. By Theorem 4-4, $B(s)$ is Hurwitz. This means that the circuits in Figs. 7-22(a) and (b) can only realize a transfer function that has an odd or even numerator polynomial and a Hurwitz denominator polynomial, such as

$$H(s) = \frac{A(s)}{B(s)} = \frac{M_1(s)}{M_2(s) + N_2(s)} \tag{7-104}$$

or

$$H(s) = \frac{A(s)}{B(s)} = \frac{N_1(s)}{M_2(s) + N_2(s)} \tag{7-105}$$

where $M_1(s)$ and $M_2(s)$ are even polynomials, $N_1(s)$ and $N_2(s)$ are odd polynomials, and $B(s) = M_2(s) + N_2(s)$ is a Hurwitz polynomial.

Consider first the case of (7-104). We can write $H(s)$ as

$$H(s) = \frac{M_1(s)/N_2(s)}{[M_2(s)/N_2(s)] + 1} \tag{7-106}$$

An identification of (7-106) and (7-101) gives

$$y_{12}(s) = -\frac{M_1(s)}{N_2(s)} \tag{7-107}$$

and

$$y_{22}(s) = \frac{M_2(s)}{N_2(s)} \tag{7-108}$$

Similarly, if $H(s)$ is given by (7-105), then $H(s)$ can be written as:

$$H(s) = \frac{\dfrac{N_1(s)}{M_2(s)}}{1 + \dfrac{N_2(s)}{M_2(s)}} \tag{7-109}$$

Comparing (7-109) and (7-101), we obtain

$$y_{12}(s) = -\frac{N_1(s)}{M_2(s)} \tag{7-110}$$

and

$$y_{22}(s) = \frac{N_2(s)}{M_2(s)} \tag{7-111}$$

Hence, the problem of realizing a voltage-ratio transfer function is reduced to a simultaneous realization of $y_{22}(s)$ and $y_{12}(s)$.[21] If $A(s)$ is given by

$$A(s) = ks^m \tag{7-112}$$

then the problem of realizing $y_{12}(s)$ and $y_{22}(s)$ simultaneously is solved in Sections 7-1-2 and 7-1-3.

Example 7-12   Realize

$$H(s) \triangleq \frac{V_o}{V_i} = \frac{1}{s^2 + s + 1} \tag{7-113}$$

by a lossless 2-port terminated by a 1 Ω load resistor.

Solution: Because the numerator of $H(s)$ of (7-113) is an even polynomial, $H(s)$ is in the form of (7-104). By (7-106), we write $H(s)$ as

$$H(s) = \frac{1}{s + (s^2 + 1)} = \frac{1/s}{1 + [(s^2 + 1)/s]} \tag{7-114}$$

Identifying the corresponding terms between (7-101) and (7-114), we obtain

$$y_{12} = -\frac{1}{s} \quad \text{and} \quad y_{22} = \frac{s^2 + 1}{s} \tag{7-115}$$

All transmission zeros of $H(s)$ are at $s = \infty$; therefore we use Cauer's first form to realize y_{22}. This involves a continued fraction expansion of $y_{22}(s)$ at $s = \infty$:

$$y_{22}(s) = \frac{s^2 + 1}{s} = s + \frac{1}{s} \tag{7-116}$$

A circuit realization of (7-113) via $y_{22}(s)$ of (7-116) is shown in Fig. 7-23. To see that Fig. 7-23 gives the voltage-ratio transfer function of (7-113), we use the voltage divider equation to obtain

$$V_o = \frac{1/(s + 1)}{[1/(s + 1)] + s} V_i$$

---

[21]By (7-56), the problem of simultaneous realization of $y_{12}(s)$ and $y_{22}(s)$ is equivalent to the problem of realizing the voltage-ratio transfer function $F(s)$ of a lossless 2-port (alone), where $F(s)$ is given by

$$F(s) = -\frac{y_{12}(s)}{y_{22}(s)} = \frac{M_1(s)}{M_2(s)}$$

for the case of (7-104), and

$$F(s) = -\frac{y_{12}(s)}{y(_{22}s)} = \frac{N_1(s)}{N_2(s)}$$

for the case of (7-105). Note that the transmission zero requirements of $F(s)$ and $H(s)$ are identical. This makes sense physically, also, because the circuit realizations of $H(s)$ and $F(s)$ differ by a resistor only.

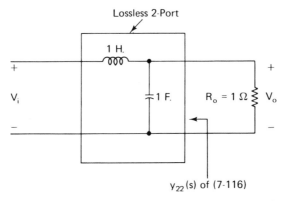

Fig. 7-23 A circuit realization of $H(s)$ of (7-113).

Hence,

$$H(s) = \frac{1}{s^2 + s + 1}$$

which is the desired function of (7-113). Notice that when all transmission zeros are at $s = \infty$, Cauer's first form should be used to realize $y_{22}(s)$. ∎

Example 7-13 Realize

$$H(s) \triangleq \frac{V_o}{V_i} = \frac{s^2}{s^2 + 3s + 1} \tag{7-117}$$

by a lossless 2-port terminated by a $1\ \Omega$ load resistor.

Solution: As in the case of Example 7-12, this problem is reduced to the simultaneous realization of

$$y_{12}(s) = -\frac{s^2}{3s} = -\frac{s}{3} \quad \text{and} \quad y_{22}(s) = \frac{1 + s^2}{3s} \tag{7-118}$$

All transmission zeros of (7-117) are at $s = 0$; therefore, Cauer's second form is used to realize y_{22} of (7-118). A circuit realization of (7-117) is given by Fig. 7-24, where $y_{22}(s)$ is expanded at $s = 0$:

$$y_{22}(s) = \frac{1}{3s} + \frac{1}{3/s} \tag{7-119}$$

To see that the circuit in Fig. 7-24 does realize the desired transfer function, the voltage-divider equation gives

$$V_o = \frac{\dfrac{1}{\dfrac{1}{3s} + 1}}{\dfrac{1}{\dfrac{1}{3s} + 1} + \dfrac{3}{s}} V_i = \frac{3s^2}{3s^2 + 3(3s + 1)} V_i$$

Hence

$$H(s) = \frac{s^2}{s^2 + 3s + 1} \qquad ∎$$

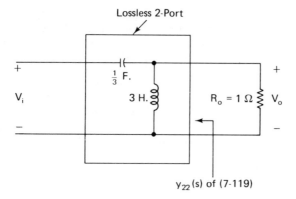

Fig. 7-24 A circuit realization of $H(s)$ of (7-117).

Example 7-14 Realize

$$H(s) = \frac{V_o}{V_i} = \frac{s}{s^3 + s^2 + 3s + 1} \qquad (7\text{-}120)$$

by a lossless 2-port terminated by a 1 Ω load resistor.

Solution: In this case, the numerator of $H(s)$ is an odd polynomial. By (7-109) through (7-111), $H(s)$ can be written as

$$H(s) = \frac{s}{(s^2 + 1) + (s^3 + 3s)} = \frac{\dfrac{s}{s^2 + 1}}{1 + \dfrac{s^3 + 3s}{s^2 + 1}} \qquad (7\text{-}121)$$

Identifying the corresponding terms between (7-121) and (7-101) leads to

$$y_{12} = \frac{s}{s^2 + 1} \quad \text{and} \quad y_{22} = \frac{s^3 + 3s}{s^2 + 1} \qquad (7\text{-}122)$$

Our problem is now reduced to a simultaneous realization of y_{12} and y_{22}. Because there is one transmission zero at $s = 0$ and two transmission zeros at $s = \infty$, we have to use a combination of Cauer's first and second forms.

It is generally preferable to realize the single transmission zero first before tackling the multiple transmission zeros. Hence, let us realize the single transmission zero at $s = 0$ first. This requires us to perform a partial continued fraction expansion at $s = 0$ on $y_{22}(s)$ until a capacitor is extracted:

$$y_{22}(s) = \frac{s^3 + 3s}{s^2 + 1} = \frac{1}{(1/3s) + z_R(s)} \qquad (7\text{-}123)$$

where the remainder impedance function $z_R(s)$ is to be realized by Cauer's first form to produce the transmission zeros at $s = \infty$:

$$z_R(s) \triangleq \frac{(2/3)s^2}{s^3 + 3s} = \frac{(2/3)s}{s^2 + 3} = \frac{1}{\dfrac{3}{2}s + \dfrac{1}{\dfrac{2}{9}s}} \qquad (7\text{-}124)$$

A circuit realization of the transfer function of (7-120), by implementing the realization of $y_{22}(s)$ as indicated by (7-123) and (7-124), is given by Fig. 7-25.

To see that the circuit in Fig. 7-25 realizes the transfer function of (7-120), we let $V_i = 1$ and perform a nodal analysis on the circuit. This gives

$$\begin{bmatrix} \dfrac{9}{2s} + \dfrac{3}{2}s + 3s & -3s \\[2mm] -3s & 1 + 3s \end{bmatrix} \begin{bmatrix} E_1 \\[2mm] V_o \end{bmatrix} = \begin{bmatrix} \dfrac{9}{2s} \\[2mm] 0 \end{bmatrix}$$

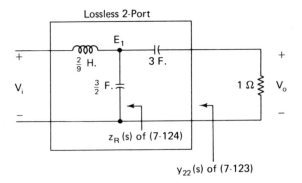

Fig. 7-25   A circuit realization of (7-120).

Hence,

$$V_o = \frac{\dfrac{27}{2}}{\left(\dfrac{9}{2}s + \dfrac{9}{2s}\right)(1 + 3s) - 9s^2}$$

$$= \frac{\dfrac{27}{2}}{\dfrac{9}{2}s^2 + \dfrac{9}{2}s + \dfrac{27}{2} + \dfrac{9}{2s}} = \frac{3s}{s^3 + s^2 + 3s + 1} \triangleq \hat{H}(s)$$

(7-125)

Because $V_i = 1$, the transfer function $\hat{H}(s)$ of the circuit is given by (7-125). A comparison of (7-125) and (7-120) shows that $\hat{H}(s)$ is a constant multiple of $H(s)$ of (7-120); therefore, the circuit in Fig. 7-25 realizes $H(s)$ of (7-120). ∎

Let us now consider briefly the case of Fig. 7-22(b) and (7-98), which is reproduced here for convenience with $R_i = 1\ \Omega$:

$$H(s) = \frac{V_o}{V_i} = \frac{z_{12}(s)}{1 + z_{11}(s)}$$

(7-126)

Suppose that the transfer function is given by

$$H(s) = \frac{A(s)}{B(s)} = \frac{M_1(s)}{M_2(s) + N_2(s)}$$

(7-127)

or

$$H(s) = \frac{A(s)}{B(s)} = \frac{N_1(s)}{M_2(s) + N_2(s)}$$

(7-128)

where $M_1(s)$ and $M_2(s)$ are even polynomials, $N_1(s)$ and $N_2(s)$ are odd polynomials, and $B(s) = M_2(s) + N_2(s)$ is a Hurwitz polynomial. If the given voltage-ratio transfer function is in the form of (7-127), then the problem of realizing (7-127) is reduced to the problem of realizing

$$z_{11}(s) = \frac{M_2(s)}{N_2(s)} \quad \text{and} \quad z_{12}(s) = \frac{M_1(s)}{N_2(s)} \tag{7-129}$$

simultaneously. Similarly, the realization of $H(s)$ of (7-128) is reduced to the simultaneous realization of

$$z_{11}(s) = \frac{N_2(s)}{M_2(s)} \quad \text{and} \quad z_{12}(s) = \frac{N_1(s)}{M_2(s)} \tag{7-130}$$

The realization procedures are the same as those discussed in Section 7-1-2.

Example 7-15 Realize

$$H(s) = \frac{V_o}{V_i} = \frac{1}{s^2 + s + 1} \tag{7-131}$$

by a circuit in the form of Fig. 7-22(b).

Solution: Because the numerator is an even polynomial, (7-127) and (7-129) apply. Hence, we write $H(s)$ as

$$H(s) = \frac{1}{s + (s^2 + 1)} = \frac{1/s}{1 + \dfrac{s^2 + 1}{s}} \tag{7-132}$$

By identifying terms between (7-126) and (7-132), we obtain

$$z_{11}(s) = \frac{s^2 + 1}{s} \quad \text{and} \quad z_{21}(s) = \frac{1}{s} \tag{7-133}$$

Because all transmission zeros are at $s = \infty$, we use Cauer's first form to realize $z_{11}(s)$. This means $z_{11}(s)$ is expanded at $s = \infty$:

$$z_{11}(s) = s + \frac{1}{s} \tag{7-134}$$

Consequently, a circuit realization of the transfer function $H(s)$ of (7-131) is shown in Fig. 7-26. ∎

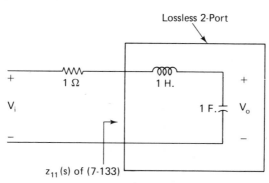

Lossless 2-Port

$z_{11}(s)$ of (7-133)

Fig. 7-26   A circuit realization of $H(s)$ of (7-131).

Example 7-16 Realize

$$H(s) = \frac{V_o}{V_i} = \frac{s^2}{s^3 + s^2 + 3s + 1} \tag{7-135}$$

by a lossless 2-port terminated by a 1 Ω source resistor.

Solution: Because the numerator of $H(s)$ is an even polynomial, we write $H(s)$ as

$$H(s) = \frac{s^2}{(s^3 + 3s) + (s^2 + 1)} = \frac{\dfrac{s^2}{s^3 + 3s}}{1 + \dfrac{s^2 + 1}{s^3 + 3s}} \tag{7-136}$$

By identifying terms between (7-126) and (7-136), we obtain

$$z_{11}(s) = \frac{s^2 + 1}{s^3 + 3s} \tag{7-137}$$

Observe that there are two transmission zeros at $s = 0$ and a single transmission zero at $s = \infty$. In general, it is preferable to realize the single transmission zero first. Hence, we use Cauer's first form to extract an element from $z_{11}(s)$ to produce the single transmission zero at $s = \infty$ first as

$$z_{11}(s) = \frac{s^2 + 1}{s^3 + 3s} = \frac{1}{s + \dfrac{1}{z_R(s)}} \tag{7-138}$$

where the remainder impedance function

$$z_R(s) = \frac{s^2 + 1}{2s}$$

is expanded by Cauer's second form as

$$z_R(s) = \frac{s^2 + 1}{2s} = \frac{1}{2s} + \frac{1}{2/s} \tag{7-139}$$

The resulting circuit realization of $H(s)$ of (7-135) is shown in Fig. 7-27. ∎

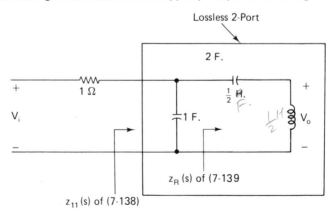

Fig. 7-27 A circuit realization of $H(s)$ of (7-135).

Example 7-17   Realize

$$H(s) = \frac{V_o}{V_i} = \frac{s^3}{s^3 + s^2 + 3s + 1} \tag{7-140}$$

by a circuit in the form of Fig. 7-22(b).

Solution: Because $H(s)$ is in the form of (7-128), (7-130) applies. Hence, we write $H(s)$ as

$$H(s) = \frac{s^3}{(s^2 + 1) + (s^3 + 3s)} = \frac{\dfrac{s^3}{s^2 + 1}}{1 + \dfrac{s^3 + 3s}{s^2 + 1}} \tag{7-141}$$

By identifying terms between (7-126) and (7-141), we obtain

$$z_{11}(s) = \frac{s^3 + 3s}{s^2 + 1}$$

Because all transmission zeros are at $s = 0$, we use Cauer's second form to realize $z_{11}(s)$. By expanding $z_{11}(s)$ at $s = 0$, we obtain

$$z_{11}(s) = \cfrac{1}{\cfrac{1}{3s} + \cfrac{1}{\cfrac{9}{2s} + \cfrac{1}{\cfrac{2}{3s}}}} \tag{7-142}$$

The resulting circuit realization of (7-140) is shown in Fig. 7-28.   ∎

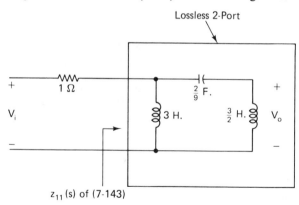

Lossless 2-Port

z_{11} (s) of (7-143)

Fig. 7-28   A circuit realization of $H(s)$ of (7-140).

7-3-2. Lossless 2-Port Terminated at Both Ends

In this section, we discuss the case of Fig. 7-22(c), which is redrawn here as Fig. 7-29 for reference. Because (7-99) and (7-100) do not give rise to simple identifications of either the z-parameters or the y-parameters of the lossless 2-port, we embark on a completely different course.

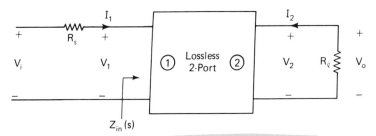

Fig. 7-29 A Darlington circuit structure.

To reduce the problem of realizing a transfer function to that of realizing a DP impedance function $Z_{in}(s)$ of Fig. 7-29, we need to introduce two coefficients: the *transmission* coefficient, and the *reflection* coefficient. The transmission coefficient is defined as the ratio of the output power P_o being dissipated in R_ℓ to the maximum *available* power P_a from the source with source resistance R_s. Clearly,

$$P_o(j\omega) = \frac{|V_o(j\omega)|^2}{R_\ell} \tag{7-143}$$

and

$$P_a(j\omega) = \frac{|V_i(j\omega)|^2}{4R_s} \tag{7-144}$$

Hence, the transmission coefficient is given by

$$|\tau(j\omega)|^2 = \frac{P_o(j\omega)}{P_a(j\omega)} = \frac{4R_s}{R_\ell} \frac{|V_o(j\omega)|^2}{|V_i(j\omega)|^2}$$

$$= \frac{4R_s}{R_\ell} |H(j\omega)|^2 \tag{7-145}$$

where $H(s)$ is the voltage-ratio transfer function

$$H(s) = \frac{V_o(s)}{V_i(s)} \tag{7-146}$$

Because the power sent to R_ℓ from the source must be less than or equal to the maximum power available from the source, we have

$$|\tau(j\omega)|^2 \leq 1 \tag{7-147}$$

The reflection coefficient is defined simply to be the complement of the transmission coefficient as

$$|\rho(j\omega)|^2 + |\tau(j\omega)|^2 = 1 \tag{7-148}$$

In sinusoidal steady state, the power P_i supplied to port ① of the lossless 2-port is equal to the power P_o supplied to the load, where

$$P_i = \text{Re}\,[Z_{in}(j\omega)]\,|I_1(j\omega)|^2 \tag{7-149}$$

By equating (7-143) and (7-149), we obtain

$$\text{Re}\,[Z_{\text{in}}(j\omega)]\,|I_1(j\omega)|^2 = \frac{|V_o(j\omega)|^2}{R_\ell}$$

or

$$R_\ell\,\text{Re}\,[Z_{\text{in}}(j\omega)] = \frac{|V_o(j\omega)|^2}{|I_1(j\omega)|^2} \tag{7-150}$$

From Fig. 7-29, we have

$$\frac{V_i}{I_1} = R_s + Z_{\text{in}}(s) \tag{7-151}$$

Combining (7-150) and (7-151) together, we obtain

$$\begin{aligned} |H(j\omega)|^2 &= \left|\frac{V_o(j\omega)}{V_i(j\omega)}\right|^2 = \left|\frac{V_o(j\omega)}{I_1(j\omega)}\right|^2 \left|\frac{I_1(j\omega)}{V_i(j\omega)}\right|^2 \\ &= \frac{R_\ell\,\text{Re}\,[Z_{\text{in}}(j\omega)]}{|R_s + Z_{\text{in}}(j\omega)|^2} \end{aligned} \tag{7-152}$$

Substituting (7-152) into (7-145) and the resulting expression into (7-148), we obtain

$$\begin{aligned} \rho(j\omega)\rho(-j\omega) &= 1 - \tau(j\omega)\tau(-j\omega) \\ &= 1 - \frac{4R_s}{R_\ell}\left|H(j\omega)\right|^2 \end{aligned} \tag{7-153}$$

$$= 1 - \frac{4R_s}{R_\ell}\frac{R_\ell\,\text{Re}\,[Z_{\text{in}}(j\omega)]}{|R_s + Z_{\text{in}}(j\omega)|^2} \tag{7-154}$$

By writing $Z_{\text{in}}(j\omega)$ as

$$Z_{\text{in}}(j\omega) = R(\omega) + jX(\omega) \tag{7-155}$$

(7-154) becomes

$$\begin{aligned} \rho(j\omega)\rho(-j\omega) &= 1 - \frac{4R_sR(\omega)}{|R_s + R(\omega) + jX(\omega)|^2} \\ &= 1 - \frac{4R_sR(\omega)}{[R_s + R(\omega)]^2 + [X(\omega)]^2} \\ &= \frac{[R_s - R(\omega)]^2 + [X(\omega)]^2}{[R_s + R(\omega)]^2 + [X(\omega)]^2} \\ &= \frac{|Z_{\text{in}}(j\omega) - R_s|^2}{|Z_{\text{in}}(j\omega) + R_s|^2} \end{aligned} \tag{7-156}$$

Equation (7-156) implies that

$$\rho(s) = \pm\frac{Z_{\text{in}}(s) - R_s}{Z_{\text{in}}(s) + R_s} \tag{7-157}$$

or that

$$Z_{\text{in}}(s) = R_s\frac{1 \pm \rho(s)}{1 \mp \rho(s)} \tag{7-158}$$

Through the transmission coefficient of (7-145) and the reflection coefficient of (7-153), we have reduced the problem of realizing a voltage-ratio transfer function $H(s)$ of (7-146) to that of realizing a DP impedance function $Z_{in}(s)$ of (7-158), bearing in mind the locations of the transmission zeros of $H(s)$. We note here that $Z_{in}(s)$ contains only one resistor R_ℓ and that the remaining elements are capacitors and inductors, as shown by Fig. 7-29.

Based on the preceding development, let us now consider a step-by-step procedure to realize transfer functions of the form[22]

$$H(s) = \frac{k s^m}{B(s)} \tag{7-159}$$

by the Darlington circuit structure of Fig. 7-29, where $B(s)$ is an nth-degree Hurwitz or modified Hurwitz polynomial and $0 \leq m \leq n$. To simplify the algebra, we let $R_s = 1\ \Omega$.

STEP 1. Find $\rho(s)$. From (7-153), we have   *find $P(s)$ given function a transfer function*

$$\rho(s)\rho(-s) = 1 - \frac{4}{R_\ell} H(s)H(-s) \tag{7-160}$$

Finding $\rho(s)$ is the most crucial step in this realization procedure. To start with, (7-160) may not have a solution. Let

$$F(s) \triangleq \rho(s)\rho(-s) \tag{7-161}$$

and

$$G(s) \triangleq 1 - \frac{4}{R_\ell} H(s)H(-s) \tag{7-162}$$

represent, respectively, the left-hand and the right-hand sides of (7-160). Clearly, both the poles and zeros of $F(s)$ are required to occur with quadrantal symmetry. Based on (7-162), the poles of $G(s)$ will also occur with quadrantal symmetry but not necessarily the zeros. This is because the numerator of $G(s)$ is only an even polynomial, not necessarily a polynomial with mirror image—one that can be written as $p(s)p(-s)$. If the zeros of $G(s)$ do not occur with quadrantal symmetry, then we can not find $\rho(s)$ from (7-160), and the procedure that we are describing will not yield a circuit realization for $H(s)$.

Let us now assume that the zeros of $G(s)$ occur with quadrantal symmetry.[23] In this case, there are more than one $\rho(s)$ satisfying (7-160). Let us

---

[22]The reason we restrict the numerator of $H(s)$ to be $k s^m$ is because we don't have enough tools to consider the general case when $A(s)$ is an mth-degree polynomial with $0 \leq m \leq n$. In Chapter 8, we see that transfer functions of many important families of filters are in the form of (7-159).

[23]The zeros of $G(s)$ will satisfy the quadrantal symmetry requirements if they do not occur on the imaginary axis of the s-plane, with the possible exception at the origin. Also, if $B(s)$ is a Hurwitz polynomial, then (7-160) will have a minimum phase solution $\rho(s)$.

choose the minimum phase $\rho(s)$ to be the solution of (7-160).[24] To do otherwise, we may need negative inductances and/or capacitances to realize the resulting DP impedance function $Z_{in}(s)$.

STEP 2. *Find* $Z_{in}(s)$. Once $\rho(s)$ is determined, (7-158) gives

$$Z_{in}(s) = \frac{1 + \rho(s)}{1 - \rho(s)} \quad \text{or} \quad Z_{in}(s) = \frac{1 - \rho(s)}{1 + \rho(s)} \tag{7-163}$$

From (7-163), there are two choices for $Z_{in}(s)$. Because one choice is the inverse of the other, we can expect that one $Z_{in}(s)$ will give R_ℓ and that the other choice of $Z_{in}(s)$ will give $1/R_\ell$ as the terminating load resistor. If there is a desired value for R_ℓ (for example, R_ℓ is equal to the input impedance of the next stage in the overall circuit design), then only one choice of $Z_{in}(s)$ will give the desired solution. If $R_\ell = 1\,\Omega$ (or if the value of R_ℓ is not important), then either choice of $Z_{in}(s)$ from (7-163) is equally valid. To determine the value $\hat{R}_\ell$ of the terminating resistor for a given choice of $Z_{in}(s)$, we have

$$\hat{R}_\ell = Z_{in}(0) \quad \text{when} \quad m = 0 \quad \text{in (7-159)} \tag{7-164}$$

$$\hat{R}_\ell = Z_{in}(\infty) \quad \text{when} \quad m = n \quad \text{in (7-159)} \tag{7-165}$$

where $\hat{R}_\ell$ either equals R_ℓ or equals $1/R_\ell$. This is because when $m = 0$ in (7-159), the transfer function is of low-pass type and all transmission zeros are at $s = \infty$. Hence, Cauer's first form is used. This means that $Z_{in}(s)$ will contain series inductors and shunt capacitors terminating with $\hat{R}_\ell$. At $s = 0$, series inductors become short circuits, and shunt capacitors become open circuits; hence, $Z_{in}(0)$ contains only the value of the terminating resistor. This is illustrated in Fig. 7-30(a). Similarly, when $m = n$, the transfer function is of high-pass type and all transmission zeros are at $s = 0$. Hence, Cauer's second form is used. This involves series capacitors and shunt inductors terminating with $\hat{R}_\ell$. At $s = \infty$, series capacitors become short circuits and shunt inductors become open circuits. Hence, $Z_{in}(\infty) = \hat{R}_\ell$, as shown in Fig. 7-30(b). Finally, for the case $0 < m < n$ in (7-159), the transfer function is a bandpass type. There is a limiting method to determine $\hat{R}_\ell$ from a given choice of $Z_{in}(s)$. However, the process is complicated and involves many calculations. In this case, it is actually better to do the realization with anyone of the two possible $Z_{in}(s)$ and find out the value of $\hat{R}_\ell$. If $\hat{R}_\ell = R_\ell$, then the design is the desired one; if not, then the other choice of $Z_{in}(s)$ from (7-163) will yield the desired circuit.

---

[24]If the zeros of $G(s)$ satisfy the quadrantal symmetry requirements, then there is one and only one minimum phase function satisfying (7-160). Recall that both the poles and zeros of a minimum phase function are not in the RH s-plane.

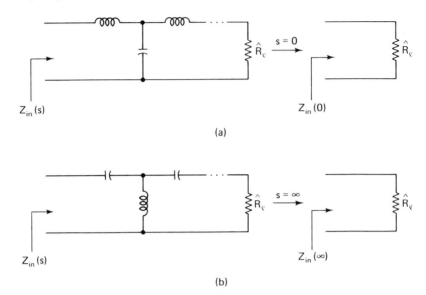

Fig. 7-30 Determination of load resistance value (a) when $m = 0$ in (7-159), and (b) when $m = n$ in (7-159).

STEP 3. *Realization of* $Z_{in}(s)$. To realize $H(s)$ of (7-159), we have to realize $Z_{in}(s)$ by a proper method to satisfy the transmission zero requirements. As in Sec. 7-1, we consider three possible cases of (7-159).

CASE 1. If $m = 0$, we use Cauer's first form.

CASE 2. If $m = n$, we use Cauer's second form.

CASE 3. If $0 < m < n$, we can either use Cauer's first form to extract $(n - m)$ dynamic elements—capacitors and inductors—first and the remainder is realized by Cauer's second form, or we can use Cauer's second form first to extract m dynamic elements and the remainder is realized by Cauer's first form.

One point to note here is that if we use the divide-and-invert procedure to find the necessary continued fraction expansion of $Z_{in}(s)$, we will find the elimination of two (highest- or lowest-power) terms in each division step. This simultaneous elimination of two terms will continue until just before the last dynamic element is extracted.

Example 7-18 Realize

$$H(s) = \frac{k}{(s^2 + 1)(s + 1)} \tag{7-166}$$

by the Darlington circuit structure of Fig. 7-29 with $R_s = 1\,\Omega$ and $R_\ell = 2\,\Omega$.

Solution: Because the transfer function of (7-166) is a low-pass type—all transmission zeros are at $s = \infty$—the resulting Darlington circuit is in the form of Fig. 7-31(a). At $s = 0$, the circuit in Fig. 7-31(a) reduces to the circuit in Fig. 7-31(b). Hence, we have

$$H(0) = \frac{R_\ell}{R_s + R_\ell} = k \qquad (7\text{-}167)$$

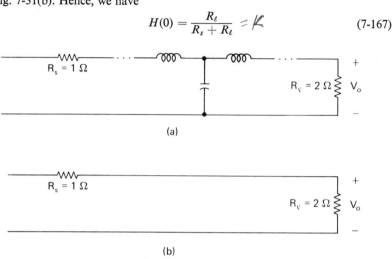

(a)

(b)

Fig. 7-31 A circuit to determine the value of k in (7-166).

Equating (7-167) with (7-166) at $s = 0$, we obtain

$$k = \frac{R_\ell}{R_s + R_\ell} = \frac{2}{3} \qquad (7\text{-}168)$$

The first step in the realization procedure is to find $\rho(s)$. From (7-160), we have

$$\rho(s)\rho(-s) = 1 - \frac{4}{R_\ell}H(s)H(-s)$$

$$= 1 - \frac{4}{2}\frac{2/3}{(s^2 + 1)(s + 1)}\frac{2/3}{(s^2 + 1)(-s + 1)}$$

$$= \frac{-s^6 - s^4 + s^2 + (1/9)}{(s^2 + 1)(s^2 + 1)(s + 1)(-s + 1)} \qquad (7\text{-}169)$$

$$= \frac{(s + 0.83)(-s + 0.83)(s^2 + 1.59)(s^2 + 0.10)}{(s^2 + 1)(s^2 + 1)(s + 1)(-s + 1)}$$

Because the zeros of the right-hand side expression of (7-169) do not occur with quadrantal symmetry, we can not obtain $\rho(s)$ from (7-169); hence, the procedure outlined in this section can not produce a circuit realization for $H(s)$ of (7-166). ∎

Example 7-19 Realize

$$H(s) = \frac{k}{s^2 + 3s + 3} \qquad (7\text{-}170)$$

by a lossless 2-port terminated with $R_s = 1\,\Omega$ and
  (a) $R_\ell = 1\,\Omega$.
  (b) $R_\ell = 2\,\Omega$.

Solution: As in Example 7-18, at $s = 0$, we have

$$H(0) = \frac{k}{3} = \frac{R_\ell}{R_\ell + R_s} \tag{7-171}$$

For case (a), when $R_\ell = 1\,\Omega$, (7-171) yields

$$k = \frac{3}{2} \tag{7-172}$$

From (7-160), we have

$$
\begin{aligned}
p(s)p(-s) &= 1 - 4\frac{3/2}{s^2 + 3s + 3}\frac{3/2}{s^2 - 3s + 3} \\
&= 1 - \frac{9}{(s^2 + 3s + 3)(s^2 - 3s + 3)} \\
&= \frac{s^4 - 3s^2}{(s^2 + 3s + 3)(s^2 - 3s + 3)} \\
&= \frac{s(s + \sqrt{3})(-s)(-s + \sqrt{3})}{(s^2 + 3s + 3)(s^2 - 3s + 3)}
\end{aligned}
\tag{7-173}
$$

Based on (7-173), $p(s)$ can be either one of the following:

$$
\begin{array}{ll}
p_1(s) = \dfrac{s(s + \sqrt{3})}{s^2 + 3s + 3} & p_2(s) = \dfrac{s(s + \sqrt{3})}{s^2 - 3s + 3} \\[2ex]
p_3(s) = \dfrac{s(-s + \sqrt{3})}{s^2 + 3s + 3} & p_4(s) = \dfrac{s(-s + \sqrt{3})}{s^2 - 3s + 3} \\[2ex]
p_5(s) = \dfrac{-s(-s + \sqrt{3})}{s^2 + 3s + 3} & p_6(s) = \dfrac{-s(-s + \sqrt{3})}{s^2 - 3s + 3} \\[2ex]
p_7(s) = \dfrac{-s(s + \sqrt{3})}{s^2 + 3s + 3} & \text{and} \quad p_8(s) = \dfrac{-s(s + \sqrt{3})}{s^2 - 3s + 3}
\end{array}
\tag{7-174}
$$

Observe that among the eight possible solutions of (7-173), as listed in (7-174), only $p_1(s)$ is a minimum phase solution. Let us choose the solution of (7-173) to be

$$p(s) = \frac{s(s + \sqrt{3})}{s^2 + 3s + 3} \tag{7-175}$$

Then the two possible DP impedance functions are given by (7-163) as

$$Z_{\text{in}1}(s) = \frac{1 + p(s)}{1 - p(s)} = \frac{2s^2 + (3 + \sqrt{3})s + 3}{(3 - \sqrt{3})s + 3} \tag{7-176a}$$

and

$$Z_{\text{in}2}(s) = \frac{1 - p(s)}{1 + p(s)} = \frac{(3 - \sqrt{3})s + 3}{2s^2 + (3 + \sqrt{3})s + 3} \tag{7-176b}$$

Because $R_\ell = 1\,\Omega$, both $Z_{\text{in}1}(s)$ and $Z_{\text{in}2}(s)$ will yield circuit realizations of $H(s)$ with proper load resistance termination. Let us first work with $Z_{\text{in}1}(s)$. All transmission zeros of $H(s)$ are at $s = \infty$; therefore, we realize $Z_{\text{in}1}(s)$ by Cauer's first form. This involves a continued fraction expansion of $Z_{\text{in}1}(s)$ at $s = \infty$:

$$
\begin{array}{r}
1.577s \\
1.268s + 3\overline{)2s^2 + 4.732s + 3} \\
2s^2 + 4.732s \qquad 0.423s \\
\hline
3\overline{)1.268s + 3} \\
1.268s \quad 1 \\
\hline
3\overline{)3} \\
3 \\
\hline
0
\end{array}
$$

or

$$
Z_{in1}(s) = 1.577s + \cfrac{1}{0.423s + \cfrac{1}{1}} \tag{7-177}
$$

A circuit realization of $H(s)$ of (7-170) based on the Cauer's first-form realization of $Z_{in1}(s)$ of (7-177) is given in Fig. 7-32(a).

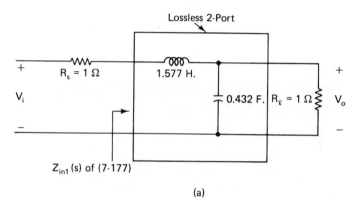

(a)

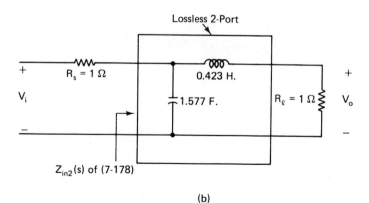

(b)

Fig. 7-32   Two Darlington circuit realizations of $H(s)$ of (7-170) with $R_s = 1\,\Omega$ and $R_\ell = 1\,\Omega$.

Next, let us consider $Z_{in2}(s)$. Because $Z_{in2}(s)$ is the inverse of $Z_{in1}(s)$, we obtain

$$Z_{in2}(s) = \cfrac{1}{1.577s + \cfrac{1}{0.423s + \cfrac{1}{1}}} \tag{7-178}$$

A circuit realization of $H(s)$ of (7-170) via $Z_{in2}(s)$ of (7-178) is shown in Fig. 7-32(b).

If the desired load resistance is $R_\ell = 2\,\Omega$, then (7-171) yields

$$k = \frac{3R_\ell}{R_s + R_\ell} = 2 \tag{7-179}$$

In this case, (7-160) becomes

$$\begin{aligned}
\rho(s)\rho(-s) &= 1 - \frac{4}{2}\frac{2}{s^2 + 3s + 3}\frac{2}{s^2 - 3s + 3} \\
&= \frac{s^4 - 3s^2 + 1}{(s^2 + 3s + 3)(s^2 - 3s + 3)} \\
&= \frac{(s^2 + \sqrt{5}\,s + 1)(s^2 - \sqrt{5}\,s + 1)}{(s^2 + 3s + 3)(s^2 - 3s + 3)}
\end{aligned} \tag{7-180}$$

The minimum phase solution of (7-180) is given by

$$\rho(s) = \frac{s^2 + \sqrt{5}\,s + 1}{s^2 + 3s + 3} \tag{7-181}$$

By (7-163), we obtain

$$Z_{in1}(s) = \frac{1 + \rho(s)}{1 - \rho(s)} = \frac{2s^2 + (3 + \sqrt{5})s + 4}{(3 - \sqrt{5})s + 2} \tag{7-182a}$$

$$Z_{in2}(s) = \frac{1 - \rho(s)}{1 + \rho(s)} = \frac{(3 - \sqrt{5})s + 2}{2s^2 + (3 + \sqrt{5})s + 4} \tag{7-182b}$$

Because $R_\ell = 2\,\Omega$, only one of the two DP impedance functions in (7-182) will be valid. And because all transmission zeros of $H(s)$ are at $s = \infty$, we know that the proper DP impedance function $Z_{in}(s)$ at $s = 0$ is equal to R_ℓ. At $s = 0$, we find

$$Z_{in1}(0) = 2 \quad \text{and} \quad Z_{in2}(0) = \frac{1}{2} \tag{7-183}$$

Hence, the proper choice is

$$\begin{aligned}
Z_{in}(s) = Z_{in1}(s) &= \frac{2s^2 + (3 + \sqrt{5})s + 4}{(3 - \sqrt{5})s + 2} \\
&= 2.618s + \cfrac{1}{0.191s + \cfrac{1}{2}}
\end{aligned} \tag{7-184}$$

A circuit realization of $H(s)$ of (7-170) by a Darlington circuit with $R_s = 1\,\Omega$ and $R_\ell = 2\,\Omega$ via (7-184) is shown in Fig. 7-33. An analysis of the circuit in Fig.

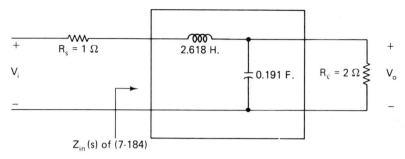

Fig. 7-33   A circuit realization of $H(s)$ of (7-170).

7-33 yields

$$H(s) = \frac{V_o}{V_i} = \frac{2}{s^2 + 3s + 3}$$

∎

Example 7-20   Realize

$$H(s) = \frac{ks^2}{s^2 + 3s + 3} \tag{7-185}$$

by a Darlington circuit with $R_s = 1\ \Omega$ and $R_\ell = 2\ \Omega$.

Solution: To simplify calculations, let us first find out the value of k in (7-185). Because the transfer function is of a high-pass type—all transmission zeros are at $s = 0$—the resulting Darlington circuit will be in the form shown in Fig. 7-34(a). At $s = \infty$, the circuit in Fig. 7-34(a) reduces to that of Fig. 7-34(b). Hence, at $s = \infty$, we have

$$H(\infty) = k = \frac{R_\ell}{R_s + R_\ell} = \frac{2}{3} \tag{7-186}$$

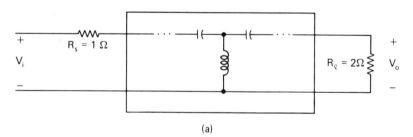

(a)

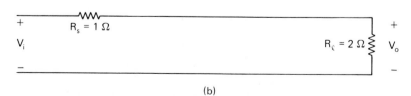

(b)

Fig. 7-34   A circuit to determine the value of k of (7-185).

From (7-160), we have

$$p(s)p(-s) = 1 - \frac{4}{2} \frac{(2/3)s^2}{(s^2 + 3s + 3)} \frac{(2/3)s^2}{(s^2 - 3s + 3)}$$

$$= \frac{(1/9)s^4 - 3s^2 + 9}{(s^2 + 3s + 3)(s^2 - 3s + 3)}$$

$$= \frac{[(1/3)s^2 + \sqrt{5}\,s + 3][(1/3)s^2 - \sqrt{5}\,s + 3]}{(s^2 + 3s + 3)(s^2 - 3s + 3)}$$

Hence,

$$p(s) = \frac{(1/3)s^2 + \sqrt{5}\,s + 3}{s^2 + 3s + 3} \qquad (7\text{-}187)$$

The two possible $Z_{in}(s)$ are given by (7-163) as

$$Z_{in1}(s) = \frac{1 + p(s)}{1 - p(s)} = \frac{(4/3)s^2 + (3 + \sqrt{5})s + 6}{(2/3)s^2 + (3 - \sqrt{5})s} \qquad (7\text{-}188a)$$

$$Z_{in2}(s) = \frac{1 - p(s)}{1 + p(s)} = \frac{(2/3)s^2 + (3 - \sqrt{5})s}{(4/3)s^2 + (3 + \sqrt{5})s + 6} \qquad (7\text{-}188b)$$

Because all transmission zeros are at $s = 0$, we have

$$Z_{in}(\infty) = R_\ell \qquad (7\text{-}189)$$

From (7-188), we have

$$Z_{in1}(\infty) = 2 \quad \text{and} \quad Z_{in2}(\infty) = \frac{1}{2} \qquad (7\text{-}190)$$

Hence, to have a load resistance of 2 Ω, we choose

$$Z_{in}(s) = Z_{in1}(s) \qquad (7\text{-}191)$$

To produce the transmission zeros at $s = 0$, we realize $Z_{in}(s)$ by Cauer's second form:

$$Z_{in}(s) = \frac{6 + (3 + \sqrt{5})s + (4/3)s^2}{(3 - \sqrt{5})s + (2/3)s^2}$$

$$= \frac{7.845}{s} + \cfrac{1}{\cfrac{0.573}{s} + \cfrac{1}{2}} \qquad (7\text{-}192)$$

A circuit realization of $H(s)$ of (7-185) via $Z_{in}(s)$ of (7-192) is shown in Fig. 7-35. ∎

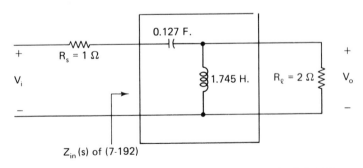

0.127 F.

$R_s = 1\,\Omega$

$+$

V_i

1.745 H.

$R_\varrho = 2\,\Omega$

$+$

V_o

$-$

$-$

Z_{in} (s) of (7-192)

Fig. 7-35 A Darlington circuit realization of $H(s)$ of (7-185).

7-4 CONCLUDING REMARKS

In this chapter, we have presented various methods for realizing transfer functions that meet certain criteria. In this section, we summarize the major results of Chapter 7.

I. RC Ladder Realization

Realizability Criteria: $H(s) = ks^m/B(s)$, where $B(s)$ is an nth-degree polynomial with simple negative real roots.

Realization Methods: Choose $z_{11}(s)$ to satisfy conditions RC1, RC2, and RC3 as stated in Section 7-1-1. If $m = 0$, use Cauer's first form to realize $z_{11}(s)$. If $m = n$, use Cauer's second form to realize $z_{11}(s)$. If $0 < m < n$, then we can either: (1) use Cauer's first form to extract $n - m$ capacitor (Cauer's first form should be stopped as soon as the $(n - m)$th capacitor is extracted), and the remainder is realized by Cauer's second form; or (2) use Cauer's second form to extract m capacitors (Cauer's second form should be terminated as soon as the mth capacitor is extracted), and the remainder is realized by Cauer's first form. We can also work with $y_{22}(s)$ instead of $z_{11}(s)$.

Realization Principle: The transmission zeros of $H(s)$ are realized by the methods used in the realization of $z_{11}(s)$, and the poles of $H(s)$ are realized by realizing the RC DP impedance function $z_{11}(s)$.

II. LC Ladder Realization

Realizability Criteria: $H(s) = ks^m/B(s)$, where $B(s)$ is an nth-degree polynomial with simple imaginary axis roots. In addition, $H(s)$ must be an even rational function.

Realization Methods: Choose $z_{11}(s)$ to satisfy conditions LC1 and LC2 as stated in Section 7-1-2. If $m = 0$, we use Cauer's first form to realize $z_{11}(s)$. If $m = n$, Cauer's second form is used to realize $z_{11}(s)$. If $0 < m < n$, we can use either: (a) Cauer's first form to extract $n - m$ elements from $z_{11}(s)$ and the remainder is realized by Cauer's second form; or (b) Cauer's second form to extract m elements from $z_{11}(s)$ and the remainder is realized by Cauer's first form. We can also work with $y_{22}(s)$ instead of $z_{11}(s)$.

Realization Principle: The transmission zeros of $H(s)$ are realized by the methods used in the realization of $z_{11}(s)$, and the poles of $H(s)$ are realized by realizing an appropriate $z_{11}(s)$.

III. Lattice Circuit Structure for All-Pass Functions

Realizability Criteria: The transfer function is given by $H(s) = p(-s)/p(s)$ where $p(s)$ is a Hurwitz polynomial.

Realization Method: The circuit structure is shown in Fig. 7-20(b), where z_a represents the series branches and z_b represents the cross-shunt branches. Let $p(s) = m(s) + n(s)$, where $m(s)$ and $n(s)$ are, respectively, the even and odd parts of $p(s)$.

1. Write $H(s)$ as

$$H(s) = \frac{m - n}{m + n} = \frac{(m/n) - 1}{(m/n) + 1}$$

Realize $z_b = m/n$ as an LC 1-port and $z_a = 1\ \Omega$.

2. Write $H(s)$ as

$$H(s) = \frac{m - n}{m + n} = \frac{1 - (n/m)}{1 + (n/m)}$$

Realize $z_a = n/m$ as an LC 1-port and $z_b = 1\ \Omega$.

IV. Lossless 2-port with Single Termination

Realizability Criteria: The transfer function $H(s)$ must be in the form of either $H(s) = M_1/(M_2 + N_2)$ or $H(s) = N_1/(M_2 + N_2)$, where M_i and N_i denote even and odd polynomials, respectively, $i = 1, 2$. In addition, $M_2 + N_2$ is a Hurwitz polynomial, and M_1 or N_1 is in the form of ks^m. Assuming that $M_2 + N_2$ is an nth-degree polynomial, then $0 \leq m \leq n$.

Realization Methods: The two circuits involved are shown in Figs. 7-22(a) and (b). The equations describing these circuits are

$$\text{Fig. 7-22(a):} \quad H(s) = -\frac{y_{12}}{1 + y_{22}}$$

$$\text{Fig. 7-22(b):} \quad H(s) = \frac{z_{12}}{1 + z_{11}}$$

If $H(s) = M_1/(M_2 + N_2)$, then write $H(s)$ as

$$H(s) = \frac{M_1/N_2}{1 + (M_2/N_2)}$$

Let $y_{22} \{z_{11}\}$ be M_2/N_2, and let $-y_{12} \{z_{12}\}$ be M_1/N_2. Then $H(s)$ is realized by a simultaneous realization of y_{22} and $-y_{12} \{z_{11}$ and $z_{12}\}$ as discussed in Section 7-1-3 {Section 7-1-2}. If $H(s) = N_1/(M_2 + N_2)$, then write $H(s)$ as

$$H(s) = \frac{N_1/M_2}{1 + (N_2/M_2)}$$

Let $y_{22}\{z_{11}\}$ be N_2/M_2 and, let $-y_{12}\{z_{12}\}$ be N_1/M_2. Then $H(s)$ is realized by a simultaneous realization of $-y_{12}$ and $y_{22}\{z_{12}$ and $z_{22}\}$.

Realization Principle: The numerator of $H(s)$ is realized by the methods used to realize $y_{22}(s)\{z_{11}(s)\}$. The denominator of $H(s)$ is realized by realizing the constructed $y_{22}(s)\{z_{11}(s)\}$.

V. Lossless 2-port with Double Terminations[25]

Realization Criteria: $H(s) = ks^m/B(s)$ where $B(s)$ is an nth-degree Hurwitz or modified Hurwitz polynomial.

Realization Methods: The basic circuit configuration is shown in Fig. 7-29. The procedures involved are:

STEP 1. Find the minimum phase solution $\rho(s)$ from

$$\rho(s)\rho(-s) = 1 - \frac{4R_s}{R_\ell}H(s)H(-s)$$

STEP 2. Form

$$Z_{in}(s) = \frac{1 \pm \rho(s)}{1 \mp \rho(s)}$$

and choose the $Z_{in}(s)$ with the desired terminating load resistance.

STEP 3. Realize $Z_{in}(s)$. If $m = 0$, use Cauer's first form. If $m = n$, use Cauer's second form. If $0 < m < n$, use a combination of Cauer's two forms.

Realization Principle: The transmission zeros of $H(s)$ are realized by the methods used in the realization of $Z_{in}(s)$. The poles of $H(s)$ are realized by realizing the constructed $Z_{in}(s)$.

REFERENCES AND FURTHER READING

[1] DESOER, C. A., and KUH, E. S. *Basic Circuit Theory.* New York: McGraw-Hill, 1969.

[2] WEINBERG, L. *Network Analysis and Synthesis.* Huntington, N.Y.: R. E. Krieger, 1975.

[3] HUMPHREYS, D. S. *The Analysis, Design, and Synthesis of Electrical Filters.* Englewood Cliffs, N.J.: Prentice-Hall, Inc., 1970.

[4] DARLINGTON, S. "Synthesis of Reactance 4-Poles." *J. Math. Phys.* 18 (1939): 257–353.

[25]Sensitivity considerations for circuits in IV and V can be found in Reference [8].

[5] HAZONY, D. "Two Extensions of the Darlington Synthesis Procedure." *IEEE Trans. Circuit Theory* CT-8 (1961): 284–88.

[6] HEINLEIN, W. E., and HOLMES, W. H. *Active Filters for Integrated Circuits: Fundamentals and Design Methods.* London: Prentice-Hall, 1974.

[7] BALABANIAN, N. *Network Synthesis.* Englewood Cliffs, N.J.: Prentice-Hall, Inc., 1958.

[8] WEYTEN, L. "Lower Bounds on the Summed Absolute and Squared Voltage Transfer Sensitivities in RLC Networks." *IEEE Trans. Circuits and Systems* CAS-25 (1978): 70–73.

PROBLEMS

7-1. (a) For the circuit shown in Fig. P7-1, find the transfer function between V_o and V_i.

(b) Find the transmission zeros of the circuit via the transfer function obtained in (a) and by inspection.

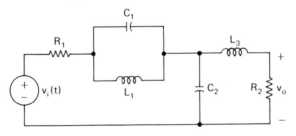

Fig. P7-1

7-2. Consider a circuit N with input $v_i(t)$ and output $v_o(t)$.

(i) If $v_i(t) = A \cos 2t$, or if $v_i(t) = B \cos 4t$, then the steady-state output $v_o(t) = 0$ for all A and B.

(ii) The impulse response of the circuit is in the form of

$$v_o(t) = a_1 \exp(-t) \cos(t + \phi_1) + a_2 \exp(-2t) \cos(5t + \phi_2)$$

Find the transfer function of the circuit.

7-3. Synthesize each of the following transfer functions by two RC ladder networks [via $z_{11}(s)$ and $y_{22}(s)$]:

(a) $H(s) = \dfrac{k}{s + 2}$

(b) $H(s) = \dfrac{ks}{s + 2}$

(c) $H(s) = \dfrac{k}{(s + 1)(s + 4)}$

(d) $H(s) = \dfrac{ks}{(s + 1)(s + 4)}$

(e) $H(s) = \dfrac{ks^2}{(s+1)(s+4)}$

(f) $H(s) = \dfrac{k}{(s+1)(s+2)(s+3)}$

(g) $H(s) = \dfrac{ks}{(s+1)(s+2)(s+3)}$

(h) $H(s) = \dfrac{ks^2}{(s+1)(s+2)(s+3)}$

(i) $H(s) = \dfrac{ks^3}{(s+1)(s+2)(s+3)}$

(j) $H(s) = \dfrac{ks}{(s+1)(s+2)(s+3)(s+4)}$

7-4. (a) Realize the transfer function

$$H(s) = \frac{3.5}{s^2 + 8s + 7}$$

by an RC ladder network.

(b) Verify your result.

7-5. (a) Realize the transfer function

$$H_1(s) = \frac{5}{s^2 + 7s + 10}$$

by an RC ladder circuit N, as shown in Fig. P7-5(a).

(b) If two identical circuits of N are cascaded together, as shown in Fig. P7-5(b), find the overall transfer function $H(s)$.

(c) Does $H(s) = H_1(s)H_1(s)$? Give your reasons.

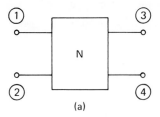

(a)

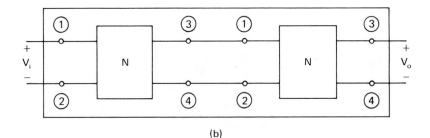

(b)

Fig. P7-5

7-6. Realize each of the following transfer functions by two LC ladder networks [via $z_{11}(s)$ and $y_{22}(s)$]:

(a) $H(s) = \dfrac{k}{s^2 + 2}$

(b) $H(s) = \dfrac{ks^2}{s^2 + 2}$

(c) $H(s) = \dfrac{k}{(s^2 + 1)(s^2 + 4)}$

(d) $H(s) = \dfrac{ks^2}{(s^2 + 1)(s^2 + 4)}$

(e) $H(s) = \dfrac{ks^4}{(s^2 + 1)(s^2 + 4)}$

(f) $H(s) = \dfrac{k}{(s^2 + 2)(s^2 + 5)(s^2 + 6)}$

(g) $H(s) = \dfrac{ks^2}{(s^2 + 2)(s^2 + 5)(s^2 + 6)}$

(h) $H(s) = \dfrac{ks^6}{(s^2 + 2)(s^2 + 5)(s^2 + 6)}$

7-7. Show that the admittance 2-port representation of Fig. 7-20 is given by (7-80) and (7-81).

7-8. Let

$$p(s) = p_0 + p_1 s + p_2 s^2 + \ldots + p_n s^n$$

be a Hurwitz polynomial. Show that the magnitude function of

$$H(s) = \frac{p(-s)}{p(s)}$$

is independent of the frequency ω.

7-9. Realize each of the following all-pass transfer functions in two ways (via z_a and z_b):

(a) $H(s) = \dfrac{s^2 - \sqrt{2}\,s + 1}{s^2 + \sqrt{2}\,s + 1}$

(b) $H(s) = \dfrac{s^2 - 3s + 3}{s^2 + 3s + 3}$

(c) $H(s) = \dfrac{-s^3 + 2s^2 - 2s + 1}{s^3 + 2s^2 + 2s + 1}$

(d) $H(s) = \dfrac{-s^3 + 6s^2 - 15s + 15}{s^3 + 6s^2 + 15s + 15}$

(e) $H(s) = \dfrac{(s^2 - 0.77s + 1)(s^2 - 1.85s + 1)}{(s^2 + 0.77s + 1)(s^2 + 1.85s + 1)}$

(f) $H(s) = \dfrac{s^4 - 10s^3 + 43s^2 - 105s + 105}{s^4 + 10s^3 + 43s^2 + 105s + 105}$

7-10. Show that the phase function of an all-pass transfer function $H(s) = p(-s)/p(s)$ is given by twice the phase function of $p(s)$ plus a constant.

7-11. Consider the transfer function

$$H(s) = \frac{-s^3 + s^2 - s + (3/8)}{s^3 + s^2 + s + (3/8)}$$

(a) Draw the pole-zero diagram of $H(s)$; i.e., locate the poles and zeros of $H(s)$ in the s-plane. [*Hint:* $(s + 0.5)$ is a factor of $s^3 + s^2 + s + (3/8)$.]

(b) Find $|H(j\omega)|$ for all ω.

(c) Sketch roughly $\phi(\omega) = -\underline{/H(j\omega)}$ for all ω.

(d) Realize $H(s)$ by two distinct lattice networks.

7-12. Realize each of the following transfer functions by a lossless 2-port terminated at only one end by a load resistor, as shown in Fig. P7-12:

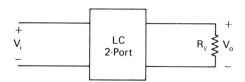

Fig. P7-12

(a) $H(s) = \dfrac{k}{s^2 + 3s + 3}$

(b) $H(s) = \dfrac{ks}{s^2 + \sqrt{2}s + 1}$

(c) $H(s) = \dfrac{ks^2}{s^2 + 4s + 4}$

(d) $H(s) = \dfrac{k}{s^3 + 6s^2 + 15s + 15}$

(e) $H(s) = \dfrac{ks}{s^3 + 6s^2 + 15s + 15}$

(f) $H(s) = \dfrac{ks^2}{s^3 + 2s^2 + 2s + 1}$

(g) $H(s) = \dfrac{ks^3}{s^3 + 2s^2 + 2s + 1}$

(h) $H(s) = \dfrac{ks^2}{(s^2 + 0.77s + 1)(s^2 + 1.85s + 1)}$

(i) $H(s) = \dfrac{ks^3}{(s + 0.77s + 1)(s^2 + 1.85s + 1)}$

(j) $H(s) = \dfrac{k}{s^4 + 10s^3 + 43s^2 + 105s + 105}$

(k) $H(s) = \dfrac{k}{(s + 1)^3}$

(l) $H(s) = \dfrac{ks}{(s + 1)^3}$

(m) $H(s) = \dfrac{ks^3}{(s + 1)^4}$

(n) $H(s) = \dfrac{ks^4}{(s + 1)^4}$

7-13. Realize each of the transfer functions in Problem 7-12 by a lossless 2-port terminated at only one end by a source resistance, as shown in Fig. P7-13.

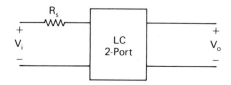

Fig. P7-13

7-14. Realize each of the following transfer functions by a lossless 2-port terminated at both ends with $R_s = R_\ell = 1\,\Omega$, as shown in Fig. P7-14:

(a) $H(s) = \dfrac{k}{s^2 + 3s + 3}$

(b) $H(s) = \dfrac{k}{s^2 + \sqrt{2}s + 1}$

(c) $H(s) = \dfrac{ks}{s^2 + 3s + 3}$

(d) $H(s) = \dfrac{ks}{s^2 + \sqrt{2}s + 1}$

(e) $H(s) = \dfrac{ks^2}{s^2 + 3s + 1}$

(f) $H(s) = \dfrac{ks^2}{s^2 + \sqrt{2}s + 1}$

(g) $H(s) = \dfrac{k}{s^3 + 2s^2 + 2s + 1}$

(h) $H(s) = \dfrac{k}{s^3 + 6s^2 + 15s + 15}$

(i) $H(s) = \dfrac{ks^3}{s^3 + 2s^2 + 2s + 1}$

(j) $H(s) = \dfrac{ks^3}{s^3 + 6s^2 + 15s + 15}$

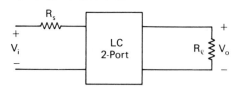

Fig. P7-14

7-15. Realize the transfer function

$$H(s) = \frac{k}{s^2 + 3s + 1}$$

by a lossless 2-port terminated at both ends with $R_s = 1\,\Omega$ and:

(a) $R_\ell = 1\,\Omega$

(b) $R_\ell = 2\,\Omega$

(c) $R_\ell = 4\,\Omega$

(d) $R_\ell = 0.5\,\Omega$

(e) $R_\ell = 0.25\,\Omega$

7-16. Realize each of the following transfer functions with a lossless 2-port terminated at both ends by $R_s = 1\ \Omega$ and $R_\ell = 2\ \Omega$:

(a) $H(s) = \dfrac{k}{(s+1)^2}$

(b) $H(s) = \dfrac{ks^2}{s^2 + 3s + 3}$

(c) $H(s) = \dfrac{k}{s^3 + 6s^2 + 15s + 15}$

(d) $H(s) = \dfrac{ks^3}{(s+1)^3}$

(e) $H(s) = \dfrac{k}{(s^2 + 0.77s + 1)(s^2 + 1.85s + 1)}$

7-17. Realize each of the following transfer functions with a lossless 2-port terminated at both ends by $R_s = 1\ \Omega$ and $R_\ell = 0.25\ \Omega$:

(a) $H(s) = \dfrac{k}{s^2 + \sqrt{2}s + 1}$

(b) $H(s) = \dfrac{ks^2}{(s+1)^2}$

(c) $H(s) = \dfrac{ks^3}{s^3 + 2s^2 + 2s + 1}$

(d) $H(s) = \dfrac{k}{s^3 + 4s^2 + 6s + 3}$

(e) $H(s) = \dfrac{k}{(s+1)^4}$

7-18. Write a computer program:

(a) to determine if a transfer function $H(s)$ is realizable by either an RC or an LC ladder network;

(b) to realize $H(s)$ if the answer to (a) is affirmative.

7-19. Write a computer program to realize an all-pass transfer function $H(s) = p(-s)/p(s)$.

7-20. Write a computer program:

(a) to determine if a transfer function $H(s)$ is realizable as a lossless 2-port terminated at both ends by resistors R_s and R_ℓ, where R_s takes on the value of either 0 or 1 Ω and $0 \le R_\ell \le \infty$;

(b) to realize $H(s)$ by a Darlington configuration if the answer to (a) is affirmative.

8

FILTER APPROXIMATION

In Chapter 7, we presented techniques to realize transfer functions. In this chapter, we examine various aspects of transfer functions and proceed to derive the transfer functions of some common filter families.

In designing a filter, the engineer must meet the signal-processing requirements with a feasible hardware implementation. Often, a simple prescription on the specifications of a filter to satisfy the signal processing requirements leads to an impossible hardware realization. As an example, let us consider a radio or a television receiver. The transmitting station is assigned a band of frequencies called a *channel* in which it must transmit its signal. Ideally, the receiver should accept and process any signal in the assigned channel and completely exclude signals at all other frequencies. Thus, the simplest specifications on the magnitude of the transfer function of the receiver are[1]

$$|H(j\omega)|^2 = A \quad \text{for } \omega_1 \leq \omega \leq \omega_2$$
$$= 0 \quad \text{otherwise} \tag{8-1}$$

where $\omega_1 \leq \omega \leq \omega_2$ is the channel of the signal to be received. However, no linear lumped circuit can produce such a transfer function *exactly*.[2] The reasons may be given in two parts, and they are: (1) any linear, lumped, and time-invariant filter containing R, L, C, and active elements has a transfer function that is a rational function of frequency; and (2) a rational function can not have a constant value over any band of frequencies unless it is con-

---

[1] Because $|H(j\omega)|^2$ is an even function, we need to consider only for $\omega \geq 0$.

[2] Note that the filter, specified by (8-1), is noncausal and hence is not physically realizable.

stant everywhere. Because no transfer functions of feasible circuits can meet the specifications of (8-1) exactly, the only alternative is to approximate (8-1) by a realizable transfer function.

Fortunately, in practice, filters are not required to meet the extremely stringent requirements such as those of (8-1) perfectly. There is always room for tolerances, no matter how small the tolerances are. For example, in the aforementioned radio or television receiver case, reception may be considered satisfactory as long as the filter response is within $\pm 5\%$ of A in the passband and below 1% of A or 40 dB down for frequencies more than $1/10$ of the bandwidth away from the band edges, namely ω_1 and ω_2. That is

$$0.95A \leq |H(j\omega)|^2 \leq 1.05A \quad \text{for} \quad \omega_1 \leq \omega \leq \omega_2 \tag{8-2a}$$

$$|H(j\omega)|^2 < 0.01A \quad \text{for} \quad \omega < \omega_1 - \frac{\omega_2 - \omega_1}{10} \triangleq \omega_A$$
$$\text{and} \quad \text{for} \quad \omega > \omega_2 + \frac{\omega_2 - \omega_1}{10} \triangleq \omega_B \tag{8-2b}$$

$$0 \leq |H(j\omega)|^2 \leq 1.05A \quad \text{for} \quad \omega_A < \omega < \omega_1$$
$$\text{and} \quad \text{for} \quad \omega_2 < \omega < \omega_B \tag{8-2c}$$

Notice that (8-2a) is a specification of the passband magnitude, (8-2b) specifies the stopband magnitude, and (8-2c) concerns the transition band. Pictorially, $|H(j\omega)|^2$ must lie within the shaded area of Fig. 8-1.

The implementation of a hardware circuit to meet filter specifications such as those prescribed in (8-2) is normally accomplished by the following two-step procedure:

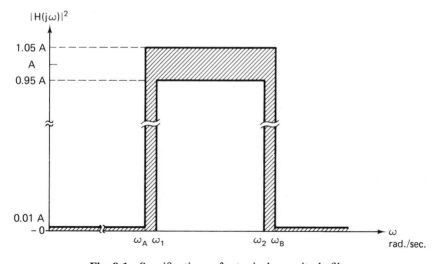

Fig. 8-1   Specifications of a typical magnitude filter

STEP 1. *Design Stage:* To find a stable and realizable transfer function whose frequency characteristics satisfy all the filter specifications.

STEP 2. *Realization Stage:* To realize the transfer function obtained in Step 1 with a feasible circuit.

In this chapter, we deal extensively with the problems associated with the design stage. Various aspects of the realization stage are discussed in this chapter as well as in Chapter 7 (passive realization), Chapter 10 (active realization), and Chapters 12 and 13 (digital realization).

For the specifications of (8-2), the first step is also an *approximation problem*—to find a stable and realizable transfer function to approximate the ideal characteristics of (8-1) within the tolerance levels specified by (8-2). There are many theorems, such as the Weierstrass approximation theorem, and constructive algorithms to approximate one function by other functions. These results can be applied to our filter design problems. However, this requires some mathematical tools that are not easy to acquire. For the very common engineering problem of finding a filter whose magnitude function is required to satisfy the specifications on various frequency bands, there are some well established design techniques that are very easy to apply. These techniques are based on some *standard* functional forms that give the basic filter functions. All that is required is a proper selection (or determination) of the coefficients for the specific problem at hand. We shall discuss some of these standard filter types.

Most of these standard filter types begin as approximations to the normalized ideal low-pass filter. The *normalized* ideal low-pass filter has a gain of one in the band of frequencies from zero to 1 rad./sec. and a gain of zero for all frequencies above 1 rad./sec. The phase shift through the filter $\phi(\omega) \triangleq -/H(j\omega)$ is linear, having a slope of 1 in the passband. For frequencies above 1 rad./sec., the phase shift is unimportant, because no signal gets through the filter anyway. Thus, the *normalized ideal low-pass* filter is characterized by

$$H(j\omega) = e^{-j\omega} \quad \text{for} \quad 0 \leq |\omega| \leq 1$$
$$= 0 \quad \text{for} \quad |\omega| > 1 \tag{8-3}$$

The magnitude and the phase characteristics of (8-3) are shown in Fig. 8-2. Once an appropriate approximation of the normalized ideal low-pass filter is obtained, then by suitable frequency transformations, this basic low-pass prototype can be converted to high-pass, bandpass, band-stop, and other more complicated frequency selective filters with multiple pass- and stop-bands, as well as other low-pass filters.[3]

---

[3] There exist no frequency transformations (in the form of a *rational* function) to convert the transfer function of a low-pass filter to that of an all-pass filter.

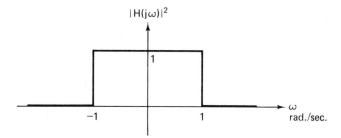

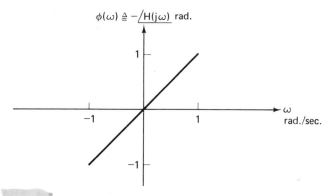

Fig. 8-2 Frequency characteristics of normalized ideal low-pass filters. (a) Magnitude function. (b) Phase function.

Because filtering is an important engineering problem, some filter approximations of (8-3) have been found to be consistently satisfactory, and their characteristics have been tabulated. Some of these common filter types are:[4]

1. The *Butterworth* filter, which is characterized by a monotonically decreasing magnitude function of ω for $\omega \geq 0$.

2. The *Chebyshev* filter, which is characterized by an equiripple magnitude function across the passband and a montonically decreasing magnitude function in the stopband.

3. The *inverse Chebyshev* filter, which is characterized by a monotonically decreasing magnitude function in the passband and an equiripple magnitude function in the stopband.

4. The *elliptic* filter (also known as the *Cauer* filter or *double Chebyshev* filter), which is characterized by a magnitude function with equal ripples in both the passband and the stopband.

---

[4] The descriptions here are applicable to low-pass filter types only.

5. The *Bessel* filter (also known as the maximally flat group delay filter), which is a Taylor series approximation to the linear phase characteristics near $s = 0$.

In this chapter, we go into some detail on the Butterworth, Chebyshev, and Bessel filters.

Recall that in Section 3-2-1, the Hilbert transform states that a minimum-phase network function is completely specified by either its magnitude function or its phase function. This means that a transfer function cannot approximate both the magnitude and the phase characteristics of the normalized ideal low-pass filter. The Butterworth, Chebyshev, inverse Chebyshev, and elliptic filters approximate the magnitude function, and the Bessel filter approximates the phase characteristics of the normalized ideal low-pass filter.

Before we proceed to discuss the various families of magnitude filters, let us consider some basic properties of the magnitude functions. The squared magnitude function of a transfer function $H(s)$ is given by[5]

$$|H(j\omega)|^2 = H(j\omega)\overline{H(j\omega)} \tag{8-4}$$

Because the coefficients of $H(s)$ are real

$$\overline{H(j\omega)} = H(\overline{j\omega}) = H(-j\omega) \tag{8-5}$$

Thus, $|H(j\omega)|^2$ can be computed by

$$|H(j\omega)|^2 = H(s)H(-s)|_{s=j\omega} \tag{8-6}$$

A transfer function $H(s)$ can always be written in factored form in terms of its poles and zeros as

$$H(s) = \frac{K(s - z_1)(s - z_2)\,\ldots}{(s - p_1)(s - p_2)\,\ldots} \tag{8-7}$$

therefore, $H(s)H(-s)$ can be written as a product of factor groups such as

$$(s - z_1)(-s - z_1) = z_1^2 - s^2 \tag{8-8}$$

When $s = j\omega$, the right-hand side of (8-8) becomes $(z_1^2 + \omega^2)$. Hence, the squared magnitude of a transfer function $H(s)$ can always be written in the form

$$|H(j\omega)|^2 = \frac{K^2(\omega^2 + z_1^2)(\omega^2 + z_2^2)\,\ldots}{(\omega^2 + p_1^2)(\omega^2 + p_2^2)\,\ldots} \tag{8-9}$$

If all poles and zeros of $H(s)$ are real, then (8-9) implies that $|H(j\omega)|^2$ is positive and real and is a function of ω^2. Let us now consider the case when some or all of the poles and zeros of $H(s)$ are complex. Because complex poles and

---

[5]To avoid square roots, we usually work with the square of the magnitude function.

zeros of any transfer function must occur in conjugate pairs[6], let us suppose $z_2 = \bar{z}_1$. Then the factors involving z_1 and z_2 can be grouped together as

$$(\omega^2 + z_1^2)(\omega^2 + z_2^2) = \omega^4 + \omega^2(z_1^2 + z_2^2) + z_1^2 z_2^2 \qquad (8\text{-}10)$$

If we write

$$z_1 = a_1 + jb_1 \qquad (8\text{-}11a)$$

where a_1 and b_1 are real numbers, then

$$z_2 = a_1 - jb_1 \qquad (8\text{-}11b)$$

$$z_1^2 = a_1^2 + 2ja_1b_1 - b_1^2 \qquad (8\text{-}11c)$$

$$z_2^2 = a_1^2 - 2ja_1b_1 - b_1^2 \qquad (8\text{-}11d)$$

Substituting (8-11) into (8-10), we obtain

$$(\omega^2 + z_1^2)(\omega^2 + z_2^2) = \omega^4 + 2(a_1^2 - b_1^2)\omega^2 + (a_1^2 + b_1^2)^2$$
$$= (\omega^2 - b_1^2)^2 + a_1^2(2\omega^2 + 2b_1^2 + a_1^2) \qquad (8\text{-}12)$$
$$\geq 0 \quad \text{for all } \omega$$

Consequently, $(\omega^2 + z_1^2)(\omega^2 + z_2^2)$ with $z_2 = \bar{z}_1$ is a polynomial of ω^2 with real coefficients, and this polynomial is greater than zero for all real ω.[7] Gathering all factors together, we have:

THEOREM 8-1 Both the numerator and the denominator polynomials of the magnitude squared function of a transfer function are polynomials of ω^2 with real coefficients, and these polynomials are greater than zero for all real ω.

The requirements stated in Theorem 8-1 must be met by any transfer function. In the process of approximating the magnitude function of a normalized ideal low-pass filter, we must be sure that the resulting magnitude function satisfies the requirements stated in Theorem 8-1, or else the approximating transfer function will be useless because it will not be realizable.

8-1 THE BUTTERWORTH APPROXIMATION

One frequently used approximation to the normalized ideal low-pass filter is the set of Butterworth functions. The nth-order Butterworth function is given by

---

[6]This is the case whenever all coefficients of a transfer function are real. Because the coefficients of a transfer function are sums and products of parameter values of elements in the circuit and the element parameter values are always real, the coefficients of a transfer function of any passive or active filter are always real. Hence, its complex poles and zeros always occur in conjugate pairs.

[7]Here, we really mean that the polynomial is greater than zero for all ω except possibly at a finite number of points where the polynomial is equal to zero. This is the interpretation hereafter.

$$B_n(\omega) = \frac{1}{1 + \omega^{2n}} \quad n = 1, 2, \ldots \tag{8-13}$$

For each value of n, the Butterworth function $B_n(\omega)$ has the previously derived properties of a squared magnitude function as stated in Theorem 8-1: Both its numerator and denominator are polynomials of ω^2 with real coefficients, and $B_n(\omega) > 0$ for all ω. Hence, a Butterworth function can be the magnitude function of a realizable transfer function.

An nth-order normalized low-pass Butterworth filter has a magnitude function given by

$$|H(j\omega)|^2 = B_n(\omega) = \frac{1}{1 + \omega^{2n}} \tag{8-14}$$

A graphical illustration of (8-14) is shown in Fig. 8-3. Observe that as $n \to \infty$, the Butterworth magnitude function approaches the ideal magnitude characteristics of Fig. 8-2(a). As the order n of the Butterworth filter increases, the magnitude function is closer to unity in the passband, the transaction band is narrower, and the magnitude function is closer to zero in the stopband. Hence, n is a parameter chosen to satisfy a set of prescribed passband and stopband specifications. Figure 8-4 is another plot of (8-14) with the vertical scale given in dB, where

$$|H(j\omega)|\ \mathrm{dB} \triangleq -10 \log |H(j\omega)|^2 \tag{8-15}$$

The phase characteristics

$$\phi(\omega) \triangleq -\underline{/H(j\omega)} \tag{8-16}$$

of an nth-order normalized low-pass Butterworth filter are shown in Fig. 8-5. Note that for ω very small, the phase function behaves almost linearly, especially for low values of n.

8-1-1. Basic Properties

Based on (8-14) and Fig. 8-3, the normalized low-pass Butterworth filter has the following basic properties:

BUTTERWORTH PROPERTY 1   For each n, we have

$$|H(j0)|^2 = 1, \quad |H(j1)|^2 = 0.5, \quad \text{and} \quad |H(j\infty)|^2 = 0 \tag{8-17}$$

This implies that the dc gain (the magnitude value at $\omega = 0$) is 1 and the 3 dB cutoff frequency is at 1 rad./sec.[8]

BUTTERWORTH PROPERTY 2   The magnitude functions of Butterworth filters are monotonically decreasing for $\omega \geq 0$. Hence, $|H(j\omega)|$ has its maximum value at $\omega = 0$.

---

[8]The cutoff frequency ω_c is the frequency where the magnitude squared function is equal to 0.5. This implies that ω_c can be calculated from the following equation: $|H(j\omega_c)|^2 = 1/2$. In terms of dB, ω_c is the point where the attenuation function is at: $-10 \log |H(j\omega_c)|^2 = -10 \log (1/2) \simeq 3$ dB.

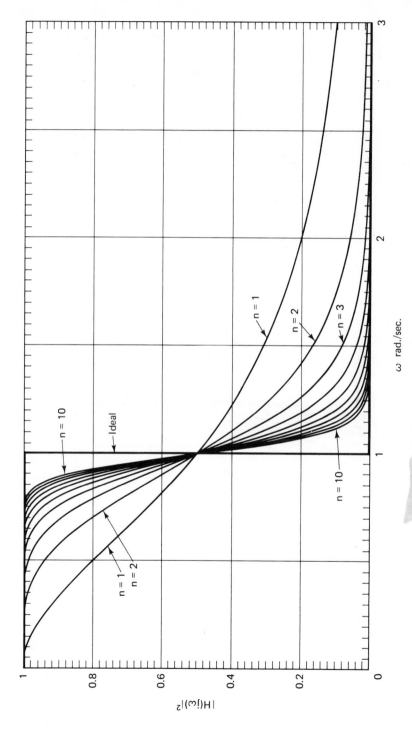

Fig. 8-3 Magnitude functions of Butterworth filters.

227

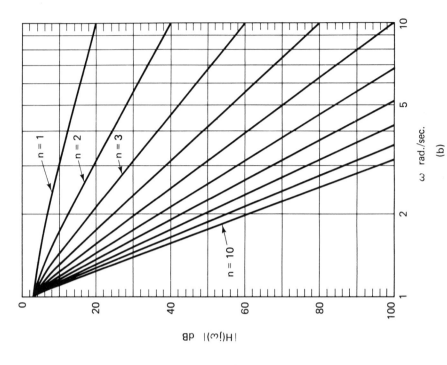

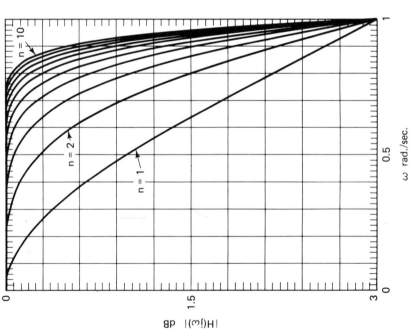

Fig. 8-4 Magnitude characteristics of Butterworth filters. (a) Passband attenuation. (b) Stopband attenuation.

228

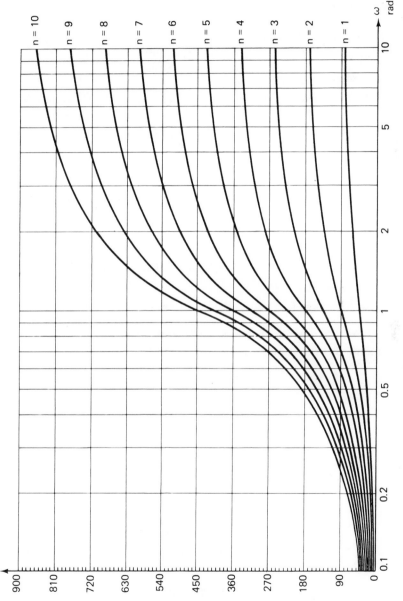

Fig. 8-5 Phase characteristics of Butterworth filters.

229

BUTTERWORTH PROPERTY 3 The first $(2n - 1)$ derivatives of an nth-order low-pass Butterworth filter are zero at $\omega = 0$. For this reason, Butterworth filters are also called *maximally flat magnitude* filters.

BUTTERWORTH PROPERTY 4 The high-frequency roll off of an nth-order Butterworth filter is $20n$ dB/decade, as illustrated in Fig. 8-6.

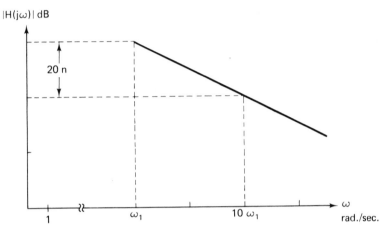

Fig. 8-6 High-frequency roll off of an nth-order Butterworth filter.

Property 1 is obvious from (8-14). To see that Property 2 is true, we differentiate (8-14) to obtain

$$\frac{d}{d\omega} |H(j\omega)|^2 = \frac{-2n\omega^{2n-1}}{(1 + \omega^{2n})^2} \qquad (8\text{-}18)$$

Observe that

$$\frac{d}{d\omega} |H(j\omega)|^2 = 2 |H(j\omega)| \frac{d}{d\omega} |H(j\omega)| \qquad (8\text{-}19)$$

Substituting (8-14) and (8-18) into (8-19), we have

$$\frac{d}{d\omega} |H(j\omega)| = \frac{1}{2 |H(j\omega)|} \frac{d}{d\omega} |H(j\omega)|^2$$

$$= -\frac{1}{2\left[\dfrac{1}{1 + \omega^{2n}}\right]^{1/2}} \frac{2n\omega^{2n-1}}{(1 + \omega^{2n})^2} \qquad (8\text{-}20)$$

$$= -\frac{n\omega^{2n-1}}{[1 + \omega^{2n}]^{3/2}}$$

Because the derivative of the magnitude function is negative for all $\omega > 0$, $|H(j\omega)|$ is a decreasing function of ω for $\omega \geq 0$. Property 3 can be shown by performing the binomial, or equivalently the Taylor series expansion[9] of $|H(j\omega)|^2$ at ω near zero:

$$|H(j\omega)|^2 = 1 - \omega^{2n} + \omega^{4n} - \ldots \tag{8-21}$$

From (8-21), we obtain

$$\left[\frac{d^k}{d\omega^k} |H(j\omega)|^2\right]\bigg|_{\omega=0} = 0 \tag{8-22}$$

for $k = 1, 2, \ldots, 2n - 1$. Finally, for Property 4, if $\omega \gg 1$, then we can approximate

$$|H(j\omega)|^2 = \frac{1}{1 + \omega^{2n}} \simeq \frac{1}{\omega^{2n}} \tag{8-23}$$

In terms of dB, (8-23) gives

$$-10 \log |H(j\omega)|^2 \simeq -10 \log \frac{1}{\omega^{2n}}$$

$$= 10 \log \omega^{2n} = 20n \log \omega \text{ dB} \tag{8-24}$$

8-1-2. Transfer Function

In Chapter 3, we presented a method to construct the minimum phase function of a given magnitude function. For convenience, we reproduce the construction procedure here:

STEP 0. Given the magnitude function of an nth-order Butterworth filter, let us form

$$h(s) \triangleq H(s)H(-s) = |H(j\omega)|^2 \big|_{\omega=s/j}$$

$$= \frac{1}{1 + \omega^{2n}}\bigg|_{\omega=s/j} = \frac{1}{1 + (-1)^n s^{2n}} \tag{8-25}$$

STEP 1. Factor $h(s)$ into first- and second-order polynomials. From (8-25), we note that $h(s)$ has no finite zeros, and the poles of $h(s)$ occur with quadrantal symmetry. Hence, the numerator of $H(s)$ is 1.

STEP 2. Assign those factors associated with the LH s-plane poles of $h(s)$ to $H(s)$. Multiply these factors together to form the denominator of $H(s)$.

Example 8-1 Find the transfer function of the third-order normalized low-pass Butterworth filter.

Solution: We follow the construction steps outlined previously with $n = 3$.

---

[9]Taylor series expansion of $f(x)$ at $x = 0$ is given by $f(x) = f(0) + f'(0)x + (1/2)f''(0)x^2 + \ldots$. If $f(x) = 1/(1 + x)$, then the expansion takes the form, $1/(1 + x) = 1 - x + x^2 - x^3 + \ldots$. In taking the Taylor expansion of (8-14), we let $x = \omega^{2n}$.

STEP 0. Form

$$H(s)H(-s) = |H(j\omega)|^2\Big|_{\omega=s/j} = \frac{1}{1-s^6}$$

STEP 1. Factor $H(s)H(-s)$ as

$$H(s)H(-s) = \frac{1}{1-s^6}$$

$$= \frac{1}{(s+1)(s^2+s+1)(-s+1)(s^2-s+1)} \tag{8-26}$$

In this factorization process, it may be worthwhile to take advantage of the properties of the pole locations of $H(s)H(-s)$.

STEP 2. Assign the LH s-plane factors $(s+1)$ and (s^2+s+1) to $H(s)$ as

$$H(s) = \frac{1}{(s+1)(s^2+s+1)}$$

Multiply these factors together to form

$$H(s) = \frac{1}{s^3+2s^2+2s+1} \tag{8-27}$$

which is the transfer function of the normalized third-order Butterworth low-pass filter.   ∎

At the heart of this process is the factorization of $H(s)H(-s)$. Observe that the poles of $H(s)H(-s)$ are the solutions of the equation

$$(-1)^n s^{2n} + 1 = 0 \tag{8-28}$$

Consider first the case when n is even. Then (8-28) reduces to

$$s^{2n} + 1 = 0$$

or

$$s^{2n} = -1 = e^{j(2k-1)\pi} \tag{8-29}$$

where k is an integer. Hence, the poles $\hat{s}_k$ of $H(s)H(-s)$ are

$$\hat{s}_k = \cos\frac{2k-1}{2n}\pi + j\sin\frac{2k-1}{2n}\pi$$

$$= \cos\hat{\theta}_k + j\sin\hat{\theta}_k \qquad k = 1, 2, \ldots, 2n \tag{8-30}$$

where

$$\hat{\theta}_k = \frac{(2k-1)\pi}{2n} \quad \text{and} \quad k = 1, 2, \ldots, 2n \tag{8-31}$$

These pole locations are shown in Figs. 8-7(a) and 8-7(b) for the cases $n = 4$ and $n = 5$, respectively. Note that $\hat{s}_{k'}$ occurs at the same pole location as that of $\hat{s}_k$ where

$$k' \triangleq 2mn + k \tag{8-32}$$

and m is an integer. Because $\hat{\theta}_k$ starts from the positive real axis and goes counterclockwise, the labeling of poles starts from the first quadrant or in

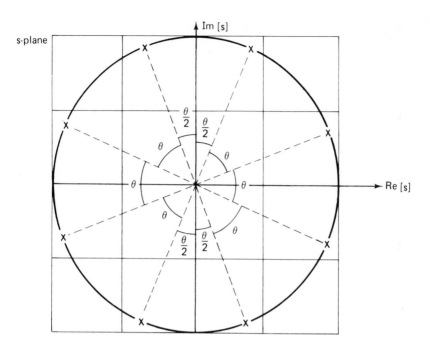

(a) n = even. No pole on real axis. In this case n = 4, θ = 45°

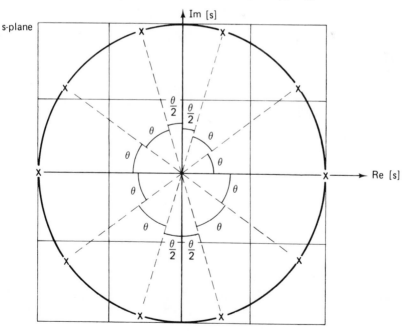

(b) n = odd. A pole as at s = −1. In this case n = 5, θ = 36°

Fig. 8-7 Pole locations of an nth-order low-pass Butterworth filter.
(a) $n = 4$. (b) $n = 5$.

233

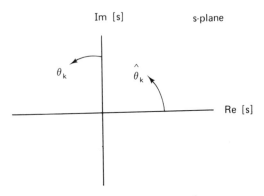

Fig. 8-8 Illustrations of θ_k and $\hat{\theta}_k$ sweeps.

the RH s-plane, as illustrated in Fig. 8-8. However, we are most interested in the LH s-plane poles. In order to extract only the LH s-plane poles, let us define

$$s_k \triangleq \hat{s}_{k+(n/2)} \tag{8-33a}$$

and

$$\theta_k \triangleq \hat{\theta}_{k+(n/2)} - \frac{\pi}{2} \tag{8-33b}$$

If we now substitute $k = 1, 2, \ldots$ into (8-33), we find that θ_k starts the angle measurement from the positive imaginary axis of the s-plane and goes counterclockwise, as shown in Fig. 8-8. In this way, θ_k sweeps the n LH s-plane poles first. In terms of θ_k, the LH s-plane poles of $H(s)H(-s)$ are given by

$$s_k \triangleq \hat{s}_{k+(n/2)} = \cos \hat{\theta}_{k+(n/2)} + j \sin \hat{\theta}_{k+(n/2)}$$

$$= \cos \left(\theta_k + \frac{\pi}{2} \right) + j \sin \left(\theta_k + \frac{\pi}{2} \right) \tag{8-34}$$

$$= -\sin \theta_k + j \cos \theta_k$$

where

$$\theta_k = \frac{2k - 1}{2n} \pi \tag{8-35}$$

and $k = 1, 2, \ldots, n$. Note that the RH s-plane poles s_k^{RH} are given by

$$s_k^{\mathrm{RH}} = \sin \theta_k + j \cos \theta_k \tag{8-36}$$

where θ_k is given by (8-35) and $k = 1, 2, \ldots, n$. In a similar manner, we can show that the LH s-plane poles of $H(s)H(-s)$ are also given by (8-34) and (8-35) when n is an odd integer in (8-28). Hence,

$$H(s) = \prod_{k=1}^{n} \frac{1}{s - s_k} = \prod_{k=1}^{n} \frac{1}{(s - \sigma_k - j\omega_k)} \tag{8-37a}$$

where

$$s_k = \sigma_k + j\omega_k \tag{8-37b}$$

$$\sigma_k = -\sin \theta_k \qquad (8\text{-}37c)$$

$$\omega_k = \cos \theta_k \qquad (8\text{-}37d)$$

order of filter

$$\theta_k = \frac{2k-1}{2n}\pi \qquad (8\text{-}37e)$$

and $k = 1, 2, \ldots, n$. Observe that

$$|s_k|^2 = \sigma_k^2 + \omega_k^2 = \sin^2 \theta_k + \cos^2 \theta_k = 1 \qquad (8\text{-}38)$$

Hence, the poles of $H(s)$ are on a unit circle.[10] If s_k is a real pole, then

$$\theta_k = \frac{\pi}{2} \quad \text{and} \quad s_k = -1 \qquad (8\text{-}39)$$

In view of (8-37e), (8-39) can occur only when n is an odd integer. On the other hand, if s_k is a complex pole, then $\overline{s_k}$ (the complex conjugate of s_k) is also a complex pole, and the product $(s - s_k)$ and $(s - \overline{s_k})$ gives

$$\begin{aligned}
(s - s_k)(s - \overline{s_k}) &= (s - \sigma_k - j\omega_k)(s - \sigma_k + j\omega_k) \\
&= s^2 - 2\sigma_k s + \sigma_k^2 + \omega_k^2 \qquad (8\text{-}40) \\
&= s^2 + (2\sin\theta_k)s + 1
\end{aligned}$$

With (8-39) and (8-40), we can write (8-37a) as

$$H(s) = \prod_{k=1}^{n/2} \frac{1}{s^2 + (2\sin\theta_k)s + 1} \qquad (8\text{-}41a)$$

when n is even, and

$$H(s) = \frac{1}{(s+1)} \prod_{k=1}^{(n-1)/2} \frac{1}{s^2 + (2\sin\theta_k)s + 1} \qquad (8\text{-}41b)$$

when n is odd, where θ_k is given by (8-37e). For example, the transfer function of the second-order normalized low-pass Butterworth filter is given by

$$H(s) = \frac{1}{s^2 + \left(2\sin\frac{\pi}{4}\right)s + 1} = \frac{1}{s^2 + \sqrt{2}s + 1} \qquad (8\text{-}42a)$$

and the third-order transfer function is

$$\begin{aligned}
H(s) &= \frac{1}{(s+1)} \frac{1}{s^2 + \left(2\sin\frac{\pi}{6}\right)s + 1} \\
&= \frac{1}{(s+1)(s^2 + s + 1)}
\end{aligned} \qquad (8\text{-}42b)$$

In view of (8-38) (that the magnitudes of the Butterworth poles are one) and (8-37e) (that the phase angles of the poles are uniformly spaced), we can locate the poles of an nth-order normalized low-pass Butterworth filter graphically as follows:

---

[10]A unit circle is a circle with a radius of one and with the origin as the center.

Steps to find the poles of BW filter Graphically

1. Construct a unit circle on the s-plane.
2. Let $\theta \triangleq \pi/n$. With angles measured counterclockwise from the positive imaginary axis, draw radial lines of angles $\theta/2, 3\theta/2, 5\theta/2, \ldots$, $[(2n - 1)/2]\theta$.
3. The intersections of these radial lines and the unit circle give the pole locations of $H(s)$. See Fig. 8-7 for examples when $n = 4$ and when $n = 5$. When n is an odd integer, the point $s = -1$ is a pole of $H(s)$.

When the frequency of a low-pass filter is scaled so that the cutoff frequency is at ω_c rad./sec. rather than at 1 rad./sec., the poles move along the radial lines to the corresponding points on a circle of radius ω_c. Thus, the pole-zero diagram remains the same under frequency scaling (to be discussed later) except for a change of scale.

8-1-3. Circuit Realization

As indicated by (8-41), the transfer function of an nth-order low pass Butterworth filter has the following two important properties:

1. The denominator polynomial is a Hurwitz polynomial.
2. All transmission zeros are at $s = \infty$.

Hence, the Darlington circuits of Sec. 7-3 can be used to realize Butterworth filters. In this section, we concentrate on the more useful case where the lossless 2-port is terminated at both ends with resistors $R_s = 1\ \Omega$ and R_ℓ as discussed in Section 7-3-2. In particular, because all transmission zeros are at $s = \infty$, the associated $Z_{in}(s)$ is realized by Cauer's first form—series inductors and shunt capacitors for the lossless 2-port. Hence, the circuit structures of passive voltage-ratio Butterworth filters are shown in Fig. 8-9, where Fig. 8-9(a) is for the case $R_\ell \geq R_s = 1\ \Omega$, Fig. 8-9(b) is for the case $R_\ell \leq R_s = 1\ \Omega$, and Fig. 8-9(c) applies only to the case when $R_\ell = R_s = 1\ \Omega$.[11]

With the choice of the minimum-phase reflection coefficients and an appropriate choice of the associated $Z_{in}(s)$, the values of the circuit elements $\tilde{C}_1$, $\tilde{L}_2, \tilde{C}_3, \tilde{L}_4, \ldots \{\hat{L}_1, \hat{C}_2, \hat{L}_3, \hat{C}_4, \ldots\}$ are given by the following set of recursive formulas:

$$\tilde{C}_{2m-1}\tilde{L}_{2m}\{\hat{L}_{2m-1}\hat{C}_{2m}\} = \frac{\alpha_{4m-3}\alpha_{4m-1}}{1 - \lambda\beta_{4m-2} + \lambda^2} \tag{8-43a}$$

$$\tilde{C}_{2m+1}\tilde{L}_{2m}\{\hat{L}_{2m+1}\hat{C}_{2m}\} = \frac{\alpha_{4m-1}\alpha_{4m+1}}{1 - \lambda\beta_{4m} + \lambda^2} \tag{8-43b}$$

---

[11]Note that for simplicity, we let $R_s = 1\ \Omega$. An impedance scaling mechanism can be used to scale R_s to any desired values.

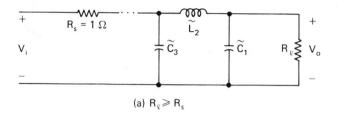

(a) $R_\ell \geqslant R_s$

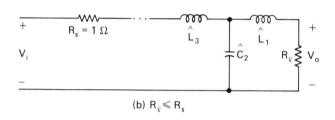

(b) $R_\ell \leqslant R_s$

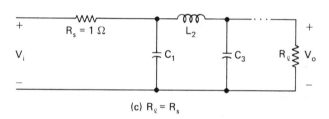

(c) $R_\ell = R_s$

Fig. 8-9   Circuit structures of low-pass Butterworth filters.

where

$$\lambda = \left(\frac{R_\ell - 1}{R_\ell + 1}\right)^{1/n} \quad \text{for Fig. 8-9(a)} \tag{8-44a}$$

$$\lambda = \left(\frac{1 - R_\ell}{1 + R_\ell}\right)^{1/n} \quad \text{for Fig. 8-9(b)} \tag{8-44b}$$

$$\alpha_i = 2 \sin \frac{\pi i}{2n} \tag{8-44c}$$

and

$$\beta_i = 2 \cos \frac{\pi i}{2n} \tag{8-44d}$$

with

$$\tilde{C}_1 = \frac{\alpha_1}{R_\ell(1 - \lambda)} \quad \text{for Fig. 8-9(a)} \tag{8-45a}$$

$$\hat{L}_1 = \frac{\alpha_1 R_\ell}{1 - \lambda} \quad \text{for Fig. 8-9(b)} \tag{8-45b}$$

and

$$m = \begin{cases} 1, 2, \ldots, \dfrac{n-1}{2} & \text{when } n \text{ is odd} \\ 1, 2, \ldots, \dfrac{n}{2} & \text{when } n \text{ is even} \end{cases} \tag{8-45c}$$

To start the recursive process of (8-43) for $m = 1, 2, \ldots$, we calculate $\tilde{C}_1$ for Fig. 8-9(a) $\{\hat{L}_1$ for Fig. 8-9(b)$\}$ from (8-45). With $m = 1$, (8-43a) gives $\tilde{L}_2 \{\hat{C}_2\}$, and in turn (8-43b) gives $\tilde{C}_3 \{\hat{L}_3\}$. Repeating (8-43a) and (8-43b) with $m = 2$ gives $\tilde{L}_4$ and $\tilde{C}_5 \{\hat{C}_4$ and $\hat{L}_5\}$. This procedure can be repeated until all the necessary circuit element values are found.

In the case when $R_\ell = R_s$, either circuit in Figs. 8-9(a) and (b) is applicable. In this case, the resulting circuit will have some symmetric properties that enable us to write down the circuit structure of the low-pass Butterworth filter from left to right, as shown in Fig. 8-9(c), where the circuit element values are given by

$$C_m = 2 \sin \left[\frac{(2m-1)\pi}{2n} \right] \quad \text{when } m \text{ is odd} \tag{8-46a}$$

and

$$L_m = 2 \sin \left[\frac{(2m-1)\pi}{2n} \right] \quad \text{when } m \text{ is even} \tag{8-46b}$$

where $m = 1, 2, \ldots, n$. Observe that (8-46) can be derived from (8-43) through (8-45) when $R_\ell = 1\ \Omega$. For convenience, Table 8-1 gives values of the circuit elements in Fig. 8-9(c) when $R_\ell = 1\ \Omega$ for $n = 1, 2, \ldots, 9$.

TABLE 8-1   Element Values for the Circuit in Fig. 8-9(c)

n	C_1	L_2	C_3	L_4	C_5	L_6	C_7	L_8	C_9
1	2.0000								
2	1.4142	1.4142							
3	1.0000	2.0000	1.0000						
4	0.7654	1.8478	1.8478	0.7654					
5	0.6180	1.6180	2.0000	1.6180	0.6180				
6	0.5176	1.4142	1.9319	1.9319	1.4142	0.5176			
7	0.4450	1.2470	1.8019	2.0000	1.8019	1.2470	0.4450		
8	0.3902	1.1111	1.6629	1.9616	1.9616	1.6629	1.1111	0.3902	
9	0.3473	1.0000	1.5321	1.8794	2.0000	1.8794	1.5321	1.0000	0.3473

8-1-4. Examples

Example 8-2 Suppose that we are to construct a normalized low-pass filter to meet:

(i) the passband specification:

$$|H(j0.5)|^2 > 0.9 \tag{8-47a}$$

(ii) the stopband specification:

$$|H(j2)|^2 < 0.01 \qquad (8\text{-}47b)$$

Find the simplest Butterworth design with $R_s = R_\ell = 1 \ \Omega$.

Solution: First, let us determine the order n of the Butterworth filter required to meet the specifications of (8-47). Recall that the magnitude function of an nth-order normalized low-pass Butterworth filter is given by

$$|H(j\omega)|^2 = \frac{1}{1 + \omega^{2n}} \qquad (8\text{-}48)$$

Hence, (8-47a) implies that[12]

$$\frac{1}{1 + (0.5)^{2n}} > 0.9$$

or

$$n \geq 2 \qquad (8\text{-}49a)$$

In a similar manner, (8-47b) implies that

$$\frac{1}{1 + 2^{(2n)}} < 0.01$$

or

$$n \geq 4 \qquad (8\text{-}49b)$$

To satisfy both conditions of (8-47), a fourth-order Butterworth filter is needed. By (8-34), the LH s-plane poles of the fourth-order normalized Butterworth filter are located at

$$s_1 = -\sin\frac{\pi}{8} + j\cos\frac{\pi}{8} = -0.3827 + j0.9239 \qquad (8\text{-}50a)$$

$$s_2 = -\sin\frac{3\pi}{8} + j\cos\frac{3\pi}{8} = -0.9239 + j0.3827 \qquad (8\text{-}50b)$$

$$s_3 = -\sin\frac{5\pi}{8} + j\cos\frac{5\pi}{8} = -0.9239 - j0.3827 \qquad (8\text{-}50c)$$

$$s_4 = -\sin\frac{7\pi}{8} + j\cos\frac{7\pi}{8} = -0.3827 - j0.9239 \qquad (8\text{-}50d)$$

Hence, the transfer function of the desired filter is given by

$$
\begin{aligned}
H(s) &= \frac{1}{(s - s_1)(s - s_2)(s - s_3)(s - s_4)} \\
&= \frac{1}{[(s - s_1)(s - s_4)][(s - s_2)(s - s_3)]} \\
&= \frac{1}{(s^2 + 0.7654s + 1)(s^2 + 1.8478s + 1)} \\
&= \frac{1}{s^4 + 2.6131s^3 + 3.4142s^2 + 2.6131s + 1}
\end{aligned}
\qquad (8\text{-}51)
$$

---

[12]We can either calculate the proper values of n to satisfy (8-47), or we can utilize the graph in Fig. 8-3 to determine n.

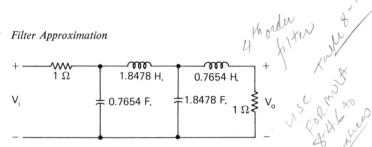

Fig. 8-10 A circuit realization of the desired filter in Example 8-2.

From Table 8-1 and Fig. 8-9(c), a circuit realization of the desired filter satisfying all the signal-processing requirements of (8-47) is shown in Fig. 8-10. ∎

Example 8-3 Suppose that a maximally flat normalized low-pass filter is desired with a passband attenuation less than 0.5 dB for $0 \leq \omega \leq 0.5$ rad./sec. and with a stopband attenuation of at least 20 dB down for $\omega \geq 4$ rad./sec. Find the desired filter circuits when

(a) $R_\ell = 2R_s$
(b) $R_\ell = 0.5R_s$

Solution: First, let us determine the order n of the Butterworth filter required to meet the specifications. The passband and the stopband specifications imply that

$$-10 \log \frac{1}{1 + (0.5)^{2n}} < 0.5 \qquad (8\text{-}52a)$$

and

$$-10 \log \frac{1}{1 + 4^{2n}} > 20 \qquad (8\text{-}52b)$$

After some algebraic manipulation of (8-52) or by referring to the graphs of Fig. 8-4, we find that $n \geq 2$ will satisfy (8-52). Hence, a second-order Butterworth filter is desired. This means that the desired transfer function is given by

$$H(s) = \frac{1}{s^2 + \sqrt{2}s + 1} \qquad (8\text{-}53)$$

For case (a), when $R_\ell = 2R_s$, we use the circuit structure of Fig. 8-9(a), where $R_s = 1 \, \Omega$ and $R_\ell = 2 \, \Omega$. The element values of $\tilde{C}_1$ and $\tilde{L}_2$ are given by (8-43) through (8-45) as

$$\lambda = \left(\frac{2 - 1}{2 + 1}\right)^{1/2} = 0.58 \qquad (8\text{-}54)$$

$$\tilde{C}_1 = \frac{\alpha_1}{R_\ell(1 - \lambda)} = \frac{2 \sin \frac{\pi}{4}}{2(1 - 0.58)} = 1.67 \text{ F.} \qquad (8\text{-}55a)$$

$$\tilde{C}_1 \tilde{L}_2 = \frac{\alpha_1 \alpha_3}{1 - \lambda \beta_2 + \lambda^2}$$

$$= \frac{4 \sin \frac{\pi}{4} \sin \frac{3\pi}{4}}{1 - 0.58\left(2 \cos \frac{\pi}{2}\right) + (0.58)^2} = 1.5$$

Hence,

$$\hat{L}_2 = \frac{1.5}{\tilde{C}_1} = 0.90 \text{ H.} \tag{8-55b}$$

The desired filter circuit is shown in Fig. 8-11(a).

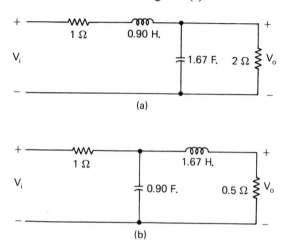

(a)

(b)

Fig. 8-11 Two circuit realizations of the desired filter of Example 8-3.

When $R_\ell = 0.5 R_s$, we use the circuit structure of Fig. 8-9(b), where $R_s = 1 \, \Omega$ and $R_\ell = 0.5 \, \Omega$. In this case, the element values of $\hat{L}_1$ and $\hat{C}_2$ can be obtained by

$$\lambda = \left(\frac{0.5}{1.5}\right)^{1/2} = 0.58 \tag{8-56}$$

$$\hat{L}_1 = \frac{\alpha_1 R_\ell}{1 - \lambda} = 1.67 \text{ H.} \tag{8-57a}$$

$$\hat{C}_2 = \frac{1.5}{\hat{L}_1} = 0.90 \text{ F.} \tag{8-57b}$$

The resulting circuit design is shown in Fig. 8-11(b).[13]

Both circuits in Fig. 8-11 are realizations of (8-53) and therefore satisfy the prescribed specifications of (8-52). ∎

8-2   THE CHEBYSHEV APPROXIMATION

A filter that uses all its degrees of freedom into making its magnitude response flat at the origin, such as a Butterworth filter, may not be the best filter. In many situations, it is more important to have the approximation uniformly good across the entire passband. A filter that has this uniform

---

[13]Observe that the circuits in Figs. 8-11(a) and (b) are *duals* of each other.

approximating property is the Chebyshev filter. The magnitude response of the Chebyshev filter ripples between two values in the passband, as shown in Fig. 8-12. The number of ripples in the passband depends on the order n of the filter. The amplitude of the ripple is a free parameter.

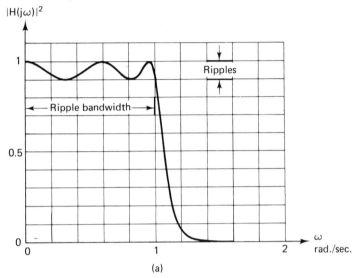

(a)

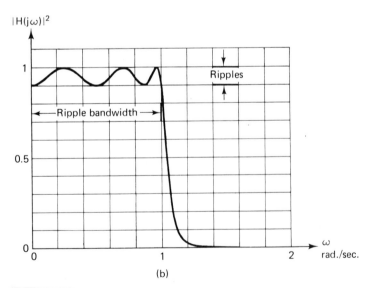

(b)

Fig. 8-12 Magnitude characteristics of Chebyshev filters. (a) $n = 5$. (b) $n = 6$.

8-2-1. Chebyshev Polynomials

It will be shown in the next few sections that Chebyshev filters are defined through the Chebyshev polynomials. In this section, we study some basic properties of Chebyshev polynomials.

The nth-order Chebyshev polynomial is given by

$$T_n(\omega) \triangleq \cos(n \cos^{-1} \omega) \qquad (8\text{-}58)$$

To see that $T_n(\omega)$ is a polynomial of ω, we define an intermediate variable

$$x \triangleq \cos^{-1} \omega \qquad (8\text{-}59)$$

Then

$$T_n(\omega) = \cos nx \qquad (8\text{-}60)$$

With the help of some trigonometry identities, (8-59) and (8-60) give

$$T_0(\omega) = \cos 0 = 1 \qquad (8\text{-}61\text{a})$$

$$T_1(\omega) = \cos x = \cos(\cos^{-1} \omega) = \omega \qquad (8\text{-}61\text{b})$$

$$T_2(\omega) = \cos 2x = 2\cos^2 x - 1 = 2\omega^2 - 1 \qquad (8\text{-}61\text{c})$$

$$T_3(\omega) = \cos 3x = -3\cos x + 4\cos^3 x = -3\omega + 4\omega^3 \qquad (8\text{-}61\text{d})$$

$$T_4(\omega) = 1 - 8\cos^2 x + 8\cos^4 x = 1 - 8\omega^2 + 8\omega^4 \qquad (8\text{-}61\text{e})$$

The recursive trigonometric relationship

$$\cos[(n+1)x] = 2\cos nx \cos x - \cos[(n-1)x] \qquad (8\text{-}62)$$

can be used to establish the Chebyshev polynomial recursive formula

$$T_{n+1}(\omega) = 2\omega T_n(\omega) - T_{n-1}(\omega) \quad n = 1, 2, \ldots \qquad (8\text{-}63)$$

With $T_0(\omega) = 1$ and $T_1(\omega) = \omega$, higher-order Chebyshev polynomials may be formed by using (8-63) repeatedly.

In view of (8-58) and (8-63), an nth-order Chebyshev polynomial has the following properties:

1. For all values of n, we have

$$0 \leq |T_n(\omega)| \leq 1 \quad \text{for} \quad 0 \leq |\omega| \leq 1 \qquad (8\text{-}64)$$

and

$$|T_n(\omega)| > 1 \quad \text{for} \quad |\omega| \geq 1 \qquad (8\text{-}65)$$

2. $T_n(\omega)$ is monotonically increasing for $\omega \geq 1$ and for all n.

3. $T_n(\omega)$ is an odd {even} polynomial of ω if n is an odd {even} integer.

4.

$$|T_n(0)| = 0 \quad \text{when } n \text{ is odd} \qquad (8\text{-}66\text{a})$$

and

$$|T_n(0)| = 1 \quad \text{when } n \text{ is even} \qquad (8\text{-}66\text{b})$$

For $|\omega| \leq 1$, $\cos^{-1} \omega$ is a real angle. Hence, $T_n(\omega)$ is the cosine of a real angle. This means that $T_n(\omega)$ oscillates between -1 and 1 for $|\omega| \leq 1$. For $|\omega| > 1$, $\cos^{-1} \omega$ is imaginary, and $\cos(n\cos^{-1}\omega)$ is a hyperbolic cosine function of a real angle. Because the hyperbolic cosine varies between 1 and ∞, $1 < |T_n(\omega)| < \infty$ for $|\omega| > 1$. Hence, property 1 is true.

Using the fact that both $\cosh(\cdot)$ and $\cosh^{-1}(\cdot)$ are monotonically increasing functions of their arguments, we can show that property 2 holds. Properties 3 and 4 are true in view of (8-63), with (8-61) as examples. As illustrations, plots of $T_n(\omega)$ versus ω for $n = 1, 2, 3$, and 4 are shown in Fig. 8-13.

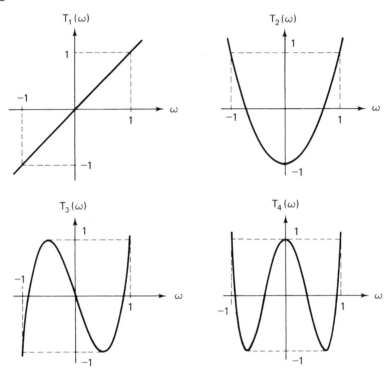

Fig. 8-13 Chebyshev polynomials.

8-2-2. Chebyshev Filters

Unlike the Butterworth functions, the Chebyshev polynomials do *not* possess all the properties of a magnitude function as stated in Theorem 8-1. However, they can be used to construct transfer functions that approximate the magnitude characteristics of normalized ideal low-pass filters. For a low-pass filter, the magnitude function must go to zero as $\omega \rightarrow \infty$. Thus, the Chebyshev polynomials should be part of the denominator polynomials of the magnitude function of the filter. A suitable squared magnitude function of the filter is

$$|H(j\omega)|^2 = \frac{1}{1 + \epsilon^2 T_n^2(\omega)} \tag{8-67}$$

where ϵ is a free parameter that sets the ripple amplitude shown in Fig. 8-12. By using the square of $\epsilon T_n(\omega)$, both the numerator and the denominator of $|H(j\omega)|^2$ are polynomials of ω^2 and have positive values. Hence, all conditions for a magnitude function as stated in Theorem 8-1 are satisfied by (8-67). This means that a valid transfer function can be extracted from (8-67). Henceforth, we call a filter having a squared magnitude function given by (8-67) *a normalized low-pass Chebyshev filter* (in short, Chebyshev filter) of order n.

Based on (8-67) and the properties of Chebyshev polynomials, an nth-order normalized low-pass Chebyshev filter has the following basic properties:

CHEBYSHEV PROPERTY 1   For $|\omega| \leq 1$, $|H(j\omega)|^2$ oscillates between $1/(1 + \epsilon^2)$ and 1. There are altogether n critical points in $0 \leq \omega \leq 1$, where $|H(j\omega)|^2$ attains either its maximum value of 1 or its minimum value of $1/(1 + \epsilon^2)$. This is the reason that Chebyshev filters are also called *equiripple filters*. As illustrations, Fig. 8-14 contains plots of $|H(j\omega)|^2$ of (8-67) versus ω for $0 \leq \omega \leq 1$. Note that the ripple bandwidth in the normalized case is 1 rad./sec. If $1/(1 + \epsilon^2) > 0.5$, which is normally the case, the 3 dB cutoff frequency ω_c of a normalized low-pass Chebyshev filter is larger than 1 rad./sec.

CHEBYSHEV PROPERTY 2   For $\omega \geq 1$, $|H(j\omega)|^2$ decreases monotonically toward zero. The high-frequency roll off is $20n$ dB/decade.

CHEBYSHEV PROPERTY 3   The squared magnitude function of an nth-order Chebyshev filter satisfies

$$|H(j1)|^2 = \frac{1}{1 + \epsilon^2} \tag{8-68}$$

$$|H(j0)|^2 = 1 \qquad \text{if } n \text{ is odd} \tag{8-69a}$$

and

$$|H(j0)|^2 = \frac{1}{1 + \epsilon^2} \quad \text{if } n \text{ is even} \tag{8-69b}$$

Given a set of passband and stopband specifications, the ripple parameter ϵ and the order of Chebyshev filter n can be determined. Normally, instead of ϵ, the maximum passband ripple attenuation $A_{\max}$ dB is given, where

$$A_{\max} \text{ dB} \triangleq -10 \log \frac{1}{1 + \epsilon^2} \tag{8-70}$$

$$= 10 \log (1 + \epsilon^2)$$

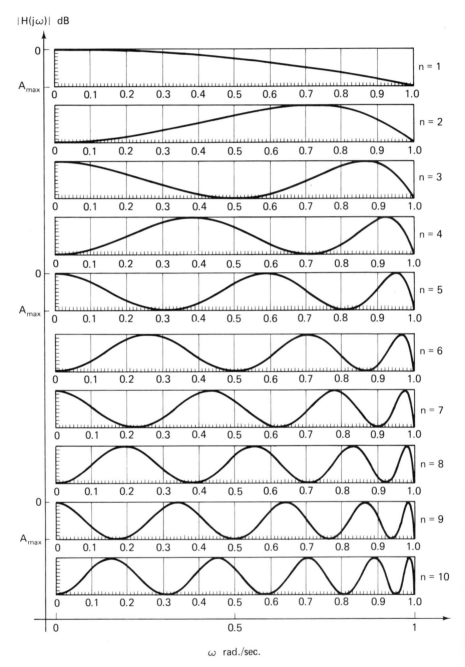

Fig. 8-14   Chebyshev passband ripples.

Hence, the ripple parameter ϵ is determined as

$$\epsilon = \sqrt{10^{(A_{max}/10)} - 1}\tag{8-71}$$

The order n of a Chebyshev filter is determined by other criteria such as dB roll off rate at high frequencies, desired cutoff frequencies, cost (number of components allowed), and other factors.

As design aids, Fig. 8-15 contains plots of the magnitude functions of Chebyshev filters for various values of passband ripple specifications.

Example 8-4 Suppose that we are to design a normalized equiripple low-pass filter to meet the following specifications:

(i) The maximum passband ripple attenuation is 1 dB.
(ii) The cutoff frequency $\omega_c \leq 1.2$ rad./sec.
(iii) The stopband attenuation is at least 40 dB for $\omega \geq 4$ rad./sec.

Find the desired magnitude function.

Solution: By (8-71), we have

$$\epsilon = \sqrt{10^{0.1} - 1} = 0.5088\tag{8-72}$$

To determine the order of the Chebyshev filter needed to satisfy the prescribed specifications, we can either use (8-67) with ϵ given by (8-72), or we can use the graphs in Fig. 8-15(e). Following the latter course, we find that condition (ii) implies that $n \geq 2$, whereas condition (iii) requires that $n \geq 3$. Hence, the third-order Chebyshev filter with ϵ given in (8-72) will satisfy all the filter specifications.

From (8-61), we have

$$T_3(\omega) = -3\omega + 4\omega^3\tag{8-73}$$

Substituting (8-72) and (8-73) into (8-67), we obtain the desired magnitude squared function

$$|H(j\omega)|^2 = \frac{1}{1 + \epsilon^2 T_3^2(\omega)}$$

$$= \frac{1}{1 + 0.2589(-3\omega + 4\omega^3)^2}\tag{8-74}$$

$$= \frac{1}{4.14\omega^6 - 6.21\omega^4 + 2.33\omega^2 + 1}\qquad\blacksquare$$

8-2-3. Transfer Function

As is in the case of a Butterworth filter, a Chebyshev filter has an all-pole transfer function—the numerator is a constant, and hence there are no finite zeros. The poles of the Chebyshev filter lie on an *ellipse* rather than on a circle as is in the case of the Butterworth filters. The major axis of the ellipse lies along the imaginary axis of the s-plane, and the minor axis lies along the

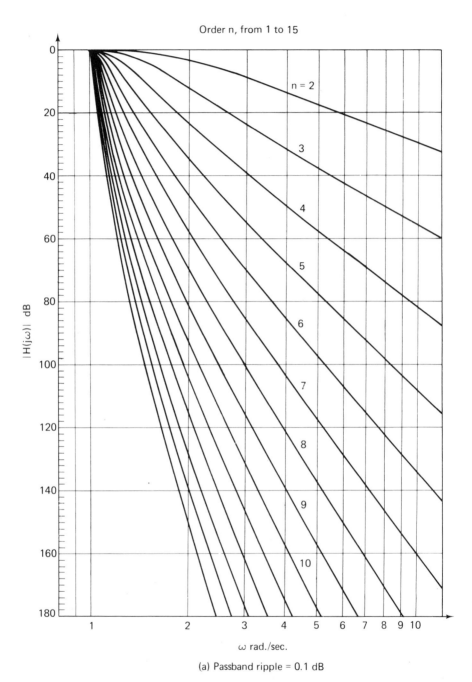

(a) Passband ripple = 0.1 dB

Fig. 8-15 Attenuation characteristics of Chebyshev filters.

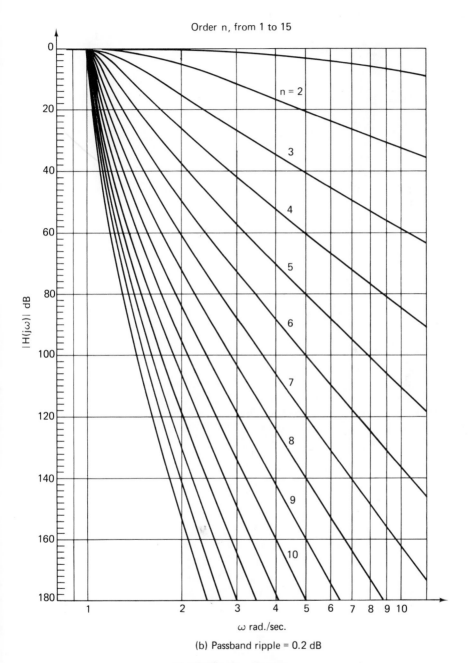

(b) Passband ripple = 0.2 dB

Fig. 8-15 (continued)

249

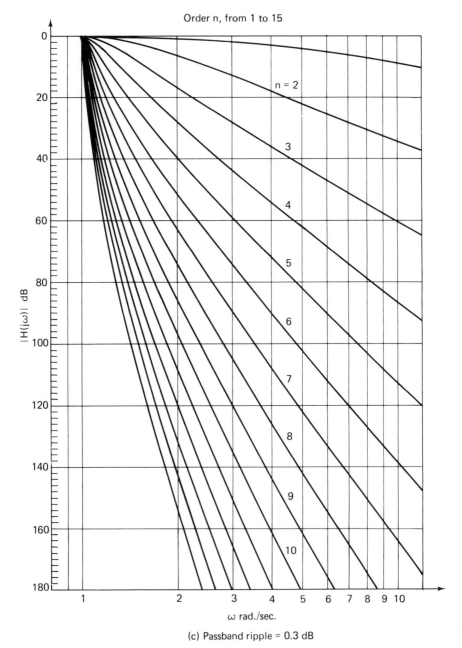

(c) Passband ripple = 0.3 dB

Fig. 8-15 (continued)

250

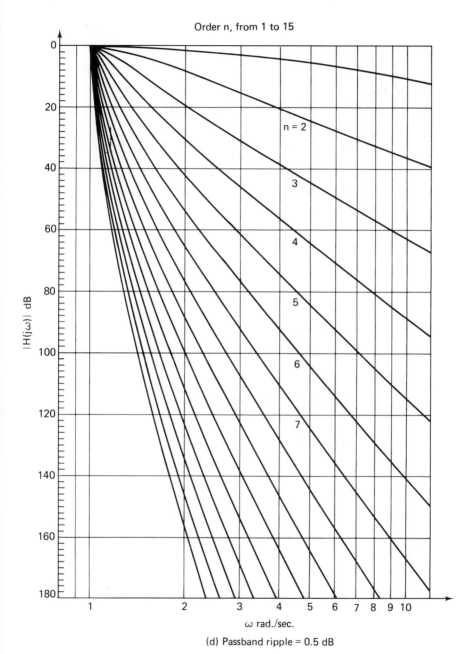

Order n, from 1 to 15

(d) Passband ripple = 0.5 dB

Fig. 8-15 (continued)

251

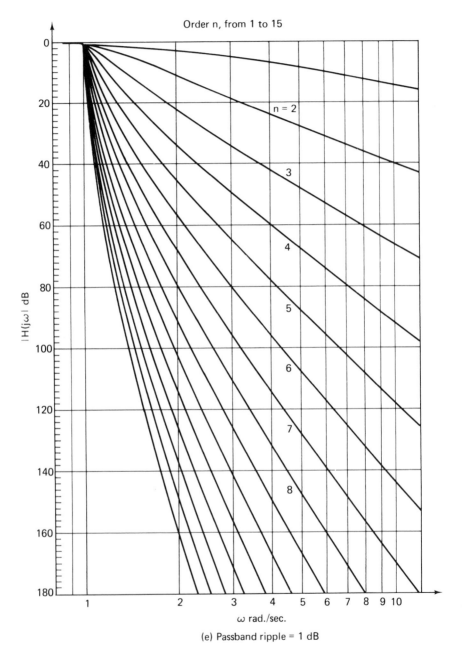

Order n, from 1 to 15

(e) Passband ripple = 1 dB

Fig. 8-15 (continued)

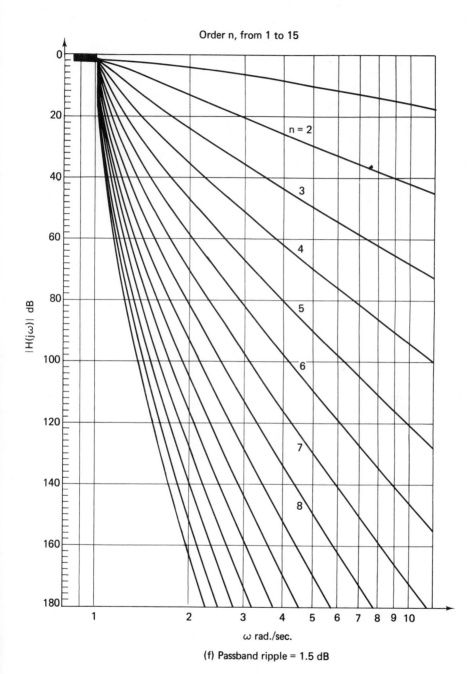

Order n, from 1 to 15

(f) Passband ripple = 1.5 dB

Fig. 8-15 (continued)

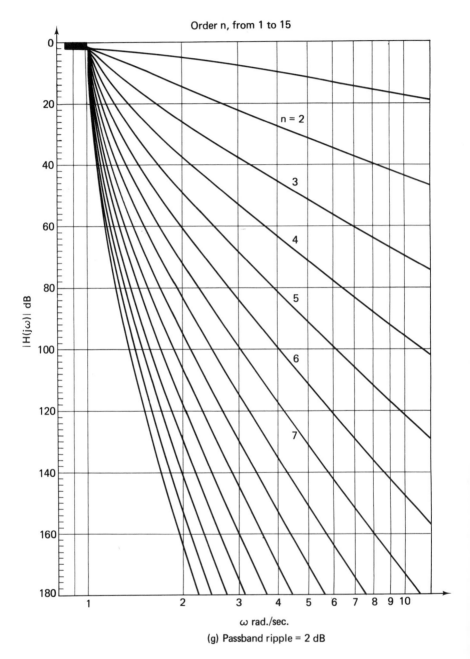

Order n, from 1 to 15

ω rad./sec.

(g) Passband ripple = 2 dB

Fig. 8-15 (continued)

254

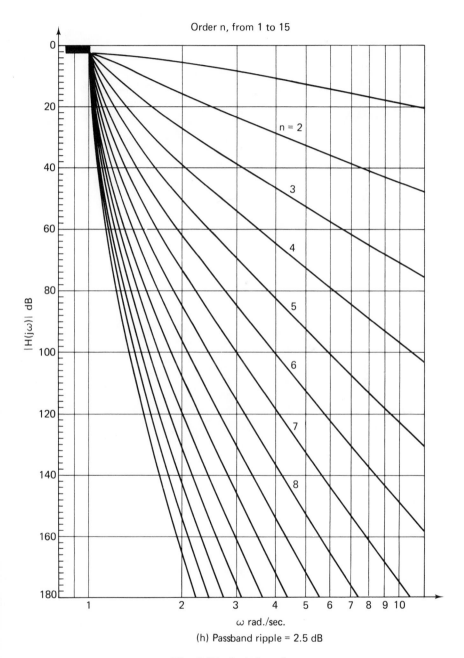

Order n, from 1 to 15

(h) Passband ripple = 2.5 dB

Fig. 8-15 (continued)

255

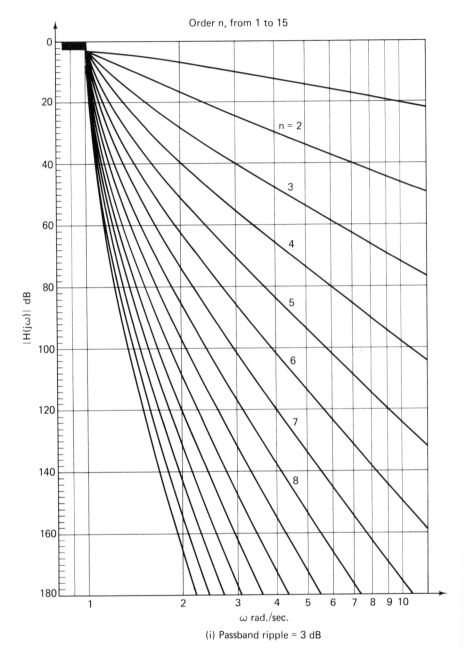

Order n, from 1 to 15

n = 2

3

4

5

6

7

8

$|H(j\omega)|$ dB

ω rad./sec.

(i) Passband ripple = 3 dB

Fig. 8-15 (continued)

real axis. It is obvious that the narrower the ellipse, the closer the poles are to the imaginary axis, and hence each individual pole will have a stronger impact, meaning that the ripples will be more pronounced. Thus, the prescribed ripple magnitude will have a strong effect on the pole locations of the resulting transfer function in the sense that the larger the ripples, the "skinnier" the ellipse will become.

To locate the poles of an nth-order Chebyshev transfer function, we first need to do some analytical work. Substituting (8-58) into (8-67), the magnitude function of an nth-order normalized low-pass Chebyshev filter is given by

$$|H(j\omega)|^2 = \frac{1}{1 + \epsilon^2 T_n^2(\omega)} = \frac{1}{1 + \epsilon^2 \cos^2 (n \cos^{-1} \omega)} \qquad (8\text{-}75)$$

Let us define a complex variable

$$\xi = \alpha + j\beta \triangleq \cos^{-1} \frac{s}{j} \qquad (8\text{-}76)$$

where $s = \sigma + j\omega$. Inverting the relationship of (8-76), we have

$$\frac{1}{j}[\sigma + j\omega] = \cos [\alpha + j\beta]$$

or

$$s = \sigma + j\omega = j \cos \alpha \cosh \beta + \sin \alpha \sinh \beta \qquad (8\text{-}77)$$

Equating the real and imaginary parts of (8-77), we obtain

$$\omega = \cos \alpha \cosh \beta \qquad (8\text{-}78a)$$
$$\sigma = \sin \alpha \sinh \beta \qquad (8\text{-}78b)$$

Substituting (8-76) into (8-75), we have

$$h(s) \triangleq H(s)H(-s) = |H(j\omega)|^2 \big|_{\omega=s/j}$$
$$= \frac{1}{1 + \epsilon^2 \cos^2 [n \cos^{-1} (s/j)]} = \frac{1}{1 + \epsilon^2 \cos^2 (n\xi)} \qquad (8\text{-}79)$$

Hence, the poles of $h(s)$ are the solutions of the equation

$$1 + \epsilon^2 \cos^2 n\xi = 0$$

or

$$(1 + j\epsilon \cos n\xi)(1 - j\epsilon \cos n\xi) = 0 \qquad (8\text{-}80)$$

The solutions of (8-80) are the solutions of the equation

$$1 \pm j\epsilon \cos n\xi = 0 \qquad (8\text{-}81)$$

Solving (8-81) is equivalent to solving

$$\cos n\xi = \cos [n\alpha + jn\beta]$$
$$= \cos n\alpha \cosh n\beta - j \sin n\alpha \sinh n\beta = \pm \frac{j}{\epsilon} \qquad (8\text{-}82)$$

Equating the real and imaginary parts of (8-82) gives

$$\cos n\alpha \cosh n\beta = 0 \tag{8-83a}$$

$$\sin n\alpha \sinh n\beta = \pm\frac{1}{\epsilon} \tag{8-83b}$$

which leads to the solutions

$$\alpha_k = \pm\frac{2k-1}{2n}\pi \tag{8-84a}$$

$$\beta_k = \pm\frac{1}{n}\sinh^{-1}\frac{1}{\epsilon} \tag{8-84b}$$

where k is a positive integer. Hence, by (8-78), the poles of an nth-order Chebyshev transfer function are at $s_k = \sigma_k + j\omega_k$, where[14]

$$\sigma_k = -\sinh\left[\frac{1}{n}\sinh^{-1}\frac{1}{\epsilon}\right]\sin\frac{2k-1}{2n}\pi \tag{8-85a}$$

$$\omega_k = \cosh\left[\frac{1}{n}\sinh^{-1}\frac{1}{\epsilon}\right]\cos\frac{2k-1}{2n}\pi \tag{8-85b}$$

and $k = 1, 2, \ldots, n$. By using the identity $\sin^2 x + \cos^2 x = 1$, (8-85) gives

$$\frac{\sigma_k^2}{\sinh^2\left[\dfrac{1}{n}\sinh^{-1}\dfrac{1}{\epsilon}\right]} + \frac{\omega_k^2}{\cosh^2\left[\dfrac{1}{n}\sinh^{-1}\dfrac{1}{\epsilon}\right]} = 1 \tag{8-86}$$

From (8-86), we conclude that all the poles $s_k = \sigma_k + j\omega_k$ are on an s-plane ellipse with

$$\text{minor axis} = a \triangleq \sinh\left[\frac{1}{n}\sinh^{-1}\frac{1}{\epsilon}\right] \tag{8-87a}$$

and

$$\text{major axis} = b \triangleq \cosh\left[\frac{1}{n}\sinh^{-1}\frac{1}{\epsilon}\right] \tag{8-87b}$$

Hence, the poles of a normalized low pass Chebyshev filter can be determined once ϵ and n are known. Figure 8-16 shows this ellipse with the vertical and the horizontal apices being given by b and a, respectively, where b and a can also be written as

$$b = \frac{1}{2}\left\{\left[\sqrt{\frac{1}{\epsilon^2}+1}+\frac{1}{\epsilon}\right]^{1/n} + \left[\sqrt{1+\frac{1}{\epsilon^2}}+\frac{1}{\epsilon}\right]^{-1/n}\right\} \tag{8-88a}$$

$$a = \frac{1}{2}\left\{\left[\sqrt{\frac{1}{\epsilon^2}+1}+\frac{1}{\epsilon}\right]^{1/n} - \left[\sqrt{1+\frac{1}{\epsilon^2}}+\frac{1}{\epsilon}\right]^{-1/n}\right\} \tag{8-88b}$$

The poles on the ellipse may be geometrically related to the poles of two Butterworth circles with radii a and b. The vertical pole position of an nth-order Chebyshev filter is equal to the vertical position of the corresponding poles of an nth-order Butterworth filter on the larger circle (with radius b),

---

[14]These are the LH s-plane poles of $h(s) = H(s)H(-s)$.

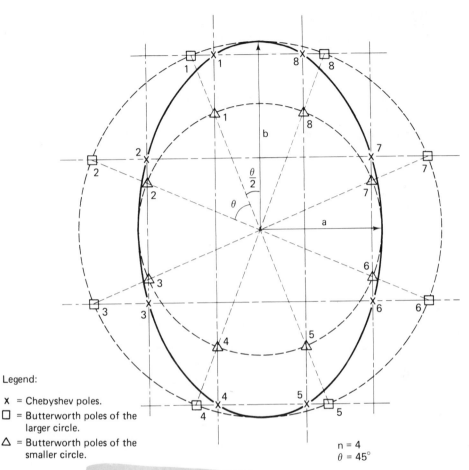

Fig. 8-16 Graphical construction of Chebyshev poles.

and the horizontal Chebyshev pole position is the horizontal position of the same Butterworth pole on the smaller circle (with radius a). See Fig. 8-16 for the construction lines. In view of the relationships between the Butterworth and the Chebyshev pole locations, an nth-order Chebyshev filter will have a negative real pole at $s = -a$ when n is an odd integer.

To find the transfer function $H(s)$ of a normalized Chebyshev low pass filter from the given squared magnitude function of (8-67), we again use the following three steps:

STEP 0. Form $H(s)H(-s) = 1/[1 + \epsilon^2 T_n^2(s/j)]$.

STEP 1. Find the poles of $H(s)H(-s)$. This can be done either graphically, by constructing a figure similar to that of Fig. 8-16 for a set of given values of n and ϵ, or analytically as indicated by (8-85).

STEP 2. Factors associated with the LH s-plane poles are assigned to $H(s)$. Hence, the transfer function is given by

$$H(s) = \prod_{\substack{\text{LH } s\text{-plane} \\ \text{poles}}} \frac{1}{(s - s_k)} \tag{8-89}$$

where s_k for $k = 1, 2, \ldots, n$ are defined by (8-85).

Example 8-5 Find the transfer function of the third-order Chebyshev filter with 1 dB passband ripples.

Solution: Because $A_{max} = 1$ dB, (8-71) gives

$$\epsilon = 0.5088 \tag{8-90}$$

From mathematical tables, we find that

$$\sinh^{-1} \frac{1}{\epsilon} = \sinh^{-1} 1.9652 = 1.4280$$

Because $n = 3$,

$$\frac{1}{n} \sinh^{-1} \frac{1}{\epsilon} = \frac{1.4280}{3} = 0.4760 \tag{8-91}$$

Again, from mathematical tables, we find that

$$\sinh \left[\frac{1}{n} \sinh^{-1} \frac{1}{\epsilon} \right] = 0.4942 \tag{8-92a}$$

$$\cosh \left[\frac{1}{n} \sinh^{-1} \frac{1}{\epsilon} \right] = 1.1154 \tag{8-92b}$$

Using (8-85), we have

$$\sigma_1 = -0.4942 \sin \frac{\pi}{6} = -0.2471 \tag{8-93a}$$

$$\omega_1 = 1.1154 \cos \frac{\pi}{6} = 0.9660 \tag{8-93b}$$

$$\sigma_2 = -0.4942 \sin \frac{\pi}{2} = -0.4942 \tag{8-94a}$$

$$\omega_2 = 1.1154 \cos \frac{\pi}{2} = 0 \tag{8-94b}$$

$$\sigma_3 = -0.4942 \sin \frac{5\pi}{6} = -0.2471 \tag{8-95a}$$

$$\omega_3 = 1.1154 \cos \frac{5\pi}{6} = -0.9660 \tag{8-95b}$$

This means that the pole locations are at

$$s_1 = \sigma_1 + j\omega_1 = -0.2471 + j0.9660 \tag{8-96a}$$

$$s_2 = \sigma_2 + j\omega_2 = -0.4942 \tag{8-96b}$$

$$s_3 = \sigma_3 + j\omega_3 = -0.2471 - j0.9660 \tag{8-96c}$$

Hence, the desired transfer function is given by

$$H(s) = \frac{k}{(s - s_1)(s - s_2)(s - s_3)}$$

$$= \frac{k}{(s + 0.4942)[(s + 0.2471)^2 + (0.9660)^2]} \qquad (8\text{-}97)$$

$$= \frac{k}{s^3 + 0.9883s^2 + 1.2384s + 0.4913} \qquad \blacksquare$$

8-2-4. Circuit Realization

From (8-89), an nth-order low-pass Chebyshev filter is characterized by an all-pole transfer function with a Hurwitz denominator polynomial. This implies that the (simplified) Darlington synthesis procedures in Section 7-3 can be used to realize Chebyshev filters. In particular, because all transmission zeros are at $s = \infty$, Cauer's first form is used to realize the lossless 2-port. A typical circuit structure to realize a voltage-ratio transfer function of a Chebyshev filter is given in Fig. 8-17. By defining

$$a = \frac{4R_\ell}{(R_\ell + 1)^2} \qquad \text{when } n \text{ is odd} \qquad (8\text{-}98a)$$

and

$$a = \frac{4R_\ell}{(R_\ell + 1)^2}[1 + \epsilon^2] \le 1 \quad \text{when } n \text{ is even} \qquad (8\text{-}98b)$$

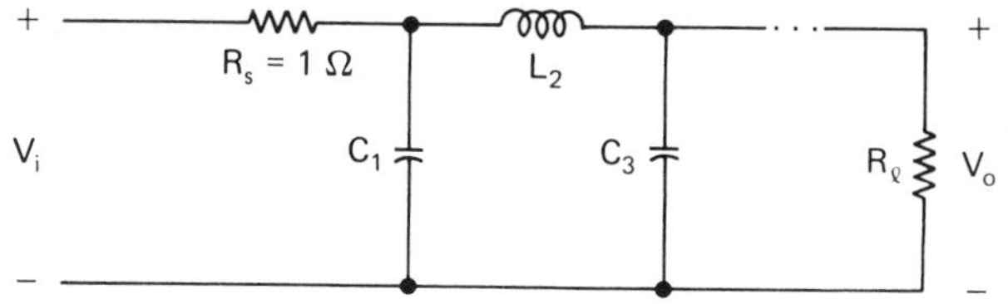

Fig. 8-17   Circuit structure of low-pass Chebyshev filters.

where R_ℓ is arbitrary, except when n is even, R_ℓ has to satisfy the inequality constraint of (8-98b), and by letting

$$\alpha_i = 2 \sin \frac{\pi i}{2n} \qquad (8\text{-}99a)$$

$$\beta_i = 2 \cos \frac{\pi i}{2n} \qquad (8\text{-}99b)$$

$$\gamma = \left[\frac{1}{\epsilon} + \sqrt{\frac{1}{\epsilon^2} + 1} \right]^{1/n} \qquad (8\text{-}99c)$$

$$\delta = \left[\sqrt{\frac{1 - a}{\epsilon^2}} + \sqrt{\frac{1 - a}{\epsilon^2} + 1} \right]^{1/n} \qquad (8\text{-}99d)$$

$$x = \gamma - \frac{1}{\gamma} \qquad (8\text{-}99e)$$

and

$$y = \delta - \frac{1}{\delta} \qquad (8\text{-}99f)$$

the element values of Fig. 8-17 can be found by a recursive relationship

$$C_{2m-1}L_{2m} = \frac{4\alpha_{4m-3}\alpha_{4m-1}}{b_{2m-1}(x,y)} \qquad (8\text{-}100a)$$

$$C_{2m+1}L_{2m} = \frac{4\alpha_{4m-1}\alpha_{4m+1}}{b_{2m}(x,y)} \qquad (8\text{-}100b)$$

with

$$C_1 = \frac{2\alpha_1}{x-y} \qquad (8\text{-}100c)$$

where the function $b_i(x,y)$ is defined by

$$b_i(x,y) \triangleq x^2 - \beta_{2i}xy + y^2 + \alpha_{2i}^2 \qquad (8\text{-}100d)$$

and

$$m = 1, 2, \ldots, \frac{n-1}{2} \quad \text{when } n \text{ is odd}$$

$$\qquad (8\text{-}100e)$$

$$= 1, 2, \ldots, \frac{n}{2} \quad \text{when } n \text{ is even}$$

Given the parameters n and ϵ of a Chebyshev filter, we can calculate all the dependent variables in (8-99). By (8-100c), we find C_1. With C_1 known and $m = 1$, we can use (8-100a) to find L_2 and then (8-100b) to find C_3. Then set $m = 2$, and repeat the process of (8-100a) and (8-100b). This process can be repeated as m is incremented. For convenience, Tables 8-2 and 8-3 give values for the circuit elements of Fig. 8-17. Table 8-2 is for the case when $A_{max} = 0.1$ dB, and Table 8-3 is for the case when $A_{max} = 1$ dB.

TABLE 8-2 Values of Circuit Elements in Chebyshev Filters when $A_{max} = 0.1$ dB

n	R_ℓ	C_1	L_2	C_3	L_4	C_5	L_6	C_7	L_8	C_9
1	1.0	0.3052								
2	0.5	1.5715	0.2880							
3	1.0	1.0316	1.1474	1.0316						
4	0.5	2.3545	0.7973	2.6600	0.3626					
5	1.0	1.1468	1.3712	1.9750	1.3712	1.1468				
6	0.5	2.5561	0.8962	3.3962	0.8761	2.8071	0.3785			
7	1.0	1.1812	1.4228	2.0967	1.5734	2.0967	1.4228	1.1812		
8	0.5	2.6324	0.9285	3.5762	0.9619	3.5095	0.8950	2.8547	0.3843	
9	1.0	1.1957	1.4426	2.1346	1.6167	2.2054	1.6167	2.1346	1.4426	1.1957

TABLE 8-3 Values of Circuit Elements in Chebyshev Filters when $A_{max} = 1$ dB

n	R_ℓ	C_1	L_2	C_3	L_4	C_5	L_6	C_7	L_8	C_9
1	1.00	1.0177								
2	0.25	3.7779	0.3001							
3	1.00	2.0236	0.9941	2.0236						
4	0.25	4.5699	0.5428	5.3680	0.3406					
5	1.00	2.1349	1.0911	3.0009	1.0911	2.1349				
6	0.25	4.7366	0.5716	6.0240	0.5764	5.5353	0.3486			
7	1.00	2.1666	1.1115	3.0936	1.1735	3.0936	1.1115	2.1666		
8	0.25	4.7966	0.5803	6.1592	0.6005	6.1501	0.5836	5.5869	0.3515	
9	1.00	2.1797	1.1192	3.1214	1.1897	3.1746	1.1897	3.1214	1.1192	2.1797

8-2-5. Examples

Example 8-6 Design and realize a Chebyshev filter to meet the specifications of Example 8-4.

Solution: From Example 8-4, we conclude that a third-order Chebyshev filter with a passband ripple height of 1 dB is needed to meet the prescribed specifications. From Table 8-3, a circuit realization is given in Fig. 8-18. Indeed, an

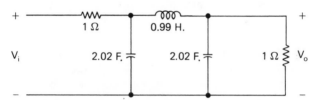

Fig. 8-18 A realization of the desired filter circuit of Example 8-6.

analysis of the circuit in Fig. 8-18 yields the transfer function

$$\hat{H}(s) = \frac{0.245}{s^3 + 0.99s^2 + 1.24s + 0.49}$$

which is a constant multiple of the transfer function obtained in Example 8-4.

■

Example 8-7 Suppose that we are to design an equiripple low-pass filter with the following specifications:

(i) The passband ripple is 0.1 dB, and the ripple bandwidth is 1 rad./sec.
(ii) For $\omega \geq 6$ rad./sec., the magnitude function is at least 20 dB down.

Find a desired filter circuit.

from fig   8-15 ⓐ   n ≥ 2

Solution: Let us first find the order of the Chebyshev filter needed to meet the prescribed specifications. By checking the design graphs of Fig. 8-15(a), we find that the second-order Chebyshev filter will satisfy all the specifications. From Fig. 8-17 and Table 8-2, a desired circuit is shown in Fig. 8-19. ∎

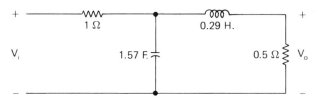

Fig. 8-19 A realization of the desired filter circuit of Example 8-7.

8-2-6. Elliptic Filters

The Butterworth and Chebyshev filters have transfer functions that are in the form of a constant divided by a polynomial. That is, all transmission zeros occur at $s = \infty$. In some cases, this is not ideal; there are some instances when one desires to have some finite transmission zeros. In 1931, Cauer showed that one could get a much better approximation to the ideal low-pass magnitude characteristics if a filter with finite frequency transmission zeros was used. He found that by a proper selection of the poles and zeros, a filter with equal ripples in *both* the pass- and the stopbands could be designed. Because the zero locations are related to the elliptic functions of classical field theory, these filters are often called *elliptic* filters. Another name commonly used is *Cauer* filters because of Cauer's original work.

The starting point for the design of elliptic filters is similar to the form for the Chebyshev filters. The magnitude function of an elliptic filter is given by

$$|H(j\omega)|^2 = \frac{1}{1 + \epsilon^2 R_n^2(\omega)} \tag{8-101}$$

where the rational function $R_n(\omega)$ is in the form of[15]

$$R_n(\omega) = \frac{\omega(\omega_1^2 - \omega^2)(\omega_2^2 - \omega^2)\ldots(\omega_k^2 - \omega^2)}{(1 - \omega_1^2\omega^2)(1 - \omega_2^2\omega^2)\ldots(1 - \omega_k^2\omega^2)} \tag{8-102a}$$

when n is odd and $k = (n - 1)/2$; and

$$R_n(\omega) = \frac{(\omega_1^2 - \omega^2)(\omega_2^2 - \omega^2)\ldots(\omega_k^2 - \omega^2)}{(1 - \omega_1^2\omega^2)(1 - \omega_2^2\omega^2)\ldots(1 - \omega_k^2\omega^2)} \tag{8-102b}$$

when n is even and $k = n/2$, where

$$0 < \omega_i < 1 \quad \text{for} \quad i = 1, 2, \ldots, k \tag{8-102c}$$

---

[15]Observe that the poles and zeros of $R_n(s)$ are symmetric with respect to the cutoff frequency $\omega_c = 1$ rad./sec.

The $2k$ conjugate pairs of critical frequencies

$$s = \pm j\omega_i \quad \text{and} \quad s = \pm j\frac{1}{\omega_i} \quad \text{for} \quad i = 1, 2, \ldots, k \quad (8\text{-}103)$$

have the following two properties:

$$|H(j\omega_i)|^2 = 1 \quad (8\text{-}104a)$$

and

$$\left|H\left(j\frac{1}{\omega_i}\right)\right|^2 = 0 \quad (8\text{-}104b)$$

In view of (8-102c) and (8-104b), the transmission zeros of normalized elliptic filters are at frequencies higher than 1 rad./sec. or in the stopband.

The design parameters in elliptic filters are the critical frequencies ω_i, where $i = 1, 2, \ldots, k$, and ϵ. These parameters are chosen to satisfy the magnitude specifications

$$A_1 \leq |H(j\omega)|^2 \leq 1 \quad \text{for} \quad |\omega| \leq \omega_{c1} \quad (8\text{-}105a)$$

and

$$|H(j\omega)|^2 \leq A_2 \quad \text{for} \quad |\omega| \geq \omega_{c2} \quad (8\text{-}105b)$$

as illustrated in Fig. 8-20(a), where ω_{c1} is the passband ripple edge, ω_{c2} is the stopband ripple edge, and

$$\omega_{c1} < 1 < \omega_{c2} \quad (8\text{-}106a)$$

$$\omega_{c1}\omega_{c2} = 1 \quad (8\text{-}106b)$$

Comparing (8-101) and (8-105a), we must have

$$A_1 = \frac{1}{1 + \epsilon^2\Delta^2} \quad (8\text{-}107)$$

where Δ is the maximum value of $|R_n(\omega)|$ for $|\omega| \leq \omega_{c1}$. From (8-102), we have

$$R_n\left(\frac{1}{\omega}\right) = \frac{1}{R_n(\omega)} \quad (8\text{-}108)$$

This implies that the minimum value of $|R_n(\omega)|$ for $|\omega| \geq \omega_{c2}$ is $1/\Delta$. Hence, (8-105b) requires that

$$A_2 = \frac{1}{1 + (\epsilon^2/\Delta^2)} \quad (8\text{-}109)$$

The derivations of the design parameters ω_i, $i = 1, 2, \ldots, k$, and ϵ to satisfy the prescribed specifications of (8-107) and (8-109) are complicated and are not pursued here.[16] An example of a fifth-order elliptic filter satisfying the conditions of (8-105) with $A_1 = 0.9$, $A_2 = 0.1$, $\omega_{c1} = 0.940$ rad./sec., and $\omega_{c2} = 1.064$ rad./sec. is shown in Fig. 8-20(b).

---

[16]See References [1], [2], [9], and [10] for more details.

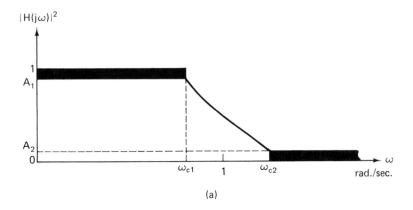

(a)

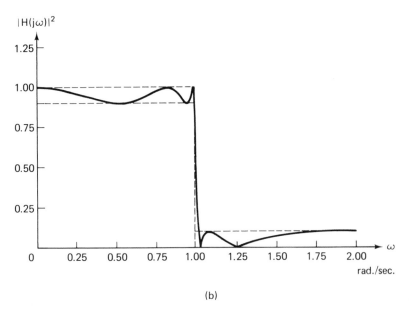

(b)

Fig. 8-20   Magnitude characteristics of elliptic filters. (a) Approximation to the ideal characteristics. (b) An example of a fifth-order elliptic
filter.

8-3   THE BESSEL APPROXIMATION

The Butterworth, the Chebyshev, and the elliptic filters approximate the
magnitude of the ideal low-pass filter. In other engineering situations, it is
more important to approximate the phase shift function specified in Fig.
8-2(b). The easiest way to relate the linear phase or constant group delay
specifications of the ideal filter to the polynomials in a transfer function is to
first write the transfer function in the polar form. That is,

$$H(j\omega) = R(\omega) + jX(\omega) = |H(j\omega)| \exp[j\underline{/H(j\omega)}]$$
$$= \exp[-\alpha(\omega) - j\phi(\omega)] \tag{8-110}$$

where

$$-\alpha(\omega) \triangleq \ell n |H(j\omega)| \tag{8-111}$$

and

$$\phi(\omega) = -\tan^{-1} \frac{X(\omega)}{R(\omega)} = -\underline{/(H(j\omega)} \tag{8-112}$$

Note that the arctangent function of $\phi(\omega)$ in (8-112) is not easy to work with. Fortunately, the group delay function $\tau(\omega)$ given by

$$\tau(\omega) = \frac{d\phi(\omega)}{d\omega} = -\frac{d}{d\omega} \tan^{-1} \frac{X(\omega)}{R(\omega)}$$

$$= \frac{1}{1 + \dfrac{X^2(\omega)}{R^2(\omega)}} \left[\frac{X(\omega)\dfrac{dR(\omega)}{d\omega} - R(\omega)\dfrac{dX(\omega)}{d\omega}}{R^2(\omega)} \right] \tag{8-113}$$

$$= \frac{X(\omega)R'(\omega) - R(\omega)X'(\omega)}{|H(j\omega)|^2}$$

is a rational function and is more amenable to manipulation, where the prime indicates the derivative with respect to ω. If it is desired to have a linear phase filter, then it is desired to have a group delay function equal to a constant.

Recall that $R(\omega)$ is an even function, $X(\omega)$ is an odd functiom, and the derivative of an even function is odd and vice versa. Furthermore, we know that the product of two even functions is even, as is the product of two odd functions. Thus, $\tau(\omega)$ is an even function. In addition, this group delay function $\tau(\omega)$ is a ratio of two polynomials in ω^2. Consequently, the problem of finding a $\tau(\omega)$ that approximates a constant is not much different from that of finding an $|H(j\omega)|^2$ that approximates a constant over the passband. The main difference is that the behavior of $\tau(\omega)$ or $\phi(\omega)$ outside the passband is not important. Before we proceed to the technical aspects of phase processing filters, it should be pointed out that not all phase filters are designed to have a linear phase. For example, most phase lead, phase lag, and nonlinear phase-compensation circuits are not designed to have linear phase characteristics.

8-3-1. Transfer Function

A straightforward approach to calculating the polynomial of a *maximally flat delay* low pass filter is to first assume a general all-pole transfer function

$$H(s) = \frac{a_0}{a_0 + a_1 s + a_2 s^2 + \ldots + a_{n-1}s^{n-1} + s^n}$$

$$= \frac{a_0}{M_2(s) + N_2(s)} \tag{8-114}$$

where
$$M_2(s) = a_0 + a_2 s^2 + \dots \tag{8-115a}$$
and
$$N_2(s) = a_1 s + a_3 s^3 + \dots . \tag{8-115b}$$
are the even and odd parts of the denominator of $H(s)$. Then $H(s)$ can be written as

$$
\begin{aligned}
H(s) &= \frac{a_0}{M_2(s) + N_2(s)} = \frac{a_0[M_2(s) - N_2(s)]}{M_2^2(s) - N_2^2(s)} \\
&= \frac{a_0 M_2(s)}{M_2^2(s) - N_2^2(s)} + \frac{-a_0 N_2(s)}{M_2^2(s) - N_2^2(s)} \\
&= M(s) + N(s)
\end{aligned}
\tag{8-116}
$$

where
$$M(s) \triangleq \frac{a_0 M_2(s)}{M_2^2(s) - N_2^2(s)} \tag{8-117a}$$
and
$$N(s) \triangleq \frac{-a_0 N_2(s)}{M_2^2(s) - N_2^2(s)} \tag{8-117b}$$

are, respectively, the even and odd parts of $H(s)$. Hence,

$$R(\omega) \triangleq \mathrm{Re}\,[H(j\omega)] = \frac{a_0 M_2(j\omega)}{M_2^2(j\omega) - N_2^2(j\omega)} \tag{8-118a}$$

$$
\begin{aligned}
X(\omega) \triangleq \mathrm{Im}\,[H(j\omega)] &= -\frac{a_0 N_2(j\omega)}{j[M_2^2(j\omega) - N_2^2(j\omega)]} \\
&= j\frac{a_0 N_2(j\omega)}{M_2^2(j\omega) - N_2^2(j\omega)}
\end{aligned}
\tag{8-118b}
$$

and
$$|H(j\omega)|^2 = \frac{a_0^2}{M_2^2(j\omega) - N_2^2(j\omega)} \tag{8-118c}$$

By substituting (8-118) into (8-113), the resultant equation can be simplified and recast to

$$\tau\left(\frac{s}{j}\right) = \frac{M_2(s)N_2'(s) - N_2(s)M_2'(s)}{M_2^2(s) - N_2^2(s)} \tag{8-119}$$

where the prime denotes derivatives with respect to s. With (8-115), (8-119) can be written as:

$$\tau\left(\frac{s}{j}\right) = \frac{a_0 a_1 + (3a_0 a_3 - a_1 a_2)s^2 + (5a_0 a_5 - 3a_1 a_4 + a_2 a_3)s^4 + \dots}{a_0^2 + (2a_0 a_2 - a_1^2)s^2 + (2a_0 a_4 - 2a_1 a_3 + a_2^2)s^4 + \dots} \tag{8-120}$$

Consider now the specific case when $n = 3$ in (8-114); (8-120) takes the form

$$\tau\left(\frac{s}{j}\right) = \frac{a_0 a_1 + (3a_0 - a_1 a_2)s^2 + a_2 s^4}{a_0^2 + (2a_0 a_2 - a_1^2)s^2 + (-2a_1 + a_2^2)s^4 - s^6} \tag{8-121}$$

Suppose that it is desired to design a unity group delay filter—$\tau(0) = 1$. In this case, (8-111) requires that $a_0 = a_1$, because

$$\tau(0) = \frac{a_0 a_1}{a_0^2} = \frac{a_1}{a_0} \tag{8-122}$$

Hence, an optimal Taylor approximation of the constant unit delay is now made by forcing as many derivatives as possible of the error function

$$e\left(\frac{s}{j}\right) \triangleq \tau\left(\frac{s}{j}\right) - \tau(0) = \tau\left(\frac{s}{j}\right) - 1$$

$$= \frac{(3a_1 - 3a_1 a_2 + a_1^2)s^2 + (a_2 + 2a_1 - a_2^2)s^4 + s^6}{a_1^2 + (2a_1 a_2 - a_1^2)s^2 + (-2a_1 + a_2^2)s^4 - s^6} \tag{8-123}$$

to vanish at $s = 0$. Alternatively, we can force the error function to have as many zeros as possible at $s = 0$. This is equivalent to having all numerator coefficients, except the one associated with the highest-degree term of $e(s/j)$, to be zero. The latter proposal gives rise to a set of simultaneous equations

$$3 - 3a_2 + a_1 = 0 \tag{8-124a}$$

$$a_2 + 2a_1 - a_2^2 = 0 \tag{8-124b}$$

Note that (8-124) is a system of *nonlinear* equations involving a_1 and a_2 as unknowns. The solution of (8-124) gives $a_2 = 6$ and $a_1 = a_0 = 15$. Thus, the desired transfer function is:

$$H(s) = \frac{a_0}{a_0 + a_1 s + a_2 s^2 + s^3} = \frac{15}{15 + 15s + 6s^2 + s^3} \tag{8-125}$$

This method is optimum. However, when the order of the filter is high, it is very difficult to obtain a set of solutions for a system of *nonlinear* simultaneous equations, such as (8-124), which invariably arise in this method.

The aforementioned method is messy, but it illustrates the basic procedure. Very often, in real life, there are no short and easy methods to replace the often clumsy and time-consuming procedures. Fortunately, in this case, an easier way has been developed. By relating the denominator of an all-pole transfer function to a certain class of Bessel polynomials, a maximally flat group delay filter results. This type of filter is called the *Bessel* filter. To be more precise, a low pass Bessel filter of order n is characterized by a transfer function

$$H(s) = \frac{k}{\hat{B}_n(s)} \tag{8-126}$$

where $\hat{B}_n(s)$ is the nth-degree Bessel polynomial and $k \triangleq \hat{B}_n(0)$. By knowing the Bessel polynomials for $n = 1$ and $n = 2$ as

$$\hat{B}_1(s) = s + 1 \tag{8-127a}$$

and

$$\hat{B}_2(s) = s^2 + 3s + 3 \tag{8-127b}$$

a Bessel polynomial of order n, $\hat{B}_n(s)$, can be found from the recursive formula

$$\hat{B}_n(s) = (2n - 1)\hat{B}_{n-1}(s) + s^2\hat{B}_{n-2}(s) \qquad (8\text{-}128)$$

For example,

$$\begin{aligned}
\hat{B}_3(s) &= (6 - 1)\hat{B}_2(s) + s^2\hat{B}_1(s) \\
&= 5(s^2 + 3s + 3) + s^2(s + 1) \qquad (8\text{-}129) \\
&= s^3 + 6s^2 + 15s + 15
\end{aligned}$$

Substituting (8-129) into (8-126), we obtain the transfer function of (8-125). Figure 8-21 gives the phase and the group delay characteristics of low pass Bessel filters of order n from $n = 1$ to $n = 10$. Observe that between $\omega = 0$ and $\omega = 1$ rad./sec., all Bessel filters of order $n \geq 2$ approximate the linear phase characteristic of Fig. 8-2(b) very well.

Note that Bessel filters of (8-126) will only produce a unity group delay

$$\tau(0) = 1 \qquad (8\text{-}130)$$

If it is desired to have

$$\tau(0) = \tau_0 \neq 1 \qquad (8\text{-}131)$$

then we need to perform a transformation[17]

$$s \mapsto \tau_0 s \qquad (8\text{-}132a)$$

or

$$\omega \mapsto \tau_0 \omega \qquad (8\text{-}132b)$$

where "$\mapsto$" means to replace s by $\tau_0 s$ or ω by $\tau_0 \omega$. In essence, (8-132) is to scale the horizontal axis of the Bessel filter's phase plots by $1/\tau_0$ while the vertical scale remains unchanged. Hence, a slope of 1 or

$$\frac{\Delta\phi(\omega)}{\Delta\omega} = 1 \qquad (8\text{-}133)$$

becomes a slope of

$$\frac{\Delta\phi(\omega)}{\Delta\omega/\tau_0} = \tau_0 \qquad (8\text{-}134)$$

For this reason, we also label the horizontal axis of Fig. 8-21 as $\tau_0\omega$ rad. in addition to ω rad./sec. Hence, the transfer function of a linear phase low pass filter with τ_0 group delay is given by

$$H(s) = \frac{k}{\hat{B}_n(\tau_0 s)} \qquad (8\text{-}135)$$

where

$$k = \hat{B}_n(0) \qquad (8\text{-}136)$$

This form of $H(s)$ makes sure that the resulting filter will have a magnitude function of a low-pass type. The degree of the denominator used in (8-135) depends on the specifications and other considerations. The larger the value

---

[17]The symbol "$\mapsto$" is used very frequently hereafter, especially in Sec. 8-4 and in Chapter 12.

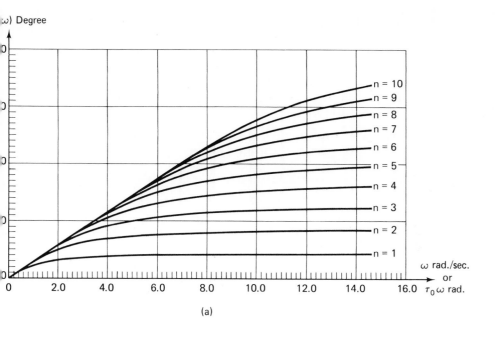

(a)

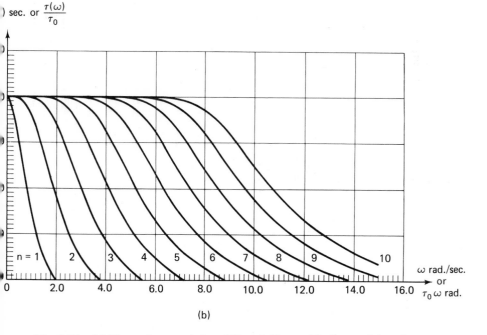

(b)

Fig. 8-21 (a) Phase characteristics of Bessel filters. (b) Group delay characteristics of Bessel filters.

of n, the better will the resulting filter approximate a constant τ_0 unit group delay over a larger frequency band, as illustrated in Fig. 8-21(b).

Example 8-8   Find the transfer function of a second-order low-pass maximally flat group delay filter with $\tau(0) = 3$.

Solution: We solve this problem in two ways. The first method employs the coefficient balancing technique, and the second method utilizes the Bessel polynomials and the frequency scaling technique of (8-132).

Assume the transfer function $H(s)$ to be of the form

$$H(s) = \frac{k}{s^2 + b_1 s + b_0} \tag{8-137}$$

By (8-119), the group delay function is given by

$$\tau\left(\frac{s}{j}\right) = \frac{(s^2 + b_0)b_1 - b_1 s(2s)}{(s^2 + b_0)^2 - b_1^2 s^2} \tag{8-138}$$

Define

$$e(s) \triangleq \tau\left(\frac{s}{j}\right) - \tau(0) = \tau\left(\frac{s}{j}\right) - 3$$

$$= \frac{-3s^4 + (3b_1^2 - b_1 - 6b_0)s^2 + b_0(b_1 - 3b_0)}{(s^2 + b_0)^2 - b_1^2 s^2} \tag{8-139}$$

Hence, we need to set

$$3b_1^2 - b_1 - 6b_0 = 0 \tag{8-140a}$$

and

$$b_1 - 3b_0 = 0 \tag{8-140b}$$

Solving (8-140), we obtain

$$b_1 = 1 \quad \text{and} \quad b_0 = \tfrac{1}{3} \tag{8-141}$$

Substituting (8-141) into (8-137), we obtain the desired transfer function $H(s)$ as

$$H(s) = \frac{k}{s^2 + s + (1/3)}$$

$$= \frac{1}{3s^2 + 3s + 1} \tag{8-142}$$

Another way to do this problem is via (8-135), where the desired transfer function is given by

$$H(s) = \frac{k}{\hat{B}_2(3s)} = \frac{k}{(3s)^2 + 3(3s) + 3}$$

$$= \frac{k}{9s^2 + 9s + 3} = \frac{1}{3s^2 + 3s + 1} \qquad \blacksquare$$

8-3-2. Design and Realization

The only design parameter of Bessel filters is of the order n. The value of n is chosen to satisfy the prescribed specifications on the phase requirements as well as the magnitude requirements.

Example 8-9 Find the lowest-order Bessel filter to meet the following specifications:

   (i) $\tau(0) = 1$ sec.
   (ii) $\tau(\omega)$ has less than 1% error for $\omega \leq 2$ rad./sec.
   (iii) $|H(j\omega)|^2 \leq 0.5$ for $\omega \geq 2$ rad./sec.

Solution: From Fig. 8-21(b), we find that $n = 5$ satisfies conditions (i) and (ii). To consider condition (iii), we have plotted the magnitude characteristics of Bessel filters in Fig. 8-22. From Fig. 8-22, we determine that $n \geq 8$ satisfies condition (iii). Hence, an eighth-order Bessel filter will meet all the prescribed requirements. ∎

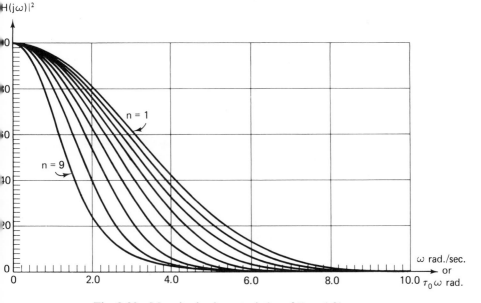

Fig. 8-22 Magnitude characteristics of Bessel filters.

Example 8-10 Find the lowest-order Bessel filter to meet the following specifications:

   (i) $\tau(0) = 2$ sec.
   (ii) $\tau(\omega)$ has less than 1% error for $\omega \leq 2$ rad./sec.
   (iii) $|H(j\omega)|^2 \leq 0.2$ for $\omega \geq 2$ rad./sec.

Solution: In view of condition (i), conditions (ii) and (iii) are equivalent to:

   (a) $\tau(\omega)$ has less than 1% error for $\tau_0\omega \leq 4$ rad.
   (b) $|H(j\omega)|^2 \leq 0.2$ for $\tau_0\omega \geq 4$ rad.

From Fig. 8-21(b), condition (a) is satisfied when $n \geq 7$, and condition (b) requires that $n \geq 5$, as shown in Fig. 8-22. Hence, a seventh-order Bessel filter is needed. ∎

Bessel filters, as presented in this section, are low-pass filters with all transmission zeros occurring at $s = \infty$. Hence, a simplified Darlington synthesis procedure with Cauer's first form, as discussed in Section 7-3, can be used to realize the resulting transfer functions. In this case, the basic circuit structure is given by Fig. 8-23. For the case of unit group delay at

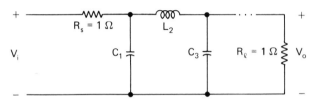

Fig. 8-23 A basic circuit structure for low-pass Bessel filters.

$\omega = 0$—when the transfer functions are given by (8-126)—the circuit element values are given by Table 8-4.

TABLE 8-4 Values of Circuit Elements in Bessel Filters

n	C_1	L_2	C_3	L_4	C_5	L_6	C_7	L_8	C_9
1	2.0000								
2	1.5774	0.4226							
3	1.2550	0.5528	0.1922						
4	1.0598	0.5116	0.3181	0.1104					
5	0.9303	0.4577	0.3312	0.2090	0.0718				
6	0.8377	0.4116	0.3158	0.2364	0.1480	0.0505			
7	0.7677	0.3744	0.2944	0.2378	0.1778	0.1104	0.0375		
8	0.7125	0.3446	0.2735	0.2297	0.1867	0.1387	0.0855	0.0289	
9	0.6678	0.3203	0.2547	0.2184	0.1859	0.1506	0.1111	0.0682	0.0230

Example 8-11 Suppose that we are to construct a second-order Bessel filter with a unity group delay at $s = 0$. Find a circuit design, and verify the result.

Solution: From (8-126) and (8-127), the transfer function of a second-order Bessel filter is given by

$$H(s) = \frac{k}{s^2 + 3s + 3} \tag{8-143}$$

From Fig. 8-23 and Table 8-4, a circuit realization of (8-143) is shown in Fig. 8-24(a).

To see that the circuit in Fig. 8-24(a) is a realization of (8-143), we let $V_i = 1$ and redraw the resultant circuit as shown in Fig. 8-24(b). A nodal analysis yields

$$V_o = \frac{1/LC}{s^2 + s\left(\dfrac{1}{L} + \dfrac{1}{C}\right) + \dfrac{2}{LC}} \tag{8-144a}$$

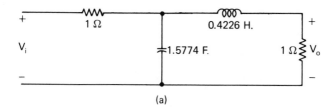

(a)

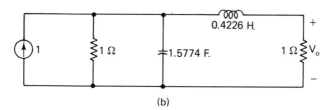

(b)

Fig. 8-24   (a) A circuit realization of a second-order Bessel filter, and (b) its equivalent circuit.

where

$$L = 0.4226 \quad \text{and} \quad C = 1.5774 \qquad (8\text{-}144\text{b})$$

By substituting (8-144b) into (8-144a), we obtain

$$V_o = \frac{1.5}{s^2 + 3s + 3}$$

Hence, the transfer function is given by

$$\hat{H}(s) = \frac{1.5}{s^2 + 3s + 3} \qquad (8\text{-}145)$$

and the circuit in Fig. 8-24(a) realizes a second-order Bessel filter.   ∎

The Bessel filters approximate the constant group delay with maximally flat property. This parallels the Butterworth filters that approximate the constant magnitude function with maximally flat property. It is also possible to approximate a constant group delay function with equal ripple property (analogous to a Chebyshev filter approximating a constant magnitude transfer function). However, we do not discuss this type of phase filter here.

8-3-3. Transitional Filters

Although the Bessel filter gives a phase shift that is much more linear than that of either the Butterworth or the Chebyshev filter, the magnitude response of the Bessel filter does not have a very sharp cut off.[18] One class

---

[18]Comparing the magnitude characteristics in Figs. 8-3 and 8-22, we see that for the same order *n*, the Butterworth filters have much sharper cutoff characteristics than those of Bessel filters. It is also known that again for the same order *n*, Chebyshev filters have sharper cutoff magnitude curves than those of Butterworth filters.

of filters make a compromise between the cutoff characteristics of the Butterworth and the phase shift characteristic of the Bessel. This compromise is accomplished by putting the poles of the filter between those of the Butterworth and those of Bessel.

As an example, consider the second-order Butterworth filter with poles at $-(1/\sqrt{2}) \pm j(1/\sqrt{2})$ as given by (8-42a). The second-order Bessel filter has poles at $-(3/2) \pm j(\sqrt{3}/2)$(see Example 8-11). The Butterworth filter is normalized to have a pole magnitude of one. Before we make the compromise, we first normalize the Bessel filter so that the pole magnitude like that for the Butterworth filter is 1. This requires normalizing the frequency by a factor of $\sqrt{3}$. (We study frequency scaling later.) The resulting normalized second-order Bessel filter's transfer function is given by

$$H(s) = \frac{1}{s^2 + \sqrt{3}\,s + 1} = \frac{1}{\left(s + \frac{\sqrt{3}}{2} + j\frac{1}{2}\right)\left(s + \frac{\sqrt{3}}{2} - j\frac{1}{2}\right)} \qquad (8\text{-}146)$$

The transitional filter has poles between

$$-\frac{1}{\sqrt{2}} \pm j\frac{1}{\sqrt{2}} \qquad \text{[from the Butterworth filter (8-42a)]}$$

and

$$-\frac{\sqrt{3}}{2} \pm j\frac{1}{2} \qquad \text{[from the Bessel filter (8-146)]}$$

A filter with the pole locations halfway between the Butterworth poles and the Bessel poles has a transfer function

$$H_T(s) = \frac{1}{\left(s + \frac{\sqrt{3} + \sqrt{2}}{4} + j\frac{1 + \sqrt{2}}{4}\right)\left(s + \frac{\sqrt{3} + \sqrt{2}}{4} - j\frac{1 + \sqrt{2}}{4}\right)}$$

$$= \frac{1}{s^2 + 1.5731s + 0.9830} \qquad (8\text{-}147)$$

Transitional filters with a transfer function such as that of (8-147) are often better as filters for tone bursts (in telecommunication systems), because good phase response means low overshoot. On the other hand, the selection of tone bursts requires fairly good frequency magnitude characteristics.

8-4 BASIC FREQUENCY AND NETWORK TRANSFORMATIONS

Although most of our discussion up to now has been centered around normalized low pass structures, this does not mean that they are the most common type of filters. Indeed, the reasons why our discussions have been so restricted are: (1) normalized low-pass filters are by far the easiest to realize; and (2) most bandpass, band-reject, and high-pass as well as other low-pass

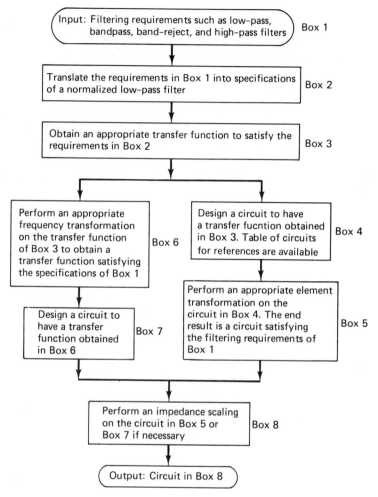

Fig. 8-25   Two filter design procedures.

filtering requirements are easily satisfied by an appropriate transformation from the normalized low-pass structure. Figure 8-25 shows two procedures to design other filters besides the normalized low-pass prototype.

8-4-1. Low-Pass to Low-Pass Transformation

This process is sometimes called *frequency scaling* or *frequency denormalization*. All filter transfer functions discussed so far are low-pass filters with cutoff frequency at 1 rad./sec. The material covered in this chapter so far would be useless if there were no simple ways of converting the normalized low-pass cutoff frequency of 1 to other low-pass frequencies. Fortunately, this can be accomplished easily. Suppose that the cutoff frequency is desired to be at ω_c rad./sec. All we need to do is to replace every ω in the normalized low-pass transfer function with ω/ω_c. The resulting low-pass transfer function will have a cutoff frequency at ω_c. For example, a low-pass Butterworth nth-order filter with unity bandwidth (cutoff frequency $= 1$) has a transfer function whose magnitude square is[19]

$$|H_N(j\omega)|^2 = \frac{1}{1 + \omega^{2n}} \qquad (8\text{-}148)$$

A low-pass nth-order Butterworth filter with bandwidth ω_c is given by

$$|H(j\omega)|^2 = \frac{1}{1 + (\omega/\omega_c)^{2n}} \qquad (8\text{-}149)$$

$$\omega \rightarrow \frac{\omega}{\omega_c} \longrightarrow$$

To see that (8-149) defines a filter with a cutoff frequency at ω_c, we simply calculate the 3 dB point ω_{3dB}, the point at which the following equation is satisfied:

$$-10 \log \frac{|H(j\omega_{3dB})|^2}{|H(j\omega_{Ref})|^2} = 3 \qquad (8\text{-}150)$$

where $\omega_{Ref} = 0$ for low-pass filters

$\phantom{where \omega_{Ref} } = \infty$ for high-pass filters

$\phantom{where \omega_{Ref} } = 0$ or ∞ for band-reject filters $\qquad (8\text{-}151)$

$\phantom{where \omega_{Ref} } =$ the center frequency for bandpass filters

After some algebraic manipulations, we find that

$$\omega_{3dB} = \omega_c \qquad (8\text{-}152)$$

Hence, the cutoff frequency or the 3 dB point is at ω_c.

With the frequency transformation

$$s \mapsto \frac{s}{\omega_c} \qquad (8\text{-}153a)$$

or

$$\omega \mapsto \frac{\omega}{\omega_c} \qquad (8\text{-}153b)$$

low pass to different low pass transformation

a capacitor with C Farads in a unity bandwidth circuit having an impedance of $1/sC$ is transformed to an ω_c bandwidth circuit branch having an impedance of

$$\frac{1}{(s/\omega_c)C} = \frac{1}{s(C/\omega_c)} \qquad (8\text{-}154a)$$

which is a capacitor with C/ω_c Farads. An inductor with L Henries in a unity bandwidth circuit has an impedance of sL, and its counterpart in a ω_c bandwidth circuit has an impedance of

$$(s/\omega_c)L = s(L/\omega_c) \qquad (8\text{-}154b)$$

---

[19] N stands for normalized low-pass prototype.

and hence is an inductor with L/ω_c Henries. Resistors and all resistive elements remain unchanged under the frequency transformation of (8-153).[20]

As is in the case of (8-132), (8-153) merely represents a change of the frequency scale; if x is a frequency point in the normalized scale, then $\omega_c x$ is the frequency point after the frequency transformation of, or the scale change indicated by, (8-153).

Example 8-12 Suppose that we are to have an equiripple filter to satisfy the following specifications:

(a) Ripple bandwidth is 1 K rad./sec.
(b) Maximum passband ripple attenuation is 0.1 dB.
(c) Minimum stopband attenuation is 40 dB for $\omega \geq 6$ K rad./sec.

(i) Find the desired transfer function.
(ii) Find a circuit realization of the desired filter.

Solution: As indicated by Fig. 8-25, let us first translate the specifications into the normalized low-pass case as follows:

(a') Ripple bandwidth is 1 rad./sec. (This implies that a frequency scaling of $\omega \mapsto \omega/1$ K or $s \mapsto s/1$ K is needed later on.)
(b') Maximum passband ripple attenuation is 0.1 dB.
(c') Minimum stopband attenuation is 40 dB for $\omega \geq 6$ rad./sec.

From Fig. 8-15(a), we find that $n \geq 3$ will satisfy conditions (a'), (b'), and (c'). To find the normalized transfer function, we use (8-71) and (8-85) to calculate the ripple parameter ϵ and the three pole locations:

$$\epsilon = \sqrt{10^{0.01} - 1} = 0.1526$$

$$s_1 = -0.4847 + j1.2062$$

$$s_2 = -0.9694$$

$$s_3 = -0.4847 - j1.2062$$

Hence,

$$H_N(s) = \frac{1.6381}{s^3 + 1.9388s^2 + 2.6295s + 1.6381} \tag{8-155}$$

By (8-153), the desired transfer function is given by

$$H(s) = H_N\left(\frac{s}{10^3}\right)$$

$$= \frac{1.6381 \times 10^9}{s^3 + (1.9388 \times 10^3 s^2) + (2.6295 \times 10^6 s) + (1.6381 \times 10^9)} \tag{8-156}$$

---

[20]The class of resistive elements includes gyrators, all four types of controlled sources, and operational amplifiers. These elements remain unchanged under *all* kinds of frequency transformations.

From Fig. 8-17 and Table 8-2, a circuit realization of the normalized design of (8-155) is shown in Fig. 8-26(a). By applying the element transformation of (8-154), a circuit implementing the desired transfer function of (8-156) is given in Fig. 8-26(b). Note that the voltage-ratio transfer function of the circuit in Fig. 8-26(b) satisfies all the prescribed specifications of conditions (a), (b), and (c). ∎

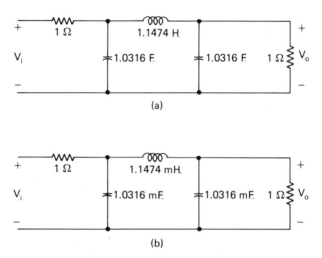

Fig. 8-26 Circuit realizations of (a) the normalized transfer function of (8-155), and (b) the desired transfer function of (8-156).

Example 8-13 Suppose that we are to design a maximally flat group delay filter to meet the following specifications:

(a) $\tau(0) = 100 \ \mu sec. = 10^{-4}$ sec.
(b) $\tau(\omega)$ has less than 3% error for $|\omega| < 20$ K rad./sec.

(i) Find the desired transfer function.
(ii) Find a circuit realization of the desired filter.

Solution: In terms of $\tau_0 \omega$, condition (b) becomes:

(b′) $\tau(\omega)$ has less than 3% error for $|\tau_0 \omega| < 2$ rad.

From Fig. 8-21(b), we find that $n = 4$ will satisfy condition (b′). The transfer function of the normalized Bessel filter is given by (8-128) as

$$H_N(s) = \frac{105}{s^4 + 10s^3 + 45s^2 + 105s + 105} \qquad (8\text{-}157)$$

To obtain the desired transfer function, we can either use (8-135) with $\tau_0 = 10^{-4}$ or (8-153) with $\omega_c = 10^4$.[21] The resulting desired transfer function is given by

$$H(s) = H_N\left(\frac{s}{10^4}\right)$$

$$= \frac{105 \times 10^{16}}{s^4 + 10^5 s^3 + (45 \times 10^8 s^2) + (105 \times 10^{12} s) + (105 \times 10^{16})}$$

(8-158)

From Fig. 8-23 and Table 8-4, a circuit realization of the normalized design of (8-157) is shown in Fig. 8-27(a). By the element transformation of (8-154), we obtain the desired filter circuit in Fig. 8-27(b). ∎

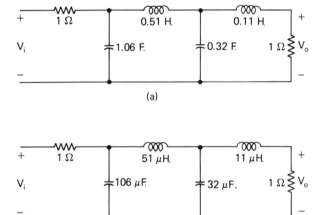

(a)

(b)

Fig. 8-27 Circuit realizations of (a) the normalized transfer function of (8-157), and (b) the desired transfer function of (8-158).

8-4-2. Low-Pass to Bandpass Transformation

The frequency transformation, which takes a normalized low-pass structure (with a single passband centered at $\omega = 0$) into a bandpass filter (with two passbands centered at ω_0 and $-\omega_0$, each possessing a bandwidth of B), is certainly not linear as in the low-pass to low-pass case. Consider the explicit transformation

$$s \mapsto \frac{s^2 + \omega_0^2}{Bs}$$

(8-159)

---

[21]Notice that in converting condition (b) to (b′), we have actually performed a frequency scaling of $\omega \mapsto 10 \, K\omega$.

where ω_0 is the desired center frequency and B is the bandwidth of the band-pass filter.[22]

The frequency transformation of (8-159) has the following important characteristics:

1. The point $\omega = 0$ is mapped to the center frequencies ω_0 and $-\omega_0$. In general, a point x is mapped to two points ω_x and $-\omega_x$, except when $x = \infty$. The point at infinity is mapped to the origin.
2. The positive {negative} imaginary axis is mapped to the intervals of (ω_0, ∞) and $(-\infty, -\omega_0)\{(0, \omega_0)$ and $(-\omega_0, 0)\}$.
3. Let $\pm\omega_x$ and $\pm\omega_{-x}$ be the images of x and $-x$ under the transformation of (8-159); then

$$\omega_0^2 = \omega_x\omega_{-x} \tag{8-160}$$

Because of (8-160), the resulting bandpass attenuation (and the phase) characteristics will not display an arithmetic symmetry but rather a geometric symmetry about ω_0.[23] If we let $x = 1$ in (8-160), then ω_1 and ω_{-1} are the pass-band edges of the resulting bandpass filter. Hence, we have

$$B = \omega_1 - \omega_{-1} \tag{8-161a}$$

and

$$\omega_0^2 = \omega_1\omega_{-1} \tag{8-161b}$$

An illustration of the basic characteristics of (8-159) is shown in Fig. 8-28.

 With the low-pass to bandpass transformation of (8-159), we can obtain the bandpass transfer function $H(s)$ from the normalized low-pass prototype $H_N(s)$ by replacing every s in $H_N(s)$ with $(s^2 + \omega_0^2)/Bs$. To obtain a desired bandpass filter circuit, we can realize the resulting transfer function $H(s)$ either by various realization techniques or simply by employing a network transformation. The latter approach is implemented by replacing every element in the normalized low-pass circuit by an appropriate set of elements in the desired bandpass circuit. To determine the replacements of a low-pass inductor of L Henries, we observe that the impedance function sL is mapped by (8-159) to an impedance function of

$$\left(\frac{s^2 + \omega_0^2}{Bs}\right)L = \frac{L}{B}s + \frac{1}{(B/\omega_0^2 L)s} \tag{8-162}$$

This, in effect, says that a low-pass inductor of L Henries is transformed into

---

[22]The bandwidth of a bandpass filter is given by the difference between the two 3 dB cutoff (positive) frequencies as $B \triangleq |\omega_{c1} - \omega_{c2}|$ where ω_{c1} and ω_{c2} are the solutions of ω_c for the following equation

$$-10 \log\frac{|H(j\omega_c)|^2}{|H(j\omega_0)|^2} = 3$$

[23]For details on the design of arithmetically symmetric bandpass filters see Reference [14].

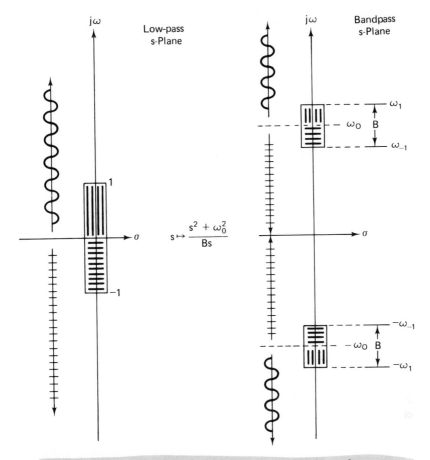

Fig. 8-28 Basic characteristics of low-pass to bandpass frequency transformation.

a series connection of an inductor and a capacitor, where the bandpass inductor and capacitor have values of

$$\frac{L}{B} \text{ Henries} \quad \text{and} \quad \frac{B}{\omega_0^2 L} \text{ Farads} \qquad (8\text{-}163)$$

respectively. Similarly, a low-pass capacitive admittance sC is mapped to an admittance function of

$$\left(\frac{s^2 + \omega_0^2}{Bs}\right)C = \frac{C}{B}s + \frac{1}{(B/\omega_0^2 C)s} \qquad (8\text{-}164)$$

Hence, a low-pass capacitor of C Farads is replaced by a parallel connection of a capacitor and an inductor with

$$\frac{C}{B} \text{ Farads} \quad \text{and} \quad \frac{B}{\omega_0^2 C} \text{ Henries} \qquad (8\text{-}165)$$

respectively. Figure 8-29 illustrates the element transformation that converts

283

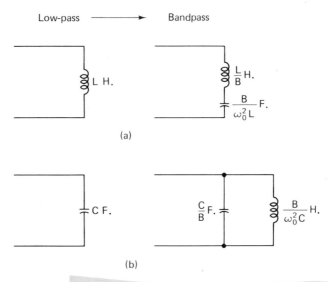

Fig. 8-29   Low-pass to bandpass element transformation.

a low-pass filter circuit into a bandpass filter circuit. Under the transformation of (8-159), resistors and all resistive elements remain unchanged.

Example 8-14 Suppose that we are to design a bandpass filter to meet the following specifications:

(a) The center frequency of the passband is at $\omega_0 = 100$ K rad./sec.
(b) The 3 dB bandwidth is 20 K rad./sec.
(c) The maximum attenuation allowed in the passband from $\omega_0 = 100$ K rad./sec. to $\omega_1 = 102.5$ K rad./sec. is 0.05 dB.
(d) The minimum attenuation required in the stopband is 10 dB for $\omega \geq \omega_2 = 120$ K rad./sec.
(e) A monotonically decreasing magnitude function for $\omega \geq \omega_0$ is required.

1. Find the transfer function of the desired filter.
2. Find a circuit realization of the desired filter.

Solution: First, let us find the desired transfer function. Condition (e) calls for a Butterworth filter. The order of the filter will be determined by conditions (a) through (d), as illustrated in Fig. 8-30(a). In general, it is much easier to determine the order n of the Butterworth filter in the domain of the normalized low-pass prototype. To do this, we need to translate conditions (a) through (d) into the language of a normalized low-pass filter. Information contained in conditions (a) and (b) is for the frequency transformation from the normalized low-pass prototype to the desired bandpass filter. These conditions are not needed

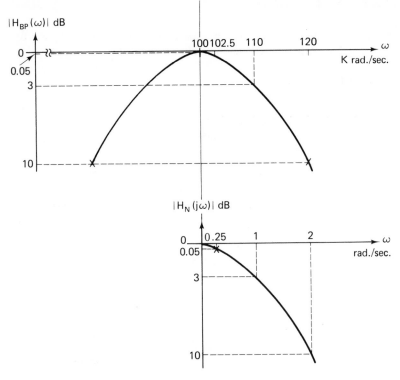

Fig. 8-30 Specifications of Example 8-14. (a) Bandpass specifications.
(b) Normalized low-pass specifications.

for the determination of n. Conditions (c) and (d) correspond to:

(c′) The maximum attenuation allowed in the passband from $\omega = 0$ to
$\omega = 0.25$ rad./sec. is 0.05 dB.

(d′) The minimum attenuation required in the stopband is 10 dB for
$\omega \geq 2$ rad./sec.

Conditions (c′) and (d′) are illustrated in Fig. 8-30(b). These conditions imply
that n has to be chosen to satisfy

$$-10 \log \left| \frac{1}{1 + (0.25)^{2n}} \right| \leq 0.05 \qquad (8\text{-}166a)$$

and

$$-10 \log \left| \frac{1}{1 + 2^{2n}} \right| > 10 \qquad (8\text{-}166b)$$

After some simple arithmetic, we find that $n \geq 2$ will satisfy both conditions in
(8-166). Consequently, the desired transfer function of the normalized low-pass
filter is given by

$$H_N(s) = \frac{1}{s^2 + \sqrt{2}s + 1} \qquad (8\text{-}167)$$

285

With $\omega_0 = 100$ K rad./sec. and a 3 dB bandwidth of 20 K rad./sec., the transfer function of the desired bandpass filter is given by

$$H_{BP}(s) = H_N\left(\frac{s^2 + 10^{10}}{2 \times 10^4 s}\right)$$

$$= \frac{1}{\left(\dfrac{s^2 + 10^{10}}{2 \times 10^4 s}\right)^2 + \sqrt{2}\left(\dfrac{s^2 + 10^{10}}{2 \times 10^4 s}\right) + 1}$$

$$= \frac{4 \times 10^8 s^2}{(s^2 + 10^{10})^2 + \sqrt{2}(s^2 + 10^{10})(2 \times 10^4 s) + (4 \times 10^8 s^2)}$$

$$= \frac{4 \times 10^8 s^2}{s^4 + (2\sqrt{2} \times 10^4 s^3) + (2.04 \times 10^{10} s^2) + (2\sqrt{2} \times 10^{14} s) + 10^{20}}$$

(8-168)

To realize the desired filter of (8-168), we first realize the normalized low-pass filter of (8-167) as shown in Fig. 8-31(a). An element transformation is applied to Fig. 8-31(a) to obtain Fig. 8-31(b). Observe that a second-order low pass filter becomes a fourth-order bandpass filter under the low-pass to bandpass transformation. ∎

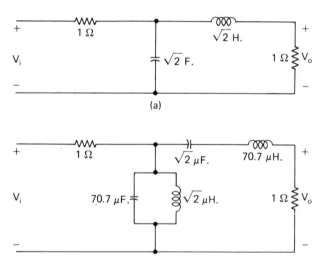

Fig. 8-31 Circuit realizations of (a) the normalized transfer function of (8-167), and (b) the desired transfer function of (8-168).

The magnitude characteristics of the normalized low-pass transfer function of (8-167) and the desired bandpass transfer function of (8-168) are shown in Fig. 8-32. Note that in the bandpass characteristics, the increasing slope for $0 \leq \omega \leq 100$ K rad./sec. is somewhat steeper than the decreasing slope for $\omega \geq 100$ K rad./sec. This is typical for bandpass filter designs obtained by (8-159). [Recall that (8-159) gives geometrically symmetric but not arithmet-

$|H_N(j\omega)|^2$

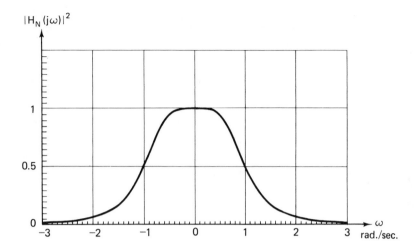

$|H_{BP}(j\omega)|^2$

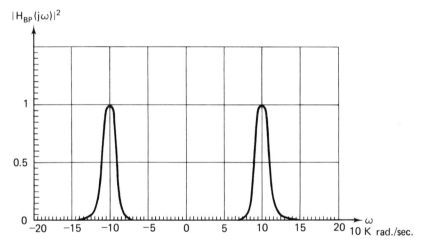

Fig. 8-32 Magnitude characteristics of (a) the normalized second-order low-pass Butterworth filter, and (b) the corresponding fourth-order bandpass Butterworth filter.

ically symmetric filter designs.] Hence, if the given specifications are arithmetically symmetric about the center frequency ω_0, then working with the frequency band for $\omega \geq \omega_0$ will ensure that the resulting filter design will satisfy all the prescribed requirements.

8-4-3. Low-Pass to Band-Reject Transformation

As is in the case of bandpass filters, it is often convenient to start with a normalized low-pass prototype and employ frequency and/or element transformation to arrive at the final band-reject model. In these cases, the frequency transformation is simply the reciprocal (or the inverse) of the low-pass to bandpass one. That is, the frequency transformation from the normalized low-pass filter to a band-reject filter is given by

$$s \mapsto \frac{Bs}{s^2 + \omega_0^2} \qquad\qquad (8\text{-}169a)$$

or

$$\omega \mapsto \frac{B\omega}{-\omega^2 + \omega_0^2} \qquad\qquad (8\text{-}169b)$$

where ω_0 is the center frequency of the rejection band and B is the rejection bandwidth. The basic properties of such a transformation are shown in Fig. 8-33.

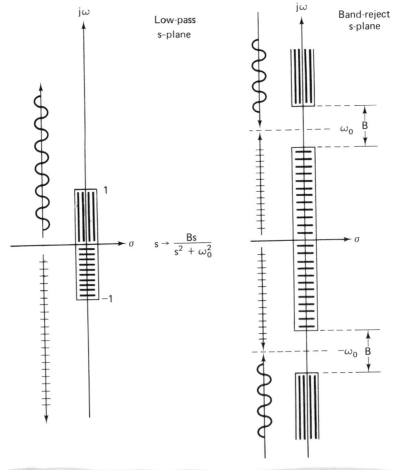

Fig. 8-33 Basic properties of low-pass to band-reject frequency transformation.

As far as the network elements are concerned, it is clear that a low-pass capacitance C Farads is transformed into a series connection of an inductor and a capacitor with values

$$\frac{1}{BC} \text{ Henries} \quad \text{and} \quad \frac{BC}{\omega_0^2} \text{ Farads} \tag{8-170}$$

as shown in Fig. 8-34(*a*). Similarly, the low-pass inductance of L Henries is replaced by a parallel connection of an inductor and a capacitor with values

$$\frac{BL}{\omega_0^2} \text{ Henries} \quad \text{and} \quad \frac{1}{BL} \text{ Farads} \tag{8-171}$$

as illustrated in Fig. 8-34(*b*). Again, resistors and all resistive elements remain unchanged.

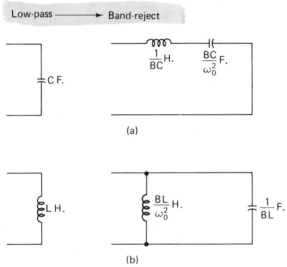

Fig. 8-34   Low-pass to band-reject element transformation.

Example 8-15   Suppose that we are to design a Butterworth band-reject filter to meet the following specifications:

  (a) The center frequency is at 1 K rad./sec.
  (b) The rejection 3 dB bandwidth is 100 rad./sec.
  (c) The minimum attenuation required in the stopband is 40 dB for 1 K rad./sec. $< \omega <$ 1010 rad./sec.
  (d) The maximum attenuation allowed in the high-frequency passband is 0.1 dB for $\omega \geq 1.2$ K rad./sec.

  1. Find the desired transfer function.
  2. Find the desired filter circuit.

Solution: With $\omega_0 = 10^3$ and $B = 10^2$, the given band-reject specifications are converted to those of the normalized low pass as follows:

(c′) The minimum attenuation is 40 dB for

$$\frac{B(1\ K)}{-(1\ K)^2 + \omega_0^2} < \omega < \frac{B(1010)}{-(1010)^2 + \omega_0^2}$$

or

$$\omega \geq \frac{100(1010)}{(1010)^2 - (1000)^2} = 5.02 \tag{8-172}$$

(d′) The maximum attenuation is 0.1 dB for

$$\omega < \frac{B(1.2\ K)}{(1.2\ K)^2 - \omega_0^2} = \frac{100(1200)}{(1200)^2 - (1000)^2} = 0.27 \tag{8-173}$$

From Fig. 8-4, condition (c′) implies that $n \geq 3$, and condition (d′) requires that $n \geq 2$. Hence, a third-order normalized low-pass Butterworth filter can serve as the prototype. The normalized transfer function is given by (8-42b) as

$$H_N(s) = \frac{1}{s^3 + 2s^2 + 2s + 1} \tag{8-174}$$

By (8-169), the desired transfer function is

$$H(s) = H_N\left(\frac{100s}{s^2 + 10^6}\right)$$

$$= \frac{1}{\left(\dfrac{100s}{s^2 + 10^6}\right)^3 + 2\left(\dfrac{100s}{s^2 + 10^6}\right)^2 + 2\left(\dfrac{100s}{s^2 + 10^6}\right) + 1} \tag{8-175}$$

$$= \frac{s^6 + (3 \times 10^6 s^4) + (3 \times 10^{12} s^2) + 10^{18}}{\begin{array}{l} s^6 + 200s^5 + (3.02 \times 10^6 s^4) + (4.01 \times 10^8 s^3) \\ \qquad + (3.02 \times 10^{12} s^2) + (2 \times 10^{14} s) + 10^{18} \end{array}}$$

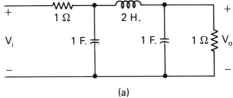

(a)

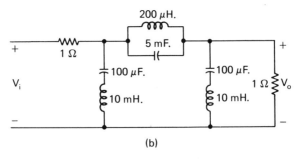

(b)

Fig. 8-35 Circuit realizations of the (a) third-order normalized low-pass Butterworth filter, and (b) sixth-order band-reject filter in Example 8-15.

A circuit realization of (8-174) is given by Table 8-1 and Fig. 8-9(c) and is shown in Fig. 8-35(a). By the element transformation of (8-170) and (8-171), we obtain the desired filter circuit in Fig. 8-35(b).   ∎

8-4-4. Low-Pass to High-Pass Transformation

Because low-pass filter characteristics are just the reciprocal of the high-pass filter characteristics, the frequency transformation of a normalized low-pass transfer function to a high-pass transfer function with a cutoff frequency at ω_c is given by

$$s \mapsto \frac{\omega_c}{s} \tag{8-176a}$$

or

$$\omega \mapsto \frac{\omega_c}{\omega} \tag{8-176b}$$

Suppose that we are to design a maximally flat second-order high-pass filter with a cutoff frequency at ω_c, as shown in Fig. 8-36. Then we start with the normalized Butterworth low-pass filter prototype:

$$H_N(s) = \frac{1}{s^2 + \sqrt{2}\,s + 1} \tag{8-177}$$

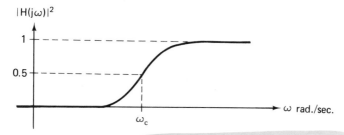

Fig. 8-36   Magnitude characteristics of a high-pass filter.

By using (8-176), we obtain our desired transfer function

$$H_{HP}(s) = \frac{1}{\left(\dfrac{\omega_c}{s}\right)^2 + \sqrt{2}\left(\dfrac{\omega_c}{s}\right) + 1} = \frac{s^2}{s^2 + \sqrt{2}\,\omega_c s + \omega_c^2} \tag{8-178}$$

In terms of network elements, a normalized low-pass capacitance of C Farads is transformed to a high-pass inductance of $1/C\omega_c$ Henries. Similarly, a normalized low-pass inductance of L Henries is transformed into a high-pass capacitance of $1/L\omega_c$ Farads. Once again, resistors and all resistive elements remain unchanged.

8-4-4-1. Inverse Chebyshev Filters.   In this subsection, we use the low-pass to high-pass frequency transformation to convert a Chebyshev filter into an inverse Chebyshev filter.

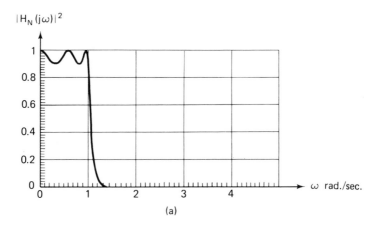

(a)

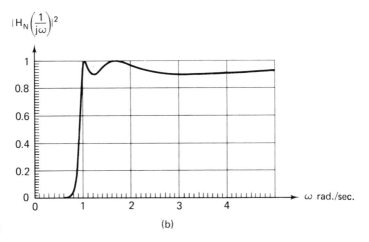

(b)

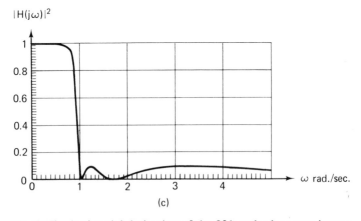

(c)

Fig. 8-37 A pictorial derivation of the fifth-order low-pass inverse Chebyshev filter from the fifth-order Chebyshev filter.

Let $|H_N(j\omega)|^2$ be the magnitude function of an nth-order low-pass Chebyshev filter with a 1 rad./sec. ripple bandwidth. A fifth-order case is shown in Fig. 8-37(a). By (8-176), the magnitude function of the nth-order high-pass Chebyshev filter with a ripple band extending from 1 rad./sec. to infinity is given by

$$|H_{HP}(j\omega)|^2 \triangleq \left|H_N\left(\frac{1}{j\omega}\right)\right|^2 = \left|H_N\left(j\frac{1}{\omega}\right)\right|^2 \qquad (8\text{-}179)$$

Figure 8-37(b) shows $|H_{HP}(j\omega)|^2$ versus ω for the case when $n = 5$. If we now subtract the high-pass magnitude function of (8-179) from 1, the resulting magnitude function is

$$|H(j\omega)|^2 = 1 - |H_{HP}(j\omega)|^2$$
$$= 1 - \left|H_N\left(j\frac{1}{\omega}\right)\right|^2 \qquad (8\text{-}180)$$

Figure 8-37(c) illustrates the behavior of $|H(j\omega)|^2$ of (8-180) for the case when $n = 5$. Observe that the resulting magnitude function is a low-pass filter with a monotonically decreasing pass band and an equiripple stop band, where the ripple starts from 1 rad./sec. and extends all the way to infinity. This type of filter is called an *inverse Chebyshev* filter. The transfer function of an inverse Chebyshev filter can be obtained from (8-180), where $H_N(s)$ represents the transfer function of a normalized low pass Chebyshev filter.

8-4-5. Impedance Scaling

So far, in all frequency transformations, resistor values remain unchanged. As shown in Figs. 8-9, 8-17, and 8-23, the normalized low-pass prototype circuits use source resistors of 1 Ω. Clearly, in real life, 1 Ω resistors are not ideal to work with. Hence, we need some mechanism to change the values of circuit elements without changing the transfer functions of the designed circuit.

Impedance scaling will not affect in any manner the transfer function.[24] Its essential aim is to raise or lower the impedance levels of all elements in a circuit by a particular value in order to match other parts of the circuit or to make the component sizes more practical for realization. For example, in Figs. 8-9, 8-17, and 8-23, if it is easier to work with A Ω resistors, then we may raise *all impedance* values of the elements in the circuits by A. For example,

1. A resistor of R Ω is now raised to AR Ω.
2. An inductor of L Henries that has an impedance value of sL is now

---

[24]This is true only for voltage-ratio and current-ratio transfer functions. Recall that in this book we consider voltage-ratio transfer functions only.

TABLE 8-5 Frequency and Element Transformations

From Normalized Low-pass Filter to:	Frequency Transformations			
		$R\ \Omega$	L H.	C F.
A low-pass filter with cutoff frequency ω_c	$s \longrightarrow \dfrac{s}{\omega_c}$	$R\ \Omega$	$\dfrac{L}{\omega_c}$ H.	$\dfrac{C}{\omega_c}$ F.
A bandpass filter with center frequency ω_0 and bandwidth B	$s \longrightarrow \dfrac{s^2 + \omega_0^2}{Bs}$	$R\ \Omega$	$\dfrac{L}{B}$ H, $\dfrac{B}{\omega_0^2 L}$ F.	$\dfrac{C}{B}$ F., $\dfrac{B}{\omega_0^2 C}$ H.
A band-reject filter with center frequency ω_0 and rejection bandwidth B	$s \longrightarrow \dfrac{Bs}{s^2 + \omega_0^2}$	$R\ \Omega$	$\dfrac{1}{BL}$ F., $\dfrac{BL}{\omega_0^2}$ H.	$\dfrac{1}{BC}$ H., $\dfrac{BC}{\omega_0^2}$ F.
A high-pass filter with cutoff frequency ω_c	$s \longrightarrow \dfrac{\omega_c}{s}$	$R\ \Omega$	$\dfrac{1}{L\omega_c}$ F.	$\dfrac{1}{C\omega_c}$ H.
Impedance scaling by A	No change	$AR\ \Omega$	AL H.	$\dfrac{C}{A}$ F.

raised to have a corresponding impedance value sAL, which is an inductor of AL Henries.

3. A capacitor of C Farads that has an impedance of $1/sC$ is now raised to have an impedance value of $A/sC = 1/[s(C/A)]$, which is a capacitor of C/A Farads.

4. An FDNR with D F^2 that has an impedance of $1/s^2D$ is now raised to a corresponding value of $A/s^2D = 1/[s^2(D/A)]$, which is an FDNR of D/A F^2.

5. VCVS and ICIS as well as ideal operational amplifiers remain unchanged.[25]

Table 8-5 summarizes all the frequency and element transformations discussed in Sec. 8-4.

Example 8-16 Find a filter circuit with $R_s = 1$ KΩ to satisfy all the conditions of Example 8-15.

Solution: The circuit in Fig. 8-35(b) satisfies all the specifications of Example 8-15 with $R_s = 1$ Ω. Hence, we need only to scale the impedance level of each element in Fig. 8-35(b) up by 1 K. The resulting circuit is shown in Fig. 8-38. ∎

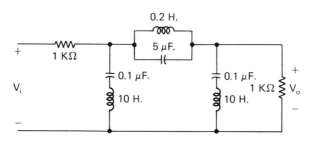

Fig. 8-38 Solution to Example 8-16.

8-4-6. Examples

Example 8-17 Suppose that we need a low-pass filter to satisfy the following conditions:

(a) The 3 dB cutoff frequency is at 20 K rad./sec.

---

[25]Observe that VCVS and ideal operational amplifiers remain unchanged under all types of frequency transformations and impedance scaling. We utilize this fact frequently in Chapter 10.

(b) The passband magnitude is within 0.1 dB of its maximum value for $\omega \leq 10$ K rad./sec.

(c) The stopband attenuation is greater than 40 dB for $\omega \geq 50$ K rad./sec.

(d) A monotonically decreasing magnitude function is required.

Find an appropriate circuit realization with the source resistor R_s being 10 KΩ.

Solution: Condition (d) requires a Butterworth filter. In terms of normalized low-pass filters, the cutoff frequency is automatically set at 1, and conditions (b) and (c) become:

(b') The passband magnitude is within 0.1 dB of its maximum value for $\omega \leq 0.5$ rad./sec.

(c') The stopband attenuation is greater than 40 dB for $\omega \geq 2.5$ rad./sec.

In terms of the normalized prototype, these conditions are represented by

$$-10 \log |H(j\omega)|^2 \leq 0.1 \quad \text{for} \quad \omega \leq 0.5 \qquad (8\text{-}181)$$

$$-10 \log |H(j\omega)|^2 > 40 \quad \text{for} \quad \omega \geq 2.5 \qquad (8\text{-}182)$$

Because of the monotonically decreasing property of Butterworth filters, (8-181) requires that

$$-\log \left| \frac{1}{1 + (0.5)^{2n}} \right| \leq 0.01$$

This means that $n \geq 3$ will satisfy condition (b'). For condition (c'), (8-182) implies that

$$-10 \log \left| \frac{1}{1 + (2.5)^{2n}} \right| > 40$$

This means that $n \geq 6$ will satisfy condition (c'). Hence, we need a Butterworth filter of order 6. From Table 8-1, we obtain the circuit in Fig. 8-39(a). The magnitude function of Fig. 8-39(b) is given by

$$|H(j\omega)|^2 = \frac{1}{1 + \omega^{12}} \qquad (8\text{-}183)$$

with the cutoff frequency being 1 rad./sec. Using element transformation to push the cutoff frequency to 20 K rad./sec., we obtain the circuit in Fig. 8-39(b), which has a magnitude function given by

$$|H(j\omega)|^2 = \frac{1}{1 + \left(\dfrac{\omega}{2 \times 10^4} \right)^{12}} \qquad (8\text{-}184)$$

Finally, impedance scaling of all elements of Fig. 8-39(b) by a factor of 10^4 raises R_s to the desired value of 10 KΩ. The resulting circuit is shown in Fig. 8-39(c). The magnitude function of Fig. 8-39(c) can be shown to be given by (8-184). Clearly, the circuit in Fig. 8-39(c) is a desired result. ∎

Example 8-18   Suppose that we need a low-pass filter to satisfy conditions (a), (b), and (c) of Example 8-17. Find a Chebyshev realization with the source resistor R_s equal to 1 KΩ.

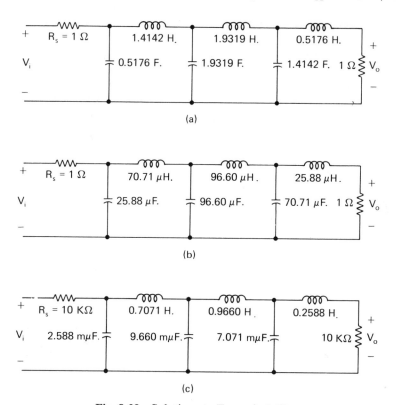

Fig. 8-39   Solutions to Example 8-17.

Solution: In terms of the normalized Chebyshev filter, condition (b) simply means 0.1 dB ripples within the passband. Hence, $A_{max} = 0.1$ dB, and by (8-71), $\epsilon = 0.1526$. Because the magnitude of a Chebyshev filter is monotonically decreasing in the stopband, condition (c) requires an integer n such that

$$-10 \log \left| \frac{1}{1 + (0.1526)^2 T_n^2(2.5)} \right| > 40 \qquad (8\text{-}185)$$

where $T_n(\omega)$ is the nth-order Chebyshev polynomial. The calculation of (8-185) in general is cumbersome. Fortunately, tables and graphs such as those in Fig. 8-15 are available in the literature. For the 0.1 dB ripple case, Fig. 8-15(a) says that $n = 5$ will satisfy (8-185). Hence, the specifications ask for a fifth-order Chebyshev filter. From Table 8-2, we obtain the normalized circuit shown in Fig. 8-40(a). To move the cutoff frequency to 20 K rad./sec., we perform an element transformation on Fig. 8-40(a) to obtain Fig. 8-40(b). Finally, an impedance scaling is carried out on Fig. 8-40(b) to obtain the final product of Fig. 8-40(c). The circuit in Fig. 8-40(c) satisfies all the filtering specifications. Note that a fifth-order Chebyshev filter can do the job of a sixth-order Butterworth filter, as shown by Examples 8-17 and 8-18. ∎

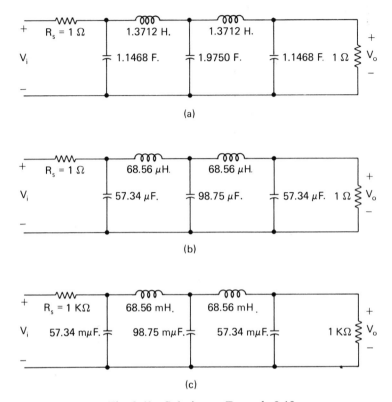

Fig. 8-40   Solution to Example 8-18.

8-5   ALL-PASS FILTERS

As shown in Fig. 8-2, one of the ideal frequency characteristics is to have a linear phase or a constant group delay function in the passband. When we design a magnitude filter, we introduce group delay distortions near the band edges. To remove these distortions, delay equalizers are needed. The most common delay equalizers are all-pass filters.

As all-pass transfer function is given by

$$H(s) = \frac{p(-s)}{p(s)} \qquad (8\text{-}186)$$

where $p(s)$ is a Hurwitz polynomial. In view of (8-186), an all-pass transfer function has the following properties:

1. For all ω, we have

$$|H(j\omega)|^2 = 1 \tag{8-187}$$

For this reason, (8-186) is called an *all-pass* transfer function.

2. If s_k is a pole of $H(s)$, then $-s_k$ is a zero of $H(s)$. Because all poles of $H(s)$ are in the LH s-plane, all zeros of $H(s)$ are in the RH s-plane. Hence, all-pass transfer functions are not minimal phase functions.

3. The phase angle $\phi(\omega) \triangleq -\underline{/H(j\omega)}$ of an all-pass function is given by

$$\phi(\omega) = 2\underline{/p(j\omega)} \tag{8-188}$$

4. Except at the points of discontinuity, $\phi(\omega)$ is a monotonically increasing function of ω.

Consider a first-order all-pass transfer function

$$H_1(s) = \frac{-s + a}{s + a} \tag{8-189}$$

where a is a real positive number. The phase and group delay functions are given respectively by

$$\phi(\omega) = 2 \tan^{-1} \frac{\omega}{a} \tag{8-190a}$$

and

$$\tau(\omega) = \frac{2/a}{1 + (\omega/a)^2} \tag{8-190b}$$

Observe that (8-190) implies that

$$\phi(0) = 0 \tag{8-191a}$$

and

$$\phi(\infty) = \pi \tag{8-191b}$$

Because $\tau(\omega)$ is the derivative of $\phi(\omega)$, we can write

$$\phi(\omega) = \int_0^\omega \tau(\omega')\, d\omega' \tag{8-192}$$

Hence, the area under the curve $\tau(\omega)$ of (8-190*b*) for $0 < \omega < \infty$ is given by

$$\phi(\infty) - \phi(0) = \pi \tag{8-193}$$

In a similar manner, the area under the curve $\tau(\omega)$ versus ω for $0 < \omega < \infty$ is $n\pi$, where n is the degree of $p(s)$ in (8-186). If a certain group delay function $\tau(\omega)$ is specified from 0 to a desired frequency ω_D rad./sec., we can calculate the area

$$\int_0^{\omega_D} \tau(\omega)\, d\omega$$

and determine approximately the minimum degree of n required for the desired all-pass transfer function. Passive realization of an all-pass voltage-ratio transfer function via a lattice circuit structure is given in Sec. 7-2.

REFERENCES AND FURTHER READING

[1] GUILLEMIN, E. A. *Synthesis of Passive Networks*. New York: Wiley, 1957.

[2] WEINBERG, L. *Network Analysis and Synthesis*. Huntington, N.Y.: R. E. Krieger, 1975.

[3] HUMPHREYS, D. S. *The Analysis, Design, and Synthesis of Electrical Filters*. Englewood Cliffs, N.J.: Prentice-Hall, Inc., 1970.

[4] CHRISTIAN, E., and EISENMANN, E. *Filter Design Tables and Graphs*. New York: Wiley, 1966.

[5] ZVEREV, A. I. *Handbook of Filter Design*. New York: Wiley, 1967.

[6] OPPENHEIM, A. V., and SCHAFER, R. W. *Digital Signal Processing*. Englewood Cliffs, N.J.: Prentice-Hall, Inc., 1975.

[7] RABINER, L. R., and GOLD, B. *Theory and Application of Digital Signal Processing*. Englewood Cliffs, N.J.: Prentice-Hall, Inc., 1975.

[8] KAWAKAMI, K. "Nomographs for Butterworth and Chebyshev Filters." *IEEE Trans. Circuit Theory* CT-10 (1963): 288–89.

[9] JOHNSON, D. E. *Introduction to Filter Theory*. Englewood Cliffs, N.J.: Prentice-Hall, Inc., 1976.

[10] DANIELS, R. W. *Approximation Methods for Electronic Filter Design*. New York: McGraw-Hill, 1974.

[11] KRALL, H. L., and FRINK, O. "A New Class of Orthogonal Polynomials: The Bessel Polynomials." *Trans. Amer. Math. Soc.* 65 (1949): 100–15.

[12] THOMSON, W. E. "Delay Network Having Maximally Flat Frequency Characteristics." *Proc. IEE* 96 (pt. 3, 1946): 487–90.

[13] STORCH, L. "Synthesis of Constant-Time Delay Ladder Network Using Bessel Polynomials," *Proc. IRE* 42 (1954): 1666–75.

[14] SZENTIRMAI, G. "The Design of Arithmetically Symmetrical Band Pass Filter." *IEEE Trans. Circuit Theory* CT-10 (1963): 367–75.

APPENDIX TO CHAPTER 8

In this Appendix,[26] we will present tables of values of Butterworth and Chebyshev filters. Each table contains three parts. Part (a) gives the pole locations of an nth order normalized low-pass filter.[27] Part (b) yields the denominator polynomial of the corresponding transfer function as a whole while part (c) presents the denominator polynomial in a factored form.

---

[26]Some tables in this Appendix are courtesy of L. Weinberg, *Network Analysis and Synthesis*, R. E. Krieger Publishing Co., 1975.

[27]Recall that a normalized low-pass Butterworth filter has a 3 dB cutoff frequency at 1 rad./sec. while a normalized low-pass Chebyshev filter has a passband ripple bandwidth of 1 rad./sec.

TABLE A8-1 Normalized Low-Pass Butterworth Filters

(a) Pole Locations

Order n	$p_{1,n}$	$p_{2,n-1}$	$p_{3,n-2}$	$p_{4,n-3}$	p_5
1	-1.00000000				
2	$-0.70710678 \pm j0.70710678$				
3	$-0.50000000 \pm j0.86602540$	-1.00000000			
4	$-0.38268343 \pm j0.92387953$	$-0.92387953 \pm j0.38268343$			
5	$-0.30901699 \pm j0.95105652$	$-0.80901699 \pm j0.58778525$	-1.00000000		
6	$-0.25881905 \pm j0.96592583$	$-0.70710678 \pm j0.70710678$	$-0.96592583 \pm j0.25881905$		
7	$-0.22252093 \pm j0.97492791$	$-0.62348980 \pm j0.78183148$	$-0.90096887 \pm j0.43388374$	-1.00000000	
8	$-0.19509032 \pm j0.98078528$	$-0.55557023 \pm j0.83146961$	$-0.83146961 \pm j0.55557023$	$-0.98078528 \pm j0.19509032$	
9	$-0.17364818 \pm j0.98480775$	$-0.50000000 \pm j0.86602540$	$-0.76604444 \pm j0.64278761$	$-0.93969262 \pm j0.34202014$	-1.00000000

(b) Denominator Polynomials $B(s) = s^n + b_{n-1}s^{n-1} + b_{n-2}s^{n-2} + \cdots + b_0$

Order n	b_0	b_1	b_2	b_3	b_4	b_5	b_6	b_7	b_8
1	1.00000000								
2	1.00000000	1.41421356							
3	1.00000000	2.00000000	2.00000000						
4	1.00000000	2.61312593	3.41421356	2.61312593					
5	1.00000000	3.23606798	5.23606798	5.23606798	3.23606798				
6	1.00000000	3.86370331	7.46410162	9.14162017	7.46410162	3.86370331			
7	1.00000000	4.49395921	10.09783468	14.59179389	14.59179389	10.09783468	4.49395921		
8	1.00000000	5.12583090	13.13707118	21.84615097	25.68835593	21.84615097	13.13707118	5.12583090	
9	1.00000000	5.75877048	16.58171874	31.16343748	41.98638573	41.98638573	31.16343748	16.58171874	5.75877048

(c) Denominator Polynomial Factors $B(s) = B_1(s)\,B_2(s)\,B_3(s)\,B_4(s)\,B_5(s)$

Order n	$B(s)$
1	$(s + 1)$
2	$(s^2 + 1.41421356s + 1)$
3	$(s^2 + s + 1)\ (s + 1)$
4	$(s^2 + 0.76536686s + 1)\ (s^2 + 1.84775907s + 1)$
5	$(s^2 + 0.61803399s + 1)\ (s^2 + 1.61803399s + 1)\ (s + 1)$
6	$(s^2 + 0.51763809s + 1)\ (s^2 + 1.41421356s + 1)\ (s^2 + 1.93185165s + 1)$
7	$(s^2 + 0.44504187s + 1)\ (s^2 + 1.24697960s + 1)\ (s^2 + 1.80193774s + 1)\ (s + 1)$
8	$(s^2 + 0.39018064s + 1)\ (s^2 + 1.11140047s + 1)\ (s^2 + 1.66293922s + 1)\ (s^2 + 1.96157056s + 1)$
9	$(s^2 + 0.34729636s + 1)\ (s^2 + s + 1)\ (s^2 + 1.53208889s + 1)\ (s^2 + 1.87938524s + 1)\ (s + 1)$

301

TABLE A8-2 Normalized Low-Pass Chebyshev Filters with 0.1 dB Passband Ripples

(a) Pole Locations

Order n	$p_{1,n}$	$p_{2,n-1}$	$p_{3,n-2}$	$p_{4,n-3}$	p_5
1	-6.55220322				
2	-1.18617812 ± j1.38094842				
3	-0.48470285 ± j1.20615528	-0.96940571			
4	-0.26415637 ± j1.12260981	-0.63772988 ± j0.46500021			
5	-0.16653368 ± j1.08037201	-0.43599085 ± j0.66770662	-0.53891432		
6	-0.11469337 ± j1.05651891	-0.31334811 ± j0.77342552	-0.42804148 ± j0.28309339		
7	-0.08384097 ± j1.04183333	-0.23491716 ± j0.83348546	-0.33946514 ± j0.46365945	-0.37677788	
8	-0.06398012 ± j1.03218136	-0.18219998 ± j0.87504111	-0.27268154 ± j0.58468377	-0.32164981 ± j0.20531364	
9	-0.05043805 ± j1.02550963	-0.14523059 ± j0.90181804	-0.22250617 ± j0.66935388	-0.27294423 ± j0.35615576	-0.29046118

(b) Denominator Polynomials $B(s) = s^n + b_{n-1}s^{n-1} + b_{n-2}s^{n-2} + \cdots + b_0$

Order n	b_0	b_1	b_2	b_3	b_4	b_5	b_6	b_7	b_8
1	6.55220322								
2	3.31403708	2.37235625							
3	1.63805080	2.62949486	1.93881142						
4	0.82850927	2.02550052	2.62679762	1.80377250					
5	0.40951270	1.43555791	2.39695895	2.77070415	1.74396339				
6	0.20712732	0.90176006	2.04784060	2.77905025	2.96575608	1.71216592			
7	0.10237818	0.56178554	1.48293374	2.70514436	3.16924598	3.18350446	1.69322441		
8	0.05178183	0.32643144	1.06662645	2.15924064	3.41845152	3.56476973	3.41291899	1.68102289	
9	0.02559454	0.19176027	0.69421123	1.73411961	2.93387298	4.19161066	3.96384487	3.64896144	1.67269928

(c) Denominator Polynomial Factors $B(s) = B_1(s) B_2(s) B_3(s) B_4(s) B_5(s)$

Order n	$B(s)$
1	$(s + 6.55220322)$
2	$(s^2 + 2.37235625s + 3.31403708)$
3	$(s^2 + 0.96940571s + 1.68974743)$ $(s + 0.96940571)$
4	$(s^2 + 0.528312273s + 1.33003138)$ $(s^2 + 1.275459977s + 0.62292460)$
5	$(s^2 + 0.33306737s + 1.19493715)$ $(s^2 + 0.871981169s + 0.63592015)$ $(s + 0.53891432)$
6	$(s^2 + 0.229386674s + 1.12938678)$ $(s^2 + 0.626696622s + 0.69637408)$ $(s^2 + 0.856082966s + 0.26336138)$
7	$(s^2 + 0.16768193s + 1.09244600)$ $(s^2 + 0.469834435s + 0.75322204)$ $(s^2 + 0.678930283s + 0.33021667)$ $(s + 0.37677788)$
8	$(s^2 + 0.127960255s + 1.06949182)$ $(s^2 + 0.364399969s + 0.79889377)$ $(s^2 + 0.545363085s + 0.41621034)$ $(s^2 + 0.64329961s + 0.14561229)$
9	$(s^2 + 0.10087611s + 1.05421401)$ $(s^2 + 0.29046118s + 0.83436770)$ $(s^2 + 0.44501235s + 0.49754361)$ $(s^2 + 0.54588846s + 0.20134548)$ $(s + 0.29046118)$

TABLE A8-3 Normalized Low-Pass Chebyshev Filters with 0.2 dB Passband Ripples

(a) Pole Locations

Order n	$p_{1,n}$	$p_{2,n-1}$	$p_{3,n-2}$	$p_{4,n-3}$	p_5
1	-4.60636099				
2	$-0.96354254 \pm j1.19516285$				
3	$-0.40731707 \pm j1.11701458$	-0.81463413			
4	$-0.22481072 \pm j1.07150422$	$-0.54274109 \pm j0.44383158$			
5	$-0.14258371 \pm j1.04741496$	$-0.37328900 \pm j0.64733805$	-0.46141058		
6	$-0.09852431 \pm j1.03354455$	$-0.26917343 \pm j0.75660712$	$-0.36769774 \pm j0.27693743$		
7	$-0.07216630 \pm j1.02491707$	$-0.20220548 \pm j0.82191968$	$-0.29219539 \pm j0.45613101$	-0.32431242	
8	$-0.05514327 \pm j1.01921190$	$-0.15703476 \pm j0.86404612$	$-0.23501912 \pm j0.57733716$	$-0.27722396 \pm j0.20273385$	
9	$-0.04351082 \pm j1.01525261$	$-0.12528442 \pm j0.89279816$	$-0.19194687 \pm j0.66265908$	$-0.23545769 \pm j0.35259353$	-0.25056884

(b) Denominator Polynomials $B(s) = s^n + b_{n-1}s^{n-1} + b_{n-2}s^{n-2} + \ldots + b_0$

Order n	b_0	b_1	b_2	b_3	b_4	b_5	b_6	b_7	b_8
1	4.60636099								
2	2.35682846	1.92708508							
3	1.15159025	2.07725754	1.62926827						
4	0.58920712	1.52213870	2.17827157	1.53510363					
5	0.28789756	1.08234729	1.86493313	2.36475740	1.49315599				
6	0.14730178	0.66110783	1.60289922	2.20817385	2.58161304	1.47079097			
7	0.07197439	0.41573867	1.11759023	2.17449134	2.55386738	2.81207554	1.45744677		
8	0.03682544	0.23654244	0.81273392	1.65937609	2.80404721	2.90162138	3.04957189	1.44884222	
9	0.01799360	0.14052449	0.51438217	1.35164765	2.28779160	3.49411391	3.25091261	3.29107898	1.44296846

(c) Denominator Polynomial Factors $B(s) = B_1(s)\, B_2(s)\, B_3(s)\, B_4(s)\, B_5(s)$

Order n	$B(s)$
1	$(s + 4.60636099)$
2	$(s^2 + 1.92708508s + 2.35682846)$
3	$(s^2 + 0.81463413s + 1.41362877)\ (s + 0.81463413)$
4	$(s^2 + 0.44962144s + 1.19866114)\ (s^2 + 1.08548218s + 0.49155436)$
5	$(s^2 + 0.28516742s + 1.11740822)\ (s^2 + 0.74657799s + 0.55839122)\ (s + 0.46141058)$
6	$(s^2 + 0.19704863s + 1.07792137)\ (s^2 + 0.53834686s + 0.64490867)\ (s^2 + 0.73539548s + 0.21189597)$
7	$(s^2 + 0.14433260s + 1.05566298)\ (s^2 + 0.40441097s + 0.71643901)\ (s^2 + 0.58439078s + 0.29343364)\ (s + 0.32431242)$
8	$(s^2 + 0.11028655s + 1.04183367)\ (s^2 + 0.31406951s + 0.77123562)\ (s^2 + 0.47003824s + 0.38855219)\ (s^2 + 0.55444791s + 0.11795414)$
9	$(s^2 + 0.08702165s + 1.03263106)\ (s^2 + 0.25056884s + 0.81278475)\ (s^2 + 0.38389374s + 0.47596066)\ (s^2 + 0.47091539s + 0.17976252)\ (s + 0.25056884)$

303

TABLE A8-4   Normalized Low-Pass Chebyshev Filters with 0.3 dB Passband Ripples

(a) Pole Locations

Order n	$p_{1,n}$	$p_{2,n-1}$	$p_{3,n-2}$	$p_{4,n-3}$	p_5
1	-3.73928318				
2	$-0.84715549 \pm j1.10348195$				
3	$-0.36463866 \pm j1.07186009$	-0.72927732			
4	$-0.20259811 \pm j1.04536452$	$-0.48911510 \pm j0.43300416$			
5	$-0.12889998 \pm j1.03048045$	$-0.33746452 \pm j0.63687195$	-0.41712909		
6	$-0.08922267 \pm j1.02170971$	$-0.24376086 \pm j0.74794342$	$-0.33298353 \pm j0.27376629$		
7	$-0.06542149 \pm j1.01618962$	$-0.18330693 \pm j0.81492080$	$-0.26488619 \pm j0.45224693$	-0.29400149	
8	$-0.05002353 \pm j1.01251401$	$-0.14245497 \pm j0.85836793$	$-0.21319892 \pm j0.57354311$	$-0.25148528 \pm j0.20140156$	
9	$-0.03948957 \pm j1.00995189$	$-0.11370569 \pm j0.88813679$	$-0.17420723 \pm j0.65919928$	$-0.21369680 \pm j0.35075261$	-0.22741138

(b) Denominator Polynomials $B(s) = s^n + b_{n-1}s^{n-1} + b_{n-2}s^{n-2} + \ldots + b_0$

Order n	b_0	b_1	b_2	b_3	b_4	b_5	b_6	b_7	b_8
1	3.73928318								
2	1.93534485	1.69431098							
3	0.93482080	1.81369083	1.45855465						
4	0.48383621	1.28205748	1.95693432	1.38342641					
5	0.23370520	0.91976859	1.60098707	2.16105841	1.34985808				
6	0.12095905	0.54930774	1.39260036	1.91754434	2.38702424	1.33193411			
7	0.05842630	0.34948247	0.94285544	1.91929792	2.23477563	2.62282530	1.32123072		
8	0.03023976	0.19528137	0.69512887	1.41506833	2.50498130	2.55297778	2.86372563	1.31432540	
9	0.01460657	0.11745564	0.42993878	1.17175288	1.96663611	3.15157757	2.87202098	3.10753913	1.30960997

(c) Denominator Polynomial Factors $B(s) = B_1(s)\,B_2(s)\,B_3(s)\,B_4(s)\,B_5(s)$

Order n	$B(s)$
1	$(s + 3.73928318)$
2	$(s^2 + 1.69431098s + 1.93534485)$
3	$(s^2 + 0.72927732s + 1.28184542)\quad(s + 0.72927732)$
4	$(s^2 + 0.40519622s + 1.13383296)\quad(s^2 + 0.98723020s + 0.42672618)$
5	$(s^2 + 0.25779995s + 1.07850517)\quad(s^2 + 0.67492904s + 0.51948818)\quad(s + 0.41712909)$
6	$(s^2 + 0.17844533s + 1.05185142)\quad(s^2 + 0.48752172s + 0.61883871)\quad(s^2 + 0.66596706s + 0.18582601)$
7	$(s^2 + 0.13084297s + 1.03692131)\quad(s^2 + 0.36661387s + 0.69769735)\quad(s^2 + 0.52977239s + 0.27469198)\quad(s + 0.29400149)$
8	$(s^2 + 0.10004706s + 1.02768697)\quad(s^2 + 0.28490993s + 0.75708892)\quad(s^2 + 0.42639785s + 0.37440548)\quad(s^2 + 0.50297056s + 0.10380743)$
9	$(s^2 + 0.07897914s + 1.02156225)\quad(s^2 + 0.22741138s + 0.80171594)\quad(s^2 + 0.34841445s + 0.46489185)\quad(s^2 + 0.42739360s + 0.16869372)\quad(s + 0.22741138)$

TABLE A8-5 Normalized Low-Pass Chebyshev Filters with 0.5 dB Passband Ripples

(a) Pole Locations

Order n	$p_{1,n}$	$p_{2,n-1}$	$p_{3,n-2}$	$p_{4,n-3}$	p_5
1	-2.86277516				
2	$-0.71281226 \pm j1.00404249$				
3	$-0.31332824 \pm j1.02192749$	-0.62645649			
4	$-0.17535307 \pm j1.01625289$	$-0.42333976 \pm j0.42094573$			
5	$-0.11196292 \pm j1.01155737$	$-0.29312273 \pm j0.62517684$	-0.36231962		
6	$-0.07765008 \pm j1.00846085$	$-0.21214395 \pm j0.73824458$	$-0.28979403 \pm j0.27021627$		
7	$-0.05700319 \pm j1.00640854$	$-0.15971939 \pm j0.80707698$	$-0.23080120 \pm j0.44789394$	-0.25617001	
8	$-0.04362008 \pm j1.00500207$	$-0.12421947 \pm j0.85199961$	$-0.18590757 \pm j0.56928794$	$-0.2192293 \pm j0.19990734$	
9	$-0.03445272 \pm j1.00400397$	$-0.09920264 \pm j0.8890628$	$-0.15198727 \pm j0.65531705$	$-0.18643998 \pm j0.34868692$	-0.19840529

(b) Denominator Polynomials $B(s) = s^n + b_{n-1}s^{n-1} + b_{n-2}s^{n-2} + \cdots + b_0$

Order n	b_0	b_1	b_2	b_3	b_4	b_5	b_6	b_7	b_8
1	2.86277516								
2	1.51620263	1.24562451							
3	0.71569379	1.53489546	1.25291297						
4	0.37905066	1.02545528	1.71686621	1.19738566					
5	0.17892345	0.75251811	1.30957474	1.93736749	1.17249093				
6	0.09476266	0.43236692	1.17186133	1.58976350	2.17184462	1.15917611			
7	0.04473086	0.28207223	0.75565110	1.64790293	1.86940791	2.41265096	1.15121758		
8	0.02369067	0.15254444	0.57356040	1.14858937	2.18401538	2.14921726	2.6567481	1.14608011	
9	0.01118272	0.09411978	0.34081930	0.98361988	1.61138805	2.78149904	2.42932969	2.90273369	1.14257051

(c) Denominator Polynomial Factors $B(s) = B_1(s)\, B_2(s)\, B_3(s)\, B_4(s)\, B_5(s)$

Order n	$B(s)$
1	$(s + 2.86277516)$
2	$(s^2 + 1.42562451s + 1.51620263)$
3	$(s^2 + 0.62645649s + 1.14244773)$ $(s + 0.62645649)$
4	$(s^2 + 0.35070614s + 1.06351864)$ $(s^2 + 0.84667952s + 0.35641186)$
5	$(s^2 + 0.22392584s + 1.03578401)$ $(s^2 + 0.58624547s + 0.47676701)$ $(s + 0.36231962)$
6	$(s^2 + 0.15530015s + 1.02302281)$ $(s^2 + 0.42428790s + 0.59001011)$ $(s^2 + 0.57958805s + 0.15699741)$
7	$(s^2 + 0.11400638s + 1.01610751)$ $(s^2 + 0.31943878s + 0.67688354)$ $(s^2 + 0.46160241s + 0.25387817)$ $(s + 0.25617001)$
8	$(s^2 + 0.08724015s + 1.01193187)$ $(s^2 + 0.24843894s + 0.74133382)$ $(s^2 + 0.37181515s + 0.35865039)$ $(s^2 + 0.43858587s + 0.08805234)$
9	$(s^2 + 0.06890543s + 1.00921097)$ $(s^2 + 0.19840529s + 0.78936466)$ $(s^2 + 0.30397454s + 0.45254057)$ $(s^2 + 0.37287997s + 0.15634244)$ $(s + 0.19840529)$

TABLE A8-6 Normalized Low-Pass Chebyshev Filters with 1.0 dB Passband Ripples

(a) Pole Locations

Order n	$p_{1,n}$	$p_{2,n-1}$	$p_{3,n-2}$	$p_{4,n-3}$	p_5
1	-1.96522673				
2	$-0.54886716 \pm j0.89512857$				
3	$-0.24708530 \pm j0.96599867$	-0.49417060			
4	$-0.13953600 \pm j0.98337916$	$-0.33686969 \pm j0.40732899$			
5	$-0.08945836 \pm j0.99010711$	$-0.23420503 \pm j0.61191985$	-0.28949334		
6	$-0.06218102 \pm j0.99341120$	$-0.16988172 \pm j0.72722747$	$-0.23206274 \pm j0.26618373$		
7	$-0.04570898 \pm j0.99528396$	$-0.12807372 \pm j0.79815576$	$-0.18507189 \pm j0.44294303$	-0.20541430	
8	$-0.03500823 \pm j0.99645128$	$-0.09969501 \pm j0.84475061$	$-0.14920413 \pm j0.56444431$	$-0.17599827 \pm j0.19820648$	
9	$-0.02766745 \pm j0.99722967$	$-0.07966524 \pm j0.87694906$	$-0.12205422 \pm j0.65089544$	$-0.14972167 \pm j0.34633423$	-0.15933047

(b) Denominator Polynomials $B(s) = s^n + b_{n-1}s^{n-1} + b_{n-2}s^{n-2} + \dots + b_0$

Order n	b_0	b_1	b_2	b_3	b_4	b_5	b_6	b_7	b_8
1	1.96522673								
2	1.10251033	1.09773433							
3	0.49130668	1.23840917	0.98834121						
4	0.27562758	0.74261937	1.45392476	0.95281138					
5	0.12282667	0.58053415	0.97439607	1.68881598	0.93682013				
6	0.06890690	0.30708064	0.93934553	1.20214039	1.93082492	0.92825096			
7	0.03070667	0.21367139	0.54861981	1.35754480	1.42879431	2.17607847	0.92312347		
8	0.01722672	0.10734473	0.44782572	0.84682432	1.83690238	1.65515567	2.42302642	0.91981131	
9	0.00767667	0.07060479	0.24418637	0.78631094	1.20160717	2.37811881	1.88147976	2.67094683	0.91754763

(c) Denominator Polynomial Factors $B(s) = B_1(s)\, B_2(s)\, B_3(s)\, B_4(s)\, B_5(s)$

Order n	$B(s)$
1	$(s + 1.96522673)$
2	$(s^2 + 1.09773433s + 1.10251033)$
3	$(s^2 + 0.49417060s + 0.99420459)$ $(s + 0.49417060)$
4	$(s^2 + 0.27907199s + 0.98650488)$ $(s^2 + 0.67373939s + 0.27939809)$
5	$(s^2 + 0.17891672s + 0.98831489)$ $(s^2 + 0.46841007s + 0.42929790)$ $(s + 0.28949334)$
6	$(s^2 + 0.12436205s + 0.99073230)$ $(s^2 + 0.33976343s + 0.55771960)$ $(s^2 + 0.46412548s + 0.12470689)$
7	$(s^2 + 0.09141796s + 0.99267947)$ $(s^2 + 0.25614744s + 0.65345550)$ $(s^2 + 0.37014377s + 0.23045013)$ $(s + 0.20541430)$
8	$(s^2 + 0.07001647s + 0.99414074)$ $(s^2 + 0.19919003s + 0.72354268)$ $(s^2 + 0.29840826s + 0.34085925)$ $(s^2 + 0.35199655s + 0.07026120)$
9	$(s^2 + 0.05533489s + 0.99523251)$ $(s^2 + 0.15933047s + 0.77538620)$ $(s^2 + 0.24410845s + 0.43856211)$ $(s^2 + 0.29944334s + 0.14236398)$ $(s + 0.15933047)$

TABLE A8-7 Normalized Low-Pass Chebyshev Filters with 1.5 dB Passband Ripples

(a) Pole Locations

Order n	$p_{1,n}$	$p_{2,n-1}$	$p_{3,n-2}$	$p_{4,n-3}$	p_5
1	-1.55692704				
2	$-0.46108873 \pm j0.84415805$				
3	$-0.21005618 \pm j0.93934594$	-0.42011237			
4	$-0.11913070 \pm j0.96761105$	$-0.28760695 \pm j0.40079762$			
5	$-0.07652815 \pm j0.97978702$	$-0.20035330 \pm j0.60554168$	-0.24765030		
6	$-0.05325112 \pm j0.98615853$	$-0.14548476 \pm j0.72191815$	$-0.19873588 \pm j0.26424038$		
7	$-0.03917029 \pm j0.98991746$	$-0.10975272 \pm j0.79385217$	$-0.15859728 \pm j0.44055472$	-0.17602970	
8	$-0.03001306 \pm j0.99232369$	$-0.08546998 \pm j0.84125141$	$-0.12791486 \pm j0.56210622$	$-0.15088586 \pm j0.19738545$	
9	$-0.02372663 \pm j0.99395816$	$-0.06831811 \pm j0.87407213$	$-0.10466942 \pm j0.64876011$	$-0.12839605 \pm j0.34519804$	-0.13663622

(b) Denominator Polynomials $B(s) = s^n + b_{n-1}s^{n-1} + b_{n-2}s^{n-2} + \cdots + b_0$

Order n	b_0	b_1	b_2	b_3	b_4	b_5	b_6	b_7	b_8
1	1.55692704								
2	0.92520563	0.92217745							
3	0.38923176	1.10298881	0.84022474						
4	0.23130141	0.60470214	1.33087103	0.81347530					
5	0.09730794	0.50419031	0.80441337	1.57113155	0.80141319				
6	0.05782535	0.24758513	0.83401695	1.00055677	1.81596761	0.79494354			
7	0.02432698	0.18365019	0.44733249	1.22429494	1.19561450	2.06289611	0.79107030		
8	0.01445634	0.08613897	0.39173725	0.69590812	1.67617801	1.39030856	2.31091937	0.78856753	
9	0.00608175	0.06034495	0.19776813	0.69725472	0.99316759	2.19012821	1.58489077	2.55957170	0.78685666

(c) Denominator Polynomial Factors $B(s) = B_1(s)\,B_2(s)\,B_3(s)\,B_4(s)\,B_5(s)$

Order n	$B(s)$
1	$(s + 1.55692704)$
2	$(s^2 + 0.92217745s + 0.92520563)$
3	$(s^2 + 0.42011237s + 0.92649440)\ (s + 0.42011237)$
4	$(s^2 + 0.23826140s + 0.95046327)\ (s^2 + 0.57521390s + 0.24335649)$
5	$(s^2 + 0.15305630s + 0.96583917)\ (s^2 + 0.40070660s + 0.40682217)\ (s + 0.24765030)$
6	$(s^2 + 0.10650224s + 0.97534434)\ (s^2 + 0.29096953s + 0.54233163)\ (s^2 + 0.39747177s + 0.10931893)$
7	$(s^2 + 0.07834059s + 0.98147089)\ (s^2 + 0.21950545s + 0.64224692)\ (s^2 + 0.31119456s + 0.21924156)\ (s + 0.17602970)$
8	$(s^2 + 0.06002613s + 0.98560709)\ (s^2 + 0.17093995s + 0.71500904)\ (s^2 + 0.25582972s + 0.33232561)\ (s^2 + 0.30177173s + 0.06172756)$
9	$(s^2 + 0.04745326s + 0.98851577)\ (s^2 + 0.13663622s + 0.76866946)\ (s^2 + 0.20933884s + 0.43184537)\ (s^2 + 0.25679210s + 0.13564724)\ (s + 0.13663622)$

307

TABLE A8-8 Normalized Low-Pass Chebyshev Filters with 2.0 dB Passband Ripples

(a) Pole Locations

Order n	$p_{1,n}$	$p_{2,n-1}$	$p_{3,n-2}$	$p_{4,n-3}$	p_5
1	-1.30756027				
2	-0.40190822 ± j0.81334508				
3	-0.18445539 ± j0.92307712	-0.36891079			
4	-0.10488725 ± j0.95795296	-0.25322023 ± j0.39679711			
5	-0.06746098 ± j0.97345572	-0.17661514 ± j0.60162872	-0.21830832		
6	-0.04697322 ± j0.98170517	-0.12833321 ± j0.71865806	-0.17530643 ± j0.26304711		
7	-0.03456636 ± j0.98662052	-0.09685278 ± j0.79120823	-0.13995632 ± j0.43908744	-0.15533980	
8	-0.02649238 ± j0.98978701	-0.07544391 ± j0.83910091	-0.11290980 ± j0.56066930	-0.13318619 ± j0.19688088	
9	-0.02094714 ± j0.99194711	-0.06031490 ± j0.87230365	-0.09240778 ± j0.64744750	-0.11335493 ± j0.34449962	-0.12062980

(b) Denominator Polynomials $B(s) = s^n + b_{n-1}s^{n-1} + b_{n-2}s^{n-2} + \cdots + b_0$

Order n	b_0	b_1	b_2	b_3	b_4	b_5	b_6	b_7	b_8
1	1.30756027								
2	0.82306043	0.80381643							
3	0.32689007	1.02219034	0.73782158						
4	0.20576511	0.51679810	1.25648193	0.71621496					
5	0.08172252	0.45934912	0.69347696	1.49954327	0.70646057				
6	0.05144128	0.21027056	0.77146177	0.86701492	1.74585875	0.70122571			
7	0.02043063	0.16612635	0.38263808	1.14459657	1.03954580	1.99366532	0.69809071		
8	0.01286032	0.07293732	0.35870428	0.59822139	1.57958072	1.21171208	2.24225293	0.69606455	
9	0.00510766	0.05437558	0.16844729	0.64446774	0.85686481	2.07674793	1.38374646	2.49128967	0.69467931

(c) Denominator Polynomial Factors $B(s) = B_1(s) B_2(s) B_3(s) B_4(s) B_5(s)$

Order n	$B(s)$
1	$(s + 1.30756027)$
2	$(s^2 + 0.80381643s + 0.82306043)$
3	$(s^2 + 0.36891079s + 0.88609517)$ $(s + 0.36891079)$
4	$(s^2 + 0.20977450s + 0.92867521)$ $(s^2 + 0.50644045s + 0.22156843)$
5	$(s^2 + 0.13492196s + 0.95216702)$ $(s^2 + 0.35323028s + 0.39315003)$ $(s + 0.21830832)$
6	$(s^2 + 0.09394643s + 0.96595153)$ $(s^2 + 0.25666642s + 0.53293883)$ $(s^2 + 0.35061285s + 0.09992612)$
7	$(s^2 + 0.06913271s + 0.97461489)$ $(s^2 + 0.19370556s + 0.63539092)$ $(s^2 + 0.27991264s + 0.21238555)$ $(s + 0.15533980)$
8	$(s^2 + 0.05298476s + 0.98038017)$ $(s^2 + 0.15088783s + 0.70978212)$ $(s^2 + 0.22581959s + 0.32709869)$ $(s^2 + 0.26637237s + 0.05650064)$
9	$(s^2 + 0.04189429s + 0.98439786)$ $(s^2 + 0.12062980s + 0.76455155)$ $(s^2 + 0.18481557s + 0.42772746)$ $(s^2 + 0.22670986s + 0.13152933)$ $(s + 0.12062980)$

TABLE A8-9 Normalized Low-Pass Chebyshev Filters with 2.5 dB Passband Ripples

(a) Pole Locations

Order n	$p_{1,n}$	$p_{2,n-1}$	$p_{3,n-2}$	$p_{4,n-3}$	p_5
1	-1.13352794				
2	$-0.35762543 \pm j0.79239886$				
3	$-0.16497445 \pm j0.91194830$	-0.32994890			
4	$-0.09398023 \pm j0.95133155$	$-0.22688835 \pm j0.39405443$			
5	$-0.06049691 \pm j0.96911059$	$-0.15838298 \pm j0.59894329$	-0.19577212		
6	$-0.04214350 \pm j0.97864714$	$-0.11513817 \pm j0.71641943$	$-0.15728167 \pm j0.26222771$		
7	$-0.03102091 \pm j0.98435581$	$-0.08691865 \pm j0.78939207$	$-0.12560108 \pm j0.43807955$	-0.13940668	
8	$-0.02377936 \pm j0.98800414$	$-0.06771789 \pm j0.83762338$	$-0.10134698 \pm j0.55968205$	$-0.11954692 \pm j0.19653420$	
9	$-0.01880433 \pm j0.99056519$	$-0.05414490 \pm j0.87108841$	$-0.08295480 \pm j0.64654551$	$-0.10175912 \pm j0.34401968$	-0.10828979

(b) Denominator Polynomials $B(s) = s^n + b_{n-1}s^{n-1} + b_{n-2}s^{n-2} + \cdots + b_0$

Order n	b_0	b_1	b_2	b_3	b_4	b_5	b_6	b_7	b_8
1	1.13352794								
2	0.75579190	0.71525087							
3	0.28338199	0.96773256	0.65989780						
4	0.18894798	0.45355237	1.20591329	0.64173716					
5	0.07084550	0.42943786	0.61232280	1.45068134	0.63353190				
6	0.04723699	0.18372756	0.72942899	0.76830555	1.69790019	0.62912669			
7	0.01771137	0.15448499	0.33601918	1.09079637	0.92336716	1.94624358	0.62648795		
8	0.01180925	0.06359602	0.33663041	0.52716439	1.51416640	1.07808152	2.19517646	0.62478230	
9	0.00442784	0.05041856	0.14748366	0.60904415	0.75700988	1.99979301	1.23266106	2.44444850	0.62361607

(c) Denominator Polynomial Factors $B(s) = B_1(s)\,B_2(s)\,B_3(s)\,B_4(s)\,B_5(s)$

Order n	$B(s)$
1	$(s + 1.13352794)$
2	$(s^2 + 0.71525087s + 0.75579190)$
3	$(s^2 + 0.32994890s + 0.85886628)\ (s + 0.32994890)$
4	$(s^2 + 0.18796046s + 0.91386400)\ (s^2 + 0.45377670s + 0.20675722)$
5	$(s^2 + 0.12099383s + 0.94283522)\ (s^2 + 0.31676595s + 0.38381823)\ (s + 0.19577212)$
6	$(s^2 + 0.08428699s + 0.95952630)\ (s^2 + 0.23027635s + 0.52651360)\ (s^2 + 0.31456334s + 0.09350090)$
7	$(s^2 + 0.06204181s + 0.96991866)\ (s^2 + 0.17383729s + 0.63069469)\ (s^2 + 0.25120216s + 0.20768932)\ (s + 0.13940668)$
8	$(s^2 + 0.04755872s + 0.97679669)\ (s^2 + 0.13545378s + 0.70619864)\ (s^2 + 0.20269397s + 0.32351521)\ (s^2 + 0.23909383s + 0.05291716)$
9	$(s^2 + 0.03760865s + 0.98157299)\ (s^2 + 0.10828979s + 0.76172668)\ (s^2 + 0.16590959s + 0.42490259)\ (s^2 + 0.20351824s + 0.12870446)\ (s + 0.10828979)$

TABLE A8-10 Normalized Low-Pass Chebyshev Filters with 3 dB Passband Ripples

(a) Pole Locations

Order n	$p_{1,n}$	$p_{2,n-1}$	$p_{3,n-2}$	$p_{4,n-3}$	p_5
1	-1.00237729				
2	$-0.32244983 \pm j0.77715757$				
3	$-0.14931010 \pm j0.90381443$	-0.29862021			
4	$-0.08517040 \pm j0.94648443$	$-0.20561953 \pm j0.39204669$			
5	$-0.05485987 \pm j0.96592748$	$-0.14362501 \pm j0.59697601$	-0.17753027		
6	$-0.03822951 \pm j0.97640602$	$-0.10444497 \pm j0.71147881$	$-0.14267448 \pm j0.26162720$		
7	$-0.02814564 \pm j0.98269568$	$-0.07886234 \pm j0.78806075$	$-0.11395938 \pm j0.43734072$	-0.12648537	
8	$-0.02157816 \pm j0.98676635$	$-0.06144939 \pm j0.83654012$	$-0.09196552 \pm j0.55895824$	$-0.10848072 \pm j0.19628003$	
9	$-0.01706520 \pm j0.98895191$	$-0.04913728 \pm j0.87019734$	$-0.07528269 \pm j0.64588414$	$-0.09234789 \pm j0.34366777$	-0.09827457

(b) Denominator Polynomials $B(s) = s^n + b_{n-1}s^{n-1} + b_{n-2}s^{n-2} + \cdots + b_0$

Order n	b_0	b_1	b_2	b_3	b_4	b_5	b_6	b_7	b_8
1	1.00237729								
2	0.70794778	0.64489965							
3	0.25059432	0.92834806	0.59724042						
4	0.17698695	0.40476795	1.16911757	0.58157986					
5	0.06264858	0.40796631	0.54893711	1.41502514	0.57450003				
6	0.04424674	0.16342991	0.69909774	0.69060980	1.66284806	0.57069793			
7	0.01566215	0.14615300	0.30001666	1.05184481	0.83114115	1.91155070	0.56842010		
8	0.01106168	0.05648135	0.32076457	0.47189898	1.46669900	0.97194732	2.16071478	0.56694758	
9	0.00391554	0.04759081	0.13138977	0.58350569	0.67893051	1.94386024	1.11232209	2.41014443	0.56594069

(c) Denominator Polynomial Factors $B(s) = B_1(s)\, B_2(s)\, B_3(s)\, B_4(s)\, B_5(s)$

Order n	$B(s)$
1	$(s + 1.00237729)$
2	$(s^2 + 0.64489965s + 0.70794778)$
3	$(s^2 + 0.29862021s + 0.83917403)\quad (s + 0.29862021)$
4	$(s^2 + 0.17034080s + 0.90308678)\quad (s^2 + 0.41123906s + 0.19598000)$
5	$(s^2 + 0.10971974s + 0.93602549)\quad (s^2 + 0.28725001s + 0.37700850)\quad (s + 0.17753027)$
6	$(s^2 + 0.07645903s + 0.95483021)\quad (s^2 + 0.20888994s + 0.52181750)\quad (s^2 + 0.28534897s + 0.08880480)$
7	$(s^2 + 0.05629129s + 0.96648298)\quad (s^2 + 0.15772468s + 0.62725902)\quad (s^2 + 0.22791876s + 0.20425365)\quad (s + 0.12648537)$
8	$(s^2 + 0.04315631s + 0.97417345)\quad (s^2 + 0.12289878s + 0.70357540)\quad (s^2 + 0.18393103s + 0.32089197)\quad (s^2 + 0.21696145s + 0.05029392)$
9	$(s^2 + 0.03413040s + 0.97950420)\quad (s^2 + 0.09827457s + 0.75965789)\quad (s^2 + 0.15056538s + 0.42283380)\quad (s^2 + 0.18469578s + 0.12663567)\quad (s + 0.09827457)$

PROBLEMS

8-1. Determine which of the following $F(\omega)$ may be a magnitude squared function of a transfer function.

(a) $F(\omega) = \dfrac{1}{\omega^4 + \omega^2 + 1}$

(b) $F(\omega) = \dfrac{1}{\omega^4 - \omega^2 + 1}$

(c) $F(\omega) = \dfrac{1 + \omega^4}{\omega^4 - 3\omega^2 + 2}$

(d) $F(\omega) = \dfrac{\omega^4 + 3\omega^2 + 2}{1 + \omega^4}$

(e) $F(\omega) = \dfrac{1 + \omega^4}{\omega^4 + 20\omega^2 + 5\omega + 1}$

(f) $F(\omega) = \dfrac{\omega^4 + \omega + 1}{\omega^4 + 20\omega^2 + 10}$

(g) $F(\omega) = \dfrac{\omega^4 - \omega + 1}{\omega^4 + 20\omega^2 + 10}$

(h) $F(\omega) = \dfrac{100 - \omega^4}{\omega^4 + 20\omega^2 + 10}$

(i) $F(\omega) = \dfrac{1 - \omega^6}{\omega^6 + 2\omega^4 + 20\omega^2 + 10}$

(j) $F(\omega) = \dfrac{\omega^2 + \omega^6}{\omega^6 + 2\omega^4 + 20\omega^2 + 10}$

8-2. (a) Find the transfer function of the nth-order normalized low-pass Butterworth filter, where $n = 1, 2, 3, \ldots, 9$.
(b) Sketch the pole-zero patterns of the nth-order normalized low-pass Butterworth filter, where $n = 1, 2, 3, \ldots, 9$.

8-3. (a) Find the minimum order of Butterworth filter to meet the following specifications:

    (i) The 3 dB cutoff frequency is at 1 rad./sec.
    (ii) The passband requirement is

$$|H(j\omega)| \geq 0.99 \quad \text{for} \quad 0 \leq \omega \leq 0.25 \text{ rad./sec.}$$

    (iii) The stopband requirement is

$$|H(j\omega)| \leq 0.001 \quad \text{for} \quad \omega \geq 2 \text{ rad./sec.}$$

(b) Find the transfer function of the desired filter.
(c) Realize the filter in (b) with $R_s = 1\ \Omega$ and $R_\ell = 1\ \Omega$.
(d) Realize the filter in (b) with $R_s = 1\ \Omega$ and $R_\ell = 3\ \Omega$.
(e) Realize the filter in (b) with $R_s = 1\ \Omega$ and $R_\ell = 0.5\ \Omega$.

8-4. Repeat Problem 8-3 with specifications (ii) and (iii) replaced by
(iia) $|H(j\omega)|^2 \geq 0.99$ for $0 \leq \omega \leq 0.25$ rad./sec.
(iiia) $|H(j\omega)|^2 \leq 0.01$ for $\omega \geq 2$ rad./sec.

8-5. Repeat Problem 8-3 with specifications (ii) and (iii) replaced by
(iib) $|H(j\omega)| \geq 0.9$ for $0 \leq \omega \leq 0.5$ rad./sec.
(iiib) $|H(j\omega)| \leq 0.1$ for $\omega \geq 1.5$ rad./sec.

8-6. Suppose that a maximally flat normalized low-pass filter is required to meet the following specifications:

(i) The passband attenuation is less than 0.1 dB for $0.05 \leq \omega \leq 0.85$ rad./sec.

(ii) The stopband attenuation is at least 50 dB for $\omega \geq 1.2$ rad./sec.

Find the minimum order of the desired filter.

8-7. (a) Find the minimum order of the normalized low-pass Butterworth filter to meet the following requirements:

(i) The passband attenuation is less than 0.01 dB for $0 \leq \omega \leq 0.3$ rad./sec. and is less than 0.1 dB for $0.3 \leq \omega \leq 0.6$ rad./sec.

(ii) The stopband attenuation is at least 40 dB for $\omega \geq 2$ rad./sec. and 60 dB for $\omega \geq 3$ rad./sec.

(b) Find a circuit realization of the desired filter.

8-8. Repeat Problem 8-7 with the following requirements:

(ia) The passband attenuation is less than 0.1 dB for $0 \leq \omega \leq 0.75$ rad./sec.

(iia) The stopband attenuation is at least 50 dB for $\omega \geq 2$ rad./sec.

8-9. (a) Find the transfer function of the nth-order low-pass Chebyshev filter with a 1 rad./sec. ripple bandwidth and with $\epsilon = 0.5$, where $n = 1, 2, \ldots, 9$.

(b) Sketch the pole-zero patterns of the transfer functions obtained in (a).

8-10. (a) Find the transfer function of the nth-order low-pass Chebyshev filter with a 1 rad./sec. ripple bandwidth and with $A_{max} = 0.1$ dB, where $n = 1, 2, \ldots, 9$.

(b) Sketch the pole-zero patterns of the transfer functions obtained in (a).

8-11. Repeat Problem 8-10 with $A_{max} = 1$ dB.

8-12. Suppose that we are to design and realize a low-pass Chebyshev filter to meet the following requirements:

(i) The ripple bandwidth is 1 rad./sec.

(ii) The passband ripple $A_{max} = 0.1$ dB.

(iii) The stopband attenuation is at least 40 dB for $\omega \geq 2$ rad./sec.

(a) Find the minimum order of the desired filter.

(b) Find the transfer function of the desired filter.

(c) Find a circuit realization of the desired filter.

8-13. Repeat Problem 8-12 with requirement (ii) replaced by one of the following:

(a) $A_{max} = 0.2$ dB.

(b) $A_{max} = 0.3$ dB.

(c) $A_{max} = 0.5$ dB.

(d) $A_{max} = 1$ dB.

(e) $A_{max} = 1.5$ dB.

(f) $A_{max} = 2$ dB

(g) $A_{max} = 2.5$ dB

(h) $A_{max} = 3$ dB

8-14. (a) Find the minimum order of an equiripple filter to meet the following requirements:

(i) The passband requirement is

$$|H(j\omega)|^2 \geq 0.955 \quad \text{for} \quad 0 \leq \omega \leq 1 \text{ rad./sec.}$$

(ii) The stopband requirement is

$$|H(j\omega)|^2 \leq 0.001 \quad \text{for} \quad \omega \geq 3 \text{ rad./sec.}$$

(b) Find a realization of the desired filter.

8-15. Repeat Problem 8-14 with requirement (i) replaced by

$$|H(j\omega)|^2 \geq 0.7079 \quad \text{for} \quad 0 \leq \omega \leq 1 \text{ rad./sec.}$$

8-16. (a) Find the minimum order of a normalized Chebyshev filter to meet the following requirements:

(i) $A_{\max} = 0.2$ dB.

(ii) The stopband attenuation is at least 60 dB for $\omega \geq 2.5$ rad./sec.

(b) Realize the desired filter.

8-17. Repeat Problem 8-16 with requirement (i) replaced by one of the following:

(a) $A_{\max} = 0.5$ dB.

(b) $A_{\max} = 1.5$ dB.

(c) $A_{\max} = 2.5$ dB.

8-18. Find the minimum order of a normalized Chebyshev filter to meet the following requirements:

(i) $A_{\max} = 0.1$ dB.

(ii) The stopband attenuation is at least 60 dB for $\omega \geq 1.4$ rad./sec.

(iii) The 3 dB frequency $\omega_c \leq 1.25$ rad./sec.

8-19. Suppose that we are to design a Chebyshev filter to meet the following requirements:

(i) The maximum passband ripple $A_{\max} = 0.3$ dB.

(ii) The ripple bandwidth is 1 rad./sec.

(iii) The 3 dB frequency $\omega_c \leq 1.2$ rad./sec.

(iv) The stopband attenuation is at least 40 dB for $\omega \geq 2$ rad./sec.

(a) Find the minimum order of the desired filter.

(b) Find the magnitude function of the desired filter.

(c) Realize the desired filter.

8-20. Repeat Problem 8-19 with requirement (i) replaced by one of the following:

(a) $A_{\max} = 0.5$ dB.

(b) $A_{\max} = 1$ dB.

(c) $A_{\max} = 2$ dB.

8-21. Suppose that we are to design a low-pass filter to meet the following requirements:

(i) The passband attenuation is less than 0.1 dB for $0 \leq \omega \leq 0.25$ rad./sec. and less than 1 dB for $0.25 \leq \omega \leq 0.75$ rad./sec.

(ii) The stopband attenuation is at least 40 dB for $\omega \geq 2$ rad./sec.

(a) Find the minimum order of the normalized low-pass Butterworth filter to meet the requirements.

(b) Find the minimum order of the normalized low-pass Chebyshev filter to meet the requirements.

8-22. Let p_1 and p_2 be the poles of a second-order maximally flat all-pole group delay filter where

$$p_1 = -\alpha + j\beta \quad \text{and} \quad p_2 = -\alpha - j\beta$$

(a) Find the group delay function $\tau(\omega)$ or $\tau(s/j)$ in terms of α and β.

(b) Find the conditions on α and β such that $\tau(\omega)$ is maximally flat at $\omega = 0$.

(c) Together with (b), find α and β such that $\tau(0) = 1$.

(d) Find the transfer function of the second-order maximally flat unit group delay [i.e., $\tau(0) = 1$] filter. *Hint:* Use (c).

(e) Find the transfer function of the second-order Bessel filter.

(f) Comment on the results obtained in (d) and (e).

(g) Together with (b), find α and β in terms of the constant $\tau_0 \triangleq \tau(0)$.

(h) Find the transfer function of the second-order maximally flat τ_0 unit group delay filter. *Hint:* Use (g).

(i) By comparing the results of (e) and (h), devise a procedure to obtain the transfer function of an nth-order maximally flat τ_0 unit group delay filter based on the Bessel polynomials.

8-23. Find the transfer function of an nth-order low-pass Bessel filter with unity group delay at $\omega = 0$, where $n = 1, 2, \ldots, 9$.

8-24. Find the transfer function of a fourth-order low-pass Bessel filter with

(a) $\tau(0) = 2$ sec.

(b) $\tau(0) = 10^{-3}$ sec.

(c) $\tau(0) = 10^{-6}$ sec.

8-25. (a) Find the minimum order of a Bessel filter to meet the following specifications:

(i) $\tau(0) = 1$ sec.

(ii) $\tau(\omega)$ has less than 2% error for $\omega \leq 2$ rad./sec.

(iii) The stopband attenuation is at least 20 dB for $\omega \geq 4$ rad./sec.

(b) Find the transfer function of the desired filter.

(c) Find a circuit realization of the desired filter.

8-26. (a) Find the minimum order of a Bessel filter to meet the following specifications:

(i) $\tau(0) = 2$ sec.

(ii) $\tau(\omega)$ has less than 1% error for $\omega \leq 2.5$ rad./sec.

(iii) The 3 dB cutoff frequency $\omega_c \leq 1.5$ rad./sec.

(iv) The stopband attenuation is at least 34 dB for $\omega \geq 3$ rad./sec.

(b) Find the transfer function of the desired filter.

8-27. (a) Find the transfer function of a second-order low-pass Bessel filter with $\tau(0) = 10$ msec.

(b) Realize the filter in (a) with a lossless 2-port terminated at both ends by $R_s = R_\ell = 1\ \Omega$.

8-28. (a) Find the transfer function of a third-order low-pass Bessel filter with $\tau(0) = 5$ msec.

(b) Realize the filter in (a) with a lossless 2-port terminated at both ends by $R_s = 1\ \Omega$ and $R_\ell = 1.5\ \Omega$.

8-29. (a) Find the transfer function $H_1(s)$ of a second-order normalized low-pass Butterworth filter.

(b) Find the transfer function $H_2(s)$ of a second-order Chebyshev filter with a 1 rad./sec. ripple bandwidth and with $A_{\max} = 0.1$ dB.

(c) Find the transfer function $H_3(s)$ of a second-order low-pass Bessel filter with a unity group delay.

(d) Find the transfer function $H_4(s)$ of a second-order low-pass transitional filter with the poles located midway between those of $H_2(s)$ and $H_3(s)$.

(e) Find the transfer function $H_5(s)$ of a second-order low-pass transitional filter with the poles located midway between those of $H_1(s)$ and $H_3(s)$.

(f) Consider the circuit shown in Fig. P8-29(a). Find the transfer function $H(s) = V_o/V_i$ in terms of L and C.

(g) Find the values of L and C to realize $H_1(s)$, $H_2(s)$, $H_3(s)$, $H_4(s)$, and $H_5(s)$.

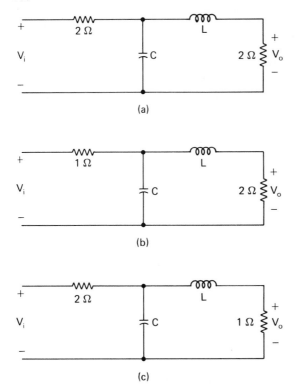

(a)

(b)

(c)

Fig. P8-29

(h) Repeat (f) and (g) for the circuit shown in Fig. P8-29(b).

(i) Repeat (f) and (g) for the circuit shown in Fig. P8-29(c).

8-30. (a) Find the transfer function of a second-order low-pass Butterworth filter with a 3 dB cutoff frequency at $\omega_c = 10^6$ rad./sec.

(b) Realize the transfer function in (a) with $R_s = R_\ell = 1\,\Omega$.

(c) Realize the transfer function in (a) with $R_s = R_\ell = 10\,\text{K}\Omega$.

(d) Realize the transfer function in (a) with $R_s = 2R_\ell = 10\,\text{K}\Omega$.

(e) Realize the transfer function in (a) with $R_s = 0.1R_\ell = 5\,\text{K}\Omega$.

8-31. Repeat Problem 8-30 for an nth-order low-pass Butterworth filter, where $n = 3, 4, \ldots, 9$.

8-32. (a) Find the transfer function of a second-order low-pass Chebyshev filter with a ripple bandwidth of $\omega_r = 10^5$ rad./sec. and with $A_{\max} = 0.1$ dB.

(b) Realize the transfer function in (a) with a suitable R_s and an $R_\ell = 10\,\text{K}\Omega$.

8-33. (a) Find the transfer function of a third-order low-pass Chebyshev filter with a ripple bandwidth $\omega_r = 10^6$ rad./sec. and $A_{\max} = 1$ dB.

(b) Realize the transfer function in (a) with a suitable R_s and an $R_\ell = 50\,\Omega$.

8-34. Suppose that we need a low-pass filter to meet the following requirements:

  (i) The passband attenuation is less than 0.1 dB for $\omega \leq 5$ K rad./sec. and is less than 0.5 dB for $\omega \leq 20$ K rad./sec.

  (ii) The stopband loss is at least 50 dB for $\omega \geq 100$ K rad./sec.

  (iii) The 3 dB cutoff frequency $\omega_c = 30$ K rad./sec.

(a) Find the minimum order of a Butterworth filter to meet the requirements.

(b) Find the transfer function of the desired Butterworth filter.

(c) Realize the desired Butterworth filter with $R_s = R_\ell = 75\,\Omega$.

(d) Find the minimum order of a Chebyshev filter to meet the requirements.

(e) Find the transfer function of the desired Chebyshev filter.

(f) Realize the desired Chebyshev filter with $R_s = 50\,\Omega$.

8-35. (a) Find the transfer function of a low-pass Bessel filter with $\tau(0) = 1$ sec. and a linear phase characteristic with less than 5% error for $\omega \leq 3$ rad./sec.

(b) Find the group delay $\tau(0)$ if a transformation

$$s \mapsto \frac{s}{10\,\text{K}}$$

is performed on the transfer function obtained in (a).

(c) Find a circuit realization of a low-pass Bessel filter with $\tau(0)$ given by (b) and a linear phase characteristic with less than 5% error for $\omega \leq 30$ K rad./sec., and with $R_s = R_\ell = 50\,\Omega$.

8-36. (a) Find the transfer function of the minimum order of a low-pass Bessel filter to meet the following requirements:

    (i) $\tau(0) = 1\ \mu\text{sec}$.

    (ii) $\tau(\omega)$ has less than 1% error for $\omega \leq 10^6$ rad./sec.

(b) Realize the desired filter.

8-37. Suppose that we need a maximally flat group delay filter to meet the following specifications:

    (i) $\tau(0) = 20\ \mu\text{sec}$.

    (ii) $\tau(\omega)$ has less than 5% error for $\omega \leq 10^5$ rad./sec.

    (iii) The 3 dB cutoff frequency $\omega_c \leq 2 \times 10^5$ rad./sec.

(a) Find the minimum order of the desired filter.

(b) Find the transfer function of the desired filter.

(c) Realize the desired filter with $R_s = R_\ell = 50\ \Omega$.

8-38. (a) Find the transfer function of a bandpass filter with a center frequency $\omega_0 = 10^5$ rad./sec. and a bandwidth $B = 10^4$ rad./sec., obtained by a low-pass to bandpass transformation from a second-order normalized low-pass Butterworth filter.

(b) Sketch the magnitude characteristics of the filter in (a).

(c) Realize the filter in (a) with $R_s = R_\ell = 10\ \text{K}\Omega$.

8-39. Repeat Problem 8-38 for a third-order normalized low-pass Butterworth filter.

8-40. (a) Find the transfer function of a bandpass filter with a center frequency $\omega_0 = 10^5$ rad./sec., a ripple bandwidth of 10^4 rad./sec., and $A_{\max} = 0.1$ dB, obtained by a low-pass to bandpass transformation from a second-order normalized low-pass Chebyshev filter.

(b) Sketch the magnitude characteristic of the filter in (a).

(c) Realize the filter in (a) with a suitable R_s and $R_\ell = 1\ \text{K}\Omega$.

8-41. Repeat Problem 8-40 for a third-order normalized low-pass Chebyshev filter with $A_{\max} = 1$ dB.

8-42. A Chebyshev bandpass filter is to be realized with the following specifications:

    (i) The ripple band is given by

$$41.4 \text{ rad./sec.} \leq \omega \leq 241.4 \text{ rad./sec.}$$

    (ii) $A_{\max} = 1$ dB.

    (iii) The loss is at least 20 dB for $\omega \geq 500$ rad./sec. and for $\omega < 20$ rad./sec.

(a) Find the center frequency ω_0 and bandwidth B.

(b) Find the normalized low-pass prototype filter specifications corresponding to the foregoing bandpass filter specifications.

(c) Find the lowest order n to meet the specifications in (b).

(d) Find a circuit realization of the desired low-pass prototype with $R_s = 1\ \Omega$ and $R_\ell = 1\ \Omega$ or $0.25\ \Omega$.

(e) Find a circuit realization of the desired bandpass filter with $R_s = 1\ \Omega$ and $R_\ell = 1\ \Omega$ or $0.25\ \Omega$.

(f) Scale the impedance level of the circuit in (e) such that $R_s = 600\ \Omega$.

8-43. Suppose that we are to design a bandpass filter to meet the following requirements:

    (i) The center frequency of the passband is at $\omega_0 = 1$ M rad./sec.

    (ii) The 3 dB bandwidth $B = 100$ K rad./sec.

    (iii) The passband attenuation is less than 0.1 dB for 0.95 M rad./sec. $\leq \omega \leq 1.05$ M rad./sec.

    (iv) The stopband attenuation is at least 40 dB for $\omega \geq 1.25$ M rad./sec.

    (a) Find the minimum order of a Butterworth bandpass filter to meet all the foregoing requirements.

    (b) Find the transfer function of the desired Butterworth filter.

    (c) Realize the desired Butterworth filter with $R_s = R_\ell = 5$ KΩ.

    (d) Find the minimum order of a Chebyshev bandpass filter to meet all the foregoing requirements.

    (e) Find the minimum order of a Chebyshev filter to meet requirements (i), (iii), and (iv).

8-44. Given the group delay characteristics in Fig. P8-44, sketch the corresponding characteristics when a low-pass to bandpass transformation of

$$s_{LP} \longrightarrow \frac{s_{BP}^2 + \omega_0^2}{B s_{BP}}$$

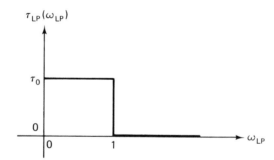

Fig. P8-44

is applied, where $s_{LP} = \sigma_{LP} + j\omega_{LP}$ and $s_{BP} = \sigma_{BP} + j\omega_{BP}$ are, respectively, the complex frequencies associated with the low-pass filter and the resultant bandpass filter, $\omega_0 = 10$ K rad./sec., and

    (a) $B = 0.05\omega_0$

    (b) $B = 0.5\omega_0$

Hint:

$$\tau_{BP}(\omega_{BP}) = \frac{d\phi_{BP}(\omega_{BP})}{d\omega_{BP}} = \frac{d\phi_{LP}(\omega_{LP})}{d\omega_{LP}}\bigg|_{\omega_{LP} = (\omega_{BP}^2 - \omega_0^2)/B\omega_{BP}} \frac{d\omega_{LP}}{d\omega_{BP}}$$

8-45. **(a)** Find the transfer function of a band-reject filter with center frequency $\omega_0 = 10$ K rad./sec. and bandwidth $B = 4$ K rad./sec., obtained by a low-pass to band-reject transformation from a second-order normalized low-pass Butterworth filter.

(b) Find a circuit realization of the desired filter.

(c) Verify that the circuit obtained in (b) indeed realized the transfer function obtained in (a).

(d) Sketch the magnitude characteristics of the desired filter.

8-46. Suppose that we need a band-reject or notch filter to meet the following specifications:

(i) The center frequency of the rejection band is at 120π rad./sec., and the 3 dB rejection bandwidth is 20π rad./sec.

(ii) The minimum loss for 118π rad./sec. $\leq \omega \leq 122\pi$ rad./sec. is 40 dB.

(iii) The passband degradation is at most 0.1 dB for $\omega \geq 150\pi$ rad./sec. and for $\omega \leq 40\pi$ rad./sec.

(a) Find the minimum order of a Butterworth filter to meet all the requirements.

(b) Find the transfer function of the desired filter.

(c) Sketch the magnitude characteristics of the desired filter.

(d) Realize the desired filter with $R_s = R_\ell = 75\ \Omega$.

8-47. **(a)** Find the transfer function of a band-reject filter to meet the following requirements:

(i) The passbands are from 0 to 3400 Hz and from 4500 Hz to ∞, with 0.1 dB ripples.

(ii) The stopband is from 3700 Hz to 4000 Hz, with a minimum loss of 30 dB.

(b) Realize the desired Chebyshev filter.

8-48. **(a)** Find the transfer function of a third-order high-pass Bessel filter with a 10 μsec. group delay.

(b) Sketch the group delay characteristics of the desired filter.

(c) Realize the desired filter with $R_s = R_\ell = 10$ KΩ.

8-49. Suppose that we need a high-pass filter to meet the following requirements:

(i) The stopband attenuation is at least 40 dB for $|\omega| \leq 100\pi$ K rad./sec.

(ii) The passband loss is at most 1 dB for $\omega \geq 120\pi$ K rad./sec.

(a) Find the minimum order of a Butterworth filter to meet the requirements.

(b) Find a circuit realization of the desired Butterworth filter in (a) with $R_s = R_\ell = 50\ \Omega$.

(c) Find the minimum order of a Chebyshev filter to meet the requirements.

(d) Realize the desired Chebyshev filter obtained in (c) with a suitable R_s and $R_\ell = 50\ \Omega$.

8-50. Write a computer program:

(a) to generate the transfer function,

(b) to locate the poles, and

(c) to produce a circuit realization with prescribed R_s and R_ℓ values of an nth order low-pass Butterworth filter with the 3 dB cutoff frequency at ω_c rad./sec.

8-51. Write a computer program:

(a) to generate the transfer function,

(b) to locate the poles, and

(c) to produce a circuit realization with a pair of prescribed and yet compatible R_s and R_ℓ values of an nth-order low-pass Chebyshev filter with ripple bandwidth ω_r rad./sec. and $A_{\max}$ dB ripples.

8-52. Write a computer program to generate the transfer function and to locate the poles of an nth-order low-pass Bessel filter with τ_0 group delay at $\omega = 0$.

8-53. Write a computer program to implement:

(a) the low-pass to low-pass transformation,

(b) the low-pass to bandpass transformation,

(c) the low-pass to band-reject transformation,

(d) the low-pass to high-pass transformation, and

(e) the impedance scaling as prescribed in Sec. 8-4 by generating the desired transfer functions and circuit realizations from their normalized low-pass counterparts.

9

SENSITIVITY

All synthesis procedures discussed so far require the use of ideal elements. Physical elements are never ideal. For example, every physical "linear" resistor has a *i-v* curve that is never exactly linear. Tolerances have to be allowed. In addition, the characteristics of a physical element depend on environmental factors such as room temperature, light intensity, etc. Hence, it is necessary to study the effect of the nonideal elements used in the hardware implementation on the desired output quantities such as transfer functions, central frequencies, bandwidths, pole and zero locations, etc.

Sensitivity is a measure of the effect on the performance of the output quantities[1] due to variations of circuit parameters such as resistor values, inductor values, capacitor values, β values of a transistor, finite open loop gain of an operational amplifier, and nonidealness of a gyrator. Certain circuit configurations are extremely sensitive and may exhibit severe distortions of output responses for small parameter variations. Other circuit structures (for example, ladder circuits) are extremely insensitive, and greatly distorted responses will occur only with large component errors or when the elements are operating beyond their capabilities.

There are basically two types of circuit parameter variations. The first and most frequently considered is the case of *incremental variation*, where the percentage changes in parameter values are assumed to be small. The second type of variation is called *large parameter variation*, where the param-

---

[1]Some output quantities are pole and zero locations, phase and magnitude responses, transfer functions, center frequencies and bandwidths, cutoff frequencies, pole-frequencies, and pole-pairs.

eter values may change drastically in comparison to their nominal values. The second case is more difficult to work with, and in this chapter we consider the incremental case only.

9-1 POLE AND ZERO SENSITIVITIES

Let $p(s)$ be a polynomial of interest, where $p(s)$ can be either the numerator or the denominator polynomial of a transfer function, as well as a magnitude function, a phase function, the real part or the imaginary part of a transfer function, etc. Let s_j be a root of $p(s)$ with multiplicity n. Then $p(s)$ can be written as

$$p(s) = (s - s_j)^n p_1(s) \qquad (9\text{-}1)$$

where $p_1(s)$ represents the products of remaining factors. An incremental change in network element values will change $p(s)$ to a new polynomial $\hat{p}(s)$, where[2]

$$\hat{p}(s) \triangleq p(s) + \delta p(s) \qquad (9\text{-}2)$$

and $\delta p(s)$ represents the change of $p(s)$ due to the changes in the circuit parameter values. Consequently, the root s_j that we are interested in will change to a new position $\hat{s}_j$. Let us denote the root displacement of s_j by

$$\delta s_j \triangleq \hat{s}_j - s_j \qquad (9\text{-}3)$$

9-1-1. Computation Techniques

To find δs_j, we can first compute $\hat{s}_j$ by solving the equation

$$\hat{p}(s) = 0 \qquad (9\text{-}4)$$

and then apply (9-3). However, solving (9-4) is in general a very difficult task. In this section, we introduce other techniques to compute δs_j approximately. By (9-1), in the neighborhood of $s = s_j$, $1/p(s)$ is approximately equal to[3]

$$\frac{1}{p(s)} \simeq \frac{L_n}{(s - s_j)^n} \qquad (9\text{-}5)$$

where

$$L_n = \frac{(s - s_j)^n}{p(s)} \bigg|_{s=s_j} = \text{a constant} \qquad (9\text{-}6)$$

is called the *Laurent constant* of $p(s)$ at s_j.[4] If all circuit parameter changes

---

[2] The symbol "δ" is used throughout this chapter to denote "small variation of."

[3] The right-hand side of (9-5) represents the most significant term of a Laurent series expansion of $1/p(s)$.

[4] Note that when s_j is a simple root of $p(s)$, the constant L_1, as defined in (9-6), is also the residue of the rational function $1/p(s)$ at the pole $s = s_j$.

are indeed small, then $\delta p(s)$, the change in $p(s)$, should be small. Hence, it is reasonable to expect that δs_j, the change in the roots, will also be small—$\hat{s}_j$ will be in the neighborhood of s_j, where (9-5) is valid. Assuming this is the case, we can evaluate (9-5) at $s = \hat{s}_j$ as

$$\frac{1}{p(\hat{s}_j)} = \frac{L_n}{(\hat{s}_j - s_j)^n} = \frac{L_n}{(\delta s_j)^n} \tag{9-7}$$

Observe that (9-7) can be rewritten as

$$\delta s_j \triangleq \hat{s}_j - s_j = [L_n p(\hat{s}_j)]^{1/n} \tag{9-8}$$

Because $\hat{s}_j$ is a root of $\hat{p}(s)$, by (9-2), we have

$$\hat{p}(\hat{s}_j) = p(\hat{s}_j) + \delta p(\hat{s}_j) = 0$$

or

$$p(\hat{s}_j) = -\delta p(\hat{s}_j) \tag{9-9}$$

A Taylor series expansion of $\delta p(\hat{s}_j)$ at s_j gives

$$\delta p(\hat{s}_j) = \delta p(s_j) + \frac{d\delta p(s)}{ds}\bigg|_{s=s_j} \delta s_j + \dots \tag{9-10}$$

$$\simeq \delta p(s_j)$$

if δs_j is indeed small. Equation (9-10) means essentially that all second-order variation terms are ignored. Substituting (9-9) and (9-10) into (9-8), we obtain

$$\delta s_j \triangleq \hat{s}_j - s_j \simeq [-L_n \, \delta p(s_j)]^{1/n} \tag{9-11}$$

As a result of small parameter variations, (9-11) implies that each root of $p(s)$ of multiplicity n becomes n simple roots situated equidistant and equiangle from each other on a circle of radius $|\delta s_j|$, centered at the nominal root s_j. If $n = 1$, then (9-11) simply gives the direction and distance of root changes.

Example 9-1 Consider the circuit in Fig. 9-1. If both C and L have a 10% tolerance, find approximately all possible pole positions.

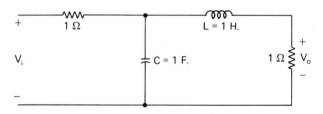

Fig. 9-1 Circuit for Example 9-1.

Solution: The transfer function is given by

$$\frac{V_o}{V_i} = \frac{1}{s^2 LC + s(L + C) + 2} \tag{9-12}$$

The poles of the circuit are the solution of the equation

$$p(s) \triangleq s^2 LC + s(L + C) + 2 = 0 \tag{9-13}$$

When $L = 1$ Henry and $C = 1$ Farad, the pole positions are

$$s_1 = -1 + j1 \quad \text{and} \quad s_2 = -1 - j1 \tag{9-14}$$

Because both L and C allow a maximum of 10% tolerance, the resultant polynomial, after parameter variations of δL and δC, is given by

$$\hat{p}(s) = s^2(L + \delta L)(C + \delta C) + s(L + \delta L + C + \delta C) + 2 \tag{9-15}$$

Subtracting (9-13) from (9-15), we obtain

$$
\begin{aligned}
\delta p(s) &= s^2(L\delta C + C\delta L + \delta L\,\delta C) + s(\delta L + \delta C) \\
&\simeq (\delta C + \delta L)s^2 + (\delta L + \delta C)s \\
&= (\delta C + \delta L)s(s + 1)
\end{aligned}
\tag{9-16}
$$

Observe that we have ignored second-order variational terms in (9-16). Evaluating $\delta p(s)$ at the nominal pole locations leads to

$$
\begin{aligned}
\delta p(s_1) &= (\delta C + \delta L)s_1(s_1 + 1) \\
&= -(\delta C + \delta L)(1 + j)
\end{aligned}
\tag{9-17a}
$$

$$
\begin{aligned}
\delta p(s_2) &= (\delta C + \delta L)s_2(s_2 + 1) \\
&= -(\delta C + \delta L)(1 - j)
\end{aligned}
\tag{9-17b}
$$

To find the possible pole positions, we need to find the Laurent constants of $p(s)$ at s_1 and s_2. With $n = 1$, (9-6) gives

$$L_{s_1} \triangleq \left.\frac{s - s_1}{p(s)}\right|_{s=s_1} = \left.\frac{1}{s - s_2}\right|_{s=s_1} = \frac{1}{j2} \tag{9-18a}$$

$$L_{s_2} \triangleq \left.\frac{s - s_2}{p(s)}\right|_{s=s_2} = \left.\frac{1}{s - s_1}\right|_{s=s_2} = -\frac{1}{j2} \tag{9-18b}$$

Substituting (9-17) and (9-18) into (9-11), we obtain

$$
\begin{aligned}
\delta s_1 &= -L_{s_1}\,\delta p(s_1) \\
&= \frac{1 + j}{j2}(\delta C + \delta L) = \frac{1 - j}{2}(\delta C + \delta L)
\end{aligned}
\tag{9-19a}
$$

$$
\begin{aligned}
\delta s_2 &= -L_{s_2}\,\delta p(s_2) \\
&= -\frac{1 - j}{j2}(\delta C + \delta L) = \frac{1 + j}{2}(\delta C + \delta L)
\end{aligned}
\tag{9-19b}
$$

Hence, the pole locations after variations are at

$$\hat{s}_1 = s_1 + \delta s_1 = s_1 + \left[\frac{1 - j}{2}(\delta C + \delta L)\right] \tag{9-20a}$$

$$\hat{s}_2 = s_2 + \delta s_2 = s_2 + \left[\frac{1 + j}{2}(\delta C + \delta L)\right] \tag{9-20b}$$

where the nominal pole locations s_1 and s_2 are given by (9-14). To find the approximate boundaries of all possible pole locations of (9-20), we consider four cases.

a. $\delta L = 0.1$, and $\delta C = 0.1$. In this case, (9-20) gives

$$s_1^a = s_1 + 0.1 - j0.1 = -0.9 + j0.9 \qquad (9\text{-}21a)$$

and

$$s_2^a = s_2 + 0.1 + j0.1 = -0.9 - j0.9 \qquad (9\text{-}21b)$$

b. $\delta L = 0.1$, and $\delta C = -0.1$. In this case, (9-17) says that $\delta p(s_1) = \delta p(s_2)$ $= 0$. Hence,

$$s_1^b = s_1 = -1 + j1 \quad \text{and} \quad s_2^b = s_2 = -1 - j1 \qquad (9\text{-}22)$$

c. $\delta L = -0.1$, and $\delta C = 0.1$. The result of this case is also given by (9-22).

d. $\delta L = -0.1$, and $\delta C = -0.1$. In this case, we have

$$s_1^d = s_1 - 0.1 + j0.1 = -1.1 + j1.1 \qquad (9\text{-}23a)$$

and

$$s_2^d = s_2 - 0.1 - j0.1 = -1.1 - j1.1 \qquad (9\text{-}23b)$$

Based on (9-20), Fig. 9-2 shows approximately all the possible pole locations of the circuit in Fig. 9-1, as illustrated by (9-21) through (9-23). ∎

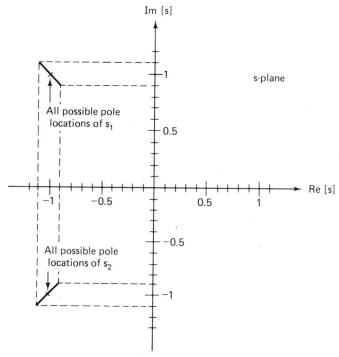

Fig. 9-2 Pole locations of the circuit in Fig. 9-1.

Example 9-2 For the circuit in Fig. 9-3, where $k = 2$, find the pole displacements if C_1 were changed by 2% to 1.02 Farads.

Solution: The transfer function of the circuit in Fig. 9-3 is given by

$$H(s) \triangleq \frac{V_o}{V_i} = \frac{k}{C_1 C_2 R_1 R_2 s^2 + (C_1 R_1 + C_2 R_2 + R_1 C_2 - k C_1 R_1)s + 1} \qquad (9\text{-}24)$$

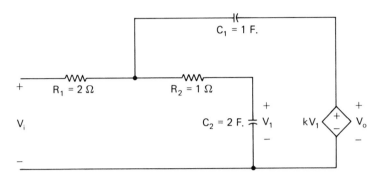

Fig. 9-3   Circuit for Examples 9-2 and 9-3.

With all circuit parameters except C_1 at nominal values, (9-24) reduces to

$$H(s) = \frac{1}{2C_1 s^2 + (3 - C_1)s + 0.5}$$

The denominator polynomial $p(s)$ is given by

$$p(s) \triangleq 2C_1 s^2 + (3 - C_1)s + 0.5 \tag{9-25}$$

At the nominal value of $C_1 = 1$ Farad, we have

$$p(s) = 2s^2 + 2s + 0.5 \tag{9-26}$$

and the poles are at

$$s_1 = s_2 = -0.5 \tag{9-27}$$

That is, $s = -0.5$ is a pole with multiplicity 2. When C_1 becomes 1.02 Farads, the denominator polynomial becomes

$$\hat{p}(s) = 2.04s^2 + 1.98s + 0.5 \tag{9-28}$$

Subtracting (9-26) from (9-28), we obtain

$$\delta p(s) = \hat{p}(s) - p(s) \\ = 0.04s^2 - 0.02s \tag{9-29}$$

From (9-6), the Laurent constant is given by

$$L_2 = \left. \frac{(s + 0.5)^2}{p(s)} \right|_{s=-0.5} = 0.5 \tag{9-30}$$

Substituting (9-29) and (9-30), the approximate new pole locations are at[5]

$$\hat{s}_{1,2} = s_{1,2} + \delta s_{1,2} \\ = s_{1,2} + [-L_2\, \delta p(s_{1,2})]^{1/2} \\ = -0.5 + [-0.5(0.02)]^{1/2} \\ = -0.5 \pm j0.1 \tag{9-31}$$

---

[5]For convenience, (9-31) actually represents two equations with the first subscript taking the upper sign and the second subscript taking the lower sign. For example, in this case, (9-31) implies that $\hat{s}_1 = -0.5 + j0.1$, and $\hat{s}_2 = -0.5 - j0.1$. This convention is used throughout this chapter.

The actual pole locations of the circuit after the variation in C_1 can be obtained by solving (9-28) and are given by

$$\bar{s}_{1,2} = \frac{-1.98 \pm \sqrt{(1.98)^2 - 4(2.04)(0.5)}}{2(2.04)} \tag{9-32}$$

$$= -0.49 \pm j0.10$$

Comparing (9-31) and (9-32), we see an excellent agreement between the approximate and the exact new pole locations ∎

As illustrated by Examples 9-1 and 9-2, we observe that the roots of a polynomial will change if the parameters in the circuit change. Let k be a parameter in the circuit subject to small variations, and $p(s, k)$ be a polynomial associated with the circuit, where we write the polynomial p as a function of k explicitly to emphasize that k is a varying parameter. Then the *root sensitivity of the root s_j of $p(s, k)$ with respect to k* is defined as

$$\hat{S}_k^{s_j} \triangleq \frac{\delta s_j}{\delta k/k}\bigg|_{k=k_0} \simeq k_0 \frac{\partial s_j}{\partial k}\bigg|_{k=k_0} \tag{9-33a}$$

or

$$\delta s_j = \left[\frac{\partial s_j}{\partial k}\bigg|_{k=k_0}\right] \delta k = \hat{S}_k^{s_j} \frac{\delta k}{k_0} \tag{9-33b}$$

where k_0 is the nominal parameter value. For example, in the case of Example 9-2,

$$\hat{S}_{C_1}^{s_1} = \frac{\delta s_1}{\delta C_1/C_1} = C_1 \frac{\delta s_1}{\delta C_1} = \frac{j0.1}{0.02} = j5 \tag{9-34a}$$

$$\hat{S}_{C_1}^{s_2} = C_1 \frac{\delta s_2}{\delta C_1} = \frac{-j0.1}{0.02} = -j5 \tag{9-34b}$$

When $p(s, k)$ is the denominator {or numerator} polynomial of a transfer function $H(s)$, then (9-33) defines the pole {or zero} sensitivity of s_j of $H(s)$.

Observe that (9-33b) provides another technique for computing the root displacements. Conceptually, the differentiation technique of (9-33b) represents a simpler method than that used in Examples 9-1 and 9-2. The problem here is in finding the functional relationship between the root s_j and the parameter k as indicated in (9-35). In a large circuit, this is a very difficult task indeed. In addition, if a digital computer is employed to do sensitivity analysis, then the derivative term of (9-33b) also presents some numerical problems. Finally, if s_j is a root with multiple multiplicity, the differentiation technique in (9-33b) may involve some mathematical difficulties.

Because the root location s_j of $p(s, k)$ depends on the value of k, we denote this relationship by writing s_j as a function of k

$$s_j = s_j(k) \tag{9-35}$$

Let k_0 be the nominal value of k. Then the nominal root location is at

$$s_{j0} \triangleq s_j(k_0) \tag{9-36}$$

If k is now changed to $k_0 + \delta k$, then the new root location is changed to

$$\hat{s}_j = s_j(k_0 + \delta k) \tag{9-37}$$

A Taylor series expansion of (9-37) yields

$$\hat{s}_j = s_j(k_0) + \left[\frac{\partial s_j}{\partial k}\bigg|_{k=k_0}\right]\delta k + \ldots \tag{9-38}$$

Hence, the pole location is changed by

$$\delta s_j = \hat{s}_j - s_j(k_0) = \left[\frac{\partial s_j}{\partial k}\bigg|_{k=k_0}\right]\delta k + \ldots \tag{9-39}$$

Comparing (9-33) and (9-39), we see that the sensitivity function defined in (9-33) contains only the first-order variational effect and can be obtained by a Taylor series expansion truncated after the first-order term.

Example 9-3 Compute the pole sensitivities with respect to the VCVS gain parameter k for the circuit in Fig. 9-3, where the nominal value of k is 4.

Solution: The transfer function of the circuit in Fig. 9-3 is given by

$$H(s) = \frac{k}{4s^2 + (8 - 2k)s + 1} \tag{9-40}$$

Hence, the pole locations as functions of k are

$$s_{1,2} = \frac{-(8 - 2k) \pm \sqrt{(8 - 2k)^2 - 16}}{8} \tag{9-41}$$

By (9-33), the pole sensitivities are given by

$$\begin{aligned}
\hat{S}_k^{s_{1,2}} &= 4 \frac{\partial s_{1,2}}{\partial k}\bigg|_{k=4} \\
&= \frac{4}{8}\left[2 \pm \frac{1}{2} \frac{2(8 - 2k)(-2)}{\sqrt{(8 - 2k)^2 - 16}}\right]\bigg|_{k=4} = 1
\end{aligned} \tag{9-42}$$

Observe that the nominal pole locations are given by (9-41) with $k = 4$ as

$$s_{1,2} = \pm j0.5 \tag{9-43}$$

From (9-33b), we obtain the pole displacements.

$$\delta s_{1,2} = \hat{S}_k^{s_{1,2}} \frac{\delta k}{k_0} = \frac{\delta k}{4} \tag{9-44}$$

This means that if k is increased by any amount, say by 1 % to 4.04, then the new pole locations

$$\begin{aligned}
\hat{s}_{1,2} &= s_{1,2} + \delta s_{1,2} \\
&= \pm j0.5 + \frac{0.04}{4} \\
&= 0.01 \pm j0.5
\end{aligned}$$

will be in the RH s-plane, and hence the circuit becomes unstable. ∎

In general, a circuit contains many nonideal elements each of which is specified by a certain tolerance level. Let $\mathbf{k} \triangleq [k_1, k_2, \ldots, k_m]$ be a vector of circuit parameters subject to small variation and $p(s, \mathbf{k})$ be a polynomial associated with the circuit. Let

$$s_j = s_j(\mathbf{k}) = s_j(k_1, k_2, \ldots, k_m) \tag{9-45}$$

represents the functional relationship between the root location s_j and the parameter vector $\mathbf{k}$. Let $\mathbf{k}_0$ be the nominal parameter vector value and

$$s_{j0} \triangleq s_j(\mathbf{k}_0) \tag{9-46}$$

be the nominal root. Suppose that the parameter vector changes from $\mathbf{k}_0$ to $\mathbf{k}_0 + \delta\mathbf{k}$; then the new root location is at

$$\hat{s}_j \triangleq s_j(\mathbf{k}_0 + \delta\mathbf{k}) \tag{9-47}$$

If $|\delta\mathbf{k}|$ is small,[6] then the new root location is approximately given by the Taylor expansion of (9-47), with the first-order terms only as

$$\hat{s}_j \simeq s_j(\mathbf{k}_0) + \left[\frac{\partial s_j}{\partial k_1}\bigg|_{\mathbf{k}=\mathbf{k}_0}\right]\delta k_1 + \left[\frac{\partial s_j}{\partial k_2}\bigg|_{\mathbf{k}=\mathbf{k}_0}\right]\delta k_2$$
$$+ \ldots + \left[\frac{\partial s_j}{\partial k_m}\bigg|_{\mathbf{k}=\mathbf{k}_0}\right]\delta k_m \tag{9-48}$$

Hence, the root displacement is

$$\delta s_j \triangleq \hat{s}_j - s_j(\mathbf{k}_0)$$
$$= \left[k_1\frac{\partial s_j}{\partial k_1}\frac{\delta k_1}{k_1} + k_2\frac{\partial s_j}{\partial k_2}\frac{\delta k_2}{k_2} + \ldots + k_m\frac{\partial s_j}{\partial k_m}\frac{\delta k_m}{k_m}\right]\bigg|_{\mathbf{k}=\mathbf{k}_0}$$
$$= \hat{S}_{k_1}^{s_j}\frac{\delta k_1}{k_1} + \hat{S}_{k_2}^{s_j}\frac{\delta k_2}{k_2} + \ldots + \hat{S}_{k_m}^{s_j}\frac{\delta k_m}{k_m} \tag{9-49}$$
$$= \sum_{i=1}^{m} \hat{S}_{k_i}^{s_j}\frac{\delta k_i}{k_i}$$

where $\hat{S}_{k_i}^{s_j}$ is the root sensitivity of s_j with respect to the parameter k_i, as defined in (9-33). Note that (9-49) is evaluated at the nominal parameter values.

Example 9-4   For the circuit in Fig. 9-4, find the pole displacements due to small variations of all circuit element values.

Solution: The voltage-ratio transfer function of the circuit in Fig. 9-4 is given by

$$H(s) = \frac{G_1 G_2}{C_1 C_2 s^2 + (C_1 G_2 + C_2 G_1 + C_2 G_2)s + G_1 G_2} \tag{9-50}$$

Let $p(s, \mathbf{k})$ denote the denominator polynomial of $H(s)$, where $\mathbf{k} = [C_1, C_2, G_1,$

---

[6]The magnitude of a vector $\mathbf{x} = [x_1, x_2, \ldots, x_m]$ is denoted by $|\mathbf{x}|$ and is given by $|\mathbf{x}| = [\sum_{i=1}^{m} x_i^2]^{1/2}$.

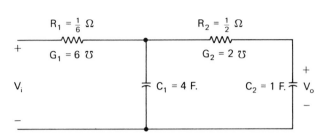

Fig. 9-4   Circuit for Examples 9-4 and 9-5.

G_2] is the parameter vector. Then

$$p(s, \mathbf{k}) = C_1 C_2 s^2 + (C_1 G_2 + C_2 G_1 + C_2 G_2)s + G_1 G_2 \qquad (9\text{-}51)$$

Hence, the pole locations are at

$$s_{1,2} = \frac{-(C_1 G_2 + C_2 G_1 + C_2 G_2) \pm \sqrt{(C_1 G_2 + C_2 G_1 + C_2 G_2)^2 - 4 C_1 C_2 G_1 G_2}}{2 C_1 C_2} \qquad (9\text{-}52)$$

At the nominal values, the poles are

$$s_1 = -2 + 1 = -1 \quad \text{and} \quad s_2 = -2 - 1 = -3 \qquad (9\text{-}53)$$

By (9-33), we obtain the following sensitivity values

$$\hat{S}^{s_1}_{C_1} = \hat{S}^{s_1}_{C_2} = \frac{1}{2}, \quad \hat{S}^{s_1}_{G_1} = -\frac{3}{4}, \quad \text{and} \quad \hat{S}^{s_1}_{G_2} = -\frac{1}{4} \qquad (9\text{-}54a)$$

$$\hat{S}^{s_2}_{C_1} = \hat{S}^{s_2}_{C_2} = \frac{3}{2}, \quad \hat{S}^{s_2}_{G_1} = -\frac{3}{4}, \quad \text{and} \quad \hat{S}^{s_2}_{G_2} = -\frac{9}{4} \qquad (9\text{-}54b)$$

With all these preliminary computations completed, the pole displacements can be obtained by (9-49) as

$$\delta s_1 = \frac{1}{2}\frac{\delta C_1}{C_1} + \frac{1}{2}\frac{\delta C_2}{C_2} - \frac{3}{4}\frac{\delta G_1}{G_1} - \frac{1}{4}\frac{\delta G_2}{G_2} \qquad (9\text{-}55a)$$

and

$$\delta s_2 = \frac{3}{2}\frac{\delta C_1}{C_1} + \frac{3}{2}\frac{\delta C_2}{C_2} - \frac{3}{4}\frac{\delta G_1}{G_1} - \frac{9}{4}\frac{\delta G_2}{G_2} \qquad (9\text{-}55b)$$

Note that if all capacitances and conductances are changed by the same percentage, then

$$\frac{\delta C_1}{C_1} = \frac{\delta C_2}{C_2} = \frac{\delta G_1}{G_1} = \frac{\delta G_2}{G_2} \qquad (9\text{-}56)$$

and (9-55) implies that

$$\delta s_1 = \delta s_2 = 0 \qquad (9\text{-}57)$$

9-1-2. Some General Results

Consider an active RLC circuit containing possibly all the four types of controlled sources. Let s_j be a root {zero or pole} of a polynomial {the numerator or the denominator polynomial of a transfer function} associated with the circuit. Then s_j is a function of all circuit parameters and is denoted by

$$s_j = s_j(R_i, L_i, C_i, \mu_i, \alpha_i, r_i, g_i) \tag{9-58}$$

where R_i, L_i, and C_i denote the individual R, L, C elements, and where μ_i, α_i, r_i, and g_i denote respectively the coefficients of each individual VCVS, ICIS, ICVS, and VCIS.

If we raise the impedance level of every element in the circuit by the same amount a, then the transfer function remains unchanged. Consequently, the root location s_j will not change. This means that

$$s_j\left(aR_i, aL_i, \frac{C_i}{a}, \mu_i, \alpha_i, ar_i, \frac{g_i}{a}\right) = s_j(R_i, L_i, C_i, \mu_i, \alpha_i, r_i, g_i) \tag{9-59}$$

Differentiating (9-59) with respect to a, we obtain

$$\left(\sum_{\mathcal{R}} R_i \frac{\partial s_j}{\partial R_i} + \sum_{\mathcal{L}} L_i \frac{\partial s_j}{\partial L_i} - \sum_{\mathcal{C}} \frac{C_i}{a^2} \frac{\partial s_j}{\partial C_i} + \sum_{\text{ICVS}} r_i \frac{\partial s_j}{\partial r_i}\right.$$
$$\left. - \sum_{\text{VCIS}} \frac{g_i}{a^2} \frac{\partial s_j}{\partial g_i}\right)\Bigg|_{(aR_i, aL_i, C_i/a, \mu_i, \alpha_i, ar_i, g_i/a)} = 0 \tag{9-60}$$

where $\sum_{\mathcal{E}}$ means sum over all elements of type $\mathcal{E}$. Setting $a = 1$, and using the notation of (9-33), (9-60) becomes

$$\sum_{\mathcal{R}} \hat{S}_{R_i}^{s_j} + \sum_{\mathcal{L}} \hat{S}_{L_i}^{s_j} - \sum_{\mathcal{C}} \hat{S}_{C_i}^{s_j} + \sum_{\text{ICVS}} \hat{S}_{r_i}^{s_j} - \sum_{\text{VCIS}} \hat{S}_{g_i}^{s_j}\Bigg|_{(R_i, L_i, C_i, \mu_i, \alpha_i, r_i, g_i)} = 0 \tag{9-61}$$

In the special case of an RC active circuit with VCVS,[7] (9-61) can be simplified to

$$\sum_{\mathcal{R}} \hat{S}_{R_i}^{s_j} = \sum_{\mathcal{C}} \hat{S}_{C_i}^{s_j} \tag{9-62}$$

when evaluated at the nominal values of all circuit parameters.

As an illustration of (9-61), consider the circuit in Fig. 9-4, which contains only two capacitors and two resistors. Equations (9-61) or (9-62) say that

$$\hat{S}_{R_1}^{s_j} + \hat{S}_{R_2}^{s_j} - \hat{S}_{C_1}^{s_j} - \hat{S}_{C_2}^{s_j} = 0 \tag{9-63}$$

where $j = 1, 2$. Note that

$$\hat{S}_{R_i}^{s_j} = \frac{\partial s_j}{\partial R_i / R_i} = R_i \frac{\partial s_j}{\partial R_i} = \frac{1}{G_i} \frac{\partial s_j}{\partial G_i} \frac{\partial G_i}{\partial R_i} \tag{9-64}$$

where

$$G_i = 1/R_i \quad \text{and} \quad \frac{\partial G_i}{\partial R_i} = -\frac{1}{R_i^2} = -G_i^2 \tag{9-65}$$

Substituting (9-65) into (9-64), we obtain

$$\hat{S}_{R_i}^{s_j} = -G_i \frac{\partial s_j}{\partial G_i} = -\hat{S}_{G_i}^{s_j} \tag{9-66}$$

---

[7] An operational amplifier can be considered as a VCVS.

Hence, (9-61) implies that, for the circuit in Fig. 9-4, we should have

$$\hat{S}^{s_j}_{G_1} + \hat{S}^{s_j}_{G_2} + \hat{S}^{s_j}_{C_1} + \hat{S}^{s_j}_{C_2} = 0 \qquad (9\text{-}67)$$

for $j = 1, 2$. From (9-54), we see that (9-67) indeed holds.

Under the general setting of (9-58), another result on root sensitivity can be obtained by frequency scaling. Let s_j be a root of the polynomial $p(s)$ of interest. The $p(s)$ must contain a factor $(s - s_j)$. If each s in $p(s)$ is scaled by a constant factor a to as,[8] then the factor becomes $(as - s_j)$. Hence, the root s_j becomes the root s_j/a. By using the element transformation as a means of implementing the frequency transformation, as indicated by the first row of Table 8-5, we have the following identity:

$$s_j(R_i, aL_i, aC_i, \mu_i, \alpha_i, r_i, g_i) = \frac{1}{a} s_j(R_i, L_i, C_i, \mu_i, \alpha_i, r_i, g_i) \qquad (9\text{-}68)$$

Differentiating (9-68) with respect to a, we obtain

$$\left(\sum_{\mathcal{L}} L_i \frac{\partial s_j}{\partial L_i} + \sum_{\mathcal{C}} C_i \frac{\partial s_j}{\partial C_i} \right)\bigg|_{(R_i, aL_i, aC_i, \mu_i, \alpha_i, r_i, g_i)} = -\frac{s_j}{a^2}\bigg|_{(R_i, L_i, C_i, \mu_i, \alpha_i, r_i, g_i)} \qquad (9\text{-}69)$$

Setting $a = 1$ in (9-69), and using the sensitivity definition of (9-33), (9-69) becomes

$$\sum_{\mathcal{L}} \hat{S}^{s_j}_{L_i} + \sum_{\mathcal{C}} \hat{S}^{s_j}_{C_i} = -s_j \qquad (9\text{-}70)$$

where (9-70) is evaluated at the nominal values of the circuit parameters. In active RC circuits, (9-70) reduces to

$$\sum_{\mathcal{C}} \hat{S}^{s_j}_{C_i} = -s_j \qquad (9\text{-}71)$$

Combining (9-62) and (9-71) together, we have

$$\sum_{\mathcal{R}} \hat{S}^{s_j}_{R_i} = \sum_{\mathcal{C}} \hat{S}^{s_j}_{C_i} = -s_j \qquad (9\text{-}72)$$

As an illustration of (9-70), consider the results of Example 9-4. From (9-53) and (9-54), we have

$$\hat{S}^{s_1}_{C_1} + \hat{S}^{s_2}_{C_1} = \tfrac{1}{2} + \tfrac{1}{2} = 1 = -s_1$$

$$\hat{S}^{s_2}_{C_2} + \hat{S}^{s_2}_{C_2} = \tfrac{3}{2} + \tfrac{3}{2} = 3 = -s_2$$

9-2 NETWORK FUNCTION SENSITIVITIES

Because network functions are ratios of polynomials, results obtained in Sec. 9-1 can be applied to both the numerator and the denominator of a network function. With this comment, we will not spend time discussing the trivial extensions of the results in Sec. 9-1 to the case of network functions. In this section, we let $F(s)$ denote the network function of interest, where

---

[8]This is equivalent to the frequency scaling or low-pass to low-pass transformation discussed in subsection 8-4-1.

$F(s)$ can be a DP impedance or admittance function, as well as a voltage-ratio transfer function. Let k be a circuit parameter subject to small variations. *The sensitivity function S_k^F of the network function $F(s, k)$ due to an incremental variation of the parameter k is defined to be*

$$S_k^F \triangleq \frac{\dfrac{\delta F(s, k)}{F(s, k)}}{\delta k / k} \simeq \frac{\partial F(s, k)}{\partial k} \frac{k}{F(s, k)} \tag{9-73}$$

Assuming that all changes are small, (9-73) says that S_k^F is equal to the percentage change in $F(s, k)$ divided by the percentage change in k. For example, if S_k^F is 0.5, then a 1 % change in the parameter k will cause a 0.5 % change in $F(s, k)$. Therefore, from the design point of view, it is necessary to keep S_k^F as small as possible. Ideally, S_k^F should be zero for every circuit parameter k. Based on the definition of (9-73), we can prove the following identities on sensitivity functions:

$$S_x^{cx} = 1, \qquad S_x^{cx^n} = n, \qquad S_x^{y+c} = \frac{y}{y + c} S_x^y,$$

$$S_x^{cy} = S_x^y, \qquad S_x^y = S_z^y S_x^z, \qquad S_x^{y^n} = n S_x^y, \tag{9-74}$$

$$S_{1/x}^y = -S_x^y, \qquad S_x^{1/y} = -S_x^y, \qquad S_x^{y/z} = S_x^y - S_x^z$$

where c and n are constants.

Because network functions are rational functions, $F(s, k)$ can be written as

$$F(s, k) = \frac{G \displaystyle\prod_{i=1}^{m} (s - z_i)}{\displaystyle\prod_{j=1}^{n} (s - p_j)} \triangleq \frac{A(s, k)}{B(s, k)} = \frac{\displaystyle\sum_{i=0}^{m} a_i s^i}{\displaystyle\sum_{j=0}^{n} b_j s^j} \tag{9-75}$$

where z_i, p_j, a_i, and b_j are functions of the parameter k, such as C_1 in Example 9-2. Taking logarithms of (9-75), we have

$$\ln F(s, k) = \ln G + \sum_{i=1}^{m} \ln (s - z_i) - \sum_{j=1}^{n} \ln (s - p_j) \tag{9-76}$$

Differentiating both sides of (9-76) with respect to k and then multiplying by k, we obtain

$$S_k^F = S_k^G - \sum_{i=1}^{m} \frac{1}{s - z_i} \hat{S}_k^{z_i} + \sum_{j=1}^{n} \frac{1}{s - p_j} \hat{S}_k^{p_j} \tag{9-77}$$

Equation (9-77) says that the contribution of a pole or zero sensitivity to the overall network function sensitivity is most significant in the neighborhood of that pole or zero.

9-2-1. Some General Results

Consider an active RLC network containing possibly all four types of controlled sources. Let $F(s)$ be a network function of interest. Then $F(s)$ will be a function of each network element and hence can be written as:

$$F(R_i, L_i, C_i, \mu_i, \alpha_i, r_i, g_i, s) \tag{9-78}$$

where the symbols R_i, L_i, C_i, μ_i, α_i, r_i, and g_i have the same meaning as those in subsection 9-1-2. If we now scale the impedance level of the network by an amount a, then (9-78) gives

$$F\left(aR_i, aL_i, \frac{C_i}{a}, \mu_i, \alpha_i, ar_i, \frac{g_i}{a}, s\right) = f(a)F(R_i, L_i, C_i, \mu_i, \alpha_i, r_i, g_i, s) \quad (9\text{-}79)$$

where

$$\begin{aligned}
f(a) &= a && \text{if } F(s) \text{ is a DP impedance function}\\
&= 1/a && \text{if } F(s) \text{ is a DP admittance function} && (9\text{-}80)\\
&= 1 && \text{if } F(s) \text{ is a voltage-ratio transfer function}
\end{aligned}$$

Differentiating (9-79) with respect to a, we obtain

$$\left(\sum_{\Re} R_i \frac{\partial F}{\partial R_i} + \sum_{\mathcal{L}} L_i \frac{\partial F}{\partial L_i} - \sum_{\mathcal{C}} \frac{C_i}{a^2} \frac{\partial F}{\partial C_i} + \sum_{\text{ICVS}} r_i \frac{\partial F}{\partial r_i}\right.$$

$$\left.- \sum_{\text{VCIS}} \frac{g_i}{a^2} \frac{\partial F}{\partial g_i}\right)\Bigg|_{(aR_i, aL_i, C_i/a, \mu_i, \alpha_i, ar_i, g_i/a, s)} \quad (9\text{-}81)$$

$$= \frac{\partial f(a)}{\partial a} F(R_i, L_i, C_i, \mu_i, \alpha_i, r_i, g_i, s)$$

Setting $a = 1$, dividing both sides of (9-81) by F, and using (9-73), we obtain

$$\sum_{\Re} S_{R_i}^F + \sum_{\mathcal{L}} S_{L_i}^F - \sum_{\mathcal{C}} S_{C_i}^F + \sum_{\text{ICVS}} S_{r_i}^F - \sum_{\text{VCIS}} S_{g_i}^F = \frac{\partial f(a)}{\partial a}\bigg|_{a=1} \quad (9\text{-}82)$$

where

$$\begin{aligned}
\frac{\partial f(a)}{\partial a}\bigg|_{a=1} &= 1 && \text{if } F \text{ is a DP impedance function}\\
&= -1 && \text{if } F \text{ is a DP admittance function} && (9\text{-}83)\\
&= 0 && \text{if } F \text{ is a voltage-ratio transfer function}
\end{aligned}$$

For an RC active filter with VCVS and operational amplifiers, (9-82) reduces to

$$\sum_{\Re} S_{R_i}^F - \sum_{\mathcal{C}} S_{C_i}^F = \frac{\partial f(a)}{\partial a}\bigg|_{a=1} \quad (9\text{-}84)$$

If in addition $F(s)$ is a voltage-ratio transfer function, then we have

$$\sum_{\Re} S_{R_i}^F = \sum_{\mathcal{C}} S_{C_i}^F \quad (9\text{-}85)$$

Equation (9-85) says that if all resistances and all capacitances are changed by the same absolute percentage value but with opposite signs, then F is unchanged. This is the reason that many active RC filters are constructed with resistive and capacitive materials having the same absolute temperature coefficient values but with opposite signs, thus ensuring that temperature variations will not alter the performance of the filter.

Next, we consider the effect of frequency scaling by a scale factor a. By subsection 8-4-1, only inductors and capacitors are affected. Therefore we have

$$F(R_i, aL_i, aC_i, \mu_i, \alpha_i, r_i, g_i, s) = F(R_i, L_i, C_i, \mu_i, \alpha_i, r_i, g_i, as) \quad (9\text{-}86)$$

Differentiating (9-86) with respect to a leads to

$$\left[\sum_{\mathcal{L}} L_i \frac{\partial F}{\partial L_i} + \sum_{\mathcal{C}} C_i \frac{\partial F}{\partial C_i} \right] \Bigg|_{(R_i, aL_i, aC_i, \mu_i, \alpha_i, r_i, g_i, s)} = s \frac{\partial F}{\partial s} \Bigg|_{(R_i, L_i, C_i, \mu_i, \alpha_i, r_i, g_i, as)} \quad (9\text{-}87)$$

Setting $a = 1$, and dividing both sides of (9-87) by F, we obtain

$$\sum_{\mathcal{L}} S_{L_i}^F + \sum_{\mathcal{C}} S_{C_i}^F = \frac{d[\ell n \, F]}{d[\ell n \, s]} \triangleq S_s^F \quad (9\text{-}88)$$

9-3 SECOND-ORDER FILTER SENSITIVITIES

To close this chapter, let us consider briefly the case of a second-order filter section, where the denominator polynomial of a transfer function is given by

$$B(s) = s^2 + b_1 s + b_0 \triangleq s^2 + \frac{\omega_0}{Q} s + \omega_0^2 \quad (9\text{-}89)$$

where

$$\omega_0 \triangleq \sqrt{b_0} \quad (9\text{-}90)$$

is called the *pole-frequency* and

$$Q \triangleq \frac{\sqrt{b_0}}{b_1} \quad (9\text{-}91)$$

is called the *pole-pair* of the second-order filter section. In the case of a band-pass filter, ω_0 is the center frequency where the magnitude function peaks and Q is inversely proportional to the bandwidth of the filter. In second-order filter sections, particularly in active filters, the Q-sensitivity and the ω_0-sensitivity, defined respectively by

$$S_x^Q \triangleq \frac{\delta Q/Q}{\delta x/x} \sim \frac{\partial[\ell n \, Q]}{\partial[\ell n \, x]} = \frac{x}{Q} \frac{\partial Q}{\partial x} \quad (9\text{-}92)$$

and

$$S_x^{\omega_0} \triangleq \frac{\delta \omega_0/\omega_0}{\delta x/x} \sim \frac{\partial[\ell n \, \omega_0]}{\partial[\ell n \, x]} = \frac{x}{\omega_0} \frac{\partial \omega_0}{\partial x} \quad (9\text{-}93)$$

where x is a circuit parameter subject to small variation, are of greater concern than the transfer function itself. This is because ω_0 and Q together describe almost all important qualitative properties of a second-order filter. Note that (9-92) and (9-93) are evaluated at the nominal parameter values.

Example 9-5 For the circuit in Fig. 9-4, find the ω_0 and Q sensitivities with respect to C_1, C_2, R_1, and R_2.

Solution: The transfer function of the circuit in Fig. 9-4 is given by

$$H(s) = \frac{\dfrac{1}{C_1 C_2 R_1 R_2}}{s^2 + \left[\dfrac{1}{C_2 R_2} + \dfrac{1}{C_1 R_1} + \dfrac{1}{C_1 R_2}\right]s + \dfrac{1}{C_1 C_2 R_1 R_2}} \qquad (9\text{-}94)$$

By identifying the corresponding terms in (9-89) and (9-94), we obtain

$$\omega_0 = \sqrt{\frac{1}{C_1 C_2 R_1 R_2}} = \sqrt{3} \qquad (9\text{-}95)$$

and

$$Q = \frac{\dfrac{1}{\sqrt{C_1 C_2 R_1 R_2}}}{\dfrac{1}{C_2 R_2} + \dfrac{1}{C_1 R_1} + \dfrac{1}{C_1 R_2}} = \frac{\sqrt{C_1 C_2 R_1 R_2}}{C_1 R_1 + C_2 R_2 + C_2 R_1} = \frac{\sqrt{3}}{4} \qquad (9\text{-}96)$$

By using (9-93), we find

$$S_{C_1}^{\omega_0} = S_{C_2}^{\omega_0} = S_{R_1}^{\omega_0} = S_{R_2}^{\omega_0} = -\frac{1}{2} \qquad (9\text{-}97)$$

$$S_{C_1}^{Q} = \frac{C_1}{Q}\left[\frac{\sqrt{C_2 R_1 R_2}}{2\sqrt{C_1}(C_1 R_1 + C_2 R_2 + C_2 R_1)} - \frac{R_1\sqrt{C_1 C_2 R_1 R_2}}{(C_1 R_1 + C_2 R_2 + C_2 R_1)^2}\right] = 0$$
$$(9\text{-}98a)$$

$$S_{C_2}^{Q} = 0 \qquad (9\text{-}98b)$$

$$S_{R_1}^{Q} = \frac{R_1}{Q}\left[\frac{\sqrt{C_1 C_2 R_2}}{2\sqrt{R_1}(C_1 R_1 + C_2 R_2 + C_2 R_1)} - \frac{(C_1 + C_2)\sqrt{C_1 C_2 R_1 R_2}}{(C_1 R_1 + C_2 R_2 + C_2 R_1)^2}\right] = -\frac{1}{2}$$
$$(9\text{-}98c)$$

$$S_{R_2}^{Q} = \frac{1}{8} \qquad (9\text{-}98d)$$

Note that (9-98a) and (9-98b) imply that the pole-pair of the circuit in Fig. 9-4 is independent of the capacitors C_1 and C_2. ∎

From (9-89), the pole locations of a second-order filter section are at

$$s_{1,2} = \frac{1}{2}\left[-\frac{\omega_0}{Q} \pm \sqrt{\left(\frac{\omega_0}{Q}\right)^2 - 4\omega_0^2}\right]$$
$$= -\frac{\omega_0}{2Q} \pm j\omega_0\sqrt{1 - \left(\frac{1}{2Q}\right)^2} \qquad (9\text{-}99)$$

If $Q > 0.5$, the poles are complex, and (9-99) implies that for large Q, the pole locations are closed to the imaginary axis. This observation has important consequences in practical terms. In passive circuits, increasing Q values requires that the elements be of better quality—the inductors and capacitors should be less lossy. In active circuits, increasing Q values requires more active elements in the realization so that the resulting network is not too sensitive.

Recall that the second-order sections of an nth-order Butterworth filter are in the form of [see (8-41)]:

$$B(s) = s^2 + (2 \sin \theta_k)s + 1 \qquad (9\text{-}100a)$$

where

$$\theta_k = \frac{(2k-1)\pi}{2n} \qquad (9\text{-}100b)$$

By identifying corresponding terms in (9-100) and (9-89), we obtain

$$\omega_0 = 1 \qquad (9\text{-}101a)$$

$$Q_k = \frac{1}{2 \sin \theta_k} \qquad (9\text{-}101b)$$

where Q_k is the pole-pair of the kth-second-order section. To be specific, let us consider the first second-order section, where

$$Q_1 = \frac{1}{2 \sin \theta_1} = \frac{1}{2 \sin (\pi/2n)} \qquad (9\text{-}102)$$

In order to have sharp cutoff magnitude characteristics, n is large. Hence, by (9-102), Q is large. Consequently, high-quality components are required to realize the first second-order section of a high-order Butterworth filter. The same implications apply to Chebyshev and Bessel filters also.

We discuss ω_0 and Q sensitivities in more detail in Chapter 10.

REFERENCES AND FURTHER READING

[1] KUH, E. S., and ROHRER, R. A. *Theory of Linear Active Networks.* San Francisco: Holden-Day, 1967.

[2] MITRA, S. K. *Analysis and Synthesis of Linear Active Networks.* New York: John Wiley, 1968.

[3] TOMOVIC, R., and VUKOBRATOVIC, M. *General Sensitivity Theory.* New York: American Elsevier, 1972.

[4] GORSKI-POPIEL, J. "Classical Sensitivity—A Collection of Formulas." *IEEE Trans. Circuit Theory* CT-10 (1963): 300–302.

[5] BLOSTEIN, M. L. "Some Bounds on Sensitivity in RLC Networks." *Proc. 1st Allerton Conf. Circuit and System Theory* (1963): 488–501.

[6] MOSCHYTZ, G. S. *Linear Integrated Networks: Fundamental.* New York: Van Nostrand Reinhold, 1974.

[7] DIRECTOR, S. W., and ROHRER, R. A. "The Generalized Adjoint Network and Network Sensitivities." *IEEE Trans. Circuit Theory* CT-16 (1969): 318–23.

[8] PARKER, S. R. "Sensitivity: Old Questions, Some New Answers." *IEEE Trans. Circuit Theory* CT-18 (1971): 27–35.

[9] BRANIN, F. A., JR., "Network Sensitivity and Noise Analysis Simplified." *IEEE Trans. Circuit Theory* CT-20 (1973): 285–88.

PROBLEMS

9-1. Consider the circuit shown in Fig. P9-1. Find the change of pole locations due to a 10% change of:

(a) The inductor L,

(b) The capacitor C,

(c) The resistor R_s,

(d) The resistor R_ℓ.

(e) If all elements are allowed to vary simultaneously within $\pm 10\%$ of their nominal values, find the regions bounding the perturbed pole locations.

(f) Verify (9-61) and (9-70) for each of the two poles of the circuit.

(g) Find the transfer function $H(s) = V_o/V_i$ of the circuit.

(h) Verify (9-83) and (9-88) for $H(s)$.

(i) Find the pole-frequency and pole-pair of the circuit.

(j) Find the pole-frequency and pole-pair sensitivities with respect to L and C.

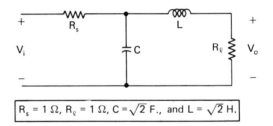

Fig. P9-1

9-2. Repeat Problem 9-1 for the circuits shown in Fig. P9-2.

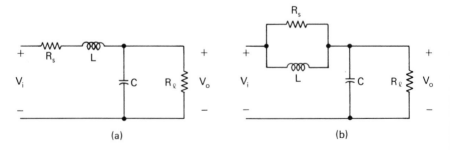

Fig. P9-2(a), (b)

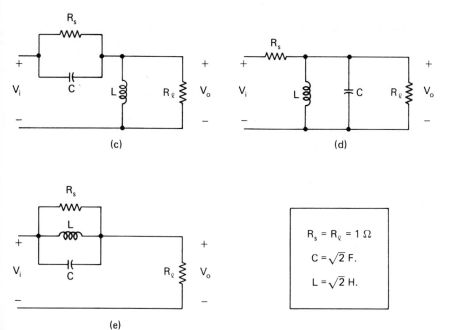

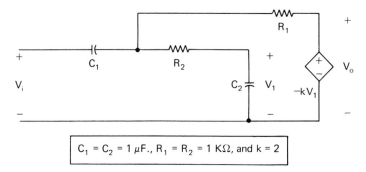

Fig. P9-2(c), (d), (e)

9-3. Consider the circuit in Fig. P9-3.

   (a) Find the transfer function $H(s)$ and the poles p_1 and p_2 of the circuit.

   (b) If C_1, C_2, R_1, and R_2 are allowed to vary simultaneously within $\pm 5\%$ and k within $\pm 1\%$ of their nominal values, find the regions bounding the perturbed pole locations.

   (c) Verify (9-72) for the poles p_1 and p_2.

   (d) Verify (9-85) and (9-88) for $H(s)$.

   (e) Find the pole-frequency ω_0 and pole-pair Q of the circuit.

   (f) Find the ω_0 and Q sensitivities with respect to k, R_1, R_2, C_1, and C_2.

Fig. P9-3

(g) If k is allowed to vary with $\pm 1\%$ of its nominal value, find the bounding regions for the perturbed ω_0 and Q values.

(h) If C_1 and C_2 are allowed to vary such that $\delta C_1/C_1 = \delta C_2/C_2$ are within $\pm 10\%$, or

$$\left| \frac{\delta C_1}{C_1} \right| = \left| \frac{\delta C_2}{C_2} \right| \le 10\%$$

find the bounding regions for the perturbed ω_0 and Q values.

(i) If R_1 and R_2 are allowed to vary such that $\delta R_1/R_1 = \delta R_2/R_2$ are within $\pm 10\%$, find the bounding regions for the perturbed ω_0 and Q values.

9-4. Repeat Problem 9-3 for the circuits shown in Fig. P9-4.

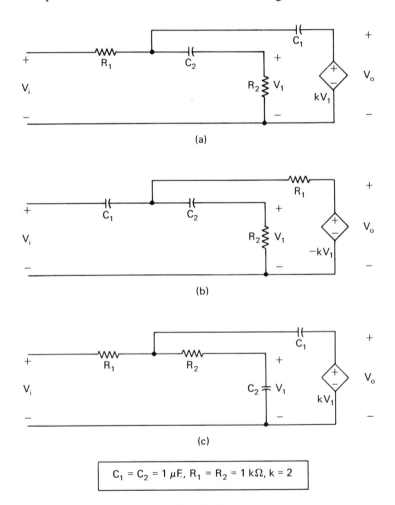

(a)

(b)

(c)

$$C_1 = C_2 = 1 \ \mu F, \ R_1 = R_2 = 1 \ k\Omega, \ k = 2$$

Fig. P9-4

9-5. Consider the attenuator circuit shown in Fig. P9-5.

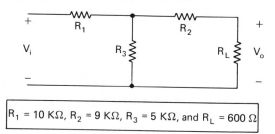

$R_1 = 10\ K\Omega,\ R_2 = 9\ K\Omega,\ R_3 = 5\ K\Omega,\ \text{and}\ R_L = 600\ \Omega$

Fig. P9-5

(a) Find the transfer function $H = V_o/V_i$.

(b) Compute the sensitivities of H with respect to resistors R_1, R_2, R_3, and R_L.

(c) If it is desired to keep the worst-case variation of H to within $\pm 5\%$, what should be the tolerance limit of each resistor assuming identical tolerance for each resistor? That is, find

$$\left|\frac{\delta R}{R}\right| = \left|\frac{\delta R_1}{R_1}\right| = \left|\frac{\delta R_2}{R_2}\right| = \left|\frac{\delta R_3}{R_3}\right| = \left|\frac{\delta R_L}{R_L}\right|$$

if $\left|\dfrac{\delta H}{H}\right| \leq 5\%$.

(d) If every resistor has a 5% tolerance, find the worst-case variation of H.

(e) Repeat (d) if every resistor has a 1% tolerance.

9-6. Suppose that a circuit is characterized by the transfer function

$$H(s) = \frac{1}{s^2 + \dfrac{1}{R_1 C_1}s + \dfrac{1}{R_1 C_1 R_2 C_2}}$$

(a) Find the worst-case percentage deviation in ω_0 and Q if the resistors may vary by $\pm 2\%$ and the capacitors by $\pm 10\%$ of their nominal values.

(b) Repeat (a) if the resistors may vary by $\pm 0.5\%$ and the capacitors by $\pm 1\%$.

(c) If it is desired to limit both ω_0 and Q deviations to within $\pm 5\%$, find the maximum tolerances on the resistors and the capacitors assuming all resistors have the same tolerance and all capacitors have the same tolerance.

(d) Repeat (c) if it is desired to limit ω_0 deviation to within $\pm 1\%$ and Q deviation to within $\pm 0.5\%$.

9-7. Prove the following sensitivity identities:

(a) $S_x^{kx} = 1$

(b) $S_x^{kx^n} = n$

(c) $S_x^y = S_\alpha^y S_x^\alpha$

(d) $S_x^{y^{-1}} = -S_x^y$

(e) $S_x^{ky} = S_x^y$

(f) $S_x^{y+k} = \dfrac{y}{y+k} S_x^y$

(g) $S_x^{\alpha/\beta} = S_x^\alpha - S_x^\beta$

(h) $S_x^{y^n} = n S_x^y$

(i) $S_{1/x}^y = -S_x^y$

where n and k are constants, and where y, α, and β are functions of x.

9-8. Consider the circuit shown in Fig. P9-8(a), where

$$\alpha \triangleq \frac{R_2}{R_1} = 2$$

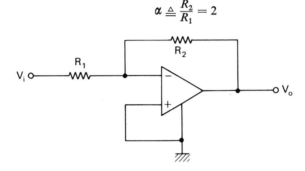

(a)

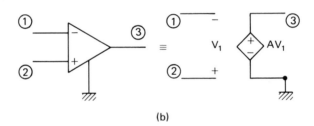

(b)

Fig. P9-8

and the operational amplifier is modeled by a VCVS with a finite gain A, as shown in Fig. P9-8(b).

(a) Find the transfer function $H = V_o/V_i$.

(b) Find the sensitivity S_A^H as a function of A. Sketch S_A^H versus A for $1 \leq A \leq 10^5$.

(c) Repeat (a) and (b) when $\alpha = 10$.

(d) Repeat (a) and (b) when $\alpha = 100$.

(e) Repeat (a) and (b) when $\alpha = 1000$.

10

ACTIVE FILTERS

Active RC filters are widely used today, particularly in the area of telephone systems, data communication systems, television, radio, and hi-fi systems. They are primarily used in low-frequency applications where inductors are not suitable because of their bulky size and low quality. With presently available active elements, the useful frequency range of active filters can be pushed from dc to roughly 100 KHz.

When active filters were first introduced, vacuum tubes were used as the active elements. Among the many drawbacks associated with vacuum tubes, the high power requirements and cost made this class of active filters extremely undesirable when compared to passive LC filters. The arrival of transistors eliminated the problem of high power. However, gain was still expensive, and active elements were used judiciously. As transistors became more economical, operation amplifiers—modular devices containing transistors and resistors—became the dominant active devices. In the early 1960s, operational amplifiers were still very expensive. Active circuit designers were constrained to minimize the number of active components in their design. Today, operational amplifiers cost very little, and the prices are still decreasing. As a consequence, there is an increasingly liberal use of active devices in circuit design. Indeed, the current trend is to use more than one active element in the design of an active filter in exchange for better functional performance such as sensitivity, stability, and fine tuning properties.

As is in the case of passive filter design, active filter design begins with an approximation of the signal-processing requirements by a real rational transfer function

$$H(s) = \frac{A(s)}{B(s)} = \frac{a_m s^m + a_{m-1} s^{m-1} + \ldots + a_1 s + a_0}{s^n + b_{n-1} s^{n-1} + \ldots + b_1 s + b_0} \qquad (10\text{-}1)$$

When $m \leq n$, (10-1) can be expressed in a product form as

$$H(s) = H_1(s)H_2(s) \dots H_K(s) \tag{10-2}$$

where $K \leq n$ and, for each $j = 1, 2, \dots, K$, $H_j(s)$ is either the transfer function of a second-order section

$$H_j(s) = \frac{a_{j2}s^2 + a_{j1}s + a_{j0}}{s^2 + b_{j1}s + b_{j0}} \tag{10-3a}$$

or the transfer function of a first-order section

$$H_j(s) = \frac{a_{j1}s + a_{j0}}{s + b_{j0}} \tag{10-3b}$$

The second-order filter section $H_j(s)$ of (10-3a) is usually characterized by two parameters

$$Q_j \triangleq \frac{\sqrt{b_{j0}}}{b_{j1}} \quad \text{and} \quad \omega_{0j} \triangleq \sqrt{b_{j0}} \tag{10-4}$$

where ω_{0j} is the *pole-frequency* and Q_j is the *pole-pair Q* of the jth second-order filter section.

There are basically two approaches to active filter design: the *direct realization approach*, which realizes the complete transfer function of (10-1) as a whole, and the *cascade approach*, which realizes the complete transfer function of (10-1) by realizing a number of first- and second-order filter sections of (10-3). In this chapter, we discuss some realization methods using these two approaches.

Before we proceed, it should be pointed out that the active filters discussed in this chapter are RC active filters. They are inductorless circuits containing resistors, capacitors, operational amplifiers, and their derived products such as VCVS, gyrators, generalized impedance converters, integrators, and summers, as discussed in Chapter 2.

For all RC active circuits with VCVS and/or operational amplifiers, impedance scaling of a circuit with a scale factor α involves:

1. replacing each resistance R Ω by a resistance αR Ω
2. replacing each capacitance C Farads (F.) by a capacitance C/α F.

A frequency scaling with a scale factor β involves replacing each capacitance C F. by a capacitance C/β F. Note that all VCVS and operational amplifiers remain unchanged under both impedance and frequency scalings. As discussed in Chapter 8, the transfer functions of the impedance scaled circuit and the original circuit are identical, whereas the transfer function of the frequency scaled circuit can be obtained from that of the original circuit by replacing each s with s/β.

$$H(s) \longrightarrow H\left(s/\beta\right)$$

10-1 DIRECT REALIZATION APPROACH

In the direct realization approach, the transfer function of (10-1) is synthesized as a whole in one step. There are many synthesis techniques using this approach. We will discuss four representative methods.

10-1-1. Direct Realization Via Passive Circuits

In Chapters 7 and 8, we presented methods to realize transfer functions with passive RCL elements. With the sole exception of the lattice structure in Sec. 7-2, all circuit realizations (including the Darlington circuits) have a ladder structure. It is known that ladder circuits have low sensitivities; unless the component errors are substantial, the output distortions are small. In this subsection, we present two basic methods to realize active filters that preserve the low-sensitivity property of ladder circuits. They are the *simulated inductance method* and the *variable-frequency scaling method*. These methods are based almost completely on passive realizations. They both require that the transfer function under consideration be realized first by a passive RLC circuit, as discussed in Chapters 7 and 8.

10-1-1-1. Simulated Inductance Methods. To eliminate inductors, the simulated inductance method simply replaces each inductor in the passive circuit realization by a synthetic inductor such as the gyrator–capacitor combination of Fig. 10-1(a) or the generalized impedance converter circuit with a resistance termination as shown in Fig. 10-1(b).[1] The result is an active filter

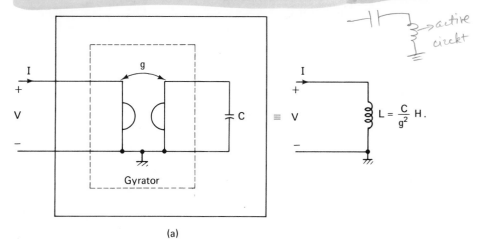

(a)

Fig. 10-1 Two synthetic grounded inductors.

---

[1]For floating inductors, see Fig. 2-11.

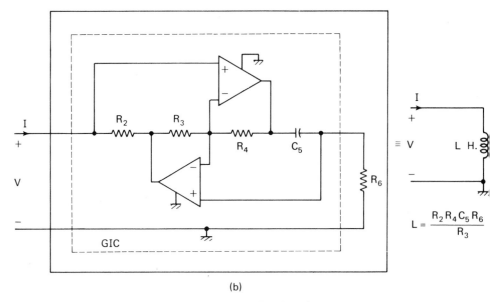

(b)

Fig. 10-1   (Continued)

circuit with a ladder structure, preserving the low structural sensitivities of a passive ladder circuit.

In practice, the simulated inductance method is applicable only to circuits where all inductors are grounded. The reason is that current technology can provide us with a reasonably good grounded synthetic inductor but floating inductor simulation is still a problem. We still do not have a practical method (not paper and pencil type) to realize a floating inductor with good stability and sensitivity behavior, especially in high-Q applications.

Example 10-1   Find an active ladder circuit realization of a fifth-order high-pass Butterworth filter with the cutoff frequency at 1 K rad./sec. and with terminating resistors $R_s = 1$ KΩ and $R_l = 4$ KΩ.

Solution: With $R_s = 1$ Ω and $R_l = 4$ Ω, a circuit realization of a fifth-order normalized low-pass Butterworth filter based on Fig. 8-9(a) and the recursive equations of (8-43) through (8-45) is shown in Fig. 10-2(a). The low-pass to high-pass element transformation of Table 8-5 with $\omega_c = 1$ K rad./sec. converts the circuit in Fig. 10-2(a) to that shown in Fig. 10-2(b). Figure 10-2(c) is obtained by performing an impedance scaling with a scale factor of 1 K on the circuit in Fig. 10-2(b). Clearly, the circuit in Fig. 10-2(c) is a passive filter satisfying the prescribed specifications. Observe that the inductance values in Fig. 10-2(c) are large. This is typical in low-frequency operations. To eliminate these large inductors, we may use the circuits in Fig. 10-1. With $g = 10^{-3}$ Mhos, a desired RC active filter with gyrators is shown in Fig. 10-2(d). Another desired active filter with GIC is shown in Fig. 10-2(e), where all the GIC are identical with

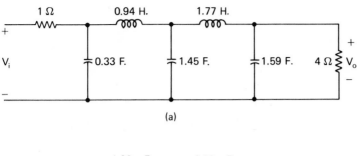

(a)

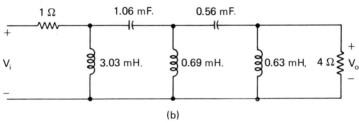

(b)

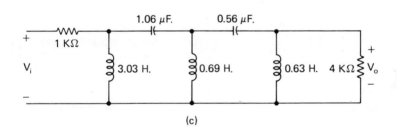

(c)

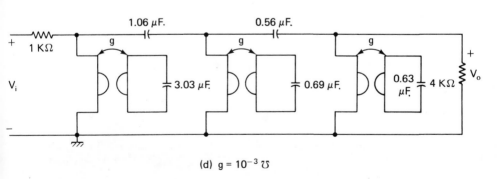

(d) $g = 10^{-3}$ ℧

Fig. 10-2 A step-by-step procedure to realize a fifth-order high-pass Butterworth active filter.

$L \rightarrow \boxed{GIC} \quad \lessgtr R_6$

transformed using

GIC Fig 10.1

$$L = \frac{R_2 R_4 C_5 R_6}{R_3}$$

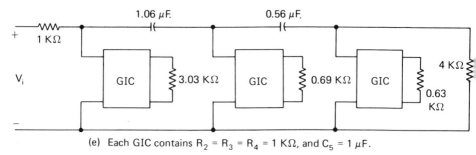

(e) Each GIC contains $R_2 = R_3 = R_4 = 1$ KΩ, and $C_5 = 1$ μF.

Fig. 10-2 (Continued)

$R_2 = R_3 = R_4 = 1$ KΩ, $C_5 = 1$ μF., and the terminating resistance values of R_6 are shown explicitly. ∎

10-1-1-2. Variable Impedance Scaling Method. The basic idea behind the variable impedance scaling method is to transform a passive RLC filter into an active filter circuit containing resistors, capacitors, and frequency-dependent negative resistors (FDNR). The transformation is obtained by dividing the impedance of each element in the passive RLC circuit realization of (10-1) by s. Steps involved in this method include a passive realization of (10-1) and the replacement of circuit elements in the passive realization according to the rules:

1. an inductor of L Henries is replaced by a resistor of L Ω;
2. a resistor of R Ω is replaced by a capacitor with $1/R$ F.; and
3. a capacitor of C F. is replaced by an FDNR of C Farad squared, or C F^2.

A circuit realization of an FDNR via an GIC is shown in Fig. 10-3.[2]

Because a voltage-ratio transfer function is unitless, impedance scaling will not affect the transfer function in any manner. Hence, the resulting active circuit with FDNR and the original passive circuit have identical transfer functions.

Note that an FDNR as realized in Fig. 10-3 is a grounded component. Hence, this method is applicable only to those passive circuits in which all capacitors are grounded.

Example 10-2 Find an active ladder circuit realization of a fifth-order low-pass Butterworth filter with the cutoff frequency at 1 K rad./sec.

---

[2]See subsection 2-2-2 for details.

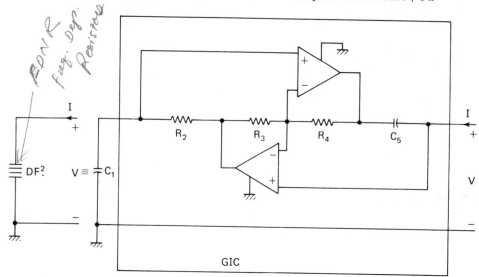

Fig. 10-3   An FDNR with $D = R_2 R_4 C_1 C_5 / R_3$.

Solution: A frequency scaling with $\omega_c = 1$ K rad./sec. converts the normalized design of Fig. 10-2(a) to the passive filter circuit shown in Fig. 10-4(a). Because the inductors are not grounded, practical application of the simulated inductance method is not possible. An alternative is to use the variable-impedance scaling method. The resulting active ladder filter circuit is shown in Fig. 10-4(b). An

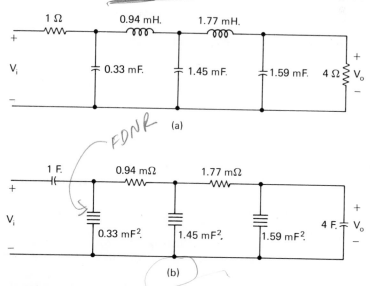

(a)

(b)

Fig. 10-4 A step-by-step procedure to realize a fifth-order low-pass Butterworth active filter.

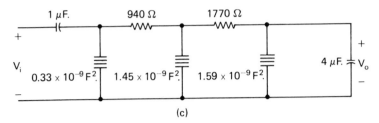

(c)

Fig. 10-4 (Continued)

impedance scaling is used to convert the element values in Fig. 10-4(b) to more reasonable numbers. Figure 10-4(c) shows the result of an impedance scaling factor of 10^6 applied to the circuit in Fig. 10-4(b). Observe that the transfer functions of all the circuits in Fig. 10-4 are identical. ∎

On many occasions, it is undesirable to have a capacitor termination such as the one in Fig. 10-4(c). To eliminate this drawback, let us consider the circuit in Fig. 10-5(a), which is a GIC 2-port terminated by an impedance Z_L. The DP impedance function is given by

$$Z_{in} = \frac{Z_2 Z_4}{Z_3 Z_5} Z_L \tag{10-5}$$

Suppose that the elements in the GIC are

$$Z_2 = R_2, \quad Z_3 = R_3, \quad Z_4 = \frac{1}{sC_4}, \quad \text{and} \quad Z_5 = R_5 \tag{10-6}$$

as shown in Fig. 10-5(b); then (10-5) becomes

$$Z_{in} = \frac{k}{s} Z_L \tag{10-7a}$$

where

$$k = \frac{R_2}{R_3 C_4 R_5} \tag{10-7b}$$

From (10-7), it is clear that a capacitor can be realized by terminating the GIC two-port with a resistor. Hence, the circuit in Fig. 10-4(c) is converted to the circuit in Fig. 10-6,[3] with a resistance termination, where

$$\frac{R_2 R_L}{R_3 C_4 R_5} = \frac{1}{4 \times 10^{-6}}$$

The GIC 2-port circuit shown in Fig. 10-5(b) functions as a variable impedance scaling device; it converts a resistor into a capacitor by impedance

---

[3]Technically, the output voltage in Fig. 10-6 should be across the input port of the GIC. The reason that we can label V_o across R_L is because the voltage across the input port and the output port of a GIC are equal.

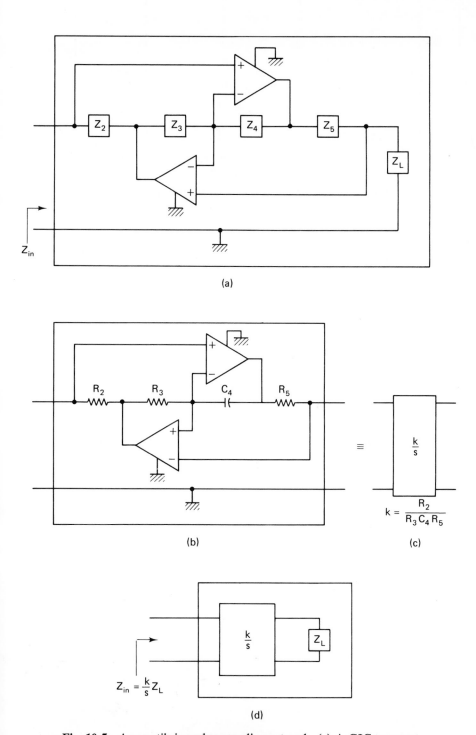

Fig. 10-5 A versatile impedance scaling network. (a) A GIC two-port with a terminating impedance Z_L. (b) A circuit for a k/s impedance scaling network. (c) Symbol for the k/s impedance scaling network. (d) Main function of a k/s impedance scaling network.

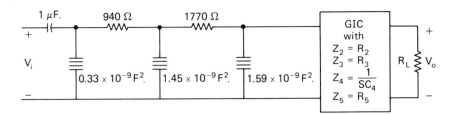

Fig. 10-6 An active circuit realization of a fifth-order low-pass Butterworth filter with a resistance termination.

scaling the resistor with an impedance scale of k/s. The symbol for this impedance scaling 2-port network is shown in Fig. 10-5(c), with its input–output relationship illustrated in Fig. 10-5(d).

Another useful impedance scaling network is shown in Fig. 10-7(a), where

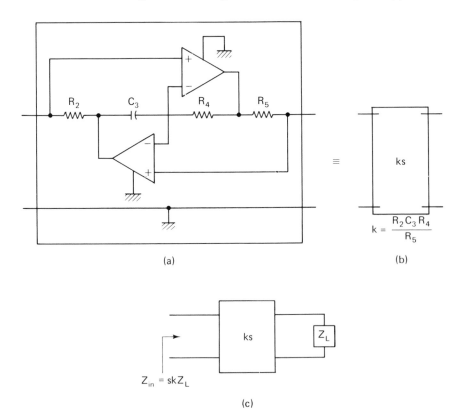

Fig. 10-7 An impedance scaling network. (a) A circuit realization of an impedance scaling network with a scale factor ks. (b) Symbol for the ks impedance scaling network. (c) The input–output relationship of the ks impedance scaling network.

the scaling factor is ks. If we terminate the 2-port circuit in Fig.10-7(a) with an impedance Z_L as illustrated in Fig. 10-7(c), then the DP impedance is given by

$$Z_{in} = skZ_L \tag{10-8a}$$

where

$$k = \frac{R_2 C_3 R_4}{R_5} \tag{10-8b}$$

This network is given the symbol shown in Fig. 10-7(b).[4]

Because of the in-place replacement procedures of both the simulated inductance method and the variable-impedance scaling method, the circuit configurations of the resulting active filter and the original passive filter are identical. This means that if we start with a passive ladder circuit, we will end up with an active ladder circuit thereby preserving the low structural sensitivity properties of passive designs.

10-1-2. Direct Realization with RC 2-Ports—Kuh's Method

Most of the direct realization methods start with a general circuit structure that possesses a versatile transfer function, one that can fit almost any desired transfer function. The branch or port characteristics in the circuit configuration are then determined by the desired transfer function. Hence, the problem of realizing a transfer function is reduced to that of realizing RC 1-port DP functions and RC multiports. Because we have not discussed any realization method for RC n-ports with $n \geq 3$, we will restrict our attention to the 1-port and 2-port cases only.[5]

Consider the circuit configuration shown in Fig. 10-8, where $\alpha > 0$ and the RC 2-port is represented by

$$\begin{bmatrix} I_1 \\ I_2 \end{bmatrix} = \begin{bmatrix} y_{11} & y_{21} \\ y_{21} & y_{22} \end{bmatrix} \begin{bmatrix} V_i \\ V_o \end{bmatrix} \tag{10-9}$$

The voltage-ratio transfer function of the circuit in Fig. 10-8 is given by

$$\frac{V_o}{V_i} = \frac{-y_{21}}{(Y_1 - \alpha Y_2) + y_{22}} = \frac{-y_{21}}{(y_{22} + Y_1) - \alpha Y_2} \tag{10-10}$$

To synthesize a voltage-ratio transfer function $H(s)$ of (10-1), we divide both the numerator $A(s)$ and the denominator $B(s)$ of (10-1) by a suitably selected polynomial $D(s)$ having simple (nonzero) negative real roots, none of

---

[4]The 2-port circuits shown in Figs. 10-5 and 10-7 function respectively as C-R and L-R mutators—if each port 2 is terminated by a resistor, then the resulting 1-ports in Figs. 10-5 and 10-7 yield a capacitor and an inductor respectively.

[5]For those interested in the 3-port cases, please consult References [13] and [14].

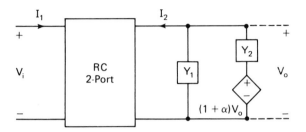

Fig. 10-8 Kuh's configuration for the direct realization of (10-1).

which coincide with the real roots of $B(s)$ as[6]

$$H(s) = \frac{A(s)}{B(s)} = \frac{A(s)/D(s)}{B(s)/D(s)} \qquad (10\text{-}11)$$

Note that there is no cancellation of terms in the denominator of the rightmost expression of (10-11). Assume that $A(s)$ is in the form[7]

$$A(s) = ks^m \qquad (10\text{-}12)$$

where $0 \leq m \leq n$, and n is the degree of the polynomial $B(s)$. Identifying the corresponding terms in (10-10) and (10-11), and using (10-12), we obtain

$$-y_{21} = \frac{ks^m}{D(s)} \qquad (10\text{-}13a)$$

$$y_{22} + (Y_1 - \alpha Y_2) = \frac{B(s)}{D(s)} \qquad (10\text{-}13b)$$

In order to realize y_{21} and y_{22} of the passive RC 2-port of Fig. 10-8 simultaneously, we must ensure that every pole of $y_{21}(s)$ is also a pole of $y_{22}(s)$. This is the reason why $D(s)$ is chosen not to have any root coinciding with the real roots of $B(s)$—to avoid cancellation in the rational function

$$F_B(s) \triangleq \frac{B(s)}{D(s)} \qquad (10\text{-}14)$$

Let

$$D(s) = (s + s_1)(s + s_2)\ldots(s + s_\ell) \qquad (10\text{-}15)$$

where

1. $s_1, s_2, \ldots, s_\ell$ are real, and $0 < s_1 < s_2 \ldots < s_\ell$;
2. s_i is not a root of $B(s)$ for $i = 1, 2, \ldots, \ell$; and
3. the integer ℓ satisfies the inequality $\ell \geq n - 1$.

---

[6]Note that $B(s)$ may have real and/or complex roots.

[7]This assumption is needed because in Chapter 7 all methods for the simultaneous realization of y_{21} and y_{22} of an RC 2-port were discussed under the assumption that the numerator $A(s)$ of the transfer function is given by (10-12). If we had developed more tools in Chapter 7, then the condition on $A(s)$ could be relaxed generously.

For economy and simplicity, we will always choose ℓ to be

$$\ell = n - 1 \qquad (10\text{-}16)$$

A partial fraction expansion of

$$\frac{B(s)}{sD(s)} = \frac{B(s)}{s(s + s_1)(s + s_2)\dots(s + s_\ell)} \qquad (10\text{-}17)$$

gives

$$\frac{B(s)}{sD(s)} = \xi_\infty + \frac{\xi_0}{s} + \frac{\xi_1}{s + s_1} + \frac{\xi_2}{s + s_2} + \dots + \frac{\xi_\ell}{s + s_\ell} \qquad (10\text{-}18)$$

Hence,

$$\frac{B(s)}{D(s)} = \xi_\infty s + \xi_0 + \frac{\xi_1 s}{s + s_1} + \frac{\xi_2 s}{s + s_2} + \dots + \frac{\xi_\ell s}{s + s_\ell} \qquad (10\text{-}19)$$

In (10-18), the ξ_is are the residues of the rational function $B(s)/[sD(s)]$ at the poles $s = -s_i$, where $i = 0, 1, 2, \dots, \ell$ with $s_0 = 0$.[8] These residues are real because the poles are real and the coefficients of the rational function $B(s)/[sD(s)]$ are real. However, not all ξ_is are positive, in general. Let $y_{22}(s)$ of the RC 2-port in Fig. 10-8 be given by

$$y_{22}(s) = k_\infty s + k_0 + \frac{k_1 s}{s + s_1} + \frac{k_2 s}{s + s_2} + \dots + \frac{k_\ell s}{s + s_\ell} \triangleq \frac{C(s)}{D(s)} \qquad (10\text{-}20)$$

where all k_i, $i = 0, 1, 2, \dots, \ell$, and ∞ are arbitrary but *positive real* numbers. Then the denominator of $y_{22}(s)$ is clearly $D(s)$, and $y_{22}(s)$ is an RC DP admittance function. Substituting (10-19) and (10-20) into (10-13b), we obtain

$$\begin{aligned}
\alpha Y_2 - Y_1 &= y_{22} - \frac{B(s)}{D(s)} \\
&= (k_\infty - \xi_\infty)s + (k_0 - \xi_0) + \frac{(k_1 - \xi_1)s}{s + s_1} \\
&\quad + \frac{(k_2 - \xi_2)s}{s + s_2} + \dots + \frac{(k_\ell - \xi_\ell)s}{s + s_\ell} \\
&\triangleq \beta_\infty s + \beta_0 + \frac{\beta_1 s}{s + s_1} + \frac{\beta_2 s}{s + s_2} + \dots + \frac{\beta_\ell s}{s + s_\ell}
\end{aligned} \qquad (10\text{-}21)$$

where

$$\beta_i \triangleq k_i - \xi_i \qquad i = 0, 1, 2, \dots, \ell, \text{ and } \infty \qquad (10\text{-}22)$$

From (10-21), we can assign those terms with positive β_is to αY_2 and those with negative β_is to Y_1.[9] This will give rise to Y_1 and Y_2 being passive RC DP admittance functions. Hence, all elements in Fig. 10-8 are determined. Consequently, the realization of the transfer function of (10-1) under the con-

---

[8] Due to (10-16), both ξ_∞ and ξ_0 are nonzero.

[9] Clearly, we can ignore those terms with zero β_i's.

straint of (10-12) is now reduced to:

1. The simultaneous realization of y_{22} and y_{21} of the RC 2-port, where $y_{21}(s)$ and $y_{22}(s)$ are given by (10-13a) and (10-20), respectively. In (10-13a), if $m = 0$, Cauer's first form should be used; if $m = n$, Cauer's second form should be used; and if $0 < m < n$, a combination of Cauer's first and second forms should be used. The realization procedures here follow those of subsections 7-1-1 and 7-1-3.
2. The realizations of two RC DP admittance functions. In these cases, either one of Foster's two forms seems to be more convenient. Of course, Cauer's forms can also be used.

In order to obtain a circuit as simple as possible, it is customary to let

$$k_i = \xi_i \quad \text{whenever} \quad \xi_i > 0 \tag{10-23}$$

Hence, the corresponding β_is will be zero. If (10-23) is adopted, then we have

$$\beta_i \geq 0 \qquad i = 0, 1, 2, \dots, \ell, \text{ and } \infty \tag{10-24}$$

Hence, $Y_1 = 0$, and all terms with nonzero β_is are assigned to $\alpha Y_2(s)$.

Example 10-3   Realize

$$H(s) = \frac{V_o}{V_i} = \frac{0.5}{s^2 + s + 1} \triangleq \frac{A(s)}{B(s)} \tag{10-25}$$

by Kuh's configuration.

Solution: From (10-16), the chosen polynomial $D(s)$ is a first-degree polynomial. Let us choose

$$D(s) = s + 0.5 \tag{10-26}$$

Then

$$-y_{21}(s) = \frac{A(s)}{D(s)} = \frac{0.5}{s + 0.5} \tag{10-27a}$$

and

$$y_{22} + Y_1 - \alpha Y_2 = \frac{B(s)}{D(s)} = \frac{s^2 + s + 1}{s + 0.5}$$

$$= s + 2 + \frac{-1.5s}{s + 0.5} \tag{10-27b}$$

Let[10]

$$y_{22}(s) = s + 2 + \frac{0.5s}{s + 0.5} \tag{10-28}$$

Then

$$\alpha Y_2 - Y_1 = y_{22} - \left(s + 2 + \frac{-1.5s}{s + 0.5} \right) = \frac{2s}{s + 0.5} \tag{10-29}$$

---

[10]Observe that different choices of $y_{22}(s)$ will give rise to different circuit realizations of (10-25).

A simple solution of (10-29) is given by[11]

$$Y_1 = 0 \tag{10-30a}$$

$$\alpha = 1 \tag{10-30b}$$

$$Y_2 = \frac{2s}{s + 0.5} = \frac{1}{0.5 + (1/4s)} \tag{10-30c}$$

At this point the problem of realizing (10-25) is reduced to the problem of realizing the DP admittance function of $Y_2(s)$ of (10-30c) and a simultaneous realization of $y_{21}(s)$ of (10-27a) and $y_{22}(s)$ of (10-28). Figure 10-9(a) shows a realization of $Y_2(s)$. Because all transmission zeros of $F(s) \triangleq -y_{21}(s)/y_{22}(s)$ are at $s = \infty$, $y_{22}(s)$ of (10-28) is realized by Cauer's first form. This requires a continued fraction expansion of $y_{22}(s)$ at $s = \infty$:

$$y_{22}(s) = s + 2 + \frac{0.5s}{s + 0.5} = \frac{s^2 + 3s + 1}{s + 0.5}$$

$$= s + \cfrac{1}{0.4 + \cfrac{1}{25s + \cfrac{1}{0.1}}} \tag{10-31}$$

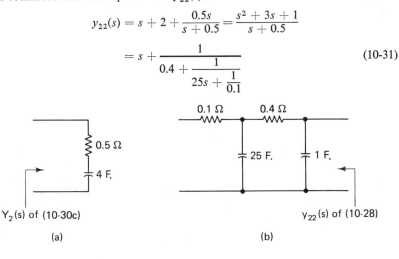

$Y_2(s)$ of (10-30c)

(a)

$y_{22}(s)$ of (10-28)

(b)

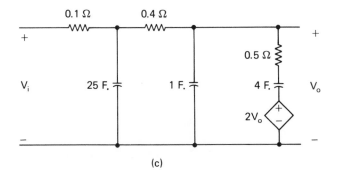

(c)

Fig. 10-9   A circuit realization of (10-25).

---

[11]Observe that there are many solutions to (10-29). For example, $Y_1 = 1$, $\alpha = 1$, and $Y_2(s) = 1 + 2s/(s + 0.5)$, is another solution.

Figure 10-9(b) shows a simultaneous realization of $y_{21}(s)$ of (10-27a) and $y_{22}(s)$ of (10-28). A circuit realization of (10-25) is shown in Fig. 10-9(c).   ∎

Example 10-4   Realize

$$H(s) = \frac{V_o}{V_i} = \frac{s}{s^2 + s + 1} \triangleq \frac{A(s)}{B(s)} \tag{10-32}$$

by Kuh's method.

Solution: Let $D(s) = s + 0.5$.

Then

$$-y_{21} = \frac{s}{s + 0.5} \tag{10-33a}$$

and

$$y_{22} + Y_1 - \alpha Y_2 = \frac{B(s)}{D(s)} = \frac{s^2 + s + 1}{s + 0.5} = s + 2 - \frac{1.5s}{s + 0.5} \tag{10-33b}$$

As in Example 10-3, a simple decomposition of (10-33b) is given by

$$y_{22}(s) = s + 2 + \frac{0.5s}{s + 0.5} \tag{10-34a}$$

$$Y_1 = 0 \tag{10-34b}$$

$$\alpha = 1 \tag{10-34c}$$

$$Y_2 = \frac{1}{0.5 + \dfrac{1}{4s}} \tag{10-34d}$$

In this case there are transmission zeros at both $s = 0$ and $s = \infty$. Hence, we use a combination of Cauer's forms to realize $y_{22}(s)$ of (10-34a). Using Cauer's first form first, we obtain

$$y_{22}(s) = \frac{s^2 + 3s + 1}{s + 0.5} = s + y_R \tag{10-35a}$$

where the remainder admittance function

$$y_R(s) = \frac{1 + 2.5s}{0.5 + s} \tag{10-35b}$$

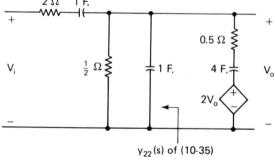

$$y_{22}(s) \text{ of } (10\text{-}35)$$

Fig. 10-10   A circuit realization of (10-32).

is realized by Cauer's second form:

$$y_R(s) = 2 + \cfrac{1}{\cfrac{1}{s} + \cfrac{1}{0.5}} \qquad (10\text{-}35c)$$

A circuit realization of (10-32) using (10-35) and Fig. 10-9(a) is shown in Fig. 10-10. ∎

From Examples 10-3 and 10-4, we observe that even with the circuit configuration fixed to be in the form of Fig. 10-8, there are many, in fact, infinitely many, circuit realizations of the transfer function of (10-1), subject to the constraint of (10-12).

10-1-3. Direct Realization with RC 1-ports

In this section, we discuss direct realization methods of (10-1) with active elements and RC 1-ports. All these methods are based on the decomposition property of Theorem 10-1, which carries the name RC:−RC decomposition.

THEOREM 10-1   Let $F(s) = C(s)/D(s)$ be a rational function with simple negative real poles. Let n_C and n_D denote the degrees of the polynomials $C(s)$ and $D(s)$, respectively. Then $F(s)$ can be expressed as

1. $F(s) = \dfrac{C(s)}{D(s)} = Z_{RC}^{(i)}(s) - Z_{RC}^{(ii)}(s)$ if $n_C \leq n_D$ $\qquad (10\text{-}36)$

2. $F(s) = \dfrac{C(s)}{D(s)} = Y_{RC}^{(1)}(s) - Y_{RC}^{(2)}(s)$ if $n_C \leq n_D + 1$ $\qquad (10\text{-}37)$

where $Z_{RC}^{(i)}$ and $Z_{RC}^{(ii)}$ $\{Y_{RC}^{(1)}$ and $Y_{RC}^{(2)}\}$ are RC DP impedance {admittance} functions, realizable by passive RC elements. ∎

The decomposition of Theorem 10-1 is obtained by a *partial fraction expansion* of $F(s)$. Those terms with positive coefficients are assigned to $Z_{RC}^{(i)}(s)$ or $Y_{RC}^{(1)}(s)$, and the remaining ones are assigned to $Z_{RC}^{(ii)}$ or $Y_{RC}^{(2)}(s)$.

Example 10-5   Let

$$Z(s) = \frac{s^2 - 2}{(s + 1)(s + 2)(s + 3)} \qquad (10\text{-}38)$$

Find the RC: −RC decomposition of $Z(s)$.

Solution: The partial fraction expansion of $Z(s)$ is given by

$$Z(s) = \frac{\xi_1}{s + 1} + \frac{\xi_2}{s + 2} + \frac{\xi_2}{s + 3} \qquad (10\text{-}39)$$

where

$$\xi_i = \frac{s^2 - 2}{(d/ds)\,[(s + 1)(s + 2)(s + 3)]}\bigg|_{s = s_i} \qquad (10\text{-}40)$$

is the residue of $Z(s)$ at the pole s_i. With $s_1 = -1$, $s_2 = -2$, and $s_3 = -3$, we obtain

$$Z(s) = \frac{-1/2}{s+1} + \frac{-2}{s+2} + \frac{7/2}{s+3} \tag{10-41}$$

Hence,

$$Z_{RC}^{(i)}(s) = \frac{7/2}{s+3} \tag{10-42a}$$

$$Z_{RC}^{(ii)}(s) = \frac{1/2}{s+1} + \frac{2}{s+2} \tag{10-42b}$$

∎

Example 10-6 Let

$$Y(s) = \frac{s^2 - 2}{(s+1)(s+2)(s+3)} \tag{10-43}$$

Find the RC:−RC decomposition of $Y(s)$.

Solution: The partial fraction expansion of $Y(s)/s$ yields

$$\frac{Y(s)}{s} = \frac{s^2 - 2}{s(s+1)(s+2)(s+3)}$$

$$= \frac{-1/3}{s} + \frac{1/2}{s+1} + \frac{1}{s+2} + \frac{-7/6}{s+3}$$

or

$$Y(s) = \frac{(1/2)s}{s+1} + \frac{s}{s+2} + \left(-\frac{1}{3}\right) + \frac{-(7/6)s}{s+3} \tag{10-44}$$

Hence,

$$Y_{RC}^{(1)}(s) = \frac{(1/2)s}{s+1} + \frac{s}{s+2} \tag{10-45a}$$

and

$$Y_{RC}^{(2)}(s) = \frac{1}{3} + \frac{(7/6)s}{s+3} \tag{10-45b}$$

∎

The realization procedures to be discussed in this section are almost identical to one another. Each starts with a circuit configuration containing RC 1-ports, VCVS, and/or operational amplifiers. The transfer function of the circuit depends explicitly on the DP admittance functions of the RC 1-ports. In addition, both the numerator and the denominator of the circuit's transfer function can be expressed as a difference of two (groups of) RC admittance functions.

To realize the prescribed transfer function $H(s)$ of (10-1), we write

$$H(s) = \frac{A(s)}{B(s)} = \frac{A(s)/D(s)}{B(s)/D(s)} \tag{10-46}$$

where $D(s)$ is an arbitrary polynomial of degree n_D having only simple negative real roots and where

$$n_D \geq \max(m, n) - 1 \tag{10-47}$$

Recall that m and n are, respectively, the degrees of the numerator polynomial

$A(s)$ and the denominator polynomial $B(s)$ in (10-1). In this case, the roots of $D(s)$ are unrestricted as long as they are simple, negative, and real. In general, the roots of $D(s)$ are chosen to coincide with those real roots of $A(s)$ and/or $B(s)$ whenever possible to simplify the resulting circuit realization. By the RC:$-$RC decomposition theorem, (10-46) can be expressed as

$$H(s) = \frac{A(s)/D(s)}{B(s)/D(s)} = \frac{Y_{RC}^{(1)}(s) - Y_{RC}^{(2)}(s)}{Y_{RC}^{(3)}(s) - Y_{RC}^{(4)}(s)} \tag{10-48}$$

By comparing the corresponding terms between the circuit's transfer function and the required transfer function of (10-48), the DP admittance functions of the RC 1-ports in each circuit configuration are determined. The remaining problems are to realize these RC 1-ports.

10-1-3-1.   Yanagisawa Method. Consider the circuit configuration given in Fig. 10-11. A node equation at node A gives

$$Y_a(V_i - V_o) + Y_b(-k_1 V_i - V_o)$$
$$- Y_c V_o + Y_d[(1 + k_2)V_o - V_o] = 0 \tag{10-49}$$

After some simple algebraic manipulations,(10-49) yields the circuit's transfer function as

$$\frac{V_o}{V_i} = \frac{Y_a - k_1 Y_b}{Y_a + Y_b + Y_c - k_2 Y_d} \tag{10-50}$$

Identifying the corresponding terms in (10-50) and (10-48), we obtain the following specifications on the admittance branches in Fig. 10-11:

$$Y_a(s) = Y_{RC}^{(1)}(s) \tag{10-51a}$$

$$Y_b(s) = \frac{1}{k_1} Y_{RC}^{(2)}(s) \tag{10-51b}$$

$$Y_c(s) = Y_{RC}^{(3)}(s) \tag{10-51c}$$

$$Y_d(s) = \frac{1}{k_2}\left[Y_{RC}^{(1)}(s) + \frac{1}{k_1}Y_{RC}^{(2)}(s) + Y_{RC}^{(4)}(s) \right] \tag{10-51d}$$

[Note that the admittance branches can also be identified as:

$$Y_a(s) = Y_{RC}^{(2)}(s) \tag{10-51a'}$$

$$Y_b(s) = \frac{1}{k_1}Y_{RC}^{(1)}(s) \tag{10-51b'}$$

$$Y_c(s) = Y_{RC}^{(4)}(s) \tag{10-51c'}$$

$$Y_d(s) = \frac{1}{k_2}\left[Y_{RC}^{(2)}(s) + \frac{1}{k_1}Y_{RC}^{(1)}(s) + Y_{RC}^{(3)}(s) \right] \tag{10-51d'}$$

Henceforth, we refer to both (10-51) and (10-51') as (10-51).]

Hence, by realizing the RC DP admittance functions of Y_a, Y_b, Y_c, and Y_d as specified by (10-51), the overall transfer function of (10-1) is realized by the circuit in Fig. 10-11.

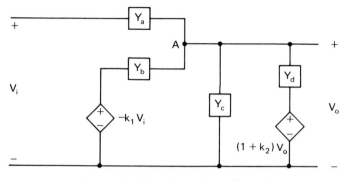

Fig. 10-11 Yanagisawa's configuration.

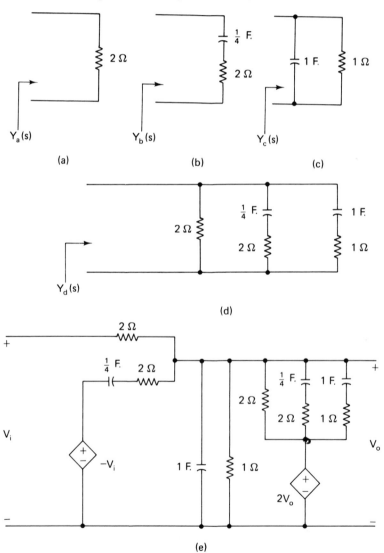

(a)   (b)   (c)

(d)

(e)

Fig. 10-12 A Yanagisawa realization of (10-52).

Example 10-7   Realize the voltage-ratio transfer function

$$H(s) = \frac{s+1}{(s+2)(s^2+s+1)} \triangleq \frac{A(s)}{B(s)} \tag{10-52}$$

by Yanagisawa's method.

Solution: By (10-47), $D(s)$ is a polynomial of degree 2. Let us choose

$$D(s) = (s+1)(s+2) \tag{10-53}$$

Then we have

$$\frac{A(s)}{sD(s)} = \frac{1}{s(s+2)} = \frac{1/2}{s} + \frac{-1/2}{s+2}$$

$$\frac{B(s)}{sD(s)} = \frac{s^2+s+1}{s(s+1)} = 1 + \frac{1}{s(s+1)} = 1 + \frac{1}{s} + \frac{-1}{s+1}$$

$$\frac{A(s)}{D(s)} = \frac{1}{2} - \frac{(1/2)s}{s+2} \tag{10-54a}$$

and

$$\frac{B(s)}{D(s)} = s + 1 - \frac{s}{s+1} \tag{10-54b}$$

Substituting (10-54) into (10-52), we obtain

$$H(s) = \frac{A(s)/D(s)}{B(s)/D(s)} = \frac{\dfrac{1}{2} - \dfrac{(1/2)s}{s+2}}{s+1 - \dfrac{s}{s+1}} \tag{10-55}$$

That is,

$$Y_{RC}^{(1)}(s) = \frac{1}{2}$$

$$Y_{RC}^{(2)}(s) = \frac{(1/2)s}{s+2}$$

$$Y_{RC}^{(3)}(s) = s + 1$$

$$Y_{RC}^{(4)}(s) = \frac{s}{s+1}$$

By (10-51), the DP admittance functions of the RC 1-ports in Fig. 10-11 are

$$Y_a(s) = \frac{1}{2}$$

$$Y_b(s) = \frac{(1/2)s}{s+2}$$

$$Y_c(s) = s + 1 \tag{10-56}$$

$$Y_d(s) = \frac{1}{2} + \frac{(1/2)s}{s+2} + \frac{s}{s+1}$$

where we have set $k_1 = k_2 = 1$. Each of these admittance functions is realized in Figs. 10-12(a) through (d). Putting everything together, the circuit in Fig. 10-12(e) realizes the transfer function of (10-52). ■

10-1-3-2. Mathews–Seifert's Method. Consider the Mathews–Seifert circuit configuration of Fig. 10-13, where $k_1 \geq 0$ and $k_2 \geq 0$. The transfer function is given by

$$H(s) \triangleq \frac{V_o}{V_i} = \frac{Y_a - k_1 Y_b}{k_2 Y_d - Y_c} = \frac{k_1 Y_b - Y_a}{Y_c - k_2 Y_d} \tag{10-57}$$

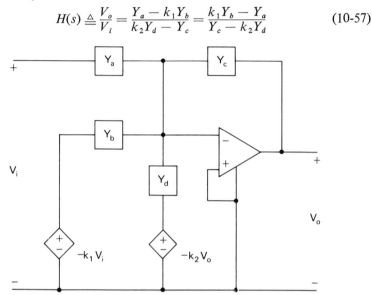

Fig. 10-13   Mathews–Seifert's circuit configuration.

In view of the similarities between (10-50) and (10-57), the realization procedures in the Mathews–Seifert's method parallel those of Yanagisawa's method very closely.

Example 10-8   Realize the voltage-ratio transfer function

$$H(s) = \frac{s+1}{s(s+2)(s+3)} \triangleq \frac{A(s)}{B(s)} \tag{10-58}$$

by Mathews–Seifert's method.

Solution: Let us choose

$$D(s) = (s+1)(s+2) \tag{10-59}$$

Then we have

$$\frac{A(s)}{D(s)} = \frac{1}{2} - \frac{(1/2)s}{s+2} \tag{10-60a}$$

$$\frac{B(s)}{D(s)} = s + \frac{2s}{s+1} \tag{10-60b}$$

and

$$H(s) = \frac{A(s)/D(s)}{B(s)/D(s)} = \frac{\dfrac{1}{2} - \dfrac{(1/2)s}{s+2}}{s + \dfrac{2s}{s+1}} \tag{10-60c}$$

Identifying the corresponding terms in (10-57) and (10-60c), we obtain[12]

$$k_1 Y_b = \frac{1}{2}$$

$$Y_a = \frac{(1/2)s}{s + 2}$$

$$Y_c = s + \frac{2s}{s + 1} \tag{10-61}$$

$$k_2 Y_d = 0$$

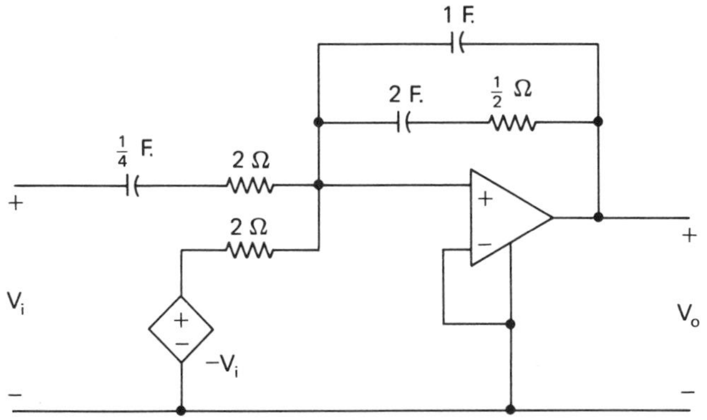

Fig. 10-14   A Mathews–Seifert realization of (10-58).

A Mathews–Seifert's realization circuit of (10-58) via (10-61) with $k_1 = 1$, $k_2 = 0$, and $Y_d = 0$ is shown in Fig. 10-14.   ∎

10-1-3-3. Lovering's Method. Another synthesis method similar to Yanagisawa's technique uses the Lovering's circuit configuration of Fig. 10-15, where the circuit's transfer function is given by[13]

$$H(s) = \frac{V_o}{V_i} = \frac{Y_b - Y_a}{Y_c - Y_d} = \frac{Y_a - Y_b}{Y_d - Y_c} \tag{10-62}$$

By comparing (10-57) and (10-62), we observe that the transfer function of Lovering's method has the same form as that of Mathews–Seifert's method. Consequently, the realization procedures of Lovering's method and Mathews–Seifert's method are identical, except for some simple modifications in symbols. We now present Lovering's method in terms of an illustrative example.

Example 10-9   Realize the transfer function of (10-58) by Lovering's method.

---

[12]Here, we use the rightmost expression of (10-57). By doing so, the resulting circuit has one less active element in this case.

[13]Observe that Y_0 does not appear in the circuit's transfer function of (10-62). This means that any *nonzero finite* value can be assigned to Y_0.

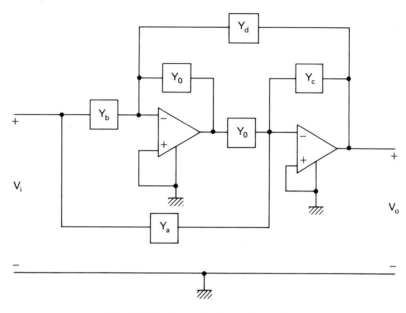

Fig. 10-15   Lovering's configuration.

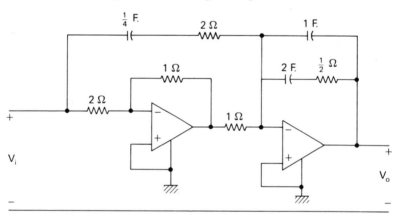

Fig. 10-16   A Lovering's realization of (10-58).

Solution: By choosing the same $D(s)$ as in Example 10-8, we obtain (10-60). A comparison of (10-60c) and (10-62) gives

$$Y_b = \frac{1}{2}$$

$$Y_a = \frac{(1/2)s}{s + 2} \tag{10-63}$$

$$Y_c = s + \frac{2s}{s + 1}$$

and

$$Y_d = 0$$

By substituting the realizations of the RC DP admittance functions of (10-63) into Fig. 10-15, we obtain a Lovering realization of (10-58) as shown in Fig. 10-16, where Y_0 is chosen to be 1.   ∎

10-1-3-4. Mitra's Method. Consider the circuit configuration of Fig. 10-17, where all the voltages shown are node-to-ground voltages. The node equations at nodes A and B are given by

$$Y_b(V_1 - V_i) + Y_d V_1 + Y_f(V_1 - V_o) = 0 \qquad (10\text{-}64)$$

$$Y_a(V_1 - V_i) + Y_c V_1 + Y_e(V_1 - V_o) = 0 \qquad (10\text{-}65)$$

From (10-64) we obtain

$$V_1 = \frac{Y_b V_i + Y_f V_o}{Y_b + Y_d + Y_f} \qquad (10\text{-}66)$$

With V_1 given by (10-66), (10-65) becomes

$$[Y_a(Y_b + Y_d + Y_f) - Y_b(Y_a + Y_c + Y_e)]V_i$$
$$= [Y_f(Y_a + Y_c + Y_e) - Y_e(Y_b + Y_d + Y_f)]V_o \qquad (10\text{-}67)$$

Hence, the transfer function of the circuit in Fig. 10-17 is given by

$$H(s) \triangleq \frac{V_o}{V_i} = \frac{Y_a(Y_b + Y_d + Y_f) - Y_b(Y_a + Y_c + Y_e)}{Y_f(Y_a + Y_c + Y_e) - Y_e(Y_b + Y_d + Y_f)} \qquad (10\text{-}68)$$

In this method, it is customary to choose the various admittance branches

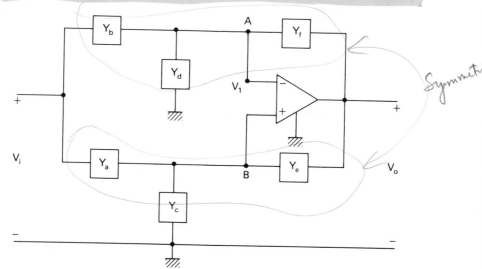

Fig. 10-17 Mitra's configuration.

such that

$$Y_a + Y_c + Y_e = Y_b + Y_d + Y_f \qquad (10\text{-}69)$$

Under the constraint of (10-69), (10-68) can be simplified to

$$H(s) \triangleq \frac{V_o}{V_i} = \frac{Y_a - Y_b}{Y_f - Y_e} = \frac{Y_b - Y_a}{Y_e - Y_f} \qquad (10\text{-}70)$$

Note that (10-70) is in the same form as that of (10-50), (10-57), and (10-62). Hence, with some modifications due to the additional constraint of (10-69), the procedures outlined in the previous realization methods are applicable here.

For the sake of clarity, we outline the steps of Mitra's method as follows:

0. Given $H(s)$ of (10-1).
1. Select an appropriate polynomial $D(s)$ of degree n_D where $n_D = \max (m, n) - 1$, and $D(s)$ has simple negative real roots.
2. Decompose both the numerator and denominator rational functions of $H(s)$ as

$$H(s) = \frac{A(s)}{B(s)} = \frac{A(s)/D(s)}{B(s)/D(s)} = \frac{Y_{RC}^{(1)} - Y_{RC}^{(2)}}{Y_{RC}^{(3)} - Y_{RC}^{(4)}} \qquad (10\text{-}71)$$

3. Identify the corresponding terms between (10-70) and (10-71) as *either*

$$Y_a = Y_{RC}^{(1)}, \quad Y_b = Y_{RC}^{(2)}, \quad Y_f = Y_{RC}^{(3)}, \quad \text{and} \quad Y_e = Y_{RC}^{(4)} \qquad (10\text{-}72a)$$

or

$$Y_b = Y_{RC}^{(1)}, \quad Y_a = Y_{RC}^{(2)} \quad Y_e = Y_{RC}^{(3)}, \quad \text{and} \quad Y_f = Y_{RC}^{(4)} \qquad (10\text{-}72b)$$

4. Find Y_c and Y_d. With (10-72a), (10-69) gives

$$
\begin{aligned}
Y_c - Y_d &= (Y_f - Y_e) - (Y_a - Y_b) \\
&= [Y_{RC}^{(3)} - Y_{RC}^{(4)}] - [Y_{RC}^{(1)} - Y_{RC}^{(2)}] \qquad (10\text{-}73a) \\
&= \frac{B(s)}{D(s)} - \frac{A(s)}{D(s)} = \frac{B(s) - A(s)}{D(s)}
\end{aligned}
$$

Similarly, if (10-72b) is adopted, (10-69) yields

$$Y_c - Y_d = \frac{A(s) - B(s)}{D(s)} \qquad (10\text{-}73b)$$

No matter which alternative of (10-72) is used, the RC:—RC decomposition theorem can be applied to the right-hand side of (10-73) to give

$$Y_c - Y_d = \pm \frac{A(s) - B(s)}{D(s)} = Y_{RC}^{(5)} - Y_{RC}^{(6)} \qquad (10\text{-}74)$$

Hence, we can identify

$$Y_c = Y_{RC}^{(5)}(s) \quad \text{and} \quad Y_d = Y_{RC}^{(6)}(s) \qquad (10\text{-}75)$$

This completes the necessary specification of Fig. 10-17.

5. Realize Y_a, Y_b, Y_c, Y_d, Y_e, and Y_f as found in Steps 3 and 4 by RC elements, as discussed in Chapter 6.

6. Finally, substitute into Fig. 10-17 the corresponding RC 1-ports realized in Step 5. The resulting circuit is a realization of the transfer function of (10-1).

$$H(s) = \frac{s+1}{s(s+2)(s+3)}$$

Example 10-10   Realize the transfer function of (10-58) by Mitra's method.

Solution: We follow the design procedure outlined in the previous paragraph.

1. Choose $D(s) = (s+1)(s+2)$.

2. Obtain

$$H(s) = \frac{\dfrac{1}{2} - \dfrac{(1/2)s}{s+2}}{s + \dfrac{2s}{s+1}} = \frac{(s+1)(s+2)}{s(s+2)(s+3)} = \frac{\dfrac{1}{s+2}}{\dfrac{s(s+3)}{s+1}}$$

$$\frac{(s+1)(s+2)}{s(s+2)(s+3)}$$

3. Using (10-72a), we obtain

$$Y_a = \frac{1}{2}, \quad Y_b = \frac{(1/2)s}{s+2}, \quad Y_f = s + \frac{2s}{s+1}, \quad \text{and} \quad Y_e = 0 \quad (10\text{-}76)$$

4. Find Y_c and Y_d as

$$Y_c - Y_d = \frac{B(s) - A(s)}{D(s)} = \frac{s(s+2)(s+3) - (s+1)}{(s+1)(s+2)}$$

$$= \frac{s^3 + 5s^2 + 5s - 1}{(s+1)(s+2)} \triangleq \frac{C(s)}{D(s)}$$

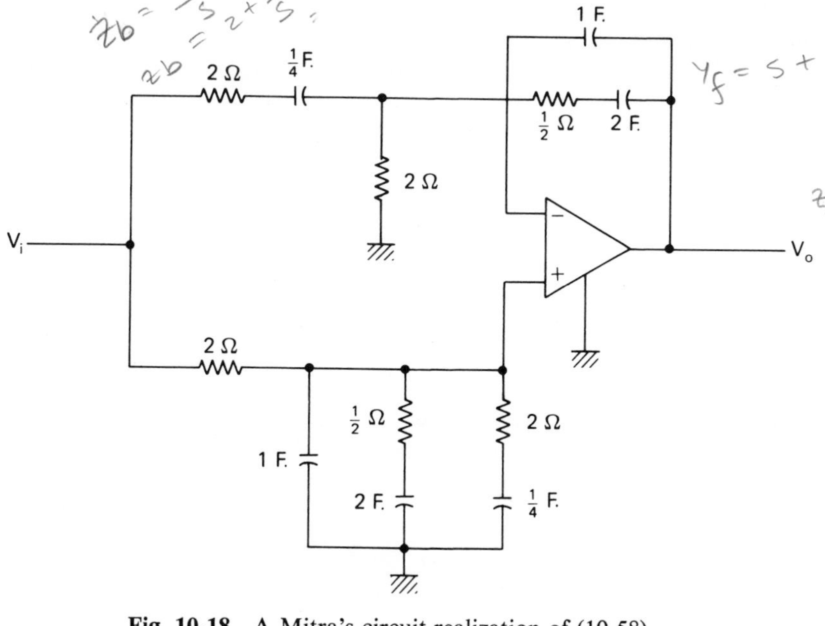

$$\frac{Y(s)}{J} = \frac{1}{s(s+2)}$$

$$Y(s) = \frac{1/2}{s} - \frac{1/2\,s}{s+2}$$

$$Y_f = s + \frac{2s}{s+1}$$

$$Y_b = \frac{2s+4}{s} = 2 + \frac{4}{s}$$

$$\frac{s+1}{2s}$$

$$Y_{a2} = \frac{1}{2} + \frac{1}{2s}$$

Fig. 10-18   A Mitra's circuit realization of (10-58).

Note that

$$\frac{C(s)}{sD(s)} = 1 + \frac{2s^2 + 3s - 1}{s(s+1)(s+2)}$$

$$= 1 + \frac{-1/2}{s} + \frac{2}{s+1} + \frac{1/2}{s+2}$$

Hence,

$$Y_c - Y_d = s + \frac{2s}{s+1} + \frac{(1/2)s}{s+2} - \frac{1}{2}$$

or

$$Y_c = s + \frac{2s}{s+1} + \frac{(1/2)s}{s+2} \qquad (10\text{-}77a)$$

$$Y_d = \tfrac{1}{2} \qquad (10\text{-}77b)$$

5. and 6. The resulting Mitra's realization circuit of (10-58) is shown in Fig. 10-18.   ∎

10-1-3-5. Some Comments. All four methods introduced in subsection 10-1-3 use the same concept, the RC:−RC decomposition technique of Theorem 10-1. These methods require absolutely no restriction on the transfer function to be realized, other than it be a real rational function of s. However, from a practical point of view, there is an important drawback, which is the large pole sensitivity with respect to the parameters of active elements, namely VCVS and operational amplifiers. This arises because the realization of complex poles in the general transfer function of (10-1) is accomplished by subtracting two rational functions, as can be seen from (10-50), (10-57), (10-62), and (10-70). In addition, the four methods are not suitable for high (pole-pair) Q circuits or narrow band filters.

Another drawback, basic to all active filters, is that a small variation in an active element's parameter, such as the coefficients of a VCVS, can easily influence a stable circuit in the borderline case to become unstable. This is particularly true if the RC:−RC decomposition of the denominator ratio $B(s)/D(s)$ gives rise to both positive and negative coefficient terms. Hence, whenever possible, we should choose $D(s)$ such that the partial fraction expansion of $B(s)/[sD(s)]$ yields positive residues only.

10-1-4. Direct Realization Via State-Variable Technique

Consider the circuit in Fig. 10-19, where all indicated voltages are node-to-ground voltages and we have assumed that n is an odd integer. If n is an even integer, then resistor R_n is connected to node B rather than to node A. The equations describing this circuit are:

$$V_k = (-1)sCRV_{k+1}$$
$$= (-1)^{n-k}(sCR)^{n-k}V_n \quad \text{for } k = 1, 2, \ldots, n-1 \qquad (10\text{-}78)$$

$$V_a = -R_a\left[\frac{V_2}{R_2} + \frac{V_4}{R_4} + \ldots + \frac{V_{n-1}}{R_{n-1}}\right] \qquad (10\text{-}79)$$

$$sC_1V_1 + \frac{V_a}{R_a} + \frac{V_i}{R_0} + \left[\frac{V_1}{R_1} + \frac{V_3}{R_3} + \ldots + \frac{V_n}{R_n}\right] = 0 \qquad (10\text{-}80)$$

Substituting (10-78) and (10-79) into (10-80), and with $C_1 = RC$, we obtain

$$(sCR)^n V_n + \frac{(sCR)^{n-1}}{R_1}V_n + \frac{(sCR)^{n-2}}{R_2}V_n$$

$$+ \frac{(sCR)^{n-3}}{R_3}V_n + \frac{(sCR)^{n-4}}{R_4}V_n + \ldots + \frac{V_n}{R_n} = -\frac{V_i}{R_0}$$

or

where

$$\frac{V_n}{V_i} = -\frac{G_0}{(sCR)^n + G_1(sCR)^{n-1} + G_2(sCR)^{n-2} + \ldots + G_n} \qquad (10\text{-}81)$$

$$G_i = \frac{1}{R_i} \quad \text{for } i = 0, 1, 2, \ldots, n$$

Note that R_a does not appear in the circuit's transfer function of (10-81). This means that R_a can be any nonzero finite positive value. From (10-81), if we take V_n as our output voltage, then the circuit in Fig. 10-19 is a low-pass filter that can be used to realize Butterworth, Chebyshev, and Bessel low-pass filters. The transfer relationships between V_k, for $k = 1, 2, \ldots, n$, and V_i can be obtained by combining (10-78) and (10-81) together. The result is:

$$H_k(s) \triangleq \frac{V_k}{V_i} = -\frac{(-1)^{n-k}G_0(sCR)^{n-k}}{(sCR)^n + G_1(sCR)^{n-1} + G_2(sCR)^{n-2} + \ldots + G_n} \qquad (10\text{-}82)$$

Note that (10-82) was derived under the assumption that n is an odd integer. If n is even, then R_n is connected to node B rather than to node A in Fig. 10-19, and the resulting transfer function is given by

$$\frac{V_k}{V_i} = \frac{(-1)^{n-k}G_0(sCR)^{n-k}}{(sCR)^n + G_1(sCR)^{n-1} + G_2(sCR)^{n-2} + \ldots + G_n} \qquad (10\text{-}83)$$

where $k = 1, 2, \ldots, n$. Except for the minus sign in front, the transfer functions of both cases are identical.

From either (10-82) or (10-83), we observe that the denominator polynomials are identical for $k = 1, 2, \ldots, n$. Hence, to realize the prescribed transfer function of (10-1), we need only to add to Fig. 10-19 a summer circuit such as the one shown in Fig. 2-15.

Note that the state-variable circuit configuration requires at least $(n + 1)$ operational amplifiers[14] in addition to a large number of resistors. This is costly. In return, the circuit provides a convenient tuning mechanism to

---

[14]In most situations, $(n + 2)$ operational amplifiers are needed for the n integrators, one sign-reversal circuit, and one summer circuit. If there is no finite nonzero transmission zero (all transmission zeros are either at $s = \infty$ or at $s = 0$ or both), then there is no need for the summer circuit. On the other hand, if the even part of the denominator polynomial $B(s)$ of the prescribed transfer function of (10-1) is zero, then the sign-reversal circuit is not needed.

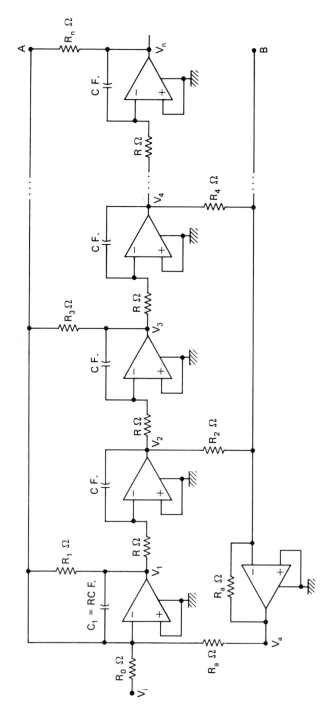

Fig. 10-19 A direct realization via state-variable technique.

adjust resistor values $R_1, R_2, \ldots, R_n$ to fit the coefficients of the prescribed transfer function.

Example 10-11 Suppose that we need an equiripple filter to meet the following requirements:

1. Ripple bandwidth is 1 K rad./sec.
2. Maximum passband ripple attenuation is 0.1 dB.
3. Minimum stopband loss is 40 dB for $\omega \geq 6$ K rad./sec.

Find an active realization via state-variable technique.

Solution: From Example 8-12, the desired transfer function is given by

$$H(s) = \frac{1.6381}{(s/10^3)^3 + 1.9388 \, (s/10^3)^2 + 2.6296(s/10^3) + 1.6381} \quad (10\text{-}84)$$

Because $n = 3$ in this case, (10-81) is applicable here. A comparison of (10-81) and (10-84) yields the following design equations:[15]

$$C_1 = RC = 10^{-3}$$
$$G_0 = 1.6381 \quad \text{or} \quad R_0 = 0.6105 \, \Omega$$
$$G_1 = 1.9388 \quad \text{or} \quad R_1 = 0.5158 \, \Omega \quad (10\text{-}85a)$$
$$G_2 = 2.6296 \quad \text{or} \quad R_2 = 0.3803 \, \Omega$$
$$G_3 = 1.6381 \quad \text{or} \quad R_3 = 0.6105 \, \Omega$$

To roughly minimize the spread of resistance values, let us choose

$$R_a = 0.5 \, \Omega, \quad R = 0.5 \, \Omega, \quad C = 2 \times 10^{-3} \, \text{F.}, \quad \text{and} \quad C_1 = 10^{-3} \, \text{F.} \quad (10\text{-}85b)$$

The resulting circuit is shown in Fig. 10-20(a), where the output voltage is taken across V_3. Figure 10-20(b) is an impedance scaled version of Fig. 10-20(a) with a scale factor of 10 K. Note that the transfer functions of both circuits in Fig. 10-20 are given by (10-84). ∎

10-2 CASCADE REALIZATION APPROACH

In the cascade realization approach, the transfer function of (10-1) is realized by cascading a sequence of first- and second-order filter sections. Figure 10-21 shows that the cascade approach reduces the problem of realizing a general transfer function of (10-1) to that of realizing a number of second-order filter sections plus perhaps a first-order section.

Cascade realization is very attractive for postdesign adjustments as each section is isolated from the others. It is also possible to design second-order

---

[15]We can set $C_1 = RC = 1$ and then perform a frequency scaling $s \longrightarrow (s/10^3)$ by replacing C F. and C_1 F. with $10^{-3} \, C$ F. and $10^{-3} \, C_1$ F., respectively.

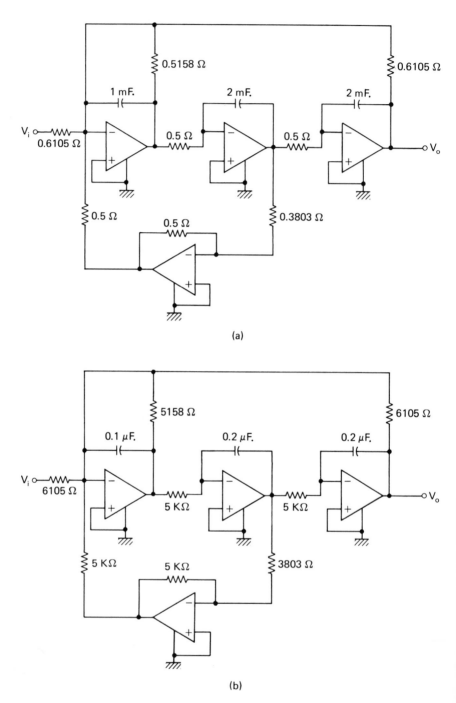

(a)

(b)

Fig. 10-20 State-variable circuit realizations for Example 10-11.

374

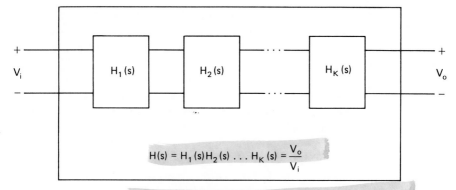

Fig. 10-21   A schematic diagram for the cascade approach.

sections with externally controlled characteristics. This allows realizations of
a number of transfer functions with a few low-order basic building blocks.
In addition, cascade realization usually produces less sensitive circuits than
those obtained by the direct approach.

The cascade approach greatly simplifies the problem of realizing general
transfer functions, because there is only a *finite* number of distinct forms for
second-order transfer function. A general second-order transfer function is
given by[16]

$$H(s) = \frac{a_2 s^2 + a_1 s + a_0}{s^2 + b_1 s + b_0} \qquad (10\text{-}86a)$$

As special cases, we have:

1. low-pass filters when $a_2 = a_1 = 0$.
2. bandpass filters when $a_2 = a_0 = 0$.
3. high-pass filters when $a_1 = a_0 = 0$.
4. low-pass notch filters when $a_1 = 0$ and $a_2 \leq a_0/b_0$.
5. high-pass notch filters when $a_1 = 0$ and $a_2 \geq a_0/b_0$.
6. all-pass filters when $-(a_1/a_2) = b_1$ and $a_0/a_2 = b_0$.

Almost all second-order filter sections make use of finite VCVS (which
can be realized by operational amplifiers) or operational amplifiers themselves.
The amplifiers are used to generate the necessary complex poles (recall that

---

[16]The transfer function of (10-86) is called a *biquadratic* transfer function, because both
its numerator and denominator are quadratic polynomials. Specifically, there are only
seven distinct forms of biquadratic transfer functions:

$$\frac{a_0}{s^2 + b_1 s + b_0}, \quad \frac{a_1 s}{s^2 + b_1 s + b_0}, \quad \frac{a_2 s^2}{s^2 + b_1 s + b_0}, \quad \frac{a_1 s + a_0}{s^2 + b_1 s + b_0},$$

$$\frac{a_2 s^2 + a_0}{s^2 + b_1 s + b_0}, \quad \frac{a_2 s^2 + a_1 s}{s^2 + b_1 s + b_0}, \quad \text{and} \quad \frac{a_2 s^2 + a_1 s + a_0}{s^2 + b_1 s + b_0} \qquad (10\text{-}86b)$$

RC filters without active devices can have only *negative real* poles) and to provide low output impedance. In the case of multiple amplifier circuits, operational amplifiers are also used to provide high-input impedance for each filter section.

In order for the cascade approach to function properly,[17] each section must have a high input impedance (the DP impedance value viewed from the input port into the filter section is large) and/or a low output impedance (the DP impedance value as seen from the output port into the filter section is small). To meet the requirements for proper cascade connections, the output voltage of each filter section is usually taken to be the output of a VCVS or an operational amplifier. This provides a very low output impedance in practice and minimizes most of the loading problems when cascading with subsequent sections.

There are basically three techniques to realize (10-86). The first technique is the direct approach where a general circuit configuration is set a priori and its individual branch characteristics are determined by the prescribed transfer function. The second technique takes into account the fact that there are only seven distinct forms of biquadratic transfer functions. A *specific* circuit (with a circuit configuration and all its element types specified) is set up for each distinct form of biquadratic transfer function of (10-86). Element values are then determined by the coefficients of the given transfer function. The third technique uses a canonical circuit (again with a circuit configuration and all its element types fixed but not the element values). Different biquadratic transfer functions are realized by choosing different sets of element values. In this section, we concentrate on the second and third techniques.

Before we proceed to discuss various synthesis methods for the realizations of the voltage-ratio biquadratic transfer functions of (10-86), we note that the pole frequency ω_0 and the pole-pair Q are given by

$$\omega_0 = \sqrt{b_0} \quad \text{and} \quad Q = \frac{\sqrt{b_0}}{b_1} \tag{10-87}$$

10-2-1. Single Amplifier Biquad[18]

In this section, we present two methods of realizing biquadratic transfer functions with passive RC elements and a *single* active device. The first one consists of a family of circuits, each dealing with a particular biquadratic transfer function. The second method involves a versatile circuit that can be used to realize a wide variety of biquadratic transfer functions.

---

[17]For the cascade approach to function perfectly, it is required that each filter section have an infinite input impedance and/or a zero output impedance.

[18]A biquad is a circuit implementing a biquadratic transfer function of (10-86).

10-2-1-1. Single Amplifier Biquad—Custom Technique. In 1955, Sallen and Key published a table of active RC circuits[19] (with a VCVS being the single active element in each circuit) to realize voltage-ratio transfer functions of the type in (10-86) with the exception of a notch filter characterized by

$$H(s) = \frac{a_2 s^2 + a_0}{s^2 + b_1 s + b_0} \tag{10-88}$$

In 1966, Kerwin and Huelsman devised a circuit realization of (10-88) with a VCVS as the only active element in the circuit.[20] We now introduce their results in a tabular form, as shown in Table 10-1.

In practice, the circuit realizations in Table 10-1 are not final products. For practical use, we need to perform frequency and impedance scalings on these circuits. Because the gain or the coefficient of a VCVS is unitless, both the frequency and the impedance scalings will not affect the coefficient of a VCVS in any manner. Hence, frequency scaling will affect only capacitors, and impedance scaling will affect both resistor and capacitor values.

Example 10-12   Realize

$$H(s) = \frac{2 \times 10^8}{s^2 + (2 \times 10^3)s + 10^8} \tag{10-89}$$

via Table 10-1.

Solution: The normalized version of (10-89) is given by

$$H_N(s) = \frac{2}{s^2 + 0.2s + 1} \tag{10-90}$$

where the frequency scaling factor of 10^4 has been used. From case A1 of Table 10-1, the design equations are

$$C_1 C_2 R_1 R_2 = 1$$
$$C_1 R_1 + C_2 R_2 + C_2 R_1 - k C_1 R_1 = 0.2 \tag{10-91}$$
$$k = 2$$

With $k = 2$, (10-91) can be rewritten as

$$C_1 C_2 R_1 R_2 = 1$$
$$C_2 R_2 + C_2 R_1 - C_1 R_1 = 0.2 \tag{10-92}$$

Because there are two equations and four unknowns, there are two degrees of freedom. Let us choose

$$C_1 = C_2 = 1 \text{ F.} \tag{10-93a}$$

Then (10-92) yields

$$R_1 = 5 \, \Omega \quad \text{and} \quad R_2 = 0.2 \, \Omega \tag{10-93b}$$

A circuit realization of $H_N(s)$ of (10-90) via (10-93) is shown in Fig. 10-22(a). To realize $H(s)$ of (10-89), we perform a frequency scaling on Fig. 10-22(a) with a

---

[19]See Reference [20].

[20]See Reference [21].

TABLE 10-1 Realization of Active Filters with a Single VCVS

Case	Transfer Function $H(s) \triangleq V_o/V_i$	Circuit Realization	Design Equations
A1	$\dfrac{G}{s^2 + bs + 1}$ (Low-pass)		$C_1 C_2 R_1 R_2 = 1$ $C_1 R_1 + C_2 R_2 + R_1 C_2$ $- kC_1 R_1 = b$ . . . . $G = k$
A2 (a)	$\dfrac{Gs}{s^2 + bs + 1}$		$C_1 C_2 R_1 R_2 (1 + k) = 1$ $C_1 R_1 + C_2 R_2 + C_2 R_1 = b$ . . . . $G = -kR_2 C_2$
(b)	(Bandpass)		$\dfrac{C_1 C_2 R_1 R_2}{1 + k} = 1$ $\dfrac{C_1 R_1 + C_2 R_2 + C_2 R_1}{1 + k} = b$ . . . . $G = -\dfrac{k}{R_2 C_2}$
A3 (High-pass)	$\dfrac{Gs^2}{s^2 + bs + 1}$		$C_1 C_2 R_1 R_2 = 1$ $C_1 R_1 + C_2 R_2 + C_2 R_1$ $- kC_2 R_2 = b$ . . . . $G = k$

378

TABLE 10-1 (Continued)

A4 (a)	$\dfrac{G(s+a)}{s^2+bs+1}$		$R_1C_1R_2C_2 = 1$ $R_1C_1 + R_1C_2 = 1/a$ $R_1C_1 + R_2C_2 + R_1C_2$ $\quad - kR_2C_2 = b$ . . . . $G = k(R_1C_1 + R_1C_2)$
(b)			$R_1C_1R_2C_2 = 1$ $R_2C_2 = 1/a$ $R_1C_1 + R_2C_2$ $\quad + R_1C_2(1-k) = b$ . . . . $G = kR_2C_2$
A5 (a)	$\dfrac{Gs(s+a)}{s^2+bs+1}$		$R_1C_1R_2C_2 = 1$ $R_2C_2 + R_1C_2 = 1/a$ $R_1C_1 + R_2C_2 + R_1C_2$ $\quad - kR_1C_1 = b$ . . . . $G = k$
(b)			$R_1C_1R_2C_2 = 1$ $R_1C_1 = a$ $R_1C_1 + R_2C_2 + R_1C_2$ $\quad - kR_2C_2 = b$ . . . . $G = k$
A6 (Band-reject)	$\dfrac{G(s^2+1)}{s^2+bs+1}$		$RC = 1$ $4(1-k) = b$ . . . . $G = k$

TABLE 10-1 (Continued)

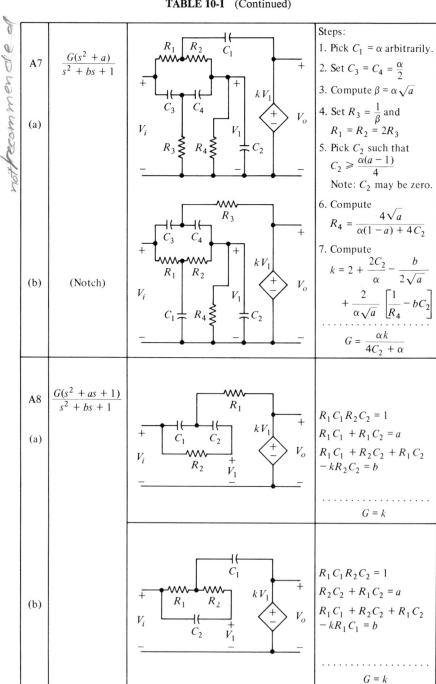

			Steps:
A7 (a)	$\dfrac{G(s^2 + a)}{s^2 + bs + 1}$		1. Pick $C_1 = \alpha$ arbitrarily. 2. Set $C_3 = C_4 = \dfrac{\alpha}{2}$ 3. Compute $\beta = \alpha\sqrt{a}$ 4. Set $R_3 = \dfrac{1}{\beta}$ and $R_1 = R_2 = 2R_3$ 5. Pick C_2 such that $C_2 \geqslant \dfrac{\alpha(a-1)}{4}$ Note: C_2 may be zero.
(b)	(Notch)		6. Compute $R_4 = \dfrac{4\sqrt{a}}{\alpha(1-a) + 4C_2}$ 7. Compute $k = 2 + \dfrac{2C_2}{\alpha} - \dfrac{b}{2\sqrt{a}}$ $+ \dfrac{2}{\alpha\sqrt{a}}\left[\dfrac{1}{R_4} - bC_2\right]$ .... $G = \dfrac{\alpha k}{4C_2 + \alpha}$
A8 (a)	$\dfrac{G(s^2 + as + 1)}{s^2 + bs + 1}$		$R_1 C_1 R_2 C_2 = 1$ $R_1 C_1 + R_1 C_2 = a$ $R_1 C_1 + R_2 C_2 + R_1 C_2$ $- kR_2 C_2 = b$ .... $G = k$
(b)			$R_1 C_1 R_2 C_2 = 1$ $R_2 C_2 + R_1 C_2 = a$ $R_1 C_1 + R_2 C_2 + R_1 C_2$ $- kR_1 C_1 = b$ .... $G = k$

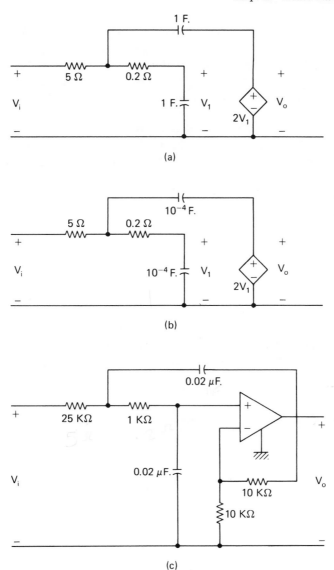

Fig. 10-22 (a) A circuit realization of (10-90). (b) and (c) Circuit realizations of (10-89).

scale factor of 10^4. The result is shown in Fig. 10-22(b). An impedance scaled version of Fig. 10-22(b) with a scale factor of 5 K is shown in Fig. 10-22(c), where the VCVS is replaced by its operational-amplifier realization. ∎

We now make some observations and comments regarding Table 10-1. Observe that the output of every circuit in Table 10-1 is across a VCVS—

across the output of an operational amplifier.[21] Because an operational amplifier has an ideal characteristic of zero output impedance (in practice, very low output impedance in normal linear mode operation), each of these circuits can be cascaded with other circuits (including some to be discussed later) without the necessity of an isolation amplifier.

Applications of all cases are simple and straightforward. Except for case A7, the process of circuit realization involves only finding a set of resistance and capacitance values to satisfy the design equations. For case A7, there is a design procedure to follow. We will illustrate this procedure in Example 10-13.

Example 10-13 Realize the transfer function

$$H(s) = \frac{G(s^2 + 10^8)}{s^2 + 2 \times 10^3 s + 4 \times 10^8} \qquad (10\text{-}94)$$

via Table 10-1.

Solution: Before we apply Table 10-1 to (10-94), let us frequency scale $H(s)$ downward by a factor of 2×10^4. This yields a "normalized" transfer function

$$H_N(s) = \frac{G(s^2 + 0.25)}{s^2 + 0.1s + 1} \qquad (10\text{-}95)$$

Note that (10-95) is obtained from (10-94) by replacing each s with $(2 \times 10^4)s$. We will now apply the realization procedure to (10-95) as follows:

STEP 0 $a = 0.25$, $\sqrt{a} = 0.5$, and $b = 0.1$.

STEP 1 Pick $C_1 = 2$ F. Hence $\alpha = 2$.

STEP 2 $C_3 = C_4 = 1$ F.

STEP 3 $\beta = \alpha\sqrt{a} = 1$.

STEP 4 $R_3 = 1 \, \Omega$, $R_1 = R_2 = 2 \, \Omega$.

STEP 5 Since $a - 1 = -0.75 \leq 0$, we may choose $C_2 = 0$.

STEP 6 With $C_2 = 0$, we obtain

$$R_4 = \frac{4\sqrt{a}}{\alpha(1 - a)} = \frac{4}{3}$$

STEP 7 The gain of the VCVS is given by

$$k = 2 - \frac{b}{2\sqrt{a}} + \frac{2}{\alpha\sqrt{a}\,R_4} = 3.4$$

---

[21]Recall that in Chapter 2, a VCVS with either a positive or a negative coefficient can be realized by an interconnection of linear resistors and an operational amplifier, as shown in Fig. 2-5.

STEP 8 $G = k = 3.4$.

Therefore, a set of component values to realize (10-95) is given by

$$C_1 = 2 \text{ F.}, \quad C_2 = 0, \quad C_3 = C_4 = 1 \text{ F.},$$
$$R_1 = R_2 = 2 \,\Omega, \quad R_3 = 1 \,\Omega, \quad R_4 = \tfrac{4}{3}\,\Omega,$$

and $k = 3.4$ (10-96a)

To realize (10-94), we frequency scale the capacitors in (10-96a) upward by 2×10^4 as

$$C_1 = 10^{-4} \text{ F.}, \quad C_2 = 0, \quad C_3 = C_4 = 0.5 \times 10^{-4} \text{ F.} \quad \text{(10-96b)}$$

A circuit realization of (10-94) via (10-96) is shown in Fig. 10-23, where all resistors and capacitors are impedance scaled up by 10 K.

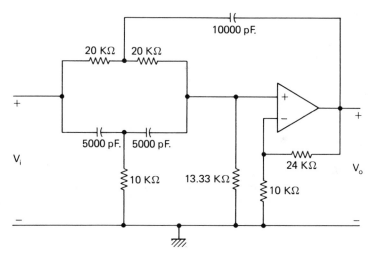

Fig. 10-23 A circuit realization of (10-94).

It can be shown that the design procedure of A7 yields the transfer function of either one of its two associated circuit configurations as

$$H(s) = \frac{G(s^2 + a)}{s^2 + b_1 s + b_0} \tag{10-97a}$$

where

$$G = \frac{\alpha}{4C_2 + \alpha} \tag{10-97b}$$

$$a = \frac{\beta^2}{\alpha^2} \tag{10-97c}$$

$$b_1 = \frac{4}{4\alpha C_2 + \alpha^2}\left[\alpha\beta\left(1 - \frac{k}{2}\right) + \frac{\alpha}{R_4} + C_2\beta\right] \tag{10-97d}$$

$$b_0 = \frac{1}{4\alpha C_2 + \alpha^2}\left[\beta^2 + \frac{4\beta}{R_4}\right] \tag{10-97e}$$

with $\alpha = 2$, $\beta = 1$ and (10-96a), (10-97) yields

$$G = 1$$

$$a = \frac{1}{4} = 0.25$$

$$b_1 = \frac{4}{0 + 4}[2(1 - 1.7) + 1.5] = 0.1$$

$$b_0 = \frac{1 + 3}{4} = 1$$

That is, the component values of (10-96a) realize the transfer function $H_N(s)$ of (10-95). Consequently, the circuit in Fig. 10-23 indeed realizes the desired transfer function of (10-94). ∎

With the exception of cases A6 and A7, each circuit contains five variables, R_1, R_2, C_1, C_2 and k. However, there are only three or four design equations constraining these variables. This implies that there are many realizations satisfying the voltage ratio transfer function. As an illustration, let us consider Example 10-14.

Example 10-14 Realize the transfer function

$$H(s) = \frac{2(s^2 + 2s + 1)}{s^2 + s + 1} \tag{10-98}$$

via Table 10-1.

Solution: We can use circuit (a) of case A8, where $a = 2$, $b = 1$, and $G = 2$. In this case, there are four constraint or design equations, as listed in (10-99):

$$R_1 C_1 R_2 C_2 = 1 \tag{10-99a}$$

$$R_2 C_2 + R_1 C_2 = a = 2 \tag{10-99b}$$

$$R_1 C_1 + R_2 C_2 + R_1 C_2 - k R_1 C_1 = b = 1 \tag{10-99c}$$

$$G = k = 2 \tag{10-99d}$$

Because there are five variables and four constraints, we have a degree of freedom. We can use this degree of freedom to set the value for one of the five variables, or we can add an extra equation to the design constraints of (10-99). Suppose that we choose the latter option and add the equation

$$R_1 C_1 = 1 \tag{10-99e}$$

to form a complete set of design equations. Notice that (10-99) is a set of five *nonlinear* equations in five variables and that, as such, there may be one and only one solution, no solution, or many solutions. In this case, there are many solutions. For example:

$$R_1 = R_2 = 1 \,\Omega, \quad C_1 = C_2 = 1 \text{ F.}, \quad \text{and} \quad k = 2 \tag{10-100}$$

and

$$R_1 = R_2 = (1/2)\,\Omega, \quad C_1 = C_2 = 2 \text{ F.}, \quad \text{and} \quad k = 2 \tag{10-101}$$

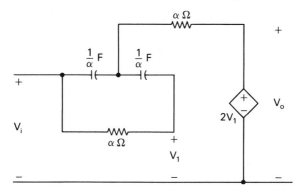

Fig. 10-24   A circuit realization of (10-98).

are solutions to the design equations of (10-99). In fact, for any positive value of α,

$$R_1 = R_2 = \alpha, \quad C_1 = C_2 = 1/\alpha, \quad \text{and} \quad k = 2 \qquad (10\text{-}102)$$

is a solution to the design equations.[22] A circuit realization of (10-98) is shown in Fig. 10-24, where α is any finite positive real number.   ∎

All circuits appearing in Table 10-1 have a common drawback. For high Q or narrow band circuits, either the gain k of the VCVS is very large (proportional to Q^2) or else the sensitivity of Q with respect to k, S_k^Q is large (at least proportional to Q). Neither case is desirable. The undesirableness of the latter case is obvious. In the former case when k is large, the practical frequency region where the circuit will function properly is small.[23] For example, when $Q = 16$, the gain of a VCVS is in the order of 250. In this case, the useful frequency range where the VCVS of Fig. 2-5 will function properly is when the open loop gain is 5000 or higher. According to the typical data sheet of an operational amplifier shown in Fig. 10-25, the useful frequency bandwidth is about 200 Hz.[24]

To illustrate the common drawback as stated in the preceding paragraph, let us consider case A1 and part (a) of case A2:

For case A1, the circuit's transfer function is given by

$$H(s) = \frac{k}{s^2 C_1 C_2 R_1 R_2 + s(C_1 R_1 + C_2 R_2 + R_1 C_2 - k C_1 R_1) + 1} \quad (10\text{-}103)$$

---

[22]Note that α is actually an impedance scaling factor.

[23]If a VCVS with a gain of k is realized by using an operational amplifier, then the frequency range where the VCVS will function properly is the frequency bandwidth where the open loop gain of the operational amplifier is roughly 20 times k or higher. In Sec. 10-3, we consider the concept of useful frequency bandwidth in more detail.

[24]For wideband operational amplifiers, the useful frequency bandwidth may be extended by a factor of 10 or more.

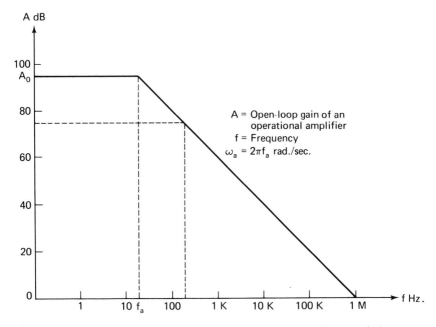

A = Open-loop gain of an
operational amplifier
f = Frequency
$\omega_a = 2\pi f_a$ rad./sec.

Fig. 10-25   A typical operation amplifier frequency characteristic.

Suppose that the desired low-pass filter has a transfer function

$$H(s) \triangleq \frac{V_o}{V_i} = \frac{G}{s^2 + (1/100)s + 1} \qquad (10\text{-}104)$$

In this case, we have $b = 0.01$ and $Q = 100$. The design equations are

$$C_1 C_2 R_1 R_2 = 1 \qquad (10\text{-}105\text{a})$$

$$b = C_1 R_1 + C_2 R_2 + R_1 C_2 - k C_1 R_1 = \frac{1}{Q} = \frac{1}{100} \qquad (10\text{-}105\text{b})$$

Let us assume that

$$C_1 = C_2 \triangleq C$$

$$R_1 = R_2 \triangleq R \qquad (10\text{-}106)$$

Then (10-105) yields

$$CR = 1 \qquad (10\text{-}107\text{a})$$

and

$$k = 3 - \frac{1}{Q} = \frac{299}{100} \simeq 3 \qquad (10\text{-}107\text{b})$$

Here the gain of the VCVS is very reasonable. However, from (10-103), we obtain

$$Q = \frac{\sqrt{C_1 C_2 R_1 R_2}}{C_1 R_1 + C_2 R_2 + R_1 C_2 - k C_1 R_1} = \frac{1}{3 - k} \qquad (10\text{-}108\text{a})$$

and hence,

$$S_k^Q = \frac{k}{3-k} = kQ \simeq 300 \qquad (10\text{-}108\text{b})$$

That is, if k varies by 1 %, then Q changes by 300 %. Clearly, this is an undesirable circuit when Q is high.

For circuit (a) of case A2, the circuit's transfer function is given by

$$\frac{V_o}{V_i} = \frac{-sC_2R_2k}{s^2C_1C_2R_1R_2(1+k) + s(C_1R_1 + C_2R_2 + C_2R_1) + 1} \qquad (10\text{-}109)$$

Suppose that the desired bandpass filter is characterized by

$$H(s) = \frac{Gs}{s^2 + (1/100)s + 1} \qquad (10\text{-}110)$$

Here, again, we have $Q = 100$ and $b = 0.01$. The design equations are

$$C_1C_2R_1R_2(1+k) = 1$$
$$b = C_1R_1 + C_2R_2 + C_2R_1 = \frac{1}{Q} = 0.01 \qquad (10\text{-}111)$$

By letting $C \triangleq C_1 = C_2$ and $R \triangleq R_1 = R_2$, we find that

$$3CR = \frac{1}{Q} \qquad (10\text{-}112\text{a})$$

and

$$k = \frac{1}{(CR)^2} - 1 = 9Q^2 - 1 \simeq 90000 \qquad (10\text{-}112\text{b})$$

In practical terms, (10-112b) says that the useful frequency range, where the circuit model behaves closely with the actual real-life circuit, is about 10 Hz, which is not much for a bandpass filter. In this case, the Q sensitivity with respect to k is very small. It can be shown that

$$S_k^Q = -\frac{1}{2}\left(\frac{k}{1+k}\right) \simeq -\frac{1}{2} \qquad (10\text{-}113)$$

10-2-1-2. Single Amplifier Biquad—Canonical Circuit Technique. In this subsection, we consider a versatile circuit introduced by Friend. The circuit configuration and its element types are all specified. The circuit produces different forms of biquadratic transfer functions depending on its element values.

Consider the circuit in Fig. 10-26. With $G_x = 1/R_x$ and

$$G_a \triangleq G_c + G_d \qquad (10\text{-}114\text{a})$$
$$G_1 \triangleq G_4 + G_5 \qquad (10\text{-}114\text{b})$$
$$G_3 \triangleq G_6 + G_7 \qquad (10\text{-}114\text{c})$$

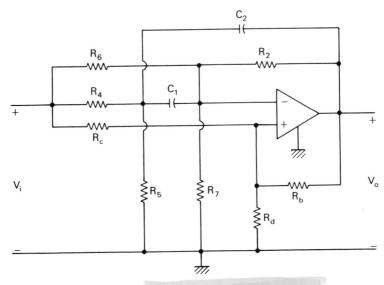

Fig. 10-26 Friend's circuit configuration.

the circuit's transfer function is given by

$$H(s) = \frac{a_2 s^2 + a_1 s + a_0}{s^2 + b_1 s + b_0}$$ (10-115)

where

$$a_2 = \frac{G_c}{G_a}$$ (10-116a)

$$a_1 = \frac{1}{C_1 C_2 G_a}[C_1 G_c(G_1 + G_2 + G_3) + C_2 G_c(G_2 + G_3)$$
$$- C_1 G_4(G_a + G_b) - (C_1 + C_2)G_6(G_a + G_b)]$$ (10-116b)

$$a_0 = \frac{1}{C_1 C_2 G_a}[G_1 G_c(G_2 + G_3) - G_1 G_6(G_a + G_b)]$$ (10-116c)

$$b_1 = \frac{1}{C_1 C_2 G_a}[(C_1 + C_2)(G_a G_2 - G_b G_3) - C_1 G_1 G_b]$$ (10-116d)

$$b_0 = \frac{1}{C_1 C_2 G_a}[G_1(G_a G_2 - G_b G_3)]$$ (10-116e)

Based on (10-114) through (10-116), let us make some observations about the circuit in Fig. 10-26. First, the circuit in Fig. 10-26 cannot realize a low-pass biquadratic transfer function. The low-pass function requires $a_2 = a_1 = 0$. From (10-116a), $a_2 = 0$ implies that $G_c = 0$. With $G_c = 0$ and $a_1 = 0$, (10-116b) requires that either $G_4 = G_6 = 0$ or $G_a + G_b = 0$. In either case,

(10-116c) implies that $a_0 = 0$. Hence, Fig. 10-26 cannot realize a low-pass biquadratic transfer function. It turns out that this is the only form of biquadratic transfer function that Fig. 10-26 cannot realize.

Another observation can be drawn from (10-114a) and (10-116a). Together, these two equations imply that the circuit in Fig. 10-26 can realize only those biquadratic transfer functions where

$$0 \leq a_2 \leq 1 \tag{10-117}$$

However, (10-117) is not a serious constraint, because a transfer function is usually realized only up to a constant multiplier. If the prescribed transfer function $H_D(s)$ has an $a_2 > 1$, we can realize $\beta H_D(s)$ where β is a constant such that $\beta a_2 < 1$. Besides, there are ways to increase the multiplier β. A case in point is shown later in Example 10-16.

Given a biquadratic transfer function of (10-115), (10-114) and (10-116) actually form a set of design equations. The problem of realization is now translated into finding a set of element values such that (10-114) and (10-116) are satisfied. Because there are eight equations and 13 unknowns, we can solve eight element values in terms of the remaining five. After some algebraic manipulations, we obtain

$$G_1 = \frac{C_2 G_a}{2G_b}\left[-b_1 + \sqrt{b_1^2 + 4b_0\left(1 + \frac{C_1}{C_2}\right)\frac{G_b}{G_a}}\right] \tag{10-118a}$$

$$G_4 = \frac{G_1 G_a}{G_a + G_b}\left[a_2 + a_0\left(1 + \frac{C_1}{C_2}\right)\frac{C_2^2}{G_1^2} - \frac{a_1 C_2}{G_1}\right] \tag{10-118b}$$

$$G_3 = \frac{C_1 C_2 G_a(a_0 - a_2 b_0)}{G_1(G_a + G_b)(a_2 - \alpha)} \tag{10-118c}$$

$$G_2 = \frac{C_1 C_2 b_0}{G_1} + \frac{G_b G_3}{G_a} \tag{10-118d}$$

$$G_5 = G_1 - G_4 \tag{10-118e}$$

$$G_6 = \alpha G_3 \tag{10-118f}$$

$$G_7 = G_3 - G_6 \tag{10-118g}$$

$$G_c = a_2 G_a \tag{10-118h}$$

$$G_d = G_a - G_c \tag{10-118i}$$

where the input quantities are the coefficients of the prescribed transfer function $(a_2, a_1, a_0, b_1, b_0)$ and five element parameters $(C_1, C_2, G_a, G_b, \alpha)$. In many cases, the element parameters have to be chosen with care. For example, the parameter

$$\alpha \triangleq \frac{G_6}{G_6 + G_7} \tag{10-119a}$$

is chosen to ensure that $G_3 > 0$. Note that (10-119a) bounds α to

$$0 \leq \alpha \leq 1 \tag{10-119b}$$

In most cases of interest, α is set to be 0 if $(a_0 - a_2 b_0) \geq 0$ and to be 1 if $(a_0 - a_2 b_0) < 0$. Recall from (10-117) that $a_2 < 1$.

In order for $G_5 \geq 0$, we have to make sure that $G_4 \leq G_1$. If a_2 is very close to unity, (10-118b) very often yields a G_4 greater than G_1, particularly when $a_1 < 0$. One way to remedy this problem is to realize a transfer function

$$\beta H(s) = \frac{\hat{a}_2 s^2 + \hat{a}_1 s + \hat{a}_0}{s^2 + b_1 s + b_0} \tag{10-120a}$$

where

$$\hat{a}_2 = \beta a_2, \quad \hat{a}_1 = \beta a_1, \quad \hat{a}_0 = \beta a_0, \quad \text{and} \quad \beta < 1 \tag{10-120b}$$

One final note on Fig. 10-26 is that in the bandpass case where $a_2 = a_0 = 0$, (10-118b) requires that $a_1 < 0$ and (10-118c) yield $G_3 = 0$. Hence, $G_6 = G_7 = 0$.

Example 10-15   Realize

$$H(s) = \frac{-s}{s^2 + 2s + 3} \tag{10-121}$$

by the circuit in Fig. 10-26.

Solution: With $a_2 = 0$, $a_1 = -1$, $a_0 = 0$, $b_1 = 2$, and $b_0 = 3$, (10-118) reduces to:

$$G_1 = \frac{C_2 G_a}{2 G_b}\left[-2 + \sqrt{4 + 12\left(1 + \frac{C_1}{C_2}\right)\frac{G_b}{G_a}}\right]$$

$$G_4 = \frac{C_2 G_a}{G_a + G_b}$$

$$G_3 = 0$$

$$G_2 = \frac{3 C_1 C_2}{G_1} \tag{10-122}$$

$$G_5 = G_1 - G_4$$

$$G_6 = G_7 = 0$$

$$G_c = 0$$

$$G_d = G_a$$

From (10-122), we can be sure that all resistors are passive if $G_a \geq G_b$. Let us choose

$$C_1 = C_2 = 1 \text{ F.}$$
$$G_a = G_b = 1 \text{ Mho} \tag{10-123a}$$

Then (10-122) yields

$$G_1 = 1.65 = \frac{1}{0.61}$$

$$G_4 = 0.5 = \frac{1}{2}$$

$$G_3 = G_6 = G_7 = 0$$

$$G_2 = 1.82 = \frac{1}{0.55} \qquad \text{(10-123b)}$$

$$G_5 = 1.15 = \frac{1}{0.87}$$

$$G_c = 0$$

$$G_d = 1$$

where all the conductances are in Mhos. A circuit realization of the bandpass function of (10-121) via (10-123) is shown in Fig. 10-27. ∎

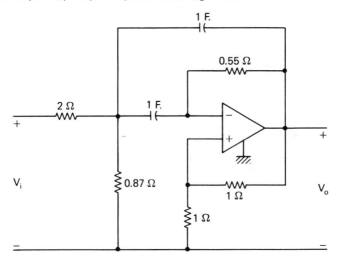

Fig. 10-27   A circuit realization of the bandpass transfer function of (10-121).

Example 10-16   Realize an all-pass transfer function

$$H(s) = \frac{s^2 - s + 1}{s^2 + s + 1} \qquad \text{(10-124)}$$

by Friend's configuration.

Solution: In practice, the circuit in Fig. 10-26 does not work for cases when $a_2 = 1$. We will see later in this case with $a_2 = 1$ that (10-118b) gives a G_4 greater than G_1. Instead of realizing $H(s)$ of (10-124), let us work with

$$H_\beta(s) \triangleq \beta H(s) = \frac{\beta s^2 - \beta s + \beta}{s^2 + s + 1} \qquad \text{(10-125)}$$

With $a_2 = a_0 = \beta$, $a_1 = -\beta$, and $b_1 = b_0 = 1$, (10-118) reduces to

$$G_1 = \frac{C_2 G_a}{2 G_b}\left[-1 + \sqrt{1 + 4\left(1 + \frac{C_1}{C_2}\right)\frac{G_b}{G_a}}\right] \tag{10-126a}$$

$$G_4 = \frac{G_1 G_a}{G_a + G_b}\left[\beta + \beta\left(1 + \frac{C_1}{C_2}\right)\frac{C_2^2}{G_1^2} + \frac{\beta C_2}{G_1}\right] \tag{10-126b}$$

$$G_3 = G_6 = G_7 = 0 \tag{10-126c}$$

$$G_2 = \frac{C_1 C_2}{G_1} \tag{10-126d}$$

$$G_5 = G_1 - G_4 \tag{10-126e}$$

$$G_c = \beta G_a \tag{10-126f}$$

$$G_d = (1 - \beta)G_a \tag{10-126g}$$

Observe that if $a_2 = \beta = 1$, (10-126b) implies that $G_4 > G_1$. Hence, we have to lower the value of the constant multiplier β until (10-126b) yields a G_4 smaller than G_1. It can be shown that with $G_b \ll G_a$, the largest allowable β is given by

$$\beta_{\max} = \frac{1}{1 + (1/Q^2)} \tag{10-127a}$$

where Q is the pole-pair of the given transfer function and in this case

$$Q = \frac{1}{2}\sqrt{\frac{G_1}{G_2}} \tag{10-127b}$$

Because the Q value of (10-124) is 1, we have $\beta_{\max} = 0.5$. Let us set $\beta = 0.5$. That is, we are actually realizing

$$\hat{H}(s) \triangleq 0.5H(s) = \frac{0.5s^2 - 0.5s + 0.5}{s^2 + s + 1} \tag{10-128}$$

With $\beta = 0.5$,

$$G_b = 10^{-6}$$
$$G_a = 1 \tag{10-129a}$$
$$C_1 = C_2 = 1 \text{ F.}$$

Equation (10-126) yields

$$G_1 = 2 = \frac{1}{0.5}$$

$$G_4 = 2 = \frac{1}{0.5}$$

$$G_3 = G_6 = G_7 = 0$$

$$G_2 = \frac{1}{2} \tag{10-129b}$$

$$G_5 = 0$$

$$G_c = 0.5 = \frac{1}{2}$$

$$G_d = 0.5 = \frac{1}{2}$$

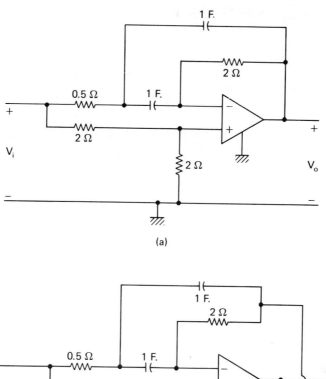

(a)

(b)

Fig. 10-28 A circuit realization of the all-pass transfer function of (a)
(10-125), and (b) (10-124), where $\beta = 0.5$.

where all conductances are in Mhos. A circuit realization of the all-pass transfer
function of (10-128) via (10-129) is shown in Fig. 10-28(a), where R_B is approximated by an open circuit. If the exact gain level of (10-124) is required, then we
can amplify that output voltage V_0 either by passing it through a VCVS amplifier
or by using the gain enhancement technique shown by the circuit in Fig. 10-28(b).

10-2-2. Multiple Amplifier Biquad

In this section, we present two multiple amplifier biquads. The basic developments of these two circuits are quite different. However, their versatilities are about the same. By taking output voltages across different nodes, these biquads can provide various biquadratic transfer functions within one circuit.

10-2-2-1. Multiple Amplifier Biquad—State-Variable Technique. Consider the circuit shown in Fig. 10-29(a), where all voltages are node-to-ground voltages. The circuit is basically an interconnection of three secondary building blocks—one summer and two integrator circuits. From left to right, the first operational amplifier is used in a summer circuit described by

$$V_1 = \frac{R_2(R + R_3)V_i + R_1(R + R_3)V_2 - R(R_1 + R_2)V_3}{R_3(R_1 + R_2)} \quad (10\text{-}130)$$

The second and third operational amplifiers are used as integrators, where

$$V_2 = -\frac{V_1}{sC_1R_8} \quad (10\text{-}131)$$

$$V_3 = -\frac{V_2}{sC_2R_9} \quad (10\text{-}132)$$

From (10-130) through (10-132) we obtain

$$\frac{V_3}{V_i} = \frac{R_2(R + R_3)}{R_3(R_1 + R_2)} \frac{1}{C_1C_2R_8R_9s^2 + \frac{R_1(R + R_3)}{(R_1 + R_2)R_3}R_9C_2s + \frac{R}{R_3}} \quad (10\text{-}133a)$$

$$\frac{V_2}{V_i} = \frac{R_2(R + R_3)}{R_3(R_1 + R_2)} \frac{-sC_2R_9}{C_1C_2R_8R_9s^2 + \frac{R_1(R + R_3)}{(R_1 + R_2)R_3}R_9C_2s + \frac{R}{R_3}} \quad (10\text{-}133b)$$

$$\frac{V_1}{V_i} = \frac{R_2(R + R_3)}{R_3(R_1 + R_2)} \frac{s^2C_1C_2R_8R_9}{C_1C_2R_8R_9s^2 + \frac{R_1(R + R_3)}{(R_1 + R_2)R_3}R_9C_2s + \frac{R}{R_3}} \quad (10\text{-}133c)$$

That is, if the output voltage is taken from the output end of the first operational amplifier, then the circuit behaves as a high-pass filter; if the output is from the second operational amplifier, we have a bandpass filter; and finally, if the output is from the third operational amplifier, then the circuit is a low-pass filter. To realize a general transfer function of the type,

$$H(s) = k\frac{s^2 + a_1s + a_0}{s^2 + b_1s + b_0} \quad (10\text{-}134)$$

we need to add an additional summer circuit to Fig. 10-29(a), as shown in Fig. 10-29(b). The output of this additional summer is a weighted sum of V_1,

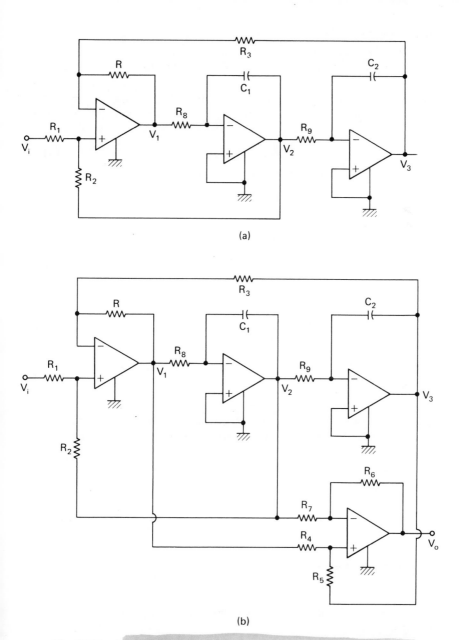

(a)

(b)

Fig. 10-29 (a) A basic multiple-amplifier biquad. (b) A complete multiple-amplifier biquad.

V_2, and V_3 and is given by

$$\frac{V_o}{V_i} = \left[\frac{R_5(R_6 + R_7)}{(R_4 + R_5)R_7}\right]\frac{V_1}{V_i} - \frac{R_6}{R_7}\frac{V_2}{V_i} + \left[\frac{R_4(R_6 + R_7)}{(R_4 + R_5)R_7}\right]\frac{V_3}{V_i}$$

$$= \left[\frac{R_2R_5(R + R_3)(R_6 + R_7)}{R_3R_7(R_1 + R_2)(R_4 + R_5)}\right]\frac{C_1C_2R_8R_9s^2 + \dfrac{(R_4 + R_5)R_6R_9C_2}{(R_6 + R_7)R_5}s + \dfrac{R_4}{R_5}}{C_1C_2R_8R_9s^2 + \dfrac{R_1(R + R_3)}{R_3(R_1 + R_2)}R_9C_2s + \dfrac{R}{R_3}}$$

$$(10\text{-}135)$$

By comparing (10-134) and (10-135), we form a set of design equations as follows:

$$\frac{R_6(R_4 + R_5)}{C_1R_8R_5(R_6 + R_7)} = a_1 \qquad (10\text{-}136a)$$

$$\frac{R_4}{C_1R_8C_2R_9R_5} = a_0 \qquad (10\text{-}136b)$$

$$\frac{R_1(R + R_3)}{C_1R_8R_3(R_1 + R_2)} = b_1 \qquad (10\text{-}136c)$$

$$\frac{R}{C_1R_8C_2R_9R_3} = b_0 \qquad (10\text{-}136d)$$

and

$$k = \frac{R_2R_5(R + R_3)(R_6 + R_7)}{R_3R_7(R_1 + R_2)(R_4 + R_5)} \qquad (10\text{-}136e)$$

Because there are only five constraints among the 12 variables, there are seven degrees of freedom. In practical situations, these degrees of freedom are used to set additional design equations corresponding to desirable properties such as minimum sensitivities, minimum spread of resistor and capacitor values, minimum sums of all resistances and capacitances used in the circuit, judicious choices of capacitor values to meet the availability requirements of capacitors, input and output impedance matching, and temperature tracking. In general, even after many additional constraints (less than seven), there are still many possible circuit realizations.

Example 10-17 Realize

$$H(s) \triangleq \frac{V_o}{V_i} = k\frac{s^2 + 2s + 3}{s^2 + 3s + 5} \qquad (10\text{-}137)$$

by the biquad circuit of Fig. 10-29, where k is arbitrary.

Solution: The design equations are

$$\frac{R_6(R_4 + R_5)}{C_1R_8R_5(R_6 + R_7)} = 2 \qquad (10\text{-}138a)$$

$$\frac{R_4}{C_1R_8C_2R_9R_5} = 3 \qquad (10\text{-}138b)$$

$$\frac{R_1(R + R_3)}{C_1 R_8 R_3(R_1 + R_2)} = 3 \qquad (10\text{-}138\text{c})$$

$$\frac{R}{C_1 R_8 C_2 R_9 R_3} = 5 \qquad (10\text{-}138\text{d})$$

There are four equations and 12 unknowns. Obviously, there are many solutions. A set of solutions is given by

$C_1 = C_2 = 1$ F.

$R_1 = R_2 = R_3 = R_5 = R_6 = R_7 = R_8 = R_9 = 1\,\Omega \qquad (10\text{-}139)$

$R_4 = 3\,\Omega$ and $R = 5\,\Omega$

With these circuit values, (10-136e) gives

$$k = \frac{3}{2} \qquad (10\text{-}140)$$

Using the element values of (10-139), a circuit realization of (10-137) is shown in Fig. 10-30. ∎

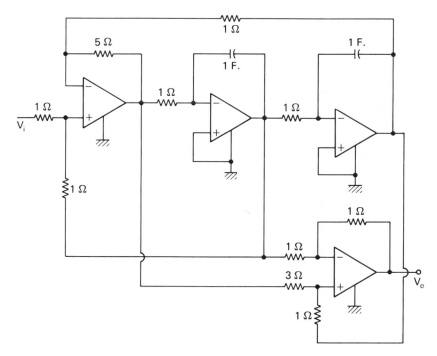

Fig. 10-30   A circuit realization of (10-137).

Example 10-18   Realize the following two transfer functions simultaneously in one circuit

$$H_1(s) = \frac{6}{s^2 + 3s + 5} \qquad (10\text{-}141\text{a})$$

$$H_2(s) = -\frac{3s}{s^2 + 3s + 5} \qquad (10\text{-}141\text{b})$$

Solution: From (10-133a) and (10-133b), we obtain the following design equations:

$$\frac{R_2(R + R_3)}{R_3(R_1 + R_2)(C_1 C_2 R_8 R_9)} = 6 \qquad (10\text{-}142\text{a})$$

$$\frac{R_1(R + R_3)}{(R_1 + R_2)R_3 C_1 R_8} = 3 \qquad (10\text{-}142\text{b})$$

$$\frac{R}{R_3 C_1 C_2 R_8 R_9} = 5 \qquad (10\text{-}142\text{c})$$

$$C_2 R_9 = 0.5 \qquad (10\text{-}142\text{d})$$

Dividing (10-142a) by (10-142b) gives

$$\frac{R_2}{R_1 C_2 R_9} = \frac{6}{3}$$

or

$$\frac{R_2}{R_1} = 2C_2 R_9 = 1$$

Hence,

$$R_1 = R_2 \qquad (10\text{-}143)$$

Substituting (10-143) into (10-142b) and (10-142d) into (10-142c), we obtain

$$\frac{R + R_3}{R_3 C_1 R_8} = 6 \qquad (10\text{-}144\text{a})$$

$$\frac{R}{R_3 C_1 R_8} = 5C_2 R_9 = 2.5 \qquad (10\text{-}144\text{b})$$

Combining the two equations in (10-144) yields

$$\frac{1}{C_1 R_8} = 6 - 2.5 = 3.5 \qquad (10\text{-}144\text{c})$$

and

$$\frac{R}{R_3} = 2.5C_1 R_8 = \frac{2.5}{3.5} = 0.71 \qquad (10\text{-}144\text{d})$$

Let

$$C_1 = C_2 = 1 \text{ F.} \qquad (10\text{-}145\text{a})$$

Then (10-142d) and (10-144c) yield

$$R_9 = 0.5 \ \Omega \quad \text{and} \quad R_8 = \frac{1}{3.5} = 0.29 \ \Omega \qquad (10\text{-}145\text{b})$$

Furthermore, if we let

$$R_2 = R_3 = 1 \ \Omega \qquad (10\text{-}145\text{c})$$

then (10-143) and (10-144d) give

$$R_1 = 1 \ \Omega \quad \text{and} \quad R = 0.71 \ \Omega \qquad (10\text{-}145\text{d})$$

Observe that the element values of (10-145) satisfy the constraint equations of (10-142). Figure 10-31 shows a circuit implementing the element values of

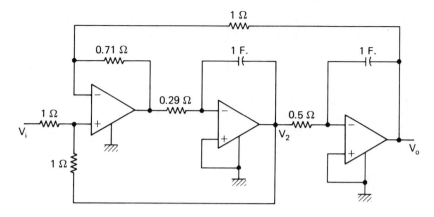

Fig. 10-31   A circuit realizing simultaneously the two transfer functions of (10-141).

(10-145). We obtain $H_1(s)$ if we take V_3 as our output voltage. With V_2 as the output, we obtain $H_2(s)$. ∎

For the multiple amplifier biquad circuit of Fig. 10-29, the pole-frequency ω_0 and the pole-pair Q can be found from (10-133):

$$\omega_0 = \sqrt{\frac{R}{R_3}\frac{1}{C_1 C_2 R_8 R_9}} \tag{10-146}$$

$$Q = \sqrt{\frac{R}{R_3}\frac{1}{C_1 C_2 R_8 R_9}}\frac{C_1 R_3 R_8 (R_1 + R_2)}{R_1 (R + R_3)}$$

$$= \sqrt{\frac{RR_3 C_1 R_8}{C_2 R_9}}\frac{R_1 + R_2}{R_1 (R + R_3)} \tag{10-147}$$

Hence, we have

$$S_{R_3}^{\omega_0} = S_{R_8}^{\omega_0} = S_{R_9}^{\omega_0} = S_{C_1}^{\omega_0} = S_{C_2}^{\omega_0} = -\frac{1}{2},$$

$$S_R^{\omega_0} = \frac{1}{2}, \quad \text{and} \quad S_x^{\omega_0} = 0 \tag{10-148}$$

where x is any variable other than R, R_3, R_8, R_9, C_1, and C_2. Also, we find that

$$S_{C_1}^{Q} = \frac{1}{2}, S_{C_2}^{Q} = -\frac{1}{2}, S_{R_8}^{Q} = \frac{1}{2}, S_{R_9}^{Q} = -\frac{1}{2}$$

$$S_{R_2}^{Q} = \frac{R_2}{R_1 + R_2} < 1, \quad S_{R_1}^{Q} = -S_{R_2}^{Q}$$

$$S_{R_3}^{Q} = \frac{1}{2}\frac{R - R_3}{R + R_3} < \frac{1}{2}, \quad \text{and} \quad S_R^{Q} = -S_{R_3}^{Q} \tag{10-149}$$

In general, multiple amplifier biquad circuits are less sensitive than single amplifier biquads. In addition, postadjustment and tuning[25] can be done easily. For example, for the biquad circuit of Fig. 10-29, with all values fixed except R_2 and R, we can use R to tune the circuit to operate at a new ω_0. Then, with this newly found value of R fixed, R_2 can be adjusted to give another desired value of Q. Commercially, this is quite desirable, because we can put all circuit elements, except R and R_2, in a closed box or on a chip. By connecting to this box externally with different values of R and R_2, as shown in Fig. 10-32, we can realize a second-order filter section with different pole-frequency ω_0 and pole-pair Q.[26] The main drawback of multiple amplifier biquad circuits is that they contain many elements, both passive and active.

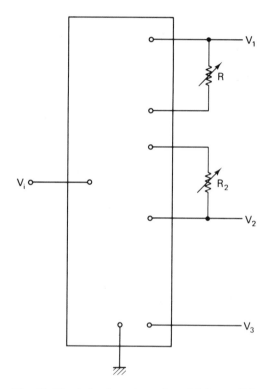

Fig. 10-32 A basic universal multiple-amplifier biquad with two external resistors for ω_0 and Q adjustments.

---

[25]Because of tolerances of circuit components, the hardware circuit does not always produce exactly the ω_0 and Q values as desired. Hence, adjustments on circuit components are necessary to nullify these inaccuracies.

In some situations, postadjustments are also needed to tune the filter to work efficiently for a different ω_0 or Q value other than the one the circuit is originally designed for.

[26]See References [25] and [26].

10-2-2-2. Multiple Amplifier Biquad—Tow's Circuit. Another versatile multiple amplifier biquad introduced by Tow is shown in Fig. 10-33(a). From left to right, this circuit consists of a "leaky" integrator, an integrator, and an inverting VCVS. To analyze the circuit in Fig. 10-33(a), we apply the principle of virtual short circuit and write KCL equations at the input node of each operational amplifier to obtain

$$\frac{V_i}{R_4} + \left(\frac{1}{R_1} + sC_1\right)V_1 + \frac{V_3}{R_3} = 0 \tag{10-150}$$

$$V_2 = -\frac{V_1}{sC_2R_2} \tag{10-151}$$

$$V_3 = -\frac{R_6}{R_5}V_2 \tag{10-152}$$

Together, (10-151) and (10-152) yield

$$V_3 = \frac{R_6}{R_5}\frac{V_1}{sC_2R_2} \tag{10-153}$$

Substituting (10-153) into (10-150), we obtain

$$\frac{V_i}{R_4} = -\left(\frac{1}{R_1} + sC_1 + \frac{R_6}{R_3R_5sC_2R_2}\right)V_1 \tag{10-154}$$

After some algebraic manipulations, we arrive at the following transfer functions:

$$\frac{V_1}{V_i} = -\frac{1}{R_4C_1}\frac{s}{s^2 + \left(\frac{1}{R_1C_1}\right)s + \left(\frac{1}{R_2R_3C_1C_2}\right)\frac{R_6}{R_5}} \tag{10-155a}$$

$$\frac{V_2}{V_i} = \frac{1}{R_2R_4C_1C_2}\frac{1}{s^2 + \left(\frac{1}{R_1C_1}\right)s + \left(\frac{1}{R_2R_3C_1C_2}\right)\frac{R_6}{R_5}} \tag{10-155b}$$

$$\frac{V_3}{V_i} = -\frac{R_6}{R_5}\left(\frac{1}{R_2R_4C_1C_2}\right)\frac{1}{s^2 + \left(\frac{1}{R_1C_1}\right)s + \left(\frac{1}{R_2R_3C_1C_2}\right)\frac{R_6}{R_5}} \tag{10-155c}$$

We now consider various second-order filter sections that can be realized by the basic circuit configuration of Fig. 10-33(a).

1. LOW-PASS. If the desired transfer function is a low-pass type, i.e.,

$$H_{LP}(s) = \frac{a_0}{s^2 + b_1s + b_0} \tag{10-156}$$

then we can choose either V_2 or V_3 as our output voltage. To be specific, let us choose V_2 to be our output. By comparing (10-156) and (10-155b), the

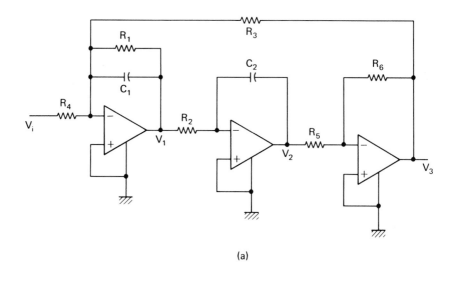

(a)

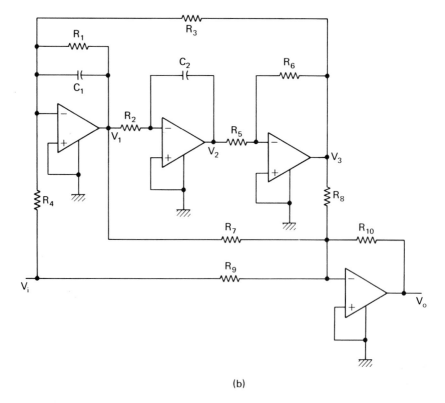

(b)

Fig. 10-33 Tow's multiple-amplifier biquad. (a) Basic circuit. (b) Complete circuit.

design equations are

$$\frac{1}{R_1 C_1} = b_1$$

$$\frac{1}{R_2 R_3 C_1 C_2} \frac{R_6}{R_5} = b_0$$

$$\frac{1}{R_2 R_4 C_1 C_2} = a_0 \qquad (10\text{-}157)$$

A solution of (10-157) is given by

$$R_1 = \frac{1}{b_1 C_1}, \quad R_2 = \frac{k_1}{\sqrt{b_0} C_2}, \quad R_3 = \frac{1}{k_1 \sqrt{b_0} C_1},$$

$$R_4 = \frac{\sqrt{b_0}}{k_1 a_0 C_1}, \quad \text{and} \quad R_5 = R_6 \qquad (10\text{-}158)$$

where C_1, C_2, R_5, and k_1 are any arbitrary positive numbers.

2. BANDPASS. If the desired transfer function is in the form of

$$H_{BP}(s) = -\frac{a_1 s}{s^2 + b_1 s + b_0} \qquad (10\text{-}159)$$

then we can select V_1 as the output. By comparing (10-159) and (10-155a), we obtain the following design equations

$$\frac{1}{R_4 C_1} = a_1$$

$$\frac{1}{R_1 C_1} = b_1$$

$$\frac{1}{R_2 R_3 C_1 C_2} \frac{R_6}{R_5} = b_0 \qquad (10\text{-}160)$$

A solution of (10-160) is

$$R_1 = \frac{1}{b_1 C_1}, \quad R_2 = \frac{k_1}{\sqrt{b_0} C_2}, \quad R_3 = \frac{1}{k_1 \sqrt{b_0} C_1},$$

$$R_4 = \frac{1}{a_1 C_1}, \quad \text{and} \quad R_5 = R_6 \qquad (10\text{-}161)$$

where C_1, C_2, R_5, and k_1 are arbitrary positive numbers.

Because lumped discrete capacitors are not available in all values, we would like to leave the capacitor values as free parameters, as was done in (10-158) and (10-161). Observe that the rightmost operational amplifier in Fig. 10-33(a) is used to realize a VCVS. In our solutions in (10-158) and (10-161), we set $R_5 = R_6$. Hence, the VCVS functions as a sign-reversal circuit. In general, $R_5 = R_6$ is between 1 KΩ and 20 KΩ. This means that in (10-158) and (10-161) the only free parameter is k_1. Very often, k_1 is used to minimize the value spread of the resistors R_1 through R_6 in Fig. 10-33(a).

Example 10-19 Realize

$$H(s) = \frac{10^9}{s^2 + 10^4 s + 10^8} \qquad (10\text{-}162)$$

by the circuit in Fig. 10-33(a).

Solution: From (10-158), a solution to the design equation of (10-157), where $b_1 = 10^4$, $b_0 = 10^8$, $a_0 = 10^9$, and $C_1 = C_2 = 0.1 \; \mu F.$, is

$$R_1 = \frac{1}{10^4 \times 10^{-7}} = 1 \; K\Omega$$

$$R_2 = \frac{k_1}{10^4 \times 10^{-7}} = k_1 \; K\Omega$$

$$R_3 = \frac{1}{k_1 \times 10^4 \times 10^{-7}} = \frac{1}{k_1} \; K\Omega \qquad (10\text{-}163)$$

$$R_4 = \frac{10^4}{k_1 \times 10^9 \times 10^{-7}} = \frac{100}{k_1} \; \Omega$$

$$R_5 = R_6 = 1 \; K\Omega$$

Without resorting to any optimization techniques, a good value for k_1 for the purpose of minimizing the spread of resistor values is $k_1 = 1$. Hence, we obtain

$$R_1 = R_2 = R_3 = R_5 = R_6 = 1 \; K\Omega$$
$$R_4 = 100 \; \Omega \qquad (10\text{-}164)$$

A circuit realization of (10-162) via (10-164) is given in Fig. 10-34. ∎

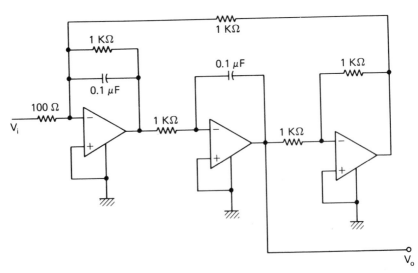

Fig. 10-34 A circuit realization of the low-pass filter of (10-162).

As indicated by (10-155), Fig. 10-33(a) can produce only bandpass and low-pass filters. However, by adding an additional summer circuit to Fig. 10-33(a), as shown in Fig. 10-33(b), we can obtain high-pass and all-pass filters as well as notch or band-reject filters. The transfer function relating V_o and V_i of Fig. 10-33(b) is given by

$$H(s) \triangleq -\frac{R_{10}}{R_9} \frac{s^2 + \frac{1}{R_1 C_1}\left[1 - \frac{R_1 R_9}{R_4 R_7}\right]s + \frac{1}{R_2 R_3 C_1 C_2}\left[1 - \frac{R_3 R_9}{R_4 R_8}\right]\frac{R_6}{R_5}}{s^2 + \left(\frac{1}{R_1 C_1}\right)s + \left(\frac{1}{R_2 R_3 C_1 C_2}\right)\frac{R_6}{R_5}} \quad (10\text{-}165)$$

Based on (10-165), we can use the circuit in Fig. 10-33(b) to realize the remaining forms of biquadratic transfer functions.

3. HIGH-PASS. If the desired transfer function is a high-pass filter,

$$H(s) = -\frac{a_2 s^2}{s^2 + b_1 s + b_0} \quad (10\text{-}166)$$

then, by comparing (10-165) and (10-166), we obtain the following design equations:

$$\frac{R_{10}}{R_9} = a_2, \quad \frac{R_1 R_9}{R_4 R_7} = 1, \quad \frac{R_3 R_9}{R_4 R_8} = 1,$$

$$\frac{1}{R_1 C_1} = b_1, \quad \text{and} \quad \frac{1}{R_2 R_3 C_1 C_2}\left(\frac{R_6}{R_5}\right) = b_0 \quad (10\text{-}167)$$

A solution of (10-167) is

$$R_1 = \frac{1}{b_1 C_1}, \quad R_2 = \frac{k_1}{\sqrt{b_0} C_2}, \quad R_3 = \frac{1}{k_1 \sqrt{b_0} C_1},$$

$$R_4 = \frac{1}{k_2 a_2 b_1 C_1}, \quad R_7 = k_2 R_{10}, \quad R_8 = \frac{k_2}{k_1}\left(\frac{b_1}{\sqrt{b_0}}\right)R_{10},$$

$$R_9 = \frac{R_{10}}{a_2}, \quad \text{and} \quad R_5 = R_6 \quad (10\text{-}168)$$

where C_1, C_2, k_1, k_2, R_5, and R_{10} are arbitrary positive numbers. As discussed before, C_1, C_2, and R_5 are not really free, but k_1, k_2, and R_{10} are completely free parameters to be set for various design considerations.

4. ALL-PASS. If the desired transfer function is specified by

$$H(s) = -k\frac{s^2 - b_1 s + b_0}{s^2 + b_1 s + b_0} \quad (10\text{-}169)$$

then the design equations are

$$\frac{R_{10}}{R_9} = k, \quad \frac{1}{R_1 C_1} = b_1, \quad \frac{R_1 R_9}{R_4 R_7} = 2,$$

$$\frac{1}{R_2 R_3 C_1 C_2}\left(\frac{R_6}{R_5}\right) = b_0, \quad \text{and} \quad \frac{R_3 R_9}{R_4 R_8} = 0 \quad (10\text{-}170)$$

A solution of (10-170) is

$$R_1 = \frac{1}{b_1 C_1}, \quad R_2 = \frac{k_1}{\sqrt{b_0} C_2}, \quad R_3 = \frac{1}{k_1 \sqrt{b_0} C_1},$$

$$R_4 = \frac{1}{k_2 2 b_1 C_1}, \quad R_7 = \frac{k_2 R_{10}}{k}, \quad R_8 = \infty = \text{an open circuit},$$

$$R_9 = \frac{1}{k} R_{10}, \quad \text{and} \quad R_5 = R_6 \tag{10-171}$$

where C_1, C_2, R_5, k_1, k_2, and R_{10} are arbitrary positive numbers, C_1, C_2, and R_5 are partially fixed, and k_1, k_2, and R_{10} are free parameters to be set for various design considerations.

5. NOTCH OR BAND-REJECT. Suppose that the desired transfer function is a notch filter of the form

$$H(s) = -\frac{a_2 s^2 + a_0}{s^2 + b_1 s + b_0} \tag{10-172}$$

By comparing (10-165) and (10-172), we obtain the following set of design equations:

$$\frac{R_{10}}{R_9} = a_2, \quad \frac{R_1 R_9}{R_4 R_7} = 1,$$

$$\left(\frac{R_{10}}{R_9}\right) \frac{1}{R_2 R_3 C_1 C_2}\left(1 - \frac{R_3 R_9}{R_4 R_8}\right)\frac{R_6}{R_5} = a_0,$$

$$\frac{1}{R_1 C_1} = b_1, \quad \text{and} \quad \frac{1}{R_2 R_3 C_1 C_2}\left(\frac{R_6}{R_5}\right) = b_0 \tag{10-173}$$

A solution to (10-173) is

$$R_1 = \frac{1}{b_1 C_1}, \quad R_2 = \frac{k_1}{\sqrt{b_0} C_2}, \quad R_3 = \frac{1}{k_1 \sqrt{b_0} C_1}, \tag{10-174}$$

$$R_4 = \frac{1}{k_2 a_2 b_1 C_1}, \quad R_7 = k_2 R_{10}, \quad R_8 = \frac{k_2 a_2 b_1}{k_1 (a_2 b_0 - a_0)}\sqrt{b_0} R_{10},$$

$$R_9 = \frac{R_{10}}{a_2}, \quad \text{and} \quad R_5 = R_6$$

where C_1, C_2, R_5, k_1, k_2, and R_{10} are arbitrary positive numbers. Note that when $a_2 b_0 < a_0$, (10-174) yields a negative value for R_8. Hence, from a practical standpoint, the circuit in Fig. 10-33(b) is able to realize a notch filter only when the coefficients satisfy the condition

$$a_2 b_0 \geq a_0 \tag{10-175}$$

Recall that in (10-155b) and (10-155c), aside from a positive constant multiplier, V_2 and V_3 of Fig. 10-33(a) are negatives of each other. Hence, if the added summer circuit in Fig. 10-33(b) is used to form a weighted sum of V_i, V_1, and V_2 rather than V_3, the constant term in the numerator polynomial of (10-165) becomes a sum of two terms rather than the present case of a

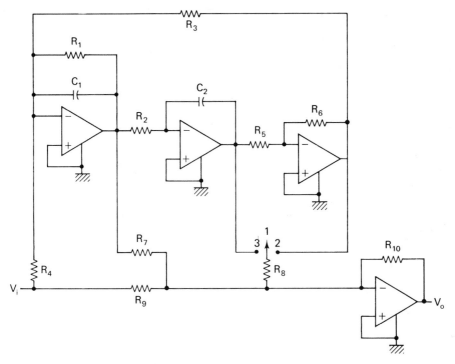

Fig. 10-35   Tow's complete circuit configuration.

difference. Consequently, we expect there would be no problem when $a_2 b_0 < a_0$. To formalize this idea, let us consider the circuit in Fig. 10-35, where the switch moves from 1 to 2 when $a_2 b_0 \geq a_0$ and from 1 to 3 when $a_2 b_0 < a_0$. In the former case, the design equations plus a set of solutions are given by (10-173) and (10-174). In the latter case, the transfer function of the circuit is given by

$$H(s) \triangleq \frac{V_o}{V_i} = -\frac{R_{10}}{R_9} \frac{s^2 + \dfrac{1}{R_1 C_1}\left[1 - \dfrac{R_1 R_9}{R_4 R_7}\right] s + \dfrac{1}{R_2 R_3 C_1 C_2}\left[\dfrac{R_6}{R_5} + \dfrac{R_3 R_9}{R_4 R_8}\right]}{s^2 + \left(\dfrac{1}{R_1 C_1}\right) s + \left(\dfrac{1}{R_2 R_3 C_1 C_2}\right)\dfrac{R_6}{R_5}}$$

$$(10\text{-}176)$$

A comparison of (10-172) and (10-176) produces a set of design equations

$$\frac{R_{10}}{R_9} = a_2, \quad \frac{R_1 R_9}{R_4 R_7} = 1,$$

$$\left(\frac{R_{10}}{R_9}\right)\frac{1}{R_2 R_3 C_1 C_2}\left(\frac{R_6}{R_5} + \frac{R_3 R_9}{R_4 R_8}\right) = a_0,$$

$$\frac{1}{R_1 C_1} = b_1, \quad \text{and} \quad \left(\frac{1}{R_2 R_3 C_1 C_2}\right)\frac{R_6}{R_5} = b_0 \qquad (10\text{-}177)$$

A solution of (10-177) is given by

$$R_1 = \frac{1}{b_1 C_1}, \quad R_2 = \frac{k_1}{\sqrt{b_0} C_2}, \quad R_3 = \frac{1}{k_1 \sqrt{b_0} C_1},$$

$$R_4 = \frac{1}{k_2 a_2 b_1 C_1}, \quad R_7 = k_2 R_{10},$$

$$R_8 = \frac{k_2}{k_1} \left(\frac{a_2 b_1}{a_0 - a_2 b_0} \right) \sqrt{b_0} R_{10}, \quad R_9 = \frac{R_{10}}{a_2}, \quad \text{and} \quad R_5 = R_6 \qquad (10\text{-}178)$$

where C_1, C_2, R_5, k_1, k_2, and R_{10} are arbitrary positive numbers. Note that with the exception of R_8, (10-178) is the same as (10-174).

Example 10-20 Realize

$$H(s) = \frac{s^2 + 3.96 \times 10^8}{s^2 + (2 \times 10^3)s + (4 \times 10^8)} \qquad (10\text{-}179)$$

Solution: Because

$$a_1 b_0 = 4 \times 10^8 > a_0 = 3.96 \times 10^8 \qquad (10\text{-}180)$$

the switch in Fig. 10-35 moves from 1 to 2, and (10-174) is applicable here. Let

$$C_1 = C_2 = 0.01 \ \mu\text{F.}, \quad R_{10} = 10 \ \text{K}\Omega, \quad \text{and} \quad k_1 = k_2 = 1$$

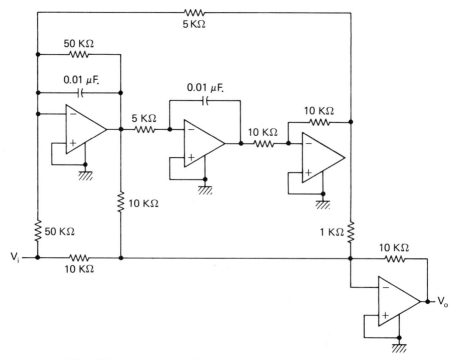

Fig. 10-36 A circuit realization of the notch filter of (10-179).

Then (10-174) gives

$$C_1 = 0.01 \ \mu F., \quad C_2 = 0.01 \ \mu F.,$$
$$R_1 = 50 \ K\Omega, \quad R_2 = 5 \ K\Omega, \quad R_3 = 5 \ K\Omega,$$
$$R_4 = 50 \ K\Omega, \quad R_5 = 10 \ K\Omega, \quad R_6 = 10 \ K\Omega, \quad (10\text{-}181)$$
$$R_7 = 10 \ K\Omega, \quad R_8 = 1 \ K\Omega, \quad R^9 = 10 \ K\Omega, \quad \text{and} \quad R_{10} = 10 \ K\Omega$$

A circuit realization of (10-179) is obtained by substituting the values of (10-181) into Fig. 10-35, as shown in Fig. 10-36. ∎

From (10-155) and (10-176), the denominator polynomial $B(s)$ for the circuits in Figs. 10-33 and 10-35 is given by

$$B(s) = s^2 + \left(\frac{1}{R_1 C_1}\right)s + \left(\frac{1}{R_2 R_3 C_1 C_2}\right)\frac{R_6}{R_5} = s^2 + \frac{\omega_0}{Q}s + \omega_0^2 \quad (10\text{-}182)$$

where

$$\omega_0 = \sqrt{\frac{1}{R_2 R_3 C_1 C_2}\left(\frac{R_6}{R_5}\right)} \quad (10\text{-}183)$$

and

$$Q = R_1 C_1 \omega_0 = R_1 \sqrt{\frac{C_1}{R_2 R_3 C_2}\left(\frac{R_6}{R_5}\right)} \quad (10\text{-}184)$$

Hence,

$$S_{R_2}^{\omega_0} = S_{R_3}^{\omega_0} = S_{C_1}^{\omega_0} = S_{C_2}^{\omega_0} = S_{C_5}^{\omega_0} = -\frac{1}{2}$$

$$S_{R_6}^{\omega_0} = \frac{1}{2} \quad (10\text{-}185)$$

and

$$S_{R_2}^{Q} = S_{R_3}^{Q} = S_{C_2}^{Q} = S_{R_5}^{Q} = -\frac{1}{2}$$

$$S_{C_1}^{Q} = S_{R_6}^{Q} = \frac{1}{2}$$

$$S_{R_1}^{Q} = 1 \quad (10\text{-}186)$$

For the purpose of postadjustments, we note that R_3 can be used to adjust the value of ω_0 and once that is done, R_1 can be used to adjust the desired pole-pair value of Q. Thus we can encapsulate the complete circuit of Fig. 10-35 with the switch positions, R_3 and R_1, placed externally, as shown in Fig. 10-37. By varying R_1 and R_3 for the desired ω_0 and Q values, Fig. 10-37 can be used to realize a wide range of filter circuits.

10-2-2-3. Some Comments. In the previous two subsections, we have introduced two single amplifier biquads (SAB) and two multiple amplifier biquads (MAB). In this subsection, we make some comments on these realization techniques.

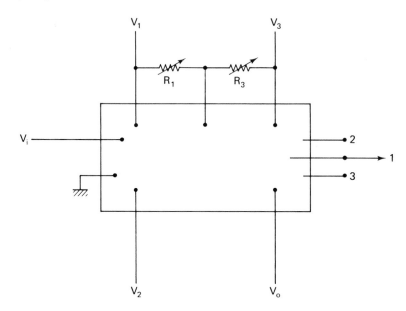

Fig. 10-37   A universal multiple-amplifier biquad with two external
resistors for ω_0 and Q adjustments.

The SAB circuits of Table 10-1 require the least number of elements in
their realizations. Tuning procedures for adjusting ω_0 and Q values can be
developed for some of these circuits. These circuits are, in general, suitable
for biquadratic functions with $Q \leq 5$.

Friend's SAB circuits use more elements than those in Table 10-1. In
return, Friend's circuits have one topology for all biquadratic functions
(except for the low-pass case). Hence, Friend's SAB circuits are suitable for
integration into chips. In general, Friend's circuits are less sensitive than those
in Table 10-1 and may be used to design filters with $Q \leq 15$. One drawback
of Friend's SAB circuits is that, except for the bandpass case, tuning procedures for ω_0 and Q adjustments are not possible.

The two MAB circuits introduced in subsection 10-2-2-2 are about the
same in performance. Tuning and adjustment procedures for ω_0 and Q values
can be developed easily. With a few external resistors, the internal parts can
be identical for a wide variety of filter circuits. Hence, MAB circuits can be
mass produced, thereby reducing their cost. This greatly compensates for the
large number of passive and active components required in the realizations.

Compared with SAB circuits, MAB circuits are less sensitive and can be
designed for higher frequency ranges. This is because the demand on the gain
levels of the operational amplifiers are less and, hence, the frequency ranges
of the MAB circuits are extended. In addition, MAB circuits may be used for
applications where the Q of the biquadratic functions are less than 50.

For higher Q values, we need to take into account the nonidealness of operational amplifiers and to provide feedback and coupling between biquadratic filter sections to reduce sensitivities. See, for example, References [27] through [30].

10-2-3. Complementary Circuit Configurations

It is generally easier and/or more economical to generate low-pass, bandpass, and high-pass filters than notch and all-pass filters. For example, the Sallen–Key table does not have a simple realization for a notch or an all-pass filter. The multiple amplifier biquad circuits require additional amplifiers to generate notch or all-pass filters. In this section, we introduce a technique to generate a band-reject or an all-pass filter from a bandpass filter via the concept of a complementary transfer function.

It has long been known that, in a passive three-terminal network with no internal connection to ground, the voltage transfer function of one input to the output must be the *complement* of the transfer function of the other input to the output. For example, in Fig. 10-38(a), we have

$$H_2(s) = 1 - H_1(s) \qquad (10\text{-}187\text{a})$$

where

$$H_1(s) = \frac{V_o}{V_1}\bigg|_{V_2=0} \qquad (10\text{-}187\text{b})$$

and

$$H_2(s) = \frac{V_o}{V_2}\bigg|_{V_1=0} \qquad (10\text{-}187\text{c})$$

Hilberman extended this complementary concept to include active circuits with ideal operational amplifiers. A special case of his result is summarized in the following theorem.

THEOREM 10-2.[27]   Let N be a three-terminal network with two input terminals V_1 and V_2 and an output terminal V_o, where all voltages are node-to-ground voltages. Suppose that N can be partitioned into two connected subnetworks: one that is not connected directly to the common ground node, and one consisting of *differential-input grounded-output* operational amplifiers, as illustrated in Fig. 10-38(b). Then we have (10-187). Note that

$$V_o = H_1(s)V_1 + H_2(s)V_2 \qquad (10\text{-}188)$$

∎

We now consider the application of Theorem 10-2 to the realization of band-reject and all-pass filters. Consider the three-terminal network N in Fig. 10-38(b). Suppose that with $V_2 = 0$ [node 2 is connected to the common

---

[27]See Reference [31].

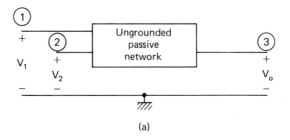

(a)

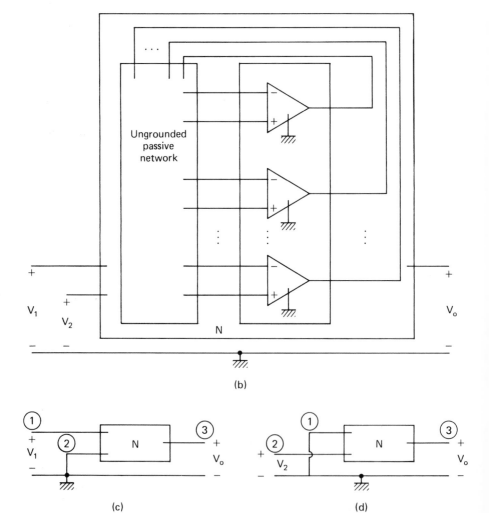

(b)

(c)

(d)

Fig. 10-38 (a) A three-terminal ungrounded passive network. (b) A partitionable three-terminal active network. (c) and (d) Complementary transfer-function networks.

ground node as shown in Fig. 10-38(c)], the transfer function is a bandpass filter given by

$$H_1(s) \triangleq \frac{V_o}{V_1}\bigg|_{V_2=0} = \frac{\alpha s}{s^2 + b_1 s + b_0} \qquad (10\text{-}189)$$

If $\alpha = b_1$, then the circuit with node 1 of N connected to the ground node, as shown in Fig. 10-38(d), yields the transfer function

$$H(s) \triangleq \frac{V_o}{V_2}\bigg|_{V_1=0} = H_2(s) = 1 - H_1(s)$$

$$= \frac{s^2 + b_0}{s^2 + b_1 s + b_0} \qquad \alpha = b_1 \qquad (10\text{-}190)$$

That is, the resultant circuit in Fig. 10-38(d) is a band-reject filter.[28] On the other hand, if $\alpha = 2b_1$, then the circuit in Fig. 10-38(d) is an all-pass filter with

$$H(s) = 1 - H_1(s) = \frac{s^2 - b_1 s + b_0}{s^2 + b_1 s + b_0} \quad \alpha = 2b_1 \qquad (10\text{-}191)$$

Note that Theorem 10-2 can be used to generate other transfer functions. For example, the transfer function

$$H(s) = \frac{s^2 + b_1 s}{s^2 + b_1 s + b_0}$$

can be obtained as the complementary transfer function of a low-pass filter characterized by

$$H_{LP}(s) = \frac{b_0}{s^2 + b_1 s + b_0}$$

Example 10-21   Consider the three-terminal network N in Fig. 10-39(a). With node 2 connected to ground, the resulting circuit is a bandpass filter characterized by

$$H(s) \triangleq \frac{V_o}{V_1}\bigg|_{V_2=0} = \frac{\left(\dfrac{G_4 G_5}{C_1 G_6}\right)s}{s^2 + \dfrac{G_1}{C_1}s + \dfrac{G_2 G_3 G_5}{G_6 C_1 C_2}} \qquad (10\text{-}192)$$

where $G_i \triangleq 1/R_i$.

(a) Construct a band-reject filter

$$H_{BR}(s) = \frac{s^2 + 1}{s^2 + s + 1} \qquad (10\text{-}193a)$$

(b) Construct an all-pass filter

$$H_{AP}(s) = \frac{s^2 - s + 1}{s^2 + s + 1} \qquad (10\text{-}193b)$$

---

[28]To generate a general notch filter, we need $H_1(s)$ to equal $(\alpha_1 s + \alpha_0)/(s^2 + b_1 s + b_0)$, where $\alpha_1 = b_1$ and $(b_0 - \alpha_0)$ is the square of the desired notch frequency. In this case, the resultant transfer function is given by $H(s) = [s^2 + (b_0 - \alpha_0)]/(s^2 + b_1 s + b_0)$.

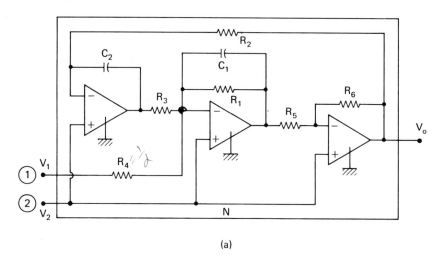

(a)

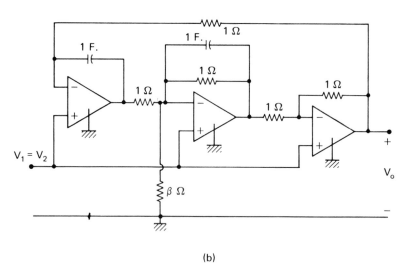

(b)

Fig. 10-39 (a) A bandpass network with node 2 connected to ground. (b) A band-reject filter of (10-193a) when $\beta = 1$ and an all-pass filter of (10-193b) when $\beta = 0.5$.

Solution: Let us first consider the band-reject filter. In this case, the desired bandpass filter is given by

$$H(s) = \frac{s}{s^2 + s + 1} \qquad (10\text{-}194)$$

Hence, the design equations are

$$\frac{G_4 G_5}{C_1 G_6} = \alpha \qquad (10\text{-}195a)$$

$$\frac{G_1}{C_1} = 1 \qquad (10\text{-}195\text{b})$$

$$\frac{G_2 G_3 G_5}{G_6 C_1 C_2} = 1 \qquad (10\text{-}195\text{c})$$

where $\alpha = 1$. A solution to (10-195) with a general α is given by

$$C_1 = C_2 = 1 \text{ F.}$$

$$R_1 = R_2 = R_3 = R_5 = R_6 = 1 \, \Omega \qquad (10\text{-}196)$$

$$R_4 = \frac{1}{\alpha} \, \Omega$$

Using Theorem 10-2 and the configuration of Fig. 10-38(d), a circuit realization of (10-193a) is shown in Fig. 10-39(b), where $\beta = 1$.

To generate the all-pass filter of (10-193b), the transfer function of the bandpass filter is required to be

$$H(s) = \frac{2s}{s^2 + s + 1} \qquad (10\text{-}197)$$

The design equations and a solution to these equations are given by (10-195) and (10-196), with $\alpha = 2$. A circuit realization of (10-193b) via the concept of complementary transfer functions is shown in Fig. 10-39(b), where $\beta = 1/2$.

∎

10-2-4. Pole-Zero Pair Selection

In order to minimize network sensitivity with respect to parameter variations, it is a common practice to decompose an nth-order active RC filter into cascadable second-order filter sections. A natural question is by what criteria should the selection of pole-zero pairs of (10-2) be made.

Consider a transfer function of n poles and m zeros:

$$H(s) = \frac{G \prod\limits_{i=1}^{m} (s - z_i)}{\prod\limits_{j=1}^{n} (s - p_j)} \qquad (10\text{-}198)$$

Taking logarithms of (10-198) gives

$$\ell\text{n} \, H(s) = \ell\text{n} \, G + \sum_{i=1}^{m} \ell\text{n} \, (s - z_i) - \sum_{j=1}^{n} \ell\text{n} \, (s - p_j)$$

Hence, we have

$$\frac{\partial \, \ell\text{n} \, H(s)}{\partial \, \ell\text{n} \, x} = \frac{\partial \, \ell\text{n} \, G}{\partial \, \ell\text{n} \, x} + \sum_{i=1}^{m} \frac{\partial \, \ell\text{n} \, (s - z_i)}{\partial \, \ell\text{n} \, x} - \sum_{j=1}^{n} \frac{\partial \, \ell\text{n} \, (s - p_j)}{\partial \, \ell\text{n} \, x} \qquad (10\text{-}199)$$

where x is any network parameter subject to small variations. Because[29]

$$\frac{\partial \ln(s - s_i)}{\partial \ln x} = -\frac{1}{s - s_i}\left(\frac{\partial s_i}{\partial \ln x}\right)$$

$$= -\frac{1}{s - s_i}\left(\frac{\partial s_i}{\partial x}\right)x = -\frac{1}{s - s_i}(\hat{S}_x^{s_i}) \qquad (10\text{-}200a)$$

and

$$\frac{\partial \ln y}{\partial \ln x} = \frac{\partial y/y}{\partial x/x} = \frac{\partial y}{\partial x}\frac{x}{y} = S_x^y \qquad (10\text{-}200b)$$

Equation (10-199) can be written as

$$S_x^{H(s)} = S_x^G + \sum_{j=1}^{n}\frac{\hat{S}_x^{p_j}}{s - p_j} - \sum_{i=1}^{m}\frac{\hat{S}_x^{z_i}}{s - z_i}$$

$$\triangleq S_x^G + F_p - F_z \qquad (10\text{-}201)$$

Hence, one obvious way to minimize the overall sensitivity function is to select the pole-zero pairs for the individual second-order functions as far apart as possible. In so doing, one will achieve a minimum contribution to the overall network sensitivity function (1) from the zero terms of F_z when s is in the neighborhood of a pole, and (2) from the pole terms of F_p when s is in the neighborhood of a zero. As is usually the case, simple things may not always work. Reducing the contribution of F_z in (10-201) may be one way to reduce the overall sensitivity function $S_x^{H(s)}$ near a pole, but it may not be the best way for other values of s. Another way of minimizing $S_x^{H(s)}$ is by a partial or even total cancellation of the pole-zero pair terms in (10-201) [i.e., to require $F_p - F_z$ to go to zero]. This can be achieved by an appropriate polynomial decomposition of each second-order function so that its own $f_p - f_z$ [the corresponding terms in (10-201) for a second-order section] goes to zero. This process essentially requires us to group a pair of poles with its closest pair of zeros. The exact procedure is quite involved and is not discussed here.[30]

10-2-5. Pole Sensitivity Considerations

For a passive filter, the circuit will remain stable for all possible element perturbations. Unfortunately, this is not true, in general, for active filters. It is possible that a paper design is stable and a hardware circuit implementing the paper design is not stable. This is basically a pole sensitivity problem. A small parameter deviation from the nominal value may move one or more pole

---

[29]See (9-49) for the definition of the root sensitivity function $\hat{S}$ and (9-73) for the sensitivity function S.

[30]See References [32] through [35].

locations to the RH s-plane and thereby cause instability to the circuit. In this subsection, we utilize some of the results obtained in Chapter 9 to reduce pole sensitivity.

If an active filter is made of n_R resistors, n_C capacitors, and n_K active elements, say VCVS or operational amplifiers, then the change of pole position p_j due to the variations of the resistors, capacitors, and active elements is

$$\delta p_j = \sum_{i=1}^{n_R} \frac{\partial p_j}{\partial R_i} \frac{\delta R_i}{R_i} R_i + \sum_{i=1}^{n_C} \frac{\partial p_j}{\partial C_i} \frac{\delta C_i}{C_i} C_i + \sum_{i=1}^{n_K} \frac{\partial p_j}{\partial K_i} \frac{\delta K_i}{K_i} K_i$$

$$= \sum_{i=1}^{n_R} \hat{S}_{R_i}^{p_j} \frac{\delta R_i}{R_i} + \sum_{i=1}^{n_C} \hat{S}_{C_i}^{p_j} \frac{\delta C_i}{C_i} + \sum_{i=1}^{n_K} \hat{S}_{K_i}^{p_j} \frac{\delta K_i}{K_i} \tag{10-202}$$

where K_i represents the gain of the ith active element in the filter circuit. From (9-72), we have

$$\sum_{i=1}^{n_R} \hat{S}_{R_i}^{p_j} = \sum_{i=1}^{n_C} \hat{S}_{C_i}^{p_j} = -p_j \tag{10-203}$$

If we assume that the passive component variations are uniform,

$$\frac{\delta R_i}{R_i} = \frac{\delta R_j}{R_j} \triangleq \frac{\delta R}{R} \qquad i, j = 1, 2, \ldots, n_R \tag{10-204a}$$

$$\frac{\delta C_i}{C_i} = \frac{\delta C_j}{C_j} \triangleq \frac{\delta C}{C} \qquad i, j = 1, 2, \ldots, n_C \tag{10-204b}$$

and that the effect of all active element variation can be lumped into the equivalent variation of a single active device

$$\sum_{i=1}^{n_K} \hat{S}_{K_i}^{p_j} \frac{\delta K_i}{K_i} = \hat{S}_K^{p_j} \frac{\delta K}{K} \tag{10-204c}$$

where K is the parameter of the equivalent active device, then (10-202) reduces to

$$\delta p_j = \hat{S}_K^{p_j} \frac{\delta K}{K} - p_j \left[\frac{\delta R}{R} + \frac{\delta C}{C} \right] \tag{10-205}$$

To ensure that pole sensitivities are minimized, a most promising method is to make

$$\frac{\delta R}{R} + \frac{\delta C}{C} = 0 \tag{10-206}$$

by using resistors and capacitors with uniformly equal but opposite temperature coefficients and to minimize $(\delta K)/K$. With great care on the operational amplifiers, we can actually make

$$\frac{\delta K}{K} \simeq 0 \tag{10-207}$$

10-3 NONIDEAL OPERATIONAL AMPLIFIER CONSIDERATION

An ideal operational amplifier has an input impedance equal to ∞, an output impedance equal to 0, and a voltage gain of ∞. All these characteristics are not possible to attain in real cases. Fortunately, though the active filters discussed so far are highly idealized, the results obtained are very close to reality in most practical cases. However, when operational amplifiers are used in high-precision circuits and/or high-frequency applications, it becomes necessary to examine the consequences of the nonideal properties of the operational amplifiers. In this section, we discuss briefly the nonideal characteristics of real operational amplifiers and the implications of these imperfections on the performance of active filters.

The principal nonideal properties of operational amplifiers that concern us are:

1. finite voltage gain;
2. frequency-dependent voltage gain;
3. finite bandwidth;
4. finite input resistance;
5. nonzero output resistance;
6. nonlinear input–output voltage relationships; and
7. noise generated by operational amplifiers.

We now examine the effect of each of these items on filter performance.

With regard to items 6 and 7, the noise generated by the operational amplifiers limits the minimum signal at which an active filter can be operated. To eliminate problems associated with the nonlinear characteristics of operational amplifiers, the signal level of an active filter is set low enough such that all the operational amplifiers involved are certain to be operating in the linear mode. Together, items 6 and 7 essentially establish the signal range within which an active filter can function satisfactorily.

Assuming that the signal strength of an active filter is properly set so that we can ignore items 6 and 7, then we can model a real operational amplifier as shown in Fig. 10-40(c), where the typical values are $r_i \simeq 1 \text{ M}\Omega$ and $r_o \simeq 100 \, \Omega$. Generally speaking, the finite input resistance and the nonzero output resistance do not have much effect on the transfer function of an active filter if the impedance level of the filter is chosen properly. In addition, the element values of the filter can be preadjusted to take into account of r_i and r_o. Thus, in almost all cases of practical interest, items 4 and 5 can be ignored. Hence, we can model a real operational amplifier by the circuit shown in Fig. 10-40(d).

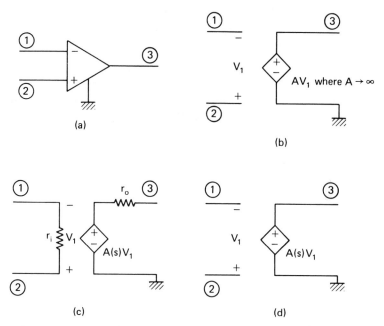

Fig. 10-40 (a) Symbol of an operational amplifier. (b) Model of an ideal operational amplifier. (c) Model of a real operational amplifier. (d) A simplified model of a real operational amplifier.

For the remainder of this section, we examine mainly the effect of finite voltage gain, frequency-dependent voltage gain, and its finite bandwidth on the performance of some typical operational amplifier circuits.

10-3-1. Inverting Voltage-Gain Amplifier

Consider the inverting voltage-gain amplifier circuit in Fig. 10-41(a). With an ideal operational amplifier, the transfer function is given by[31]

$$H_i(s) = -\frac{R_b}{R_a} \tag{10-208}$$

Let us now replace the operational amplifier with its simplified model, as shown in Fig. 10-41(b). The circuit equations are

$$\frac{V_i + V_1}{R_a} = -\frac{V_1 + V_o}{R_b} \tag{10-209a}$$

$$V_o = A(s)V_1 \tag{10-209b}$$

---

[31]In this subsection, $H_i(s)$ and $H_n(s)$ represent, respectively, the transfer functions of the circuits with *i*deal and *n*onideal operational amplifiers. A nonideal operational amplifier is modeled by Fig. 10-40(d).

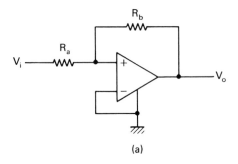

(a)

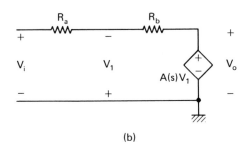

(b)

Fig. 10-41 An inverting voltage-gain amplifier.
(a) Schematic. (b) Modeled circuit.

Substituting (10-209b) into (10-209a) and rearranging terms, we obtain

$$\frac{V_o}{V_i} = -\frac{R_b}{R_a\left[1 + \frac{1}{A(s)}\left(\frac{R_b}{R_a} + 1\right)\right]}$$

$$= -\frac{\beta}{1 + \frac{\beta + 1}{A(s)}} \tag{10-210a}$$

where

$$\beta \triangleq \frac{R_b}{R_a} \tag{10-210b}$$

is (the absolute value of) the voltage gain of the idealized circuit. We now consider the effect of finite voltage gain, finite bandwidth, and frequency-dependent voltage gain of the operational amplifier on the inverting voltage-gain amplifier circuit.

(a) CONSEQUENCE OF FINITE GAIN. Suppose $A(s) = A_0$ is a very large but finite positive constant. Then (10-210) can be written as

$$H_n(s) = \frac{V_o}{V_i} = -\frac{\beta}{1 + \frac{\beta + 1}{A_0}} = -\beta\left[1 - \frac{\beta + 1}{A_0} + \frac{(\beta + 1)^2}{A_0^2} - \cdots\right] \tag{10-211}$$

If a precise inverting voltage gain G is desired, then the necessary ratio β of R_b/R_a can be solved from (10-211) as

$$\frac{R_b}{R_a} = \beta = -\frac{G(A_0 + 1)}{A_0 + G} \tag{10-212}$$

Note that here G is a negative number and $G = -\beta$ in the idealized circuit. In general, A_0 is very large compared with $\beta + 1$. Therefore, the infinite series in (10-211) can be approximated by the first term, or

$$H_n(s) = -\beta\left[1 - \frac{\beta + 1}{A_0}\right] \tag{10-213}$$

This means that the gain error ϵ (true gain − idealized gain) and the fractional gain error ϵ_f are given by

$$\epsilon = \frac{\beta(\beta + 1)}{A_0} \tag{10-214a}$$

and

$$\epsilon_f \triangleq \frac{\epsilon}{\beta} = \frac{\beta + 1}{A_0} \tag{10-214b}$$

Note that the nominal value of A_0 is generally very large. Hence, the gain error and the fractional gain error due to idealizing the operational amplifier is rather small for low to medium-high voltage-gain amplifiers. However, when $|G|$ is very large, as demanded by some high-Q filters, the VCVS should be designed according to (10-212), where A_0 is the minimum open-loop gain value of the operational amplifier over the frequency band of interest. From (10-214b), we observe that as the precision requirement becomes more stringent for a particular voltage gain G, we need to increase A_0. Consequently, the useful frequency bandwidth (where the VCVS performs satisfactorily) decreases.

(b) CONSEQUENCE OF NONIDEAL OPERATIONAL AMPLIFIER ITEMS 1 TO 3. To increase the useful operative frequency bandwidth, we need to take into account the frequency dependence of the open-loop gain of operational amplifiers. This can be done by assuming that $A(s)$ is a truly frequency-dependent function. For the operational amplifiers characterized by Fig. 10-25, $A(s)$ is approximately given by

$$A(s) = \frac{A_0\omega_a}{s + \omega_a} \tag{10-215a}$$

where typical values for a monolithic operational amplifier are

$$A_0 = 50000, \quad \omega_a = 20(2\pi) = 40\pi \text{ rad./sec.} \tag{10-215b}$$

and $A_0\omega_a$ is called the *gain-bandwidth product* of the operational amplifier.

In this case, we can write (10-210) as

$$H_n(s) = -\frac{\beta A(s)}{1 + \beta + A(s)} = -\frac{\beta A_0 \omega_a}{(1 + \beta)(s + \omega_a) + A_0 \omega_a}$$

$$= -\frac{\beta A_0 \omega_a}{(1 + \beta)} \frac{1}{s + \left[1 + \dfrac{A_0}{1 + \beta}\right]\omega_a} \qquad (10\text{-}216a)$$

$$= -\frac{\alpha \beta \omega_a}{s + (1 + \alpha)\omega_a}$$

where

$$\alpha \triangleq \frac{A_0}{1 + \beta} \qquad (10\text{-}216b)$$

Thus the magnitude transfer function is given by

$$|H_n(j\omega)| = \frac{\alpha \beta \omega_a}{\sqrt{\omega^2 + (1 + \alpha)^2 \omega_a^2}}$$

$$= \frac{\alpha \beta}{\sqrt{(1 + \alpha)^2 + (\omega/\omega_a)^2}} \qquad (10\text{-}217)$$

Let ϵ_p be the maximum allowable voltage-gain magnitude percentage error due to the analysis with ideal operational amplifiers. Then the frequency ω in the useful frequency bandwidth where the voltage-gain amplifier meets the ϵ_p requirement satisfies the equation

$$\frac{\alpha \beta}{\sqrt{(1 + \alpha)^2 + \left(\dfrac{\omega}{\omega_a}\right)^2}} \geq \left(1 - \frac{\epsilon_p}{100}\right)\beta$$

or

$$\frac{\alpha^2}{(1 + \alpha)^2 + \left(\dfrac{\omega}{\omega_a}\right)^2} \geq \left(1 - \frac{\epsilon_p}{100}\right)^2 \qquad (10\text{-}218)$$

If ϵ_p is small (say less than 5), then the right-hand side of (10-218) can be approximated by

$$\left(1 - \frac{\epsilon_p}{100}\right)^2 \simeq 1 - \frac{\epsilon_p}{50} \qquad (10\text{-}219)$$

The largest frequency ω_1 such that the voltage-gain amplifier meets the ϵ_p requirement can be computed from (10-218) and (10-219) as

$$\frac{\alpha^2}{(1 + \alpha)^2 + \left(\dfrac{\omega_1}{\omega_a}\right)^2} \geq 1 - \frac{\epsilon_p}{50}$$

or

$$\frac{1}{\left(\dfrac{1 + \alpha}{\alpha}\right)^2 + \left(\dfrac{\omega_1}{\alpha \omega_a}\right)^2} \geq 1 - \frac{\epsilon_p}{50} \qquad (10\text{-}220)$$

Note that α is given by (10-216b). If the desired voltage gain β is not too excessive (say $\beta/A_0 \leq 0.05$), then

$$\frac{1 + \alpha}{\alpha} \simeq 1 \qquad (10\text{-}221)$$

and (10-220) can be simplified to

$$\frac{1}{1 + \left(\frac{\omega_1}{\alpha\omega_a}\right)^2} \geq 1 - \frac{\epsilon_\rho}{50} \qquad (10\text{-}222)$$

Inverting (10-222) yields

$$1 + \left(\frac{\omega_1}{\alpha\omega_a}\right)^2 \leq \frac{1}{1 - \frac{\epsilon_\rho}{50}} \simeq 1 + \frac{\epsilon_\rho}{50} \qquad (10\text{-}223)$$

Solving for ω_1, we obtain

$$\omega_1 \leq \alpha\omega_a\sqrt{\frac{\epsilon_\rho}{50}}$$

or

$$\omega_1 \simeq \frac{A_0\omega_a\sqrt{0.02\epsilon_\rho}}{\beta + 1} \qquad (10\text{-}224)$$

Example 10-22   Consider the inverting voltage gain amplifier circuit in Fig. 10-41, where the operational amplifier is characterized by Fig. 10-25. If the desired voltage-amplifier gain is 50 within $\pm 1\%$, find the useful frequency bandwidth.

Solution: From Fig. 10-25, we obtain $A_0 = 50000$ and $\omega_a = 20(2\pi) = 40\pi$ rad./sec. For a 1% tolerance, (10–224) indicates that the useful frequency bandwidth is from 0 to

$$\omega_1 \simeq \frac{50000}{51}(40\pi)\sqrt{0.02} \simeq 17423$$

or

$$f_1 \triangleq \frac{\omega_1}{2\pi} = 2773 \text{ Hz.} \qquad \blacksquare$$

10-3-2. Noninverting Voltage-Gain Amplifier

Consider the noninverting voltage-gain amplifier circuit shown in Fig. 10-42(a). The transfer function of the circuit with an ideal operational amplifier is given by

$$H_i(s) = \frac{V_o}{V_i} = \frac{R_1 + R_2}{R_1} \triangleq \gamma \qquad (10\text{-}225)$$

If the operational amplifier is replaced by its simplified model, as shown in

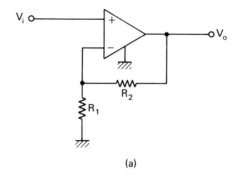

(a)

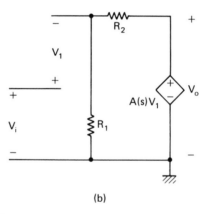

(b)

Fig. 10-42 A noninverting voltage-gain amplifier. (a) Schematic. (b) Modeled circuit.

Fig. 10-42(b), then the transfer function is

$$H_n(s) = \frac{R_1 + R_2}{R_1 + \dfrac{1}{A(s)}[R_1 + R_2]} = \frac{\gamma}{1 + \dfrac{\gamma}{A(s)}} \qquad (10\text{-}226)$$

Consider the case when the operational amplifier is assumed to have an infinite bandwidth; that is, $A(s) = A_0$. Then (10-226) yields

$$H_n(s) = \gamma\left[1 - \frac{\gamma}{A_0} + \ldots\right] \simeq \gamma\left[1 - \frac{\gamma}{A_0}\right] \qquad (10\text{-}227)$$

where we have assumed that the desired voltage gain γ is small compared to A_0. Hence, the percentage error in assuming an ideal operational amplifier is approximately given by

$$\epsilon_p\% = \frac{100\gamma}{A_0}\% \qquad (10\text{-}228)$$

As in the case of the inverting voltage-gain amplifier, we need a larger A_0 to produce a higher-precision noninverting voltage-gain amplifier.

For higher-frequency applications, the open-loop gain function $A(s)$ of an operational amplifier is more accurately described by (10-215). In this case, (10-226) becomes

$$H_n(s) = \frac{\gamma}{1 + \dfrac{\gamma(s + \omega_a)}{A_0 \omega_a}} = \frac{A_0 \omega_a \gamma}{\gamma s + (A_0 + \gamma)\omega_a}$$

$$= \frac{A_0}{\left(\dfrac{s}{\omega_a}\right) + \left(1 + \dfrac{A_0}{\gamma}\right)} \tag{10-229a}$$

and

$$|H_n(j\omega)| = \frac{A_0}{\sqrt{\left(\dfrac{\omega}{\omega_a}\right)^2 + \left(1 + \dfrac{A_0}{\gamma}\right)}} \tag{10-229b}$$

To stay within an ϵ_p voltage-gain magnitude percentage error, the largest useful frequency ω_1 satisfies the equation

$$\frac{A_0^2}{\left(\dfrac{\omega_1}{\omega_a}\right)^2 + \left(1 + \dfrac{A_0}{\gamma}\right)^2} \geq \left(1 - \frac{\epsilon_p}{100}\right)^2 \gamma^2$$

or

$$\frac{\hat{\alpha}^2}{\left(\dfrac{\omega_1}{\omega_a}\right)^2 + (1 + \hat{\alpha})^2} \geq \left(1 - \frac{\epsilon_p}{100}\right)^2 \tag{10-230a}$$

where

$$\hat{\alpha} \triangleq \frac{A_0}{\gamma} \tag{10-230b}$$

Note that (10-230a) has the same format as that of (10-218). Hence, ω_1 is approximately given by

$$\omega_1 \simeq \hat{\alpha}\omega_a \sqrt{\frac{\epsilon_p}{50}} \simeq \frac{A_0 \omega_a \sqrt{0.02\epsilon_p}}{\gamma} \tag{10-231}$$

and all the conclusions in the inverting voltage-gain amplifier case apply equally to the present case of noninverting voltage-gain amplifiers.

10-3-3. Integrator

Consider the integrator circuit in Fig. 10-43(a), where, with an ideal operational amplifier, the transfer function is given by

$$H_i(s) = -\frac{1}{sRC} \tag{10-232a}$$

For $\omega \geq 0$, we have

$$|H_i(j\omega)| = \frac{1}{\omega RC} \tag{10-232b}$$

$$\phi_i(\omega) \triangleq -\underline{/H_i(j\omega)} = -90° \tag{10-232c}$$

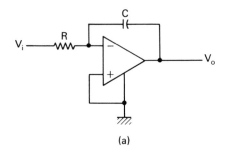

(a)

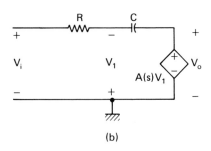

(b)

Fig. 10-43 An inverting integrator.
(a) Schematic. (b) Modeled circuit.

By replacing the operational amplifier with its simplified model, we obtain
the circuit shown in Fig. 10-43(b). To simplify the analysis, let us assume that
$A(s) = a_0 \gg 1$. For $\omega > 0$, we have

$$H_n(s) = \frac{V_o}{V_i} = -\frac{1}{\dfrac{1}{a_0} + sRC\left(1 + \dfrac{1}{a_0}\right)} \qquad (10\text{-}233a)$$

$$|H_n(j\omega)| = \frac{1}{\sqrt{\left(\dfrac{1}{a_0}\right)^2 + (\omega RC)^2\left(1 + \dfrac{1}{a_0}\right)^2}}$$

$$\simeq \frac{1}{\sqrt{\left(\dfrac{1}{a_0}\right)^2 + (\omega RC)^2}} \qquad (10\text{-}233b)$$

$$= \frac{1}{\omega RC} \frac{1}{\sqrt{\left(\dfrac{1}{\omega RC a_0}\right)^2 + 1}}$$

and

$$\phi_n(\omega) \triangleq -\underline{/H_n(j\omega)} = \tan^{-1}(a_0\omega RC) \qquad (10\text{-}233c)$$

We now consider the effect of finite open-loop gain on the useful bandwidth
of the integrator.

To maintain the integrator to within ϵ_p percentage magnitude error, the generic frequency point ω has to satisfy

$$|H_n(j\omega)| \geq \left(1 - \frac{\epsilon_p}{100}\right)|H_i(j\omega)| \qquad (10\text{-}234)$$

Substituting (10-232b) and (10-233b) into (10-234) gives

$$\frac{1}{\omega RC}\frac{1}{\sqrt{1 + \left(\frac{1}{\omega RC a_0}\right)^2}} \geq \left(1 - \frac{\epsilon_p}{100}\right)\frac{1}{\omega RC}$$

or

$$\frac{1}{1 + \left(\frac{1}{\omega RC a_0}\right)^2} \geq \left(1 - \frac{\epsilon_p}{100}\right)^2 \qquad (10\text{-}235)$$

Inverting, we obtain

$$1 + \left(\frac{1}{\omega RC a_0}\right)^2 \leq \frac{1}{\left(1 - \frac{\epsilon_p}{100}\right)^2} \simeq 1 + \frac{\epsilon_p}{50}$$

or

$$\frac{1}{\omega RC a_0} \leq \sqrt{\frac{\epsilon_p}{50}} = \sqrt{0.02\epsilon_p} \qquad (10\text{-}236)$$

Hence, the *minimum* frequency point ω_2 where the integrator meets the ϵ_p requirement is given by

$$\omega_2 = \frac{1}{RC a_0}\sqrt{\frac{50}{\epsilon_p}} \qquad (10\text{-}237)$$

That is, the useful frequency bandwidth for an integrator with a finite gain and an infinite bandwidth operational amplifier is from $f_2 \triangleq \omega_2/2\pi$ Hz. to infinity. If $a_0 = \infty$, then the integrator magnitude will function properly for all ω. On the other hand, the finite bandwidth property of a real operational amplifier will place a lower-frequency limit on the satisfactory performance of the integrator's magnitude function. Note that from (10-236), we need a larger a_0 to produce a higher-precision integrator.

Another factor to consider for an integrator is its phase angle. If a maximum error of ϵ_ϕ degree is allowed, then the generic frequency point ω has to satisfy

$$|\phi_n(\omega) - \phi_i(\omega)| \leq \epsilon_\phi$$

or

$$|\tan^{-1}(a_0\omega RC) - 90°| \leq \epsilon_\phi \qquad (10\text{-}238)$$

A minimum frequency value ω_3 such that the integrator meets the ϵ_ϕ phase error tolerance requirement can be computed from (10-238). For example, when $\epsilon_\phi = 1°$, we have

$$a_0\omega_3 RC \geq \tan 89° = 57.29$$

or

$$\omega_3 = \frac{57.29}{a_0 RC} \qquad (10\text{-}239)$$

Example 10-23   For the integrator circuit in Fig. 10-43, where $RC = 10^{-3}$ and the operational amplifier is characterized by Fig. 10-25, find the frequency range where the magnitude error is less than 1 % and the phase error is less than 2°.

Solution: From (10-237) and (10-238), the integrator will meet both the magnitude and the phase tolerance requirements if the following equations are satisfied:

$$\omega \geq \frac{\sqrt{50}}{RC a_0} = \frac{7.07 \times 10^3}{a_0} \qquad (10\text{-}240a)$$

and

$$\omega \geq \frac{\tan 88°}{RC a_0} = \frac{28.64 \times 10^3}{a_0} \qquad (10\text{-}240b)$$

where a_0 is the minimum open-loop gain of the operational amplifier within the useful frequency bandwidth of the integrator. Clearly, for the two equations in (10-240), we need only to deal with (10-240b). Recall that the open-loop gain of the operational amplifier involved is characterized by

$$A(s) = \frac{A_0}{1 + (s/\omega_a)} \qquad (10\text{-}241a)$$

and

$$|A(j\omega)| = \frac{A_0}{\sqrt{1 + (\omega/\omega_a)^2}} \qquad (10\text{-}241b)$$

where

$$A_0 = 50000 \quad \text{and} \quad \omega_a = 20(2\pi) = 40\pi \text{ rad./sec.} \qquad (10\text{-}241c)$$

Let the useful frequency bandwidth of the integrator be from ω_m to ω_M rad./sec. Then the design equations are from (10-240b):

$$\omega_m = \frac{28.64 \times 10^3}{a_0} \qquad (10\text{-}242a)$$

and from (10-241b):

$$a_0 = \frac{A_0}{\sqrt{1 + (\omega_M/\omega_a)^2}} \simeq \frac{A_0 \omega_a}{\omega_M}$$

or

$$\omega_M = \frac{A_0 \omega_a}{a_0} = \frac{2\pi \times 10^6}{a_0} \qquad (10\text{-}242b)$$

Note that (10-242b) was derived because $|A(j\omega)|$ is a decreasing function of ω and that the ratio of ω_M to ω_a is generally very large compared to 1. Because there are two equations and three unknowns (a_0, ω_m, and ω_M), there is a degree of freedom. From (10-242), we observe that if a_0 becomes larger, then both ω_m and ω_M become smaller. For example, if a_0 is chosen to be 10^3, then $\omega_m = 28.64$ and $\omega_M = 2000\pi$ rad./sec. On the other hand, if $a_0 = 10^4$, then $\omega_m = 2.864$ and $\omega_M = 200\pi$ rad./sec. For most voice circuits, a good choice in this case would probably be $a_0 = 250$, which yields a useful frequency bandwidth from

$$f_m \triangleq \frac{\omega_m}{2\pi} = \frac{28.64 \times 10^3}{(250)(2\pi)} = 18.23 \text{ Hz}.$$

to

$$f_M \triangleq \frac{\omega_M}{2\pi} = \frac{2\pi \times 10^6}{(250)(2\pi)} = 4000 \text{ Hz}. \qquad \blacksquare$$

10-3-4. Friend's Bandpass Filter Section

Consider the bandpass circuit in Fig. 10-44(a), which is a special case of Friend's biquad circuit. Suppose that the desired transfer function has a denominator

$$D(s) = s^2 + b_1 s + b_0 = s^2 + \left(\frac{\omega_0}{Q}\right)s + \omega_0^2 \qquad (10\text{-}243a)$$

where

$$\omega_0 = \sqrt{b_0} \quad \text{and} \quad Q = \frac{\omega_0}{b_1} = \frac{\sqrt{b_0}}{b_1} \qquad (10\text{-}243b)$$

are the pole-frequency and pole-pair of the circuit. From (10-114) through (10-118), a circuit design is obtained by letting

$$C_1 = C_2 = C$$
$$G_1 = G_a = Q^2 G_b \qquad (10\text{-}244)$$
$$G_b = G_2$$

where we have assumed the terminologies of subsection 10-2-1-2. With (10-244) and an ideal operational amplifier, the denominator of the circuit is characterized by (10-243), with

$$b_1 = \frac{1}{C^2 G_a}[2CG_a G_2 - CG_1 G_b] = \frac{G_b}{C} \qquad (10\text{-}245a)$$

$$b_0 = \frac{1}{C^2 G_a}[G_1 G_2 G_a] = \frac{G_a G_b}{C^2} \qquad (10\text{-}245b)$$

$$Q = \frac{\sqrt{b_0}}{b_1} = \sqrt{\frac{G_a}{G_b}} \qquad (10\text{-}245c)$$

and

$$\omega_0 = \frac{\sqrt{G_a G_b}}{C} = \frac{QG_b}{C} \qquad (10\text{-}245d)$$

Let us now replace the operational amplifier with its simplified model, as shown in Fig. 10-44(b). The transfer function in this case has the denominator

$$\hat{D}(s) = s^2 + \hat{b}_1 s + \hat{b}_0 = s^2 + \left(\frac{\hat{\omega}_0}{\hat{Q}}\right)s + \hat{\omega}_0^2 \qquad (10\text{-}246a)$$

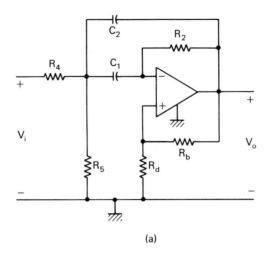

(a)

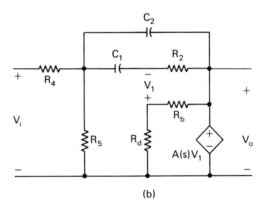

(b)

Fig. 10-44 Friend's bandpass biquad circuit. (a) Schematic. (b) Modeled circuit.

where

$$\hat{b}_1 = \frac{CQ^2G_b^2 + \dfrac{1}{A(s)}[CG_b^2(Q^2 + 1)(Q^2 + 2)]}{C^2Q^2G_b + \dfrac{1}{A(s)}[C^2G_b(Q^2 + 1)]} \qquad (10\text{-}246b)$$

and

$$\hat{b}_0 = \frac{Q^4G_b^3 + \dfrac{1}{A(s)}[Q^2G_b^3(Q^2 + 1)]}{C^2Q^2G_b + \dfrac{1}{A(s)}[C^2G_b(Q^2 + 1)]} \qquad (10\text{-}246c)$$

Assuming that the original Q is large enough that $Q^2 \gg 2$ and the working frequency is low enough that $|A(j\omega)| \gg 1$, then (10-246) can be approximated closely as

$$\hat{b}_1 \simeq \frac{CQ^2G_b^2\left[1 + \dfrac{Q^2}{A(s)}\right]}{C^2Q^2G_b\left[1 + \dfrac{1}{A(s)}\right]} \tag{10-247a}$$

$$\simeq \frac{G_b}{C}\left[1 + \frac{Q^2}{A(s)}\right] = \frac{\omega_0}{Q}\left[1 + \frac{Q^2}{A(s)}\right]$$

$$\hat{b}_0 \simeq \frac{Q^4G_b^3\left[1 + \dfrac{1}{A(s)}\right]}{C^2Q^2G_b\left[1 + \dfrac{1}{A(s)}\right]} \tag{10-247b}$$

$$= \frac{Q^2G_b^2}{C^2} = \omega_0^2$$

where we have utilized (10-245) to simplify the expressions in (10-247). Substituting (10-247) into (10-246a), we obtain

$$\hat{D}(s) = s^2 + \frac{\omega_0}{Q}\left[1 + \frac{Q^2}{A(s)}\right]s + \omega_0^2 \tag{10-248}$$

Assume that the open-loop gain of the operational amplifier is given by

$$A(s) = \frac{A_0\omega_a}{s + \omega_a} \tag{10-249}$$

Then (10-248) becomes

$$\hat{D}(s) = s^2 + \frac{\omega_0}{Q}\left[1 + \frac{Q^2(s + \omega_a)}{A_0\omega_a}\right]s + \omega_0^2$$

$$= s^2\left[1 + \frac{\omega_0 Q}{A_0\omega_a}\right] + \frac{\omega_0}{Q}\left[1 + \frac{Q^2}{A_0}\right]s + \omega_0^2 \tag{10-250}$$

$$= \left(1 + \frac{\omega_0 Q}{A_0\omega_a}\right)\left[s^2 + \frac{\omega_0\left(1 + \dfrac{Q^2}{A_0}\right)s}{Q\left(1 + \dfrac{\omega_0 Q}{A_0\omega_a}\right)} + \frac{\omega_0^2}{1 + \dfrac{\omega_0 Q}{A_0\omega_a}}\right]$$

Therefore, by taking into account the finite gain and finite bandwidth of an operational amplifier, the actual pole-frequency $\hat{\omega}_0$ and pole-pair $\hat{Q}$ are given by

$$\hat{\omega}_0 = \frac{\omega_0}{\sqrt{1 + \dfrac{\omega_0 Q}{A_0\omega_a}}} \tag{10-251a}$$

and

$$\hat{Q} = \frac{\omega_0}{\sqrt{1 + \dfrac{\omega_0 Q}{A_0\omega_a}}}\left(\frac{Q}{\omega_0}\right)\frac{1 + \dfrac{\omega_0 Q}{A_0\omega_a}}{1 + \dfrac{Q^2}{A_0}} \tag{10-251b}$$

$$= Q\frac{\sqrt{1 + \dfrac{\omega_0 Q}{A_0\omega_a}}}{1 + \dfrac{Q^2}{A_0}}$$

From (10-251a), we note that as the desired $\omega_0 Q = b_0/b_1$ increases, the actual pole-frequency decreases and will be at 0.707 of the desired value when

$$\omega_0 Q = A_0 \omega_a \qquad (10\text{-}252)$$

By taking derivatives of $\hat{Q}$ with respect to A_0 and ω_a, it can be shown that the actual pole-pair $\hat{Q}$ decreases as A_0 decreases and that a lower cutoff frequency ω_a enhances the actual $\hat{Q}$ factor.

If $\omega_0 Q$ is small compared with the gain-bandwidth product $A_0 \omega_a$ of the operational amplifier involved, and if $Q^2 \ll A_0$, then we can approximate (10-251) as

$$\hat{\omega}_0 \simeq \omega_0 \left[1 - \frac{1}{2} \left(\frac{\omega_0 Q}{A_0 \omega_a} \right) \right] \qquad (10\text{-}253a)$$

and

$$
\hat{Q} \simeq Q \left[1 + \frac{1}{2} \left(\frac{\omega_0 Q}{A_0 \omega_a} \right) \right] \left(1 - \frac{Q^2}{A_0} \right)
$$
$$
\simeq Q \left[1 + \frac{1}{2} \left(\frac{\omega_0 Q}{A_0 \omega_a} \right) - \frac{Q^2}{A_0} \right] \qquad (10\text{-}253b)
$$

Hence, the percentage ω_0 and Q errors due to idealizing the operational amplifier in the circuit are given respectively by

$$
\epsilon_{\omega_0} \% = \frac{\hat{\omega}_0 - \omega_0}{\omega_0} (100\%)
$$
$$
= -\frac{50 \omega_0 Q}{A_0 \omega_a} \% \qquad (10\text{-}254a)
$$

and

$$
\epsilon_Q \% = \frac{\hat{Q} - Q}{Q} (100\%)
$$
$$
= \frac{100 Q}{A_0} \left[\frac{1}{2} \left(\frac{\omega_0}{\omega_a} \right) - Q \right] \% \qquad (10\text{-}254b)
$$

As expected, (10-254) indicates that absolute ω_0 and Q errors decrease with increasing A_0.

Example 10-24 Consider the circuit in Fig. 10-44, where the operational amplifier is characterized by Fig. 10-25. Suppose that the desired center frequency is at 3500 Hz. and that Q is 10. Find the percentage errors in ω_0 and Q due to idealizing the operational amplifier.

Solution: Because $A_0 = 50000$ and $\omega_a = 40\pi$ rad./sec.,

$$\omega_0 Q = 3500(2\pi)10 = 70000\pi$$

is small compared to the gain-bandwidth product of the operational amplifier

$$A_0 \omega_a = 2\pi \times 10^6$$

In addition, $Q^2 = 100 \ll A_0$. Hence, (10-254) is applicable, and we obtain

$$\epsilon_{\omega_0}\% = -\frac{50(70000\pi)}{2 \times 10^6} = -1.75\%$$

$$\epsilon_Q\% = \frac{100(10)}{50000}\left[\frac{7000\pi}{2(40\pi)} - 10\right] \simeq 1.75\% \quad\blacksquare$$

To remedy the ω_0 and Q deviations from the desired values due to the nonideal properties of the operational amplifier in the circuit, we can predistort the ω_0 and Q values. For example, if the desired values are ω_{0d} and Q_d, then the pole-frequency ω_0 and pole-pair Q values for Friend's circuit design equations (with an ideal operational amplifier) are given by

$$\omega_0 = \frac{\omega_{0d}}{1 - \frac{1}{2}\left(\frac{\omega_{0d}Q_d}{A_0\omega_a}\right)} \simeq \omega_{0d}\left[1 + \frac{1}{2}\left(\frac{\omega_{0d}Q_d}{A_0\omega_a}\right)\right] \tag{10-255a}$$

and

$$Q = \frac{Q_d}{1 + \frac{1}{2}\left(\frac{\omega_{0d}Q_d}{A_0\omega_a}\right) - \frac{Q_d^2}{A_0}} \simeq Q_d\left[1 - \frac{1}{2}\left(\frac{\omega_{0d}Q_d}{A_0\omega_a}\right) + \frac{Q_d^2}{A_0}\right] \tag{10-255b}$$

In this way, the end circuit with a real operational amplifier will yield the desired ω_{0d} and Q_d values provided that

$$\omega_{0d}Q_d \ll A_0\omega_a \quad\text{and}\quad Q_d^2 \ll A_0 \tag{10-256}$$

10-4   ACTIVE CIRCUITS WITHOUT CAPACITORS

From the previous section, it is clear that for high-frequency applications we need to take into account the nonideal properties of operational amplifiers. For most operational amplifiers with T compensation, Fig. 10-25 presents a typical open-loop gain characteristic $A(s)$, where

$$A(s) = \frac{A_0\omega_a}{s + \omega_a} = \frac{A_0}{1 + (s/\omega_a)} \tag{10-257}$$

Observe that (10-257) says that the transfer relationship of an operational amplifier includes the effect of an RC network with one capacitor, which leads us to conclude that we can design a biquad circuit with resistors and two operational amplifiers (without using capacitors). This class of filters is called *active R*.

In this section, we present two biquad active R circuits. The first one is a bandpass filter that has a very simple structure and is suitable for high-frequency and high-Q applications. The second biquad has the versatility similar to that of Tow's multiple amplifier biquad circuit.

10-4-1. A High-Q High-Frequency Bandpass Active R Biquad Circuit

Consider the circuit in Fig. 10-45. The circuit equations are

$$V_i = V_1 + A_2(s)V_2 \qquad (10\text{-}258)$$

$$V_o = V_2 + \frac{R_1 A_2(s)V_2}{R_1 + R_2} \qquad (10\text{-}259)$$

$$V_o = A_1(s)V_1 \qquad (10\text{-}260)$$

Solving V_1 and V_2 in terms of V_o, (10-259) and (10-260) yield

$$V_1 = \frac{V_o}{A_1(s)} \qquad (10\text{-}261a)$$

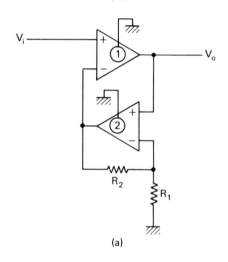

(a)

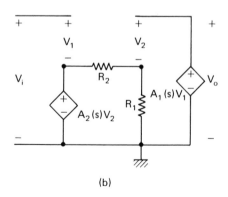

(b)

Fig. 10-45 A high-frequency high-Q active R bandpass circuit.

$$V_2 = \frac{V_o}{1 + \dfrac{R_1 A_2(s)}{R_1 + R_2}} \tag{10-261b}$$

By substituting (10-261) into (10-258), we obtain

$$V_i = \frac{V_o}{A_1(s)} + \frac{A_2(s)V_o}{1 + \dfrac{R_1 A_2(s)}{R_1 + R_2}}$$

$$= \left[\frac{1}{A_1(s)} + \frac{A_2(s)}{1 + \gamma A_2(s)} \right] V_o \tag{10-262a}$$

$$= \frac{1 + \gamma A_2(s) + A_1(s)A_2(s)}{A_1(s)[1 + \gamma A_2(s)]} V_o$$

where

$$\gamma = \frac{R_1}{R_1 + R_2} \tag{10-262b}$$

Hence, the transfer function of the circuit in Fig. 10-45 is given by

$$H(s) = \frac{V_o}{V_i} = \frac{A_1(s)[1 + \gamma A_2(s)]}{A_1(s)A_2(s) + \gamma A_2(s) + 1} \tag{10-263}$$

Let the open-loop gains $A_1(s)$ and $A_2(s)$ of the two operational amplifiers be identical and be given by

$$A_1(s) = A_2(s) = A(s) = \frac{A_0 \omega_a}{s + \omega_a} \triangleq \frac{B}{s + \omega_a} \tag{10-264a}$$

where

$$B = A_0 \omega \tag{10-264b}$$

is the gain-bandwidth product of the operational amplifiers. Then (10-263) becomes

$$H(s) = \frac{B(s + \omega_a + \gamma B)}{B^2 + \gamma B(s + \omega_a) + (s + \omega_a)^2}$$

$$= \frac{B[s + (\omega_a + \gamma B)]}{s^2 + (\gamma B + 2\omega_a)s + (\omega_a^2 + \gamma B\omega_a + B^2)} \tag{10-265}$$

Because $2\omega_a$ is very small compared with $\gamma B = \gamma A_0 \omega_a$ for a very wide range of γ values (say $\gamma \geq 200/A_0 \simeq 0.004$), we can approximate (10-265) by

$$H(s) \simeq \frac{B(s + \gamma B)}{s^2 + \gamma Bs + B^2} = \frac{(s/B) + \gamma}{(s/B)^2 + \gamma(s/B) + 1} \tag{10-266}$$

Note that we can obtain (10-266) from (10-263) if we assume that

$$A(s) = \frac{B}{s} = A_1(s) = A_2(s) \tag{10-267}$$

That is, (10-266) is a good approximation to (10-265) if the frequency of interest $\omega \gg \omega_a$.

From (10-266), we obtain the pole-frequency and the pole-pair of the biquad circuit as

$$\omega_0 = B = A_0\omega_a \qquad (10\text{-}268a)$$

$$Q = \frac{1}{\gamma} = \frac{R_1 + R_2}{R_1} \qquad (10\text{-}268b)$$

For operational amplifiers characterized by Fig. 10-25, the center frequency is given by

$$f_0 \triangleq \frac{\omega_0}{2\pi} = 1 \text{ MHz.}$$

That is, the circuit in Fig. 10-45 is indeed intended for high-frequency applications only. Note that it is possible to adjust the gain-bandwidth product B of operational amplifiers with various compensation schemes.

From (10-268b), we observe that the circuit in Fig. 10-45 can only realize filters with $Q \geq 1$. If $Q \gg 1$, then $\gamma \ll 1$ and (10-266) can be further approximated by

$$H(s) \simeq \frac{Bs}{s^2 + \gamma Bs + B^2} \qquad (10\text{-}269)$$

This means that the circuit in Fig. 10-45 is a good bandpass filter for high-Q and high-frequency applications.

10-4-2. An Active R Biquad Circuit

In this subsection, we introduce an active R biquad circuit. This biquad circuit can provide simultaneously a low-pass and a bandpass output. With an additional summing amplifier circuit, it can provide all forms of biquadratic transfer functions.[32]

Consider the circuit in Fig. 10-46, where R_4 and R_5 are constrained by

$$R_4 = (1 - \beta)R \qquad (10\text{-}270a)$$

$$R_5 = \beta R \qquad (10\text{-}270b)$$

with

$$0 < \beta < 1 \qquad (10\text{-}270c)$$

The two operational amplifiers are assumed to be identical and are characterized by the open-loop gain

$$A(s) = \frac{A_0\omega_a}{s + \omega_a} = \frac{B}{s + \omega_a} \qquad (10\text{-}271)$$

---

[32]If the closed-loop gain of the summing amplifier circuit is low, then we can consider the operational amplifier used in the summing circuit as an ideal operational amplifier without adverse consequences.

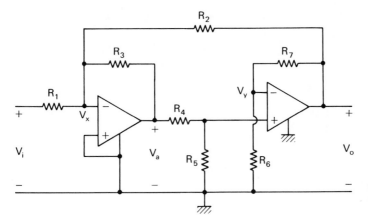

Fig. 10-46   An active R biquad circuit.

With the node-to-ground voltages indicated in Fig. 10-46, the circuit equations are

$$\frac{V_i - V_x}{R_1} + \frac{V_o - V_x}{R_2} + \frac{V_a - V_x}{R_3} = 0 \qquad (10\text{-}272\text{a})$$

$$\frac{V_o - V_y}{R_7} = \frac{V_y}{R_6} \qquad (10\text{-}272\text{b})$$

$$V_a = -\frac{A_0 \omega_a}{s + \omega_a} V_x \qquad (10\text{-}272\text{c})$$

$$V_o = \frac{A_0 \omega_a}{s + \omega_a}(\beta V_a - V_y) \qquad (10\text{-}272\text{d})$$

After a lengthy computation, (10-272) yields

$$\frac{V_a}{V_i} = \frac{a_1 s + a_0}{s^2 + b_1 s + b_0} \qquad (10\text{-}273\text{a})$$

and

$$\frac{V_o}{V_i} = \frac{\alpha_0}{s^2 + b_1 s + b_0} \qquad (10\text{-}273\text{b})$$

where

$$a_1 = \frac{A_0 \omega_a}{1 + \dfrac{R_1}{R_2} + \dfrac{R_1}{R_3}} \qquad (10\text{-}274\text{a})$$

$$a_0 = \frac{A_0 \omega_a^2}{1 + \dfrac{R_1}{R_2} + \dfrac{R_1}{R_3}}\left(1 + \frac{A_0}{1 + \dfrac{R_7}{R_6}}\right) \qquad (10\text{-}274\text{b})$$

$$b_1 = 2\omega_a + \omega_a A_0\left(\frac{1}{1 + \dfrac{R_3}{R_2} + \dfrac{R_3}{R_1}} + \frac{1}{1 + \dfrac{R_7}{R_6}}\right) \qquad (10\text{-}274\text{c})$$

$$b_0 = \frac{\omega_a^2\left[\left(A_0 + 1 + \dfrac{R_3}{R_2} + \dfrac{R_3}{R_1}\right)\left(A_0 + 1 + \dfrac{R_7}{R_6}\right) + \dfrac{R_3}{R_2}\beta A_0^2\left(1 + \dfrac{R_7}{R_6}\right) - A_0^2\right]}{\left(1 + \dfrac{R_3}{R_2} + \dfrac{R_3}{R_1}\right)\left(1 + \dfrac{R_7}{R_6}\right)}$$

(10-274d)

and

$$\alpha_0 = \frac{A_0^2\omega_a^2\beta}{1 + \dfrac{R_1}{R_2} + \dfrac{R_1}{R_3}}$$

(10-274e)

In general, A_0 is very large compared to resistor ratios and ω_a. Hence, we can approximate (10-274) as

$$a_1 = \frac{B}{1 + \dfrac{R_1}{R_2} + \dfrac{R_1}{R_3}}$$

(10-275a)

$$a_0 = \frac{B^2}{\left(1 + \dfrac{R_1}{R_2} + \dfrac{R_1}{R_3}\right)\left(1 + \dfrac{R_7}{R_6}\right)}$$

(10-275b)

$$b_1 = B\left(\frac{1}{1 + \dfrac{R_3}{R_2} + \dfrac{R_3}{R_1}} + \frac{1}{1 + \dfrac{R_7}{R_6}}\right)$$

(10-275c)

$$b_0 = \frac{\dfrac{R_3}{R_2}\beta B^2}{1 + \dfrac{R_3}{R_2} + \dfrac{R_3}{R_1}}$$

(10-275d)

and

$$\alpha_0 = \frac{\beta B^2}{1 + \dfrac{R_1}{R_2} + \dfrac{R_1}{R_3}}$$

(10-275e)

From (10-275), the pole-frequency and the pole-pair of the circuit are

$$\omega_0 = \sqrt{b_0} = \sqrt{\frac{\dfrac{R_3}{R_2}\beta B^2}{1 + \dfrac{R_3}{R_2} + \dfrac{R_3}{R_1}}}$$

(10-276a)

and

$$Q = \frac{\sqrt{b_0}}{b_1} = \frac{\left(1 + \dfrac{R_7}{R_6}\right)\sqrt{\dfrac{R_3}{R_2}\beta\left(1 + \dfrac{R_3}{R_2} + \dfrac{R_3}{R_1}\right)}}{2 + \dfrac{R_3}{R_2} + \dfrac{R_3}{R_1} + \dfrac{R_7}{R_6}}$$

(10-276b)

The sensitivity functions of ω_0 and Q can be computed from (10-276). The results are

$$|S_x^{\omega_0}| \leq 0.5 \quad \text{and} \quad |S_x^{Q}| \leq 1$$

(10-277)

where x stands for A_0, ω_a, B, and any resistor value. That is, the active R circuit in Fig. 10-46 has good passive and active sensitivity properties.

Note that if we take V_o as the output, the circuit is a low-pass filter characterized by (10-273b). On the other hand, if we take V_a as the output, then the circuit will function like a bandpass filter if

$$a_0 \ll b_0 \tag{10-278}$$

By substituting (10-275) into (10-278), we obtain the requirement for the circuit to perform as a bandpass filter as

$$\frac{R_1}{R_2}\beta\left(1 + \frac{R_7}{R_6}\right) \gg 1 \tag{10-279}$$

Low-Pass. Now we consider procedures to realize biquadratic transfer functions with the circuit in Fig. 10-46. Let us first consider the low-pass case. Suppose that the desired low-pass filter is given by (10-273b). Then the design equations can be derived from (10-275) as

$$1 + \frac{R_1}{R_2} + \frac{R_1}{R_3} = \frac{\beta B^2}{\alpha_0}$$

implying that

$$1 + \frac{R_3}{R_2} + \frac{R_3}{R_1} = \frac{R_3}{R_1}\left(\frac{\beta B^2}{\alpha_0}\right) \tag{10-280}$$

$$\frac{1}{1 + \frac{R_7}{R_6}} = \frac{b_1}{B} - \frac{R_1}{R_3}\frac{\alpha_0}{\beta B^2}$$

or that

$$1 + \frac{R_7}{R_6} = \frac{1}{\dfrac{b_1}{B} - \dfrac{R_1}{R_3}\left(\dfrac{\alpha_0}{\beta B^2}\right)} \tag{10-281}$$

Substituting (10-280) and (10-281) into (10-275d), we obtain

$$b_0 = \frac{R_3\beta B^2}{R_2}\frac{1}{1 + \frac{R_3}{R_2} + \frac{R_3}{R_1}}$$

$$= \frac{R_3\beta B^2}{R_2}\frac{R_1\alpha_0}{R_3\beta B^2} = \frac{R_1}{R_2}\alpha_0$$

or

$$\frac{R_1}{R_2} = \frac{b_0}{\alpha_0} \tag{10-282}$$

With (10-282), (10-280) and (10-281) yield

$$\frac{R_1}{R_3} = \frac{\beta B^2}{\alpha_0} - \frac{R_1}{R_2} - 1 = \frac{\beta B^2}{\alpha_0} - \frac{b_0}{\alpha_0} - 1 \tag{10-283}$$

and

$$\frac{R_7}{R_6} = \frac{1}{\dfrac{b_1}{B} - \dfrac{R_1}{R_3}\left(\dfrac{\alpha_0}{\beta B^2}\right)} - 1 \tag{10-284}$$

To ensure that the resistor ratios in (10-282) through (10-284) are positive, we need to satisfy the following two equations:

$$\beta B^2 - b_0 - \alpha_0 > 0 \tag{10-285a}$$

and

$$1 > \frac{b_1}{B} - \frac{\beta B^2 - b_0 - \alpha_0}{\beta B^2} > 0 \tag{10-285b}$$

With $0 < \beta < 1$, (10-285) forms the realizability criteria for the circuit in Fig. 10-46 to function as a low-pass filter. Notice that (10-285a) and the right half of (10-285b) are satisfied if β is set to

$$\frac{\beta B^2 - b_0 - \alpha_0}{\beta B^2} = \frac{b_1}{yB} \tag{10-286a}$$

or

$$\beta = \frac{b_0 + \alpha_0}{B^2 - \dfrac{b_1 B}{y}} \tag{10-286b}$$

where

$$y > 1 \tag{10-286c}$$

In this case, a design procedure is:

1. Given the desired low-pass biquadratic transfer function (α_0, b_1, b_0) and the operational amplifier parameters (ω_a, A_0, or $B = \omega_a A_0$).
2. Check if the realizability conditions in (10-285) can be satisfied with $0 < \beta < 1$. If affirmative, find an appropriate β value from (10-286).
3. Choose R, R_3, and R_6 arbitrarily.[33]
4. Find R_4 and R_5 from (10-270), R_1 from (10-283), R_2 from (10-282), and R_7 from (10-284).

Example 10-25 Find an active R realization of

$$H(s) = \frac{2 \times 10^{12}}{s^2 + 10^5 s + 10^{12}} \tag{10-287}$$

Solution: Assuming that the operational amplifiers are characterized by Fig. 10-25, then the given parameters are

$$\alpha_0 = 2 \times 10^{12}, \quad b_1 = 10^5, \quad b_0 = 10^{12}, \quad \text{and} \quad B = 2\pi \times 10^6$$

[33]The values of R, R_3, and R_6 are generally chosen (1) to minimize the spread of resistor values, and (2) to minimize the effect of finite input impedance and nonzero output impedance of the operational amplifiers in the circuit.

With these given parameters, (10-285a) requires that

$$\beta > \frac{b_0 + \alpha_0}{B^2} = \frac{3}{4\pi^2} \qquad (10\text{-}288)$$

Because

$$\frac{b_1}{B} = \frac{1}{20\pi} < 1$$

(10-285b) will be satisfied if

$$\beta B^2 - b_0 - \alpha_0 = \frac{\beta b_1 B}{y} \qquad (10\text{-}289a)$$

where

$$y \geq 1 \qquad (10\text{-}289b)$$

or

$$\beta = \frac{3 \times 10^{12}}{4\pi^2 \times 10^{12} - \dfrac{2\pi \times 10^{11}}{y}} \qquad (10\text{-}290)$$

Clearly, the β value in (10-290) must also meet the condition set by the (10-288). To see how to choose the value for y properly, we use (10-284), (10-283), and (10-286a) as

$$\frac{R_7}{R_6} = \frac{1}{\dfrac{b_1}{B} - \dfrac{R_1}{R_3}\dfrac{\alpha_0}{\beta B^2}} - 1$$

$$= \frac{1}{\dfrac{b_1}{B} - \dfrac{\beta B^2 - b_0 - \alpha_0}{\beta B^2}} - 1 \qquad (10\text{-}291)$$

$$= \frac{1}{\dfrac{b_1}{B} - \dfrac{b_1}{yB}} - 1$$

$$= \frac{B}{b_1} \frac{1}{1 - \dfrac{1}{y}} - 1$$

To ensure that the approximation employed in obtaining (10-275d) does not cause significant errors, we need to have a large ratio for R_7 over R_6. Hence, we should choose y very close to (and greater than) 1.

Let $y = 1.1$; then (10-290) gives

$$\beta = 0.077 \qquad (10\text{-}292)$$

Note that (10-288) is satisfied by (10-292). From (10-282) through (10-284), we obtain

$$\frac{R_1}{R_2} = \frac{1}{2} = 0.5 \qquad (10\text{-}293a)$$

$$\frac{R_1}{R_3} = 2\pi^2\beta - 1.5 = 0.022 \qquad (10\text{-}293b)$$

and

$$\frac{R_7}{R_6} = 690.15 \qquad \text{(10-293c)}$$

It can be shown that with the resistor ratios of (10-293) and β of (10-292), the realizability condition of (10-285) is satisfied. Let $R = 10$ K. Then (10-270) yields

$$R_4 = 9230\ \Omega \qquad \text{(10-294a)}$$

$$R_5 = 770\ \Omega \qquad \text{(10-294b)}$$

In addition, let

$$R_3 = 25\ \text{K}\Omega \qquad \text{(10-294c)}$$

and

$$R_6 = 250\ \Omega \qquad \text{(10-294d)}$$

Then (10-293) gives

$$R_7 = 172.54\ \text{K}\Omega \qquad \text{(10-294e)}$$

$$R_1 = 550\ \Omega \qquad \text{(10-294f)}$$

$$R_2 = 1100\ \Omega \qquad \text{(10-294g)}$$

A circuit realization of (10-286) via the element values of (10-294) is shown in Fig. 10-47. ∎

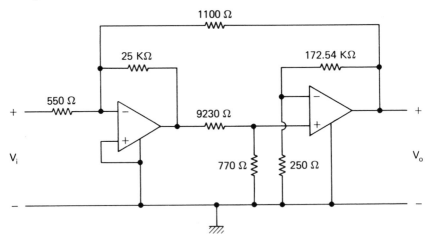

Fig. 10-47   An active R circuit realization of (10-286).

Bandpass. If the desired transfer function is a bandpass filter,

$$H(s) = \frac{a_1 s}{s^2 + b_1 s + b_0} \qquad \text{(10-295)}$$

then we can derive a set of design equations from (10-275) and (10-279) as

$$1 + \frac{R_1}{R_2} + \frac{R_1}{R_3} = \frac{B}{a_1} \qquad \text{(10-296a)}$$

or

$$1 + \frac{R_3}{R_2} + \frac{R_3}{R_1} = \frac{R_3}{R_1}\frac{B}{a_1} \qquad (10\text{-}296\text{b})$$

$$1 + \frac{R_7}{R_6} = \frac{1}{\dfrac{b_1}{B} - \dfrac{R_1}{R_3}\left(\dfrac{a_1}{B}\right)} \qquad (10\text{-}296\text{c})$$

$$\frac{R_1}{R_2} = \frac{b_0}{Ba_1\beta} \qquad (10\text{-}296\text{d})$$

From (10-296), we obtain

$$\frac{R_1}{R_2} = \frac{b_0}{Ba_1\beta} \qquad (10\text{-}297\text{a})$$

$$\frac{R_1}{R_3} = \frac{B}{a_1} - \frac{b_0}{Ba_1\beta} - 1 \qquad (10\text{-}297\text{b})$$

$$\frac{R_7}{R_6} = \frac{1}{\dfrac{b_1}{B} - \dfrac{R_1}{R_3}\left(\dfrac{a_1}{B}\right)} - 1 \qquad (10\text{-}297\text{c})$$

To ensure that (10-297) yields positive ratios, we require that

$$B - \frac{b_0}{\beta B} - a_1 > 0 \qquad (10\text{-}298\text{a})$$

$$1 > \frac{1}{B}\left[b_1 - \left(B - \frac{b_0}{\beta B} - a_1\right)\right] > 0 \qquad (10\text{-}298\text{b})$$

Notice here also that (10-298a) and the right half of (10-298b) are satisfied if

$$B - \frac{b_0}{\beta B} - a_1 = \frac{b_1}{y} \qquad (10\text{-}299\text{a})$$

or

$$\beta = \frac{b_0}{B\left(B - \dfrac{b_1}{y} - a_1\right)} \qquad (10\text{-}299\text{b})$$

where

$$y > 1 \qquad (10\text{-}299\text{c})$$

In this case, (10-297c), (10-297b), and (10-299a) yield

$$\begin{aligned}
\frac{R_7}{R_6} &= \frac{1}{\dfrac{b_1}{B} - \dfrac{a_1}{B}\dfrac{B}{a_1} - \dfrac{b_0}{Ba_1\beta} - 1} \\[2ex]
&= \frac{1}{\dfrac{b_1}{B} - \dfrac{b_1}{By}} - 1 \qquad (10\text{-}299\text{d}) \\[2ex]
&= \frac{B}{b_1}\frac{1}{1 - \dfrac{1}{y}} - 1
\end{aligned}$$

An appropriate value for y is determined jointly by (10-299b) to yield a β value between 0 and 1 and by (10-279) to satisfy the requirement of a bandpass filter.

Let us now give a design procedure for the circuit in Fig. 10-46 to perform as a bandpass filter:

1. Given the desired transfer function (a_1, b_1, b_0) and the operational amplifier parameters $(\omega_a, A_0, \text{ or } B = \omega_a A_0)$.
2. Check the realizability criteria of (10-298) with $0 < \beta < 1$. Find an appropriate β value if possible.
3. Choose R_1, R_3, and R_6.
4. Find R_4 and R_5 from (10-270), R_1 from (10-297b), R_2 from (10-297a), and R_7 from (10-297c).

Example 10-26   Find an active R realization of

$$H(s) = \frac{10^5 s}{s^2 + 10^5 s + 10^{12}} \tag{10-300}$$

Solution: From (10-299), the value of β to satisfy the realizability conditions of (10-298) is given by

$$\beta = \frac{1}{2\pi\left(2\pi - 0.1 - \dfrac{0.1}{y}\right)} \tag{10-301a}$$

where

$$y > 1 \tag{10-301b}$$

and where we have assumed that

$$B = 2\pi \times 10^6 \tag{10-302}$$

For the circuit to function as a bandpass filter, (10-279) requires that the ratio R_7/R_6 be large. From (10-299d), this means that y should be chosen to be close to 1. Let $y = 1.1$; then

$$\beta = \frac{1}{2\pi\left(2\pi - 0.1 - \dfrac{0.1}{1.1}\right)} = 0.026 \tag{10-303}$$

Note that (10-298b) is satisfied by (10-303). From (10-297), we obtain

$$\frac{R_1}{R_2} = \frac{10^{12}}{2\pi \times 10^6 (10^5) 0.026} = 61.2 \tag{10-304a}$$

$$\frac{R_1}{R_3} = \frac{2\pi \times 10^6}{10^5} - 61.2 - 1 = 0.632 \tag{10-304b}$$

$$\frac{R_7}{R_6} = \frac{2\pi \times 10^6}{10^5}(1 + 10) - 1 = 690.5 \tag{10-304c}$$

Let us choose

$$R = 10 \text{ K}\Omega$$

Then (10-270) gives

$$R_4 = 9739 \, \Omega \qquad\qquad (10\text{-}305a)$$

$$R_5 = 261 \, \Omega \qquad\qquad (10\text{-}305b)$$

Let

$$R_3 = 20 \, K\Omega \qquad\qquad (10\text{-}305c)$$

and

$$R_6 = 200 \, \Omega \qquad\qquad (10\text{-}305d)$$

Then (10-304) yields

$$R_1 = 12.64 \, K\Omega \qquad\qquad (10\text{-}305e)$$

$$R_2 = 207 \, \Omega \qquad\qquad (10\text{-}305f)$$

$$R_7 = 138 \, K\Omega \qquad\qquad (10\text{-}305g)$$

A circuit realization of (10-300) via (10-305) is shown in Fig. 10-48. From (10-275b), we find the ignored term

$$
\begin{aligned}
a_0 &= \frac{B^2}{\dfrac{B}{a_1}\left(1 + \dfrac{R_7}{R_6}\right)} \\
&= \frac{(2\pi \times 10^6)(10^5)}{691.5} = 9.1 \times 10^8 \qquad (10\text{-}306)
\end{aligned}
$$

Hence, the dc gain

$$\frac{a_0}{b_0} = 9.1 \times 10^{-4}$$

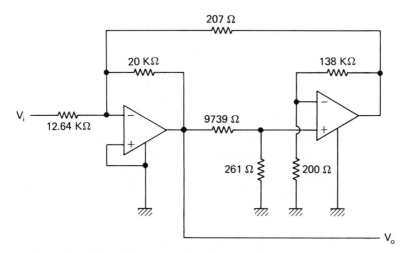

Fig. 10-48   An active R bandpass filter.

is rather small compared with the midband gain

$$\frac{a_1}{b_1} = 1$$

of the bandpass filter. That is, the circuit in Fig. 10-48 is a good realization of (10-300). ∎

REFERENCES AND FURTHER READING

[1] MITRA, S. K. *Active Inductorless Filters.* New York: IEEE Press, 1971.

[2] MITRA, S. K. *Analysis and Synthesis of Linear Active Networks.* New York: John Wiley, 1968.

[3] SU, K. L. *Active Network Synthesis.* New York: McGraw-Hill, 1965.

[4] HUELSMAN, L. P. *Theory and Design of Active RC Circuits.* New York: McGraw-Hill, 1968.

[5] HILBURN, J. L., and JOHNSON, D. E. *Manual of Active Filter Design.* New York: McGraw-Hill, 1973.

[6] HEINLEIN, W. E., and HOLMES, W. H. *Active Filters For Integrated Circuits.* London: Prentice-Hall, 1974.

[7] MOSCHYTZ, G. S. *Linear Integrated Networks: Fundamental.* New York: Van Nostrand Reinhold, 1974.

[8] MOSCHYTZ, G. S. *Linear Integrated Network: Design.* New York: Van Nostrand Reinhold, 1975.

[9] JOHNSON, D. E. *Introduction to Filter Theory.* Englewood Cliffs, N.J.: Prentice-Hall, Inc., 1976.

[10] BRUTON, L. T. "Network Transfer Functions Using the Concept of Frequency Dependent Negative Resistance." *IEEE Trans. Circuit Theory* CT-16 (1969): 406–8.

[11] BRUTON, L. T., and TRELEAVEN, D. "Active Filter Design Using Generalized Impedance Converter." *EDN*, (Feb. 5, 1973): 68–75.

[12] KUH, E. S. "Transfer Function Synthesis of Active RC Networks." *1960 IRE International Record* 8 (pt. 2): 134–38.

[13] HAZONY, D., and JOSEPH, R. D. "Transfer Matrix Synthesis with Active RC Networks." *SIAM J. Appl. Math.* 14 (1966): 739–61.

[14] MITRA, S. K. "Transfer Function Synthesis Using a Single Operational Amplifier." *Electronic Letters* 3 (1967): 333–34.

[15] YANAGISAWA, T. "RC Active Networks Using Current Inversion Type Negative Impedance Converters." *IRE Trans. Circuit Theory* CT-4 (1957): 140–44.

[16]   MATHEWS, M. V., and SEIFERT, W. W. "Transfer Function Synthesis with Computer Amplifiers and Passive Networks." *Proc. Western Joint Computer Conference* (March 1955): 7–12.

[17]   LOVERING, W. F. "Analog Computer Simulation of Transfer Functions." *Proc. IEEE* 53 (1965): 306.

[18]   MITRA, S. K. "Active RC Filters Employing a Single Operational Amplifier as the Active Element." *Proc. Hawaii International Conference on System Science* (1968): 433–36.

[19]   BROWN, G. C. "Sensitivity in Active RC Filters." *Electronic Letters* 3 (1967): 298–99.

[20]   SALLEN, R. P., and KEY, E. L. "A Practical Method of Designing RC Active Filters." *IRE Trans. Circuit Theory* CT-2 (1955): 74–85.

[21]   KERWIN, W. J., and HUELSMAN, L. P. "The Design of High Performance Active RC Band Pass Filters." *1966 IEEE International Convention Record* 14 (pt. 10): 74–80.

[22]   FRIEND, J. J., HARRIS, C. A., and HILBERMANN, D. "STAR: An Active Biquadratic Filter Section." *IEEE Trans. Circuit and Systems* CAS-22 (1975): 115–21.

[23]   KERWIN, W. J., HUELSMAN, L. P., and NEWCOMB, R. W. "State-Variable Synthesis for Insensitive Integrated Circuit Transfer Functions." *IEEE J. Solid State Circuits* SC-2 (1967): 87–92.

[24]   TOW, J. "A Step-by-Step Active-Filter Design." *IEEE Spectrum* 6 (1969): 64–68.

[25]   THOMAS, L. C. "The Biquad: Part I—Some Practical Design Considerations." *IEEE Trans. Circuit Theory* CT-18 (1971): 350–57.

[26]   THOMAS, L. C. "The Biquad: Part II—A Multipurpose Active Filtering System." *IEEE Trans. Circuit Theory* CT-18 (1971): 358–61.

[27]   GIRLING, F. E. J., and GOOD, E. F. "The Leapfrog or Active Ladder Synthesis." *Wireless World* (July 1970): pp. 285–87.

[28]   ADAMS, R. L. "On Reduced Sensitivity Active Filters." *14th Midwest Symp. on Circuit Theory*, Univeristy of Denver, Colorado (May 1971): 14.3-1 to 3-8.

[29]   SZENTIRMAI, G. "Synthesis of Multiple-Feedback Active Filters." *Bell Syst. Tech. J.* 52 (1973): 527–55.

[30]   LAKER, K. R., and GHAUSI, M. S. "Synthesis of a Low Sensitivity Multi-loop Feedback Active RC Filter." *IEEE Trans. Circuit and Systems* CAS-21 (1974): 252–59.

[31]   HILBERMAN, D. "Input and Ground as Complements in Active Filter." *IEEE Trans. Circuit Theory* CT-20 (1973): 540–47.

[32] MOSCHYTZ, G. S. "Second Order Pole-Zero Pair Section for *n*th Order Minimum Sensitivity Networks." *IEEE Trans. Circuit Theory* CT-17 (1970): 527–34.

[33] LEE, S. C. "Sensitivity Minimization in Active RC Integrated Circuit Design." *Proc. 4th Annual Allerton Conference on Circuit and System Theory* (1966): 269–81.

[34] LUEDER, E. "A Decomposition of a Transfer Function Minimizing Distortion and Inband Losses." *Bell·System Tech. J.* 49 (1970): 455–69.

[35] HALFIN, S. "An Optimization Method for Cascaded Filters." *Bell System Tech. J.* 49 (1970): 185–90.

[36] GRAEME, J. G., TOBEY, G. E., and HUELSMAN, L. P. *Operational Amplifier Design and Application.* New York: McGraw-Hill, 1971.

[37] GRAEME, J. D. *Applications of Operational Amplifiers: Third Generation Techniques.* New York: McGraw-Hill, 1973.

[38] ROBERGE, J. K. *Operational Amplifier: Theory and Practice.* New York: John Wiley, 1975.

[39] STOUT, D. F., and KAUFMAN, M. *Handbook of Operational Amplifier Circuit Design.* New York: McGraw-Hill, 1976.

[40] MOSCHYTZ, G. S. "The Operational Amplifier in Linear Active Networks." *IEEE Spectrum* 7 (1970): 42–50.

[41] SOUNDARARAJAN, K., and RAMAKRISHNA, K. "Characteristics of Nonideal Operational Amplifiers." *IEEE Trans. Circuit and Systems* CAS-21 (1974): 69–75.

[42] BUDAK, A., and PETRELA, D. M. "Frequency Limitations of Active Filters Using Operational Amplifiers." *IEEE Trans. Circuit Theory* CT-19 (1972): 322–28.

[43] GRAY, P. R., and MEYER, R. G. "Recent Advances in Monolithic Operational Amplifier Design." *IEEE Trans. Circuit and Systems* CAS-21 (1974): 317–27.

[44] FLEISCHER, P. E. "Sensitivity Minimization in a Single Amplifier Biquad Circuit." *IEEE Trans. Circuit and Systems* CAS-23 (1976): 45–55.

[45] SRINIVASAGOPALAN, P., and MARTENS, G. O. "A Comparison of a Class of Active Filters with Respect to Operational Amplifier Gain-Bandwidth Product." *IEEE Trans. Circuit and Systems* CAS-21 (1974): 377–81.

[46] GEFFE, P. R. "Exact Synthesis with Real Amplifiers." *IEEE Trans. Circuit and Systems* CAS-21 (1974): 369–76.

[47] RAO, K. R., and SRINIVASAN, S. "Low-Sensitivity Active Filters Using the Operational Amplifier Pole." *IEEE Trans. Circuit and Systems* CAS-21 (1974): 260–62.

[48]   SCHAUMANN, R. "Low Sensitivity High Frequency Tunable Active Filter Without External Capacitors." *IEEE Trans. Circuit and Systems* CAS-22 (1975): 39–44.

[49]   MITRA, A. K., and AATRE, V. K. "Low Sensitivity High Frequency Active R Filters." *IEEE Trans. Circuit and Systems* CAS-23 (1976): 670–76.

PROBLEMS

10-1. Find an active ladder circuit realization of an nth-order low-pass Butterworth filter with the 3 dB cutoff frequency $f_c = 8$ KHz. and the terminating load resistor $R_\ell = 600 \, \Omega$, where $n = 2, 3, 4, 5$, and 6.

10-2. Find an active ladder circuit realization of an nth-order low-pass Chebyshev filter with 0.1 dB ripples, ripple bandwidth $f_r = 3.4$ KHz., and a terminating load resistor $R_\ell = 600 \, \Omega$, where $n = 2, 3, 4, 5$, and 6.

10-3. Find an active ladder circuit realization of an nth-order high-pass Butterworth filter with the 3 dB cutoff frequency $f_c = 10$ KHz. and the terminating resistor $R_\ell = 600 \, \Omega$, where $n = 2, 3, 4, 5$, and 6.

10-4. Find an active ladder circuit realization of an nth-order high-pass Chebyshev filter with 1 dB ripples for $f_r \geq 10$ KHz. and the terminating resistor $R_\ell = 600 \, \Omega$.

10-5. Replace each passive ladder circuit in Fig. P10-5 with an active ladder circuit having the same overall transfer function. The active circuits may

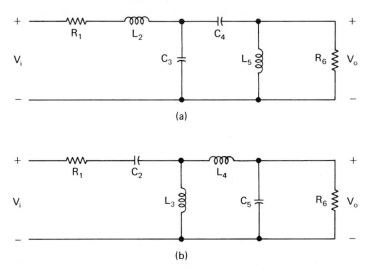

(a)

(b)

Fig. P10-5(a), (b)

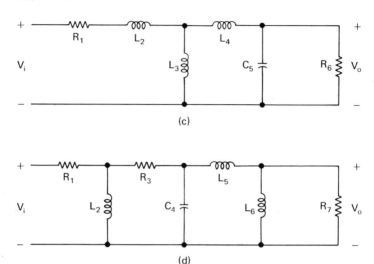

Fig. P10-5(c), (d)

contain resistors, capacitors, ks and k/s impedance scaling 2-ports, gyrators, and FDNRs only.

10-6. Realize the following filters with Kuh's configuration:

(a) A second-order Butterworth low-pass filter with a dc gain of 10 and a 3 dB cutoff frequency $\omega_c = 10$ K rad./sec.

(b) A third-order low-pass Chebyshev filter with 0.1 dB ripples, bandwidth $\omega_r = 10$ K rad./sec., and a dc gain of 5.

(c) A fourth-order bandpass Butterworth filter with center frequency $\omega_0 = 8$ K rad./sec., bandwidth $B = 2$ K rad./sec., and a midband gain of 1.

(d) A fourth-order high-pass Butterworth filter with a high frequency gain of 1 and a 3 dB cutoff frequency at $\omega_c = 10$ K rad./sec.

10-7. Realize the following transfer functions with Kuh's configurations:

(a) $H(s) = \dfrac{1}{(s^2 + 1)(s + 1)^2}$

(b) $H(s) = \dfrac{1}{(\hat{s} + 1)(\hat{s} + 2)(\hat{s} + 3)}$ where $\hat{s} = \dfrac{s}{10000}$

(c) $H(s) = \dfrac{1}{(s + 1)^3}$

(d) $H(s) = \dfrac{s^2}{(s + 1)^3}$

(e) $H(s) = \dfrac{s^2}{s^2 + 3s + 3}$

10-8. Realize the following transfer functions by Yanagisawa's method:

(a) $H(s) = \dfrac{1}{(s + 1)^3}$

(b) $H(s) = \dfrac{1}{(\hat{s} + 1)(\hat{s}^2 + 1)}$ where $\hat{s} = \dfrac{s}{1000}$

(c) $H(s) = \dfrac{s + 1}{(s + 2)(s^2 + 3)}$

(d) $H(s) = \dfrac{(s + 1)^2}{(s + 2)(s^2 + 3)}$

(e) $H(s) = \dfrac{\hat{s}^2 + 1}{(\hat{s} + 1)(\hat{s}^2 + 3\hat{s} + 3)}$ where $\hat{s} = \dfrac{s}{4000}$

(f) $H(s) = \dfrac{s^2 + 1}{s^2 + \sqrt{2}\,s + 1}$

(g) $H(s) = \dfrac{s^3 + 1}{s(s + 1)^3}$

(h) $H(s) = \dfrac{s^3}{(s + 1)(s^2 + 3s + 1)}$

(i) $H(s) = \dfrac{\hat{s}^2 - 3\hat{s} + 3}{\hat{s}^2 + 3\hat{s} + 3}$ where $\hat{s} = \dfrac{s}{10000}$

(j) $H(s) = \dfrac{-s^3 + 2s^2 - 2s + 4}{s^3 + 2s^2 + 2s + 4}$

10-9. Realize the transfer functions in Problem 10-8 by Mathews–Seifert's method.

10-10. Realize the transfer functions in Problem 10-8 by Lovering's method.

10-11. Realize the transfer functions in Problem 10-8 by Mitra's method.

10-12. (a) Realize the transfer function

$$H(s) = \frac{(s + 1)^2}{(s^2 + 1)(s + 3)}$$

by Mathew–Seifert's method of Fig. 10-13 with $D(s) = (s + 1)(s + 3)$, $k_1 = 0$, and $k_2 = 1$.

(b) Find the pole sensitivities $\hat{S}^{p_1}_{k_2}$, $\hat{S}^{p_2}_{k_2}$ and $\hat{S}^{p_3}_{k_2}$, where $p_1 = j$, $p_2 = -j$, and $p_3 = -3$ are the poles of the network.

(c) Find the conditions under which the pole locations of p_1 and p_2 may be perturbed to the RH s-plane, and hence the circuit becomes unstable.

10-13. Realize the following transfer functions via the state-variable technique:

(a) $H(s) = \dfrac{1}{(s + 1)^3}$

(b) $H(s) = \dfrac{s}{(s + 1)(s^2 + 1)}$

(c) $H(s) = \dfrac{2\hat{s}^2}{(\hat{s} + 2)(\hat{s}^2 + 1)}$ where $\hat{s} = \dfrac{s}{10^4}$

(d) $H(s) = \dfrac{3s^4}{(s + 1)(s + 2)(s^2 + 3s + 3)}$

(e) $H(s) = \dfrac{s^4}{(s^2 + 1)(s^2 + 3s + 3)}$

(f) $H(s) = \dfrac{s^2 + 1}{(s + 2)(s^2 + 3s + 3)}$

(g) $H(s) = \dfrac{\mathfrak{s}^2 - 3\mathfrak{s} + 3}{\mathfrak{s}^2 + 3\mathfrak{s} + 3}$ where $\mathfrak{s} = \dfrac{s}{5000}$

(h) $H(s) = \dfrac{s^3 - 6s^2 + 15s - 15}{s^3 + 6s^2 + 15s + 15}$

(i) $H(s) = \dfrac{1}{(\mathfrak{s}^2 + 0.77\mathfrak{s} + 1)(\mathfrak{s}^2 + 1.85\mathfrak{s} + 1)}$ where $\mathfrak{s} = \dfrac{s}{10^4}$

(j) $H(s) = \dfrac{s^2}{(s + 1)^2 (s + 2)^2}$

10-14. Realize the following second-order transfer functions via Table 10-1:

(a) $H(s) = \dfrac{6}{s^2 + 3s + 3}$

(b) $H(s) = \dfrac{2}{\mathfrak{s}^2 + \sqrt{2}\,\mathfrak{s} + 1}$ where $\mathfrak{s} = \dfrac{s}{10^4}$

(c) $H(s) = \dfrac{10^8}{s^2 + 100s + 10^8}$

(d) $H(s) = \dfrac{6s}{s^2 + 3s + 3}$

(e) $H(s) = \dfrac{2\mathfrak{s}}{\mathfrak{s}^2 + \sqrt{2}\,\mathfrak{s} + 1}$ where $\mathfrak{s} = \dfrac{s}{10^4}$

(f) $H(s) = \dfrac{10^3 s}{s^2 + 100s + 10^8}$

(g) $H(s) = \dfrac{3\mathfrak{s}^2}{\mathfrak{s}^2 + 3\mathfrak{s} + 3}$ where $\mathfrak{s} = \dfrac{s}{10^5}$

(h) $H(s) = \dfrac{s^2}{s^2 + \sqrt{2}\,s + 1}$

(i) $H(s) = \dfrac{2s^2}{s^2 + 100s + 10^8}$

(j) $H(s) = \dfrac{s + 2}{s^2 + 3s + 4}$

(k) $H(s) = \dfrac{s(s + 2)}{s^2 + 5s + 2}$

(l) $H(s) = \dfrac{\mathfrak{s}^2 + 1}{\mathfrak{s}^2 + 0.1\mathfrak{s} + 1}$ where $\mathfrak{s} = \dfrac{s}{10^4}$

(m) $H(s) = \dfrac{s^2 + (120\pi)^2}{s^2 + 10\pi s + (120\pi)^2}$

(n) $H(s) = \dfrac{s^2 + (120\pi)^2}{s^2 + 10\pi s + (240\pi)^2}$

(o) $H(s) = \dfrac{s^2 + 5}{s^2 + 5s + 2}$

(p) $H(s) = \dfrac{s^2 + 2}{s^2 + 5s + 5}$

(q) $H(s) = \dfrac{s^2 + 3s + 1}{s^2 + 5s + 1}$

(r) $H(s) = \dfrac{s^2 + 5s + 1}{s^2 + 3s + 1}$

10-15. Realize the following transfer functions by cascading second-order sections obtained from Table 10-1:

(a) $H(s) = \dfrac{2}{(s^2 + 0.77s + 1)(s^2 + 1.85s + 1)}$

(b) $H(s) = \dfrac{2}{(s^2 + 3s + 3)(s^2 + \sqrt{2}\,s + 1)}$

(c) $H(s) = \dfrac{2\hat{s}^2}{(\hat{s}^2 + 3\hat{s} + 3)(\hat{s}^2 + \sqrt{2}\,\hat{s} + 1)}$ where $\hat{s} = \dfrac{s}{10^4}$

(d) $H(s) = \dfrac{s(s^2 + 1)}{(s^2 + 0.77s + 1)(s^2 + 1.85s + 1)}$

(e) $H(s) = \dfrac{s^2(s^2 + 1)}{(s^2 + 3s + 3)(s^2 + \sqrt{2}\,s + 1)}$

(f) $H(s) = \dfrac{1}{(\hat{s}^2 + 0.77\hat{s} + 1)(\hat{s}^2 + 1.85\hat{s} + 1)(\hat{s}^2 + \sqrt{2}\,\hat{s} + 1)}$

   where $\hat{s} = \dfrac{s}{10^4}$

(g) $H(s) = \dfrac{s^2}{(s^2 + 3s + 3)(s^2 + \sqrt{2}\,s + 1)^2}$

(h) $H(s) = \dfrac{10}{(s^2 + s + 1)^3}$

10-16. Consider the transfer function

$$H(s) = \frac{10^8}{s^2 + 10^\alpha s + 10^8}$$

(a) With $\alpha = 4$, realize $H(s)$ via Table 10-1.
(b) Find the ω_0 and Q sensitivities with respect to the gain of the VCVS.
(c) Repeat (a) and (b) with $\alpha = 3$.
(d) Repeat (a) and (b) with $\alpha = 2$.
(e) Repeat (a) and (b) with $\alpha = 1$.

10-17. Repeat Problem 10-16 with

$$H(s) = \frac{10^\alpha s}{s^2 + 10^\alpha s + 10^8}$$

10-18. Repeat Problem 10-16 with

$$H(s) = \frac{s^2}{s^2 + 10^\alpha s + 10^8}$$

10-19. Realize the following transfer functions by Friend's circuit configuration of Fig. 10-26:

(a) $H(s) = \dfrac{100s}{s^2 + 100s + 10^6}$

(b) $H(s) = \dfrac{s^2 - 100s + 10^6}{s^2 + 100s + 10^6}$

(c) $H(s) = \dfrac{s^2 + 10^6}{s^2 + 100s + 10^6}$

(d) $H(s) = \dfrac{s^2}{s^2 + 100s + 10^6}$

(e) $H(s) = \dfrac{100s(s^2 + 10^6)}{(s^2 + 100s + 10^6)^2}$

(f) $H(s) = \dfrac{s^2}{(s^2 + 100s + 10^6)^2}$

10-20. (a) Realize the transfer function

$$H(s) = \frac{s^2 + \omega_1^2}{s^2 + 100s + 10^6} = \frac{s^2 + 10^4}{s^2 + 100s + 10^6}$$

by Friend's circuit configuration.

(b) Find the ω_1, ω_0, and Q sensitivities with respect to the the capacitors C_1 and C_2.

10-21. Realize the following transfer functions via the multiple amplifier biquads of Fig. 10-29.

(a) $H(s) = \dfrac{6}{s^2 + 3s + s}$

(b) $H(s) = \dfrac{1}{\hat{s}^2 + \sqrt{2}\hat{s} + 1}$ where $\hat{s} = \dfrac{s}{10^4}$

(c) $H(s) = \dfrac{s}{(s + 2)^2}$

(d) $H(s) = \dfrac{6\hat{s}}{\hat{s}^2 + 3\hat{s} + 3}$ where $\hat{s} = \dfrac{s}{10^5}$

(e) $H(s) = \dfrac{s^2}{(s + 2)^2}$

(f) $H(s) = \dfrac{\hat{s}^2}{\hat{s}^2 + \sqrt{2}\hat{s} + 1}$ where $\hat{s} = \dfrac{s}{10^4}$

(g) $H(s) = \dfrac{s^2 + 3}{s^2 + 3s + 3}$

(h) $H(s) = \dfrac{\hat{s}^2 + 1}{\hat{s}^2 + \sqrt{2}s + 1}$ where $\hat{s} = \dfrac{s}{120\pi}$

(i) $H(s) = \dfrac{s + 1}{s^2 + 3s + 1}$

(j) $H(s) = \dfrac{s^2 + \sqrt{2}s + 1}{s^2 + 3s + 3}$

10-22. Realize the following two transfer functions simultaneously in one biquad circuit (use Fig. 10-29):

$$H_1(s) = \frac{2}{\hat{s}^2 + \sqrt{2}\hat{s} + 1}$$

and

$$H_2(s) = \frac{4\hat{s}}{\hat{s}^2 + \sqrt{2}\hat{s} + 1}$$

where $\hat{s} = \dfrac{s}{10^5}$.

10-23. Realize the following three transfer functions simultaneously in one biquad circuit (use Fig. 10-29):

$$H_1(s) = \frac{6}{s^2 + 3s + 3}$$

$$H_2(s) = \frac{2s}{s^2 + 3s + 3}$$

and

$$H_3(s) = \frac{3s^2}{s^2 + 3s + 3}$$

10-24. Realize the following four transfer functions simultaneously in one complete biquad circuit (use Fig. 10-29):

$$H_1(s) = \frac{10^6}{s^2 + 100s + 10^6}$$

$$H_2(s) = \frac{200s}{s^2 + 100s + 10^6}$$

$$H_3(s) = \frac{2s^2}{s^2 + 100s + 10^6}$$

and

$$H_4(s) = \frac{s^2 + 10^6}{s^2 + 100s + 10^6}$$

10-25. (a) Realize the transfer function

$$H(s) = \frac{10^8}{s^2 + 100s + 10^8}$$

by a biquad circuit (use Fig. 10-29).

(b) Find the ω_0 and Q sensitivities with respect to all resistors and capacitors.

(c) Find the pole sensitivities with respect to all resistors and capacitors.

(d) Verify (9-72) for this case.

10-26. (a) Use the biquad circuit of Fig. 10-29 to realize a second-order band-pass filter with a midband gain of 10, center frequency $\omega_0 = 10N$ K rad./sec., and a pole-pair $Q = 5N$, where N is an integer. *Note:* The transfer function of such a filter is given by

$$H(s) = \frac{G(\omega_0/Q)s}{s^2 + (\omega_0/Q)s + \omega_0^2}$$

where G is the midband gain and $\omega_0/Q = 2$ K rad./sec. is the bandwidth.

(b) A cable is carrying 10 channels with a frequency assignment, as shown in Fig. P10-26(a), where $\#N$ denotes channel N. To process this cable signal into intelligent messages, we use a bank of bandpass filters (BPF), as shown in Fig. P10-26(b). Suppose that the filter in (a) is used to implement the BPFs. Find the transfer function of each channel's bandpass filter, each with a midband gain of 10, bandwidth 2 K rad./sec., and center frequency at 10 N K rad./sec. (for channel N).

(c) Find circuit realizations of the BPFs in (b) in the form of Fig. 10-29 such that the circuit realization of BPF $\#i$ has only *one element* different from that of BPF $\#k$, where $i \neq k = 1, 2, \ldots, 10$.

Cable signal
frequency spectrum

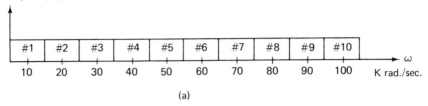

(a)

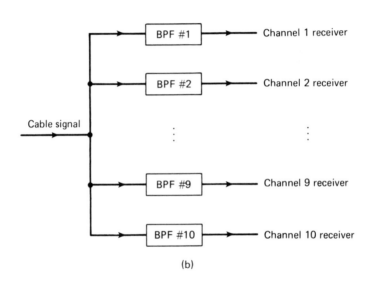

(b)

Fig. P10-26

10-27. Suppose that a bank of band elimination filters (BEF) are required to remove a base frequency and its harmonics. The desired transfer functions are in the form

$$H(s) = \frac{s^2 + \omega_0^2}{s^2 + (\omega_0/Q)s + \omega_0^2}$$

where $\omega_0 = 120N\pi$ rad./sec., the elimination bandwidth $\omega_0/Q = 10\pi$ rad./sec., and $N = 1, 2, 3, 4,$ and 5. Find circuit realizations of these five filters in the form of Fig. 10-29 such that the circuit realization of the ith-filter has at most three elements different from that of the kth-filter, where $i \neq k = 1, 2, 3, 4,$ and 5.

10-28. Realize the transfer functions in Problem 10-21 by Tow's multiple amplifier biquad.

10-29. Realize the following two transfer functions simultaneously in a Tow's multiple amplifier biquad:

$$H_1(s) = \frac{10^8}{s^2 + 100s + 10^8}$$

and

$$H_2(s) = \frac{200s}{s^2 + 100s + 10^8}$$

10-30. Repeat Problem 10-29 with the following two transfer functions:

$$H_1(s) = \frac{10^9}{s^2 + 200s + 10^8}$$

and

$$H_2(s) = \frac{s^2 - 200s + 10^8}{s^2 + 200s + 10^8}$$

10-31. Repeat Problem 10-29 with the following two transfer functions:

$$H_1(s) = \frac{s^2 + 10^6}{s^2 + 100s + 10^8}$$

and

$$H_2(s) = \frac{200s}{s^2 + 100s + 10^8}$$

10-32. Realize the following three transfer functions simultaneously in a Tow's multiple amplifier biquad:

$$H_1(s) = \frac{10^{10}}{s^2 + 400s + 10^{10}}$$

$$H_2(s) = \frac{1000s}{s^2 + 400s + 10^{10}}$$

and

$$H_3(s) = \frac{2s^2}{s^2 + 400s + 10^{10}}$$

10-33. Consider the 3-port circuit in Fig. 10-39(a). By using the concept of complementary transfer function:

(a) Construct an all-pass filter

$$H_A(s) = \frac{s^2 - 3s + 3}{s^2 + 3s + 3}$$

(b) Construct a band-reject filter

$$H_B(s) = \frac{s^2 + 3}{s^2 + 3s + 3}$$

10-34. Find the transfer function V_o/V_i for the circuit shown in Fig. P10-34,

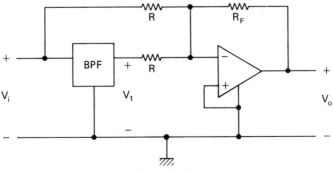

Fig. P10-34

where the BPF is characterized by

$$\frac{V_1}{V_i} = H_{BPF}(s) = -\frac{(\omega_0/Q)s}{s^2 + (\omega_0/Q)s + \omega_0^2}$$

10-35. Consider the inverting voltage-gain amplifier circuit shown in Fig. 10-41, where the operational amplifier is characterized by Fig. 10-25.

  (a) Find the useful frequency range if the desired voltage gain is within $\pm 1\%$ of $|G|$, where $-G = 1, 5, 10, 50, 100, 200, 500$, and 1000.

  (b) Plot the results of (a) with $|G|$ being the independent variable.

  (c) Repeat (a) and (b) if the accuracy required is changed to $\pm 5\%$.

10-36. Consider the noninverting voltage-gain amplifier of Fig. 10-42(a), where the operational amplifier is characterized by Fig. 10-25.

  (a) Find the useful frequency range if the desired voltage gain is within $\pm 1\%$ of its nominal gain value G, where $G = 1, 5, 10, 50, 100, 200, 500$, and 1000.

  (b) Plot the result of (a) with G being the independent variable.

  (c) Repeat (a) and (b) if the required accuracy is $\pm 5\%$.

10-37. Consider the integrator circuit in Fig. 10-43, where $RC = 10^{-4}$ and the operational amplifier is characterized by Fig. 10-25.

  (a) Find the useful frequency range if the magnitude error is required to be less than $\pm 1\%$ and the phase error is less than $\pm 1°$.

  (b) Repeat (a) if $RC = 10^{-2}, 10^{-3}, 10^{-5}, 10^{-6}$, and 10^{-7}.

  (c) Plot the results of (b).

10-38. Repeat Problem 10-37 if the magnitude error is to be less than $\pm 5\%$ and the phase error less than $\pm 3°$.

10-39. If the operational amplifier is characterized by Fig. 10-25, find a realization of

$$H(s) = \frac{2s}{s^2 + 0.1s + 1}$$

via circuit (a) of Case A2 of Table 10-1 that will yield the largest useful frequency range. *Hint:* Optimize the useful frequency range with respect to the VCVS gain k.

10-40. (a) If the operational amplifier is modeled by Fig. 10-40(d), with $A(s) = A_0$, find the transfer function of the integrator circuit shown in Fig. P10-40.

  (b) Consider the biquad circuit in Fig. 10-29(a), where the two operational amplifiers in the integrator circuits are assumed to be characterized by (a) and the remaining operational amplifier is assumed to be ideal. Find the transfer functions

$$H_1(s) = \frac{V_1}{V_i}, \quad H_2(s) = \frac{V_2}{V_i}, \quad \text{and} \quad H_3(s) = \frac{V_3}{V_i}$$

  (c) Based on the results of (b), find the effects of the finite operational

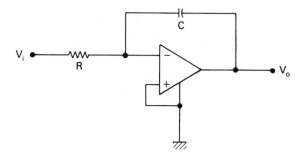

Fig. P10-40

amplifier gain on the pole-frequency ω_0 and pole-pair Q of the circuit.

(d) If $A_0 = 500$, find a realization for

$$H(s) = \frac{2}{\hat{s}^2 + \sqrt{2}\hat{s} + 1}$$

where $\hat{s} = \dfrac{s}{2K}$.

(e) Find the ω_0 and Q sensitivities of the circuit in (d) with respect to A_0.

(f) Repeat (d) and (e) for the following transfer function:

$$H(s) = \frac{2}{\hat{s}^2 + \sqrt{2} \times 10^{-2}\hat{s} + 1}$$

where $\hat{s} = \dfrac{s}{2K}$.

10-41. Suppose that an operational amplifier is modeled by Fig. P10-41(a), where A_0 and τ are constants.

(a) Find the transfer function of the integrator circuit shown in Fig. P10-41(b).

(b) Find the transfer function of the summer circuit shown in Fig. P10-41(c).

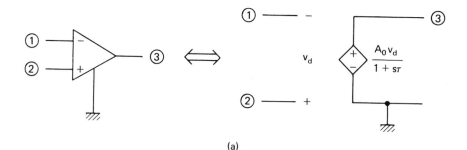

(a)

Fig. P10-41(a)

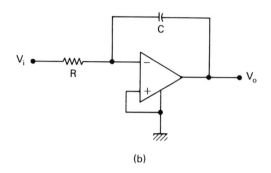

(b)

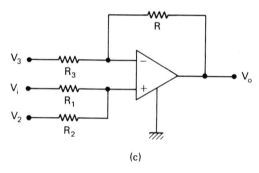

(c)

Fig. P10-41(b), (c)

(c) Find the transfer functions

$$H_1(s) = \frac{V_1}{V_i}, \quad H_2(s) = \frac{V_2}{V_i}, \quad \text{and} \quad H_3(s) = \frac{V_3}{V_i}$$

of the biquad circuit in Fig. 10-29(a), where the operational amplifiers are identically modeled by Fig. P10-41(a).

(d) Based on the results of (c), find $H_1(s)$, $H_2(s)$, and $H_3(s)$ if $\tau \to 0$.

(e) Repeat (d) if $A_0 \to \infty$ and $\tau \to 0$.

10-42. Suppose that an operational amplifier is characterized by an open-loop gain

$$A(s) = \frac{A_0 \omega_a}{s + \omega_a}$$

where $A_0 = 50000$ and $\omega_a = 40\pi$ rad./sec.

(a) Find an active R biquad circuit realization of

$$H(s) = \frac{Bs}{s^2 + \gamma Bs + B^2}$$

where $B = A_0 \omega_a$ and $\gamma = 0.01$.

(b) Find the Q sensitivity with respect to A_0.

(c) Find the pole sensitivities with respect to B.

(d) Repeat (a), (b), and (c) with $\gamma = 0.1$.

(e) Repeat (a), (b), and (c) with $\gamma = 0.001$.

10-43. Suppose that an operational amplifier is characterized by an open-loop gain

$$A(s) = \frac{A_0 \omega_a}{s + \omega_a}$$

where $A_0 = 50000$ and $\omega_a = 40\pi$ rad./sec. Find an active R biquad realization for each of the following transfer functions:

(a) $H(s) = \dfrac{2 \times 10^{10}}{s^2 + 10^3 s + 10^{10}}$

(b) $H(s) = \dfrac{3 \times 10^{12}}{s^2 + 10^5 s + 10^{12}}$

(c) $H(s) = \dfrac{10^{14}}{s^2 + 10^5 s + 10^{14}}$

(d) $H(s) = \dfrac{10^3 s}{s^2 + 10^3 s + 10^{10}}$

(e) $H(s) = \dfrac{2 \times 10^5 s}{s^2 + 10^5 s + 10^{12}}$

(f) $H(s) = \dfrac{10^5 s}{s^2 + 10^5 s + 10^{14}}$

10-44. Suppose that an operational amplifier is characterized by an open-loop gain

$$A(s) = \frac{A_0 \omega_a}{s + \omega_a}$$

where $A_0 = 50000$ and $\omega_a = 40\pi$ rad./sec.

(a) Realize the transfer function

$$H(s) = \frac{10^{10}}{s^2 + \sqrt{2} \times 10^5 s + 10^{10}}$$

by an active R biquad circuit.

(b) Find the ω_0 and Q sensitivities with respect to A_0 and ω_a.

(c) Find the pole sensitivities with respect to A_0 and ω_a.

10-45. Repeat Problem 10-44 with

$$H(s) = \frac{10^6 s}{s^2 + 10^5 s + 10^{14}}$$

11

INTRODUCTION
TO DIGITAL FILTERS

A digital filter is a digital signal processor that converts a sequence of numbers called the *input* to another sequence of numbers called the *output*. Many theoretical concepts of digital filtering have been known since the days of Laplace. However, the technology of that time could not utilize this body of knowledge. As digital computers came onto the scene, digital filters began to proliferate. Seismic scientists made notable use of digital filtering concepts to solve many interesting problems. Picture processing uses digital filtering techniques to improve the clarity of pictures obtained from remote sensings, interplanetary communications, and x-ray films. Other areas of applications include speech processing, mapping, radar, sonar, and various fields of medical technology.

A digital filter can be implemented as software, such as a subroutine on a digital computer, or as hardware, such as a circuit containing registers, multipliers, and summers. For a number of years, software implementation was the only possible mode of performing digital filtering. Today, software implementation is still the dominant mode. Large-scale digital filters are invariably implemented on a general-purpose or a special-purpose digital computer. However, the rapid development of very large-scale integrated circuit technologies have opened up the area of hardware implementation of digital filters. Currently, the industry can produce adders, shift registers, and multiplier chips needed for the hardware implementation of digital filters at reasonable cost. In addition, general-purpose digital signal processing chips and number-crunching microprocessors are on the horizon. In view of the past history of the IC industry, it is foreseeable that these components may cost much less and perform much better in the future. Consequently, hardware and software implementations may be combined together to yield low-cost and yet efficient digital filters.

11-1   DIGITAL SIGNALS AND SYSTEMS

As mentioned in Chapter 1, a filter is a signal processor that enhances some signals and attenuates others. A signal may be a continuous function of an independent variable, which we usually call *time*, such as voltage and current waveforms in analog filters. These signals are called *continuous-time* signals. On the other hand, a signal may be defined for a finite or at most a countably infinite number of time instants only. This type of signal is called a *discrete-time* signal. Some examples of discrete-time signals are: the annual GNP of a nation shown in Fig. 11-1(a), the monthly unemployment rate in Fig. 11-1(b), the population chart of a small village shown in Fig. 11-1(c), and the monthly automobile production of a company in Fig. 11-1(d). Among the main sources of discrete-time signals are those obtained by sampling a continuous-time signal. A case in point is shown in Fig. 11-2.

Digital signals are discrete-time signals whose values are *quantized*. The output of an A/D converter, which samples a continuous-time input signal and generates a sequence of finite-length binary numbers, is a typical digital signal. The essence of an A/D converter is shown in Fig. 11-3(a). If the sampler samples at the rate of one sample per μsec. and the quantizer has an input–output relationship as given by Fig. 11-3(b), then given a continuous-time signal $\hat{x}(t)$ as in Fig. 11-3(c), the corresponding discrete-time signal $x_1(nT)$ and the output digital signal $x(nT)$ are shown, respectively, in Figs. 11-3(d) and (e). Some other typical digital signals are those shown in Fig. 11-1(c) and (d), where the quantized levels are respectively per person and per car. Strictly speaking, digital computers can handle digital signals only.

Because there are only a finite number of quantized signal levels, errors arise in any system that handles digital signals. Consequently, one of the design considerations of a digital filter is the number of bits or the number of quantized levels needed to represent a digital signal. The larger the number of bits used, the more accurate the representation of the signal and the costlier the filter. Clearly, there is a trade-off between accuracy and cost.

In this book, we do not consider the quantization effect of a digital filter. This essentially means that we have an *infinite-bit* representation of numbers. Thus, we treat digital signals as if they are discrete-time signals. In other words, we make no distinction between the words "discrete-time" and "digital," and we use the word "digital" hereafter.

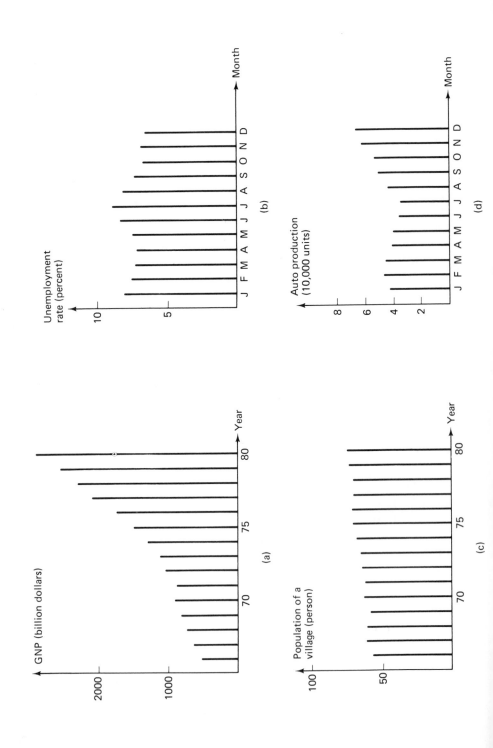

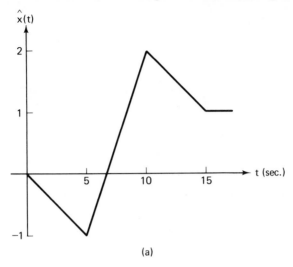

(a)

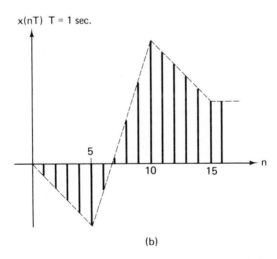

(b)

Fig. 11-2   Sampling of a continuous signal. (a) A continuous signal. (b) Its corresponding sampled sequence.

No matter how they arise, digital signals can be considered as sequences of numbers. The notations used to describe digital signals are[1]

$$x(n) \text{ or } \{x(n)\} \tag{11-1a}$$

---

[1]Strictly speaking, $\{x(n)\}$ denotes the complete sequence, and $x(n)$ denotes the sequence value at the nth point. However, for convenience, we use both $x(n)$ and $\{x(n)\}$ to denote the sequence of x.

In this book, we consider one-dimensional digital sequences only. That is, the values of the sequences depend on one independent variable only.

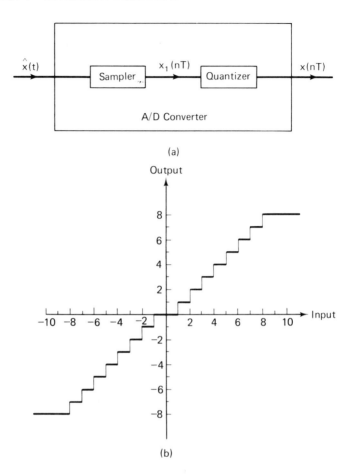

Fig. 11-3 The function of an A/D converter. (a) Schematic.
(b) Input–output relationship of the quantizer.

and

$$x(nT) \text{ or } \{x(nT)\} \tag{11-1b}$$

Note that (11-1b) applies to signals with uniform time intervals, whereas
(11-1a) applies to signals with uniform as well as nonuniform time spacings.[2]

Some important sequences are:

1. the *unit impulse* sequence $\delta(n)$ defined by

$$\delta(n) = 0 \quad n \neq 0$$
$$= 1 \quad \text{when } n = 0 \tag{11-2}$$

---

[2]We consider exclusively digital signals with uniform time spacings only. For those
who are interested in systems where the time intervals between signal samples are not
identical, please consult Reference [23].

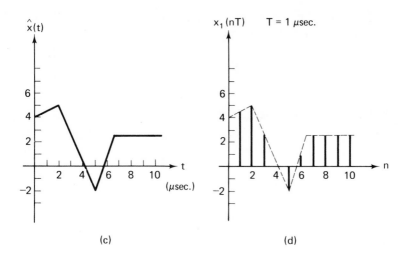

(c)   (d)

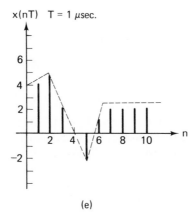

(e)

Legend: $\hat{x}(t)$ = continuous-time signal, input to the A/D converter.
$x(nT)$ = discrete-time signal, output of the sampler.
$x(nT)$ = digital signal, output of the A/D converter.

Fig. 11-3   (c), (d), and (e) An example.

Observe that a sequence $x(n)$ given by

$$\{x(n)\} = \{\ldots, x(-1), x(0), x(1), \ldots\}$$

can be written in terms of the unit impulse sequence as

$$x(n) = \sum_{k=-\infty}^{\infty} x(k)\, \delta(n-k) \qquad (11\text{-}3)$$

2. the *unit step* sequence $u(n)$ defined by

$$u(n) = 1 \quad \text{when } n \geq 0$$
$$= 0 \quad \text{when } n < 0 \qquad (11\text{-}4)$$

Based on the definitions in (11-2) and (11-4), the relationships between the unit impulse and the unit step sequences are

$$u(n) = \sum_{k=-\infty}^{n} \delta(k) \qquad (11\text{-}5a)$$

$$\delta(n) = u(n) - u(n-1) \qquad (11\text{-}5b)$$

3. an *exponential* sequence

$$x(n) = a^n \quad \text{when } n \geq 0$$
$$= 0 \quad \text{when } n < 0 \qquad (11\text{-}6a)$$

where *a* may be real or complex. Note that an exponential sequence can be expressed as

$$x(n) = a^n u(n) \qquad (11\text{-}6b)$$

4. *sinusoidal* sequences with period *P*

$$x_1(n) = A_1 \cos (2\pi n/P) \qquad (11\text{-}7a)$$

$$x_2(n) = A_2 \sin (2\pi n/P) \qquad (11\text{-}7b)$$

If *P* is a positive rational number, say $P = \alpha/\beta$, where both α and β are two relatively primed positive integers, then the sequences in (11-7) repeat every α sample. That is,

$$x_k(n) = x_k(n + m\alpha) \qquad (11\text{-}8)$$

where $k = 1, 2$ and *m* is an integer. On the other hand, if *P* is an irrational positive number, then the sequences in (11-7) do not repeat themselves. Therefore, sinusoidal digital sequences are *not* necessarily periodic sequences.

Just like continuous-time functions, digital signals or sequences are subjected to arithmetic operations. Let $x \triangleq \{x(n)\}$ and $y \triangleq \{y(n)\}$ be two sequences, and let α be a scalar. Then we define:

1. sum and difference of two sequences

$$x \pm y \triangleq \{x(n) \pm y(n)\} \qquad (11\text{-}9a)$$

2. multiplication of a sequence by a scalar

$$\alpha x \triangleq \{\alpha x(n)\} \qquad (11\text{-}9b)$$

3. multiplication and division of two sequences

$$xy \triangleq \{x(n)\, y(n)\} \qquad (11\text{-}9c)$$

$$\frac{x}{y} \triangleq \{x(n)/y(n)\} \qquad (11\text{-}9d)$$

In the "time" domain, a digital system is characterized by a set of *difference* equations.[3] This means that given an input sequence and the initial conditions of the system, the set of difference equations will yield a unique output sequence.[4] For example, consider the system characterized by

$$y(n) - ay(n-1) = x(n) \qquad (11\text{-}10a)$$

$$y(0) = 1 \qquad (11\text{-}10b)$$

where $x(n)$ and $y(n)$ are, respectively, the input and the output sequences as shown in Fig. 11-4. If the input sequence is a unit step

$$x(n) = 1 \quad \text{for } n \geq 0$$
$$= 0 \quad \text{for } n < 0 \qquad (11\text{-}11)$$

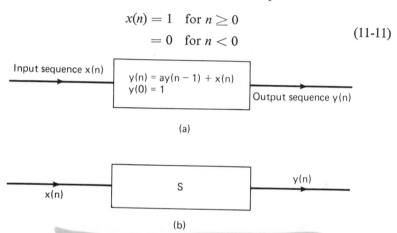

Fig. 11-4 A digital system. (a) A specific case. (b) A general case.

then the output sequence can be computed from (11-10) for $n = 1, 2,$ ... as

$$y(1) = ay(0) + x(1) = a + 1$$
$$y(2) = ay(1) + x(2) = a(a+1) + 1$$
$$= a^2 + a + 1$$

$$\vdots \qquad (11\text{-}12)$$

$$y(k) = ay(k-1) + x(k)$$

$$= a^k + a^{k-1} + a^{k-2} + \ldots + 1 = \left(\sum_{i=0}^{k} a^i \right)$$

---

[3]Recall that a continuous-time system such as that of an active or a passive RLC circuit is characterized by a set of *differential* equations in the time domain.

[4]In this book, all difference equations are assumed to be linear and time-invariant.

If $|a| < 1$, then (11-12) can be written as

$$y(k) = \left(\sum_{i=0}^{k} a^i\right) = \left(\sum_{i=0}^{\infty} a^i\right) - \left(\sum_{i=k+1}^{\infty} a^i\right)$$

$$= \left(\sum_{i=0}^{\infty} a^i\right) - a^{k+1}\left(\sum_{j=0}^{\infty} a^j\right) \qquad (11\text{-}13)$$

$$= \left(1 - a^{k+1}\right)\left(\sum_{i=0}^{\infty} a^i\right) = \frac{1 - a^{k+1}}{1 - a}$$

Basically, a single-input single-output digital system S is an algorithm for converting one sequence of numbers to another sequence of numbers, as shown in Fig. 11-4(b), where the input sequence is called $x(n)$ and the output sequence is called $y(n)$. Let $y_1(n)$ and $y_2(n)$ be, respectively, the zero-state responses[5] due to the input sequences $x_1(n)$ and $x_2(n)$. Then S is said to be *linear* if the zero-state output sequence $y(n)$ due to the input sequence

$$x(n) \triangleq a_1 x_1(n) + a_2 x_2(n) \qquad (11\text{-}14a)$$

is given by

$$y(n) \triangleq a_1 y_1(n) + a_2 y_2(n) \qquad (11\text{-}14b)$$

S is said to be *time-invariant* if the zero-state output $y(n)$ due to the input sequence

$$x(n) \triangleq x_1(n - n_0) \qquad (11\text{-}15a)$$

is given by

$$y(n) \triangleq y_1(n - n_0) \qquad (11\text{-}15b)$$

Let $h(n)$ be the zero-state response to $\delta(n)$. The time-invariant property of the system leads us to conclude that $h(n - k)$ is the zero-state response to $\delta(n - k)$. By (11-3) and by the linearity property of the system, the zero-state output sequence due to an input sequence of $x(n)$ written as

$$x(n) = \sum_{k=-\infty}^{\infty} x(k)\,\delta(n - k) \qquad (11\text{-}16)$$

is given by

$$y(n) = \sum_{k=-\infty}^{\infty} x(k)\,h(n - k) \qquad (11\text{-}17a)$$

This means that a linear and time-invariant digital system S can be characterized by an *impulse response* $h(n)$, which is the output sequence of S when the input is a unit impulse sequence and all initial conditions of S are zero. By a change of variable, (11-17a) can also be written as

$$y(n) = \sum_{k=-\infty}^{\infty} x(n - k)\,h(k) \qquad (11\text{-}17b)$$

---

[5] A zero-state response is an output of the system when all initial conditions of the system are zero.

Both equations of (11-17) are called the *convolution sum* of the two sequences $x(n)$ and $h(n)$ and are denoted by

$$y(n) = x(n) * h(n) \tag{11-17c}$$

Finally, a linear and time-invariant digital system S is *stable* if its impulse response $h(n)$ satisfies the condition

$$\sum_{n=-\infty}^{\infty} |h(n)| < \infty \qquad \text{Stability} \tag{11-18}$$

and is *causal* if

$$h(n) = 0 \quad \text{for } n < 0 \qquad \text{Causal} \tag{11-19}$$

Note that if (11-18) is violated, then we can find a bounded input sequence $x(n)$, where

$$\sum_{n=-\infty}^{\infty} |x(n)|^2 = K < \infty, \tag{11-20a}$$

to yield an unbounded output sequence $y(n)$ such that

$$\sum_{n=-\infty}^{\infty} |y(n)|^2 \longrightarrow \infty \tag{11-20b}$$

Example 11-1   Let the system S be characterized by[6]

$$y(n) - ay(n-1) = x(n) \tag{11-21a}$$

$$y(-1) = 0 \tag{11-21b}$$

Find the impulse response $h(n)$ of S, and discuss the stability and causality conditions of S.

Solution: Because the initial condition of S is zero, as given by (11-21b), when

$$x(n) = \delta(n) \tag{11-22}$$

the output sequence $y(n)$ will be the impulse response $h(n)$. From (11-21), we obtain

$$y(0) = ay(-1) + \delta(0) = 0 + 1 = 1$$
$$y(1) = ay(0) + \delta(1) = a + 0 = a$$
$$y(2) = ay(1) + \delta(2) = a^2 + 0 = a^2$$

Progressing inductively, we obtain

$$y(n) = a^n \quad \text{for } n \geq 0 \tag{11-23a}$$

To consider the case when $n < -1$, we write (11-21) and (11-22) as

$$y(n-1) = a^{-1}[y(n) - \delta(n)]$$

---

[6]The zero initial condition of the system S is given by (11-21b), where we have assumed that the initial time is when $n = 0$. Recall that for the continuous-time case, the initial conditions are given at the point $t = 0-$.

with

$$y(-1) = 0$$

This gives

$$y(-2) = a^{-1}[y(-1) - \delta(-1)] = a^{-1}(0 - 0) = 0$$
$$y(-3) = a^{-1}[y(-2) - \delta(-2)] = 0$$

Clearly, we have

$$y(n) = 0 \quad \text{for } n < 0 \tag{11-23b}$$

Hence, the impulse response $h(n)$ of the system S characterized by (11-21) is given by

$$h(n) = a^n u(n) \tag{11-24}$$

In view of (11-24), the system S is causal for all a and is stable when $|a| < 1$. ∎

11-2 Z-TRANSFORM

The z-transform method is a very useful tool in solving linear difference equations. It reduces the solutions of such equations into those of algebraic equations. The application of z-transforms to a set of difference equations is analogous to the application of Laplace transforms to a set of differential equations.

The z-transform $X(z)$ of a sequence $x(n)$ is defined to be[7]

$$X(z) \triangleq \sum_{n=-\infty}^{\infty} x(n)z^{-n} \tag{11-25}$$

where z is a complex variable. Hence, $X(z)$ is complex.

Example 11-2   Find the z-transform of the sequence $x(n)$ given by

$$x(n) = (\cos n\phi + \sin n\phi)u(n) \tag{11-26}$$

Solution: From (11-25), we have

$$X(z) = \sum_{n=-\infty}^{\infty} x(n)z^{-n} = \sum_{n=0}^{\infty} (\cos n\phi + \sin n\phi)z^{-n}$$

$$= \sum_{n=0}^{\infty} \left[\frac{e^{jn\phi} + e^{-jn\phi}}{2} + \frac{e^{jn\phi} - e^{-jn\phi}}{2j} \right] z^{-n} \tag{11-27}$$

$$= \sum_{n=0}^{\infty} \left[\frac{1-j}{2} e^{jn\phi} z^{-n} \right] + \sum_{n=0}^{\infty} \left[\frac{1+j}{2} e^{-jn\phi} z^{-n} \right]$$

If

$$|z^{-1}| < 1 \quad \text{or} \quad |z| > 1 \tag{11-28a}$$

then

$$|e^{\pm j\phi} z^{-1}| < 1 \tag{11-28b}$$

---

[7]We use the convention that the z-transform of a time sequence $x(n)$ is denoted by $X(z)$; a time sequence is denoted by a lower-case letter, and its z-transform is denoted by the corresponding upper-case letter.

and (11-27) can be simplified to

$$X(z) = \frac{1-j}{2} \frac{1}{1 - e^{j\phi}z^{-1}} + \frac{1+j}{2} \frac{1}{1 - e^{-j\phi}z^{-1}}$$

$$= \frac{1 - (\cos \phi)z^{-1} + (\sin \phi)z^{-1}}{1 - (e^{j\phi} + e^{-j\phi})z^{-1} + z^{-2}} \qquad (11\text{-}29)$$

$$= \frac{1 + (\sin \phi - \cos \phi)z^{-1}}{1 - 2(\cos \phi)z^{-1} + z^{-2}} \qquad \blacksquare$$

Clearly, $X(z)$ is defined for those values of z or z^{-1} for which the power series in (11-25) converges. For example, $X(z)$ of (11-27) is defined only if (11-28a) is satisfied. By writing z in its polar form

$$z = re^{j\theta} \qquad (11\text{-}30)$$

(11-25) becomes

$$X(z) = \sum_{n=-\infty}^{\infty} x(n)r^{-n}e^{-j\theta n} \qquad (11\text{-}31)$$

Hence, $X(z)$ is defined for those values of z with radius r in the z-plane such that

$$\sum_{n=-\infty}^{\infty} |x(n)r^{-n}| < \infty \qquad (11\text{-}32)$$

The totality of all z such that (11-32) holds is called the *region of convergence* for the sequence $x(n)$. In the case of Example 11-2, the region of convergence is $r > 1$ in the z-plane.

Example 11-3   Find the region of convergence for the pulse sequence

$$h(n) = a \quad 0 \le n < N - 1$$
$$= 0 \quad \text{elsewhere} \qquad (11\text{-}33)$$

where a is real.

Solution:

$$H(z) = \sum_{n=-\infty}^{\infty} h(n)z^{-n} = \sum_{n=0}^{N-1} az^{-n}$$

Hence,

$$H(re^{j\theta}) = \sum_{n=0}^{N-1} ar^{-n}e^{-j\theta n} \qquad (11\text{-}34)$$

Because (11-34) involves only a finite sum (the number of terms in the summation is finite), $H(z)$ is defined for all $r < \infty$. Hence, the region of convergence is the entire z-plane. $\blacksquare$

Example 11-4   Find the region of convergence for the exponential sequence

$$h(n) = a^n \quad \text{for } 0 \le n < \infty$$
$$= 0 \quad \text{for } n < 0 \qquad (11\text{-}35)$$

Solution: Because

$$H(re^{j\theta}) = \sum_{n=-\infty}^{\infty} h(n)r^{-n}e^{-j\theta n} = \sum_{n=0}^{\infty} a^n r^{-n}e^{-j\theta n} = \sum_{n=0}^{\infty} (ar^{-1})^n e^{-j\theta n} \quad (11\text{-}36)$$

the region of convergence is the values of z with radius r such that

$$\sum_{n=0}^{\infty} \left| \frac{a}{r} \right|^n < \infty \quad (11\text{-}37)$$

Clearly, (11-37) is satisfied if and only if

$$\left| \frac{a}{r} \right| < 1 \quad (11\text{-}38)$$

Hence, the region of convergence of $h(n)$ of (11-35) is the exterior of a circle with radius $|a|$ in the z-plane, as shown in Fig. 11-5(a). ∎

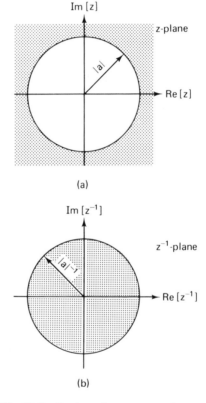

(a)

(b)

Fig. 11-5 Region of convergence for an exponential sequence. (a) In the z-plane. (b) In the z^{-1}-plane.

The region of convergence for a causal sequence $x(n)$—with $x(n) = 0$ for $n < 0$—is everywhere outside a certain circle with radius R in the z-plane.[8] A case in point is given by Example 11-4. The value of R depends on the pole locations of $X(z)$.[9] For the sequence considered in Example 11-4, the z-transform $H(z)$ of the sequence $h(n)$ is given by

$$H(z) = \sum_{n=0}^{\infty} a^n z^{-n}$$

$$= \frac{1}{1 - az^{-1}}$$

(11-39)

Hence, the pole of $H(z)$ is located at the point $z = a$, which is the boundary of the region of convergence for the sequence.

In most physical digital systems including digital filters, causal sequences form the basis of all signals involved in the processing. For convenience, the z-transforms of some of the frequently used causal sequences are listed in Table 11-1, together with their regions of convergence. In general, we will assume that we are working within the area in the z-plane where the z-transforms of all sequences involved are defined, and hence we can ignore the problems associated with the regions of convergence.

From Table 11-1, we observe that the z-transform of a sequence is a rational function of either z or z^{-1}. Thus, if we know the poles and zeros of the z-transform $X(z)$ of a sequence $x(n)$, we can construct $X(z)$ up to a constant multiple rather easily. For example, if $X(z)$ has poles $p_1, p_2, \ldots, p_N$ and zeros $z_1, z_2, \ldots, z_M$, then $X(z)$ can be written in the factored form as:

$$X(z) = \frac{\alpha \prod_{i=1}^{M} (1 - z_i z^{-1})}{\prod_{k=1}^{N} (1 - p_k z^{-1})}$$

(11-40a)

or

$$X(z) = \frac{\alpha z^{(N-M)} \prod_{i=1}^{M} (z - z_i)}{\prod_{k=1}^{N} (z - p_k)}$$

(11-40b)

where α is a constant. In digital filter applications, (11-40a) is preferred, because a shift register or a unit of a tapped delay line is an implementation

---

[8] The region of convergence can be located in the z^{-1}-plane also. For a causal sequence, the region of convergence is everywhere inside a certain circle with radius $\bar{R}$ in the z^{-1}-plane. For example, the region of convergence of the exponential sequence in Example 11-4 is everywhere inside the circle with radius $|a|^{-1}$ in the z^{-1}-plane, as shown in Fig. 11-5(b).

[9] A pole {zero} of a z-transformed function $X(z)$ is the location z_1 in the z-plane, where $X(z_1) = \infty$ {$X(z_1) = 0$}.

TABLE 11-1 Z-Transform Pairs of Some Causal Sequences

Causal Sequence $x(n)$	Z-Transforms of Causal Sequences	Radius of Convergence
$\{x(n) = 0 \text{ for } n < 0\}$	$X(z) = \sum_{n=-\infty}^{\infty} x(n)z^{-n} = \sum_{n=0}^{\infty} x(n)z^{-n}$	$\lvert z \rvert > R \text{ or } \lvert z^{-1} \rvert < \dfrac{1}{R}$
$x(n) = \delta(n)$	$X(z) = 1$	$R = 0$
$x(n) = \delta(n - m)$	$X(z) = z^{-m}$	$R = 0$
$x(n) = u(n)$	$X(z) = \dfrac{z}{z - 1} = \dfrac{1}{1 - z^{-1}}$	$R = 1$
$x(n) = a^n u(n)$	$X(z) = \dfrac{z}{z - a} = \dfrac{1}{1 - az^{-1}}$	$R = \lvert a \rvert$
$x(n) = nu(n)$	$X(z) = \dfrac{z}{(z - 1)^2} = \dfrac{z^{-1}}{(1 - z^{-1})^2}$	$R = 1$
$x(n) = [a^n \sin n\omega T]u(n)$	$X(z) = \dfrac{az \sin \omega T}{z^2 - 2az \cos \omega T + a^2}$ $= \dfrac{az^{-1} \sin \omega T}{a^2 z^{-2} - 2az^{-1} \cos \omega T + 1}$	$R = \lvert a \rvert$
$x(n) = [a^n \cos n\omega T]u(n)$	$X(z) = \dfrac{z(z - a \cos \omega T)}{z^2 - 2az \cos \omega T + a^2}$ $= \dfrac{1 - az^{-1} \cos \omega T}{a^2 z^{-2} - 2az^{-1} \cos \omega T + 1}$	$R = \lvert a \rvert$

of the operator z^{-1}. By multiplying together the factors in (11-40a), we obtain

$$X(z) = \frac{\displaystyle\sum_{i=0}^{M} a_i z^{-i}}{1 + \displaystyle\sum_{k=1}^{N} b_k z^{-k}} \tag{11-41}$$

We use mainly (11-41) for general digital filter design.

11-2-1. Properties of z-Transform

In this subsection, we discuss the various properties associated with z-transforms.

Uniqueness Property: Let $X_1(z)$ and $X_2(z)$ be the z-transforms of $x_1(n)$ and $x_2(n)$, respectively. Then $X_1(z) = X_2(z)$ if and only if $x_1(n) = x_2(n)$ for $-\infty < n < \infty$. This means that for each sequence $x(n)$, there corresponds one and only one z-transformed function $X(z)$.

Linearity Property: Z-transform is a linear operation. If $X_1(z)$ and $X_2(z)$ are the z-transforms of $x_1(n)$ and $x_2(n)$, respectively, then the z-transform $X(z)$ of

$$x(n) \triangleq a_1 x_1(n) + a_2 x_2(n) \tag{11-42a}$$

where a_1 and a_2 are constants, is given by

$$X(z) = a_1 X_1(z) + a_2 X_2(z) \tag{11-42b}$$

Example 11-5   Find $X(z)$, the z-transform of

$$x(n) = [\cos n\phi + \alpha \sin n\phi]u(n) \tag{11-43}$$

via Table 11-1, where α is a constant.

Solution: From Table 11-1, the z-transforms $X_1(z)$ and $X_2(z)$ of the sequences

$$x_1(n) = [\cos n\phi]u(n)$$

and

$$x_2(n) = [\sin n\phi]u(n)$$

are given by

$$X_1(z) = \frac{1 - z^{-1} \cos \phi}{z^{-2} - 2z^{-1}(\cos \phi) + 1} \tag{11-44a}$$

and

$$X_2(z) = \frac{z^{-1} \sin \phi}{z^{-2} - 2z^{-1}(\cos \phi) + 1} \tag{11-44b}$$

By the property of linearity, we obtain

$$X(z) = X_1(z) + \alpha X_2(z) = \frac{1 + (\alpha \sin \phi - \cos \phi)z^{-1}}{z^{-2} - 2z^{-1}(\cos \phi) + 1} \tag{11-45}$$

Note that (11-45) is identical to (11-29) when $\alpha = 1$.   ∎

Shift Property: Let $X_1(z)$ be the z-transform of $x_1(n)$. Then the z-transform $X(z)$ of

$$x(n) \triangleq x_1(n - m) \implies z^{-m} \text{ for causal system} \tag{11-46a}$$

is given by

$$X(z) = z^{-m} X_1(z) + x_1(-m) + x_1(-m + 1)z^{-1}$$
$$+ \ldots + x_1(-1)z^{-m+1} \tag{11-46b}$$

If $x_1(n)$ is a causal sequence, then (11-46b) reduces to

$$X(z) = z^{-m} X_1(z) \tag{11-46c}$$

Example 11-6   Let S be a digital system characterized by

$$y(n) + b_1 y(n - 1) + b_2 y(n - 2) = a_0 x(n) + a_1 x(n - 1) \tag{11-47}$$

Assuming that both $x(n)$ and $y(n)$ are causal sequences, find the relationship between $X(z)$ and $Y(z)$, the z-transforms of $x(n)$ and $y(n)$, respectively.

Solution: By the shift property, the z-transform of (11-47) gives

$$Y(z) + b_1 z^{-1} Y(z) + b_2 z^{-2} Y(z) = a_0 X(z) + a_1 z^{-1} X(z)$$

or

$$(1 + b_1 z^{-1} + b_2 z^{-2}) Y(z) = (a_0 + a_1 z^{-1}) X(z)$$

Hence,

$$\frac{Y(z)}{X(z)} = \frac{a_0 + a_1 z^{-1}}{1 + b_1 z^{-1} + b_2 z^{-2}} \tag{11-48}$$

∎

Convolution Property: Let $X_1(z)$ and $X_2(z)$ be the z-transforms of $x_1(n)$ and $x_2(n)$, respectively. Then the z-transform $X(z)$ of

$$x(n) = x_1(n) * x_2(n)$$

$$= \sum_{k=-\infty}^{\infty} x_1(k) x_2(n-k) \tag{11-49a}$$

$$= \sum_{k=-\infty}^{\infty} x_1(n-k) x_2(k)$$

is given by

$$X(z) = X_1(z) X_2(z) \tag{11-49b}$$

Example 11-7   Let $x(n)$ be the input to a linear time-invariant digital system, with an impulse response $h(n)$. Let $X(z)$ and $H(z)$ be the z-transforms of $x(n)$ and $h(n)$, respectively. Find the z-transform $Y(z)$ of the zero-state output sequence $y(n)$.

Solution: From (11-17), the output $y(n)$ is given by

$$y(n) = x(n) * h(n)$$

Hence, the convolution property yields

$$Y(z) = H(z) X(z) \tag{11-50}$$

∎

The z-transform $H(z)$ of the impulse response of a linear time-invariant system is called the *transfer function* of the system. In view of (11-50), the transfer function of a system is given as a ratio of the z-transforms of the zero-state output response and the associated input of the system. For example, from (11-48), the system S in Example 11-6 has a transfer function given by

$$H(z) = \frac{Y(z)}{X(z)} = \frac{a_0 + a_1 z^{-1}}{1 + b_1 z^{-1} + b_2 z^{-2}} \tag{11-51}$$

This means that if a set of difference equations representing a system S is given, we can find the transfer function of the system S. Conversely, if we are given the transfer function of the system S,

$$H(z) = \frac{Y(z)}{X(z)} = \frac{\sum_{i=0}^{M} a_i z^{-i}}{1 + \sum_{k=1}^{N} b_k z^{-k}} \tag{11-52}$$

we can find the difference equation characterizing the system S as follows:

$$\left(1 + \sum_{k=1}^{N} b_k z^{-k}\right) Y(z) = \left(\sum_{i=0}^{M} a_i z^{-i}\right) X(z)$$

$$y(n) + \sum_{k=1}^{N} [b_k y(n-k)] = \sum_{i=0}^{M} [a_i x(n-i)]$$

or

$$y(n) + b_1 y(n-1) + \ldots + b_N y(n-N)$$
$$= a_0 x(n) + a_1 x(n-1) + \ldots + a_M x(n-M) \tag{11-53}$$

That is, a system S can be characterized either by a difference equation or by a transfer function. Note that the transfer function of a system can yield the impulse response of the system only. In order to find a unique output sequence, we need to know the input sequence and the initial conditions of the system.

11-2-2. Inverse Z-Transform

Z-transforms are tools for the analysis of linear and time-invariant digital systems. At the end of an analysis, the output sequences rather than their corresponding z-transforms are desired. The process of finding a sequence associated with a function of z is called the *inverse z-transform*. Formally, the inverse z-transform $x(n)$ of $X(z)$ is defined to be

$$x(n) = \frac{1}{2\pi j} \oint_C X(z) z^{n-1} \, dz \tag{11-54}$$

where the integral in (11-54) is a contour integral over a closed path C. For simplicity, C can be a circle in the region of convergence of $X(z)$ in the z-plane.

Direct evaluation of (11-54) is impractical if not impossible. In general, (11-54) is *not* used directly to find the inverse z-transform of $X(z)$. In this subsection, we present four methods to implement (11-54).

Residue Method: Let $X(z)$ be a rational function of z. Then (11-54) can be evaluated by the residue theorem, which states that

$$x(n) = \frac{1}{2\pi j} \oint_C X(z) z^{n-1} \, dz \triangleq \frac{1}{2\pi j} \oint_C F_n(z) \, dz$$
$$= \sum \text{residues of } F_n(z) \text{ at all poles of } F_n(z) \text{ inside } C \tag{11-55a}$$

where

$$F_n(z) = X(z) z^{n-1} \tag{11-55b}$$

and $n = \ldots, -1, 0, 1, \ldots$.

Example 11-8   Find the inverse z-transform of

$$X(z) = \frac{1}{1 - az^{-1}} = \frac{z}{z - a} \qquad (11\text{-}56)$$

by the residue method.

Solution: Let

$$F_n(z) \triangleq X(z)z^{n-1} = \frac{z^n}{z - a} \qquad (11\text{-}57)$$

Then (11-55) implies that $x(n)$ is the sum of residues of $F_n(z)$ at all poles of $F_n(z)$ inside some circle C. For simplicity, we choose C to be a circle of radius greater than $|a|$ in the z-plane. For $n \geq 0$, the closed path C encloses only one pole at $z = a$, as shown in Fig. 11-6(a). Hence, (11-55a) gives

$$
\begin{aligned}
x(n) &= \text{residue of } F_n(z) \text{ at } z = a \\
&= (z - a)F_n(z)|_{z=a} = z^n|_{z=a} \qquad (11\text{-}58) \\
&= a^n \quad \text{for } n \geq 0
\end{aligned}
$$

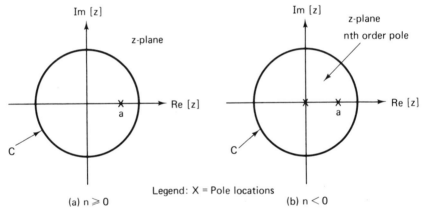

Legend: X = Pole locations

(a) $n \geqslant 0$ (b) $n < 0$

Fig. 11-6   Pole locations of $F_n(z)$ of (11-57). (a) For $n \geq 0$. (b) for $n < 0$.

For $n < 0$, $F_n(z)$ can be written as

$$F_n(z) = \frac{1}{z^{|n|}(z - a)} \qquad (11\text{-}59)$$

That is, there is a simple pole at $z = a$ and a pole at $z = 0$ with multiplicity $|n|$, as shown in Fig. 11-6(b). Hence,

$$x(n) = \zeta_a + \zeta_0 \qquad (11\text{-}60)$$

where ζ_a and ζ_0 are, respectively, the residues of $F_n(z)$ at $z = a$ and $z = 0$.[10]

---

[10]The residue of a complex function $G(z)$ at a pole $z = p_0$ of multiplicity n is given by

$$\frac{1}{(n - 1)!} \frac{d^{n-1}}{dz^{n-1}} \left[(z - p_0)^n G(z) \right] \Big|_{z = p_0}$$

When $n = -1$, we have[11]

$$\zeta_a = (z - a)F_n(z)\bigg|_{z=a} = \frac{1}{z}\bigg|_{z=a} = a^{-1} \tag{11-61a}$$

$$\zeta_0 = zF_n(z)\bigg|_{z=0} = \frac{1}{z - a}\bigg|_{z=0} = -a^{-1} \tag{11-61b}$$

Hence,

$$x(-1) = \zeta_a + \zeta_0 = a^{-1} - a^{-1} = 0 \tag{11-62}$$

When $n = -2$, we have

$$F_n(z) = \frac{1}{z^2(z - a)} \tag{11-63a}$$

$$\zeta_a = (z - a)F_n(z)\bigg|_{z=a} = \frac{1}{z^2}\bigg|_{z=a} = a^{-2} \tag{11-63b}$$

and

$$\begin{aligned}\zeta_0 &= \frac{d}{dz}[z^2F_n(z)]\bigg|_{z=0} = \frac{d}{dz}\left[z^2\frac{1}{z^2(z - a)}\right]\bigg|_{z=0} \\ &= \frac{d}{dz}\left(\frac{1}{z - a}\right)\bigg|_{z=0} = -\frac{1}{(z - a)^2}\bigg|_{z=0} = -a^{-2}\end{aligned} \tag{11-63c}$$

Hence,

$$x(-2) = a^{-2} - a^{-2} = 0 \tag{11-63d}$$

It turns out that for every $n < 0$, we have

$$\zeta_a = -\zeta_0 \tag{11-64a}$$

Hence,

$$x(n) = 0 \quad \text{for } n < 0 \tag{11-64b}$$

From (11-58) and (11-64), the inverse z-transform of $X(z)$ of (11-56) is given by

$$x(n) = a^n u(n) \tag{11-65}$$

This result can be verified easily by consulting Table 11-1. ∎

Long-Division Method: Suppose that $X(z)$ is given by

$$X(z) = \frac{a_0 + a_1z^{-1} + a_2z^{-2} + \ldots + a_Mz^{-M}}{b_0 + b_1z^{-1} + b_2z^{-2} + \ldots + b_Nz^{-N}} \tag{11-66}$$

where $M \leq N$. Then long division of the numerator by the denominator of $X(z)$ yields[12]

$$X(z) = x_0 + x_1z^{-1} + x_2z^{-2} + \ldots \tag{11-67}$$

By comparing (11-67) and (11-25), we obtain

$$\begin{aligned}x(n) &= x_n \quad \text{for } n \geq 0 \\ &= 0 \quad \text{for } n < 0\end{aligned} \tag{11-68}$$

---

[11]See (4-48).

[12]In each step of the long-division process, we eliminate the lowest-power term of z^{-1}.

Example 11-9   Find the inverse z-transform of

$$X(z) = \frac{1}{1 - az^{-1}} \tag{11-69}$$

by the long-division method.

Solution: Dividing the numerator of $X(z)$ by the denominator of $X(z)$, we obtain

$$
\begin{array}{r}
1 + az^{-1} + a^2z^{-2} + \cdots \\
1 - az^{-1} \overline{)1} \\
1 - az^{-1} \\
\overline{az^{-1}} \\
az^{-1} - a^2z^{-2} \\
\overline{a^2z^{-2}} \\
a^2z^{-2} - a^3z^{-3} \\
\overline{a^3z^{-3}}
\end{array}
$$

Hence, $X(z)$ can be written as

$$X(z) = 1 + az^{-1} + a^2z^{-2} + \cdots$$

or

$$x(n) = a^n u(n) \qquad \blacksquare$$

In general, this method will not provide answers for $x(n)$ when n is large unless one is willing to carry out an extensive long division to reach the nth stage. Hence, this method is seldom used unless one just wants to know the values of the first few terms in the sequence.

Power Series Method: Let $X(z)$ be the z-transform of a sequence $x(n)$. Define $X_1(z^{-1})$ as

$$X_1(z^{-1}) \triangleq X(z) = \sum_{n=-\infty}^{\infty} x(n)z^{-n} \tag{11-70}$$

A Taylor series expansion of $X_1(z^{-1})$ about the point $z^{-1} = 0$ gives

$$X_1(z^{-1}) = \alpha_0 + \alpha_1 z^{-1} + \alpha_2 z^{-2} + \cdots \tag{11-71a}$$

where

$$\alpha_k = \frac{1}{k!} \frac{\partial^{(k)} X_1(z^{-1})}{[\partial z^{-1}]^{(k)}}\bigg|_{z^{-1}=0}$$

$$\triangleq \frac{1}{k!} X_1^{(k)}(0) \tag{11-71b}$$

By comparing (11-70) and (11-71), we obtain

$$
\begin{aligned}
x(n) &= \alpha_n \quad \text{for } n \geq 0 \\
&= 0 \quad\ \text{for } n < 0
\end{aligned} \tag{11-72}
$$

Example 11-10   Find the inverse z-transform of

$$X(z) = \frac{1}{1 - az^{-1}} \tag{11-73}$$

by the power series method.

Solution: By (11-70) and (11-71),

$$X_1(z^{-1}) = \frac{1}{1 - az^{-1}}$$

$$= X_1(0) + X_1^{(1)}(0)z^{-1} + \frac{1}{2!}X_1^{(2)}(0) \qquad (11\text{-}74)$$

$$+ \ldots + \frac{1}{k!}X_1^{(k)}(0)z^{-k} + \ldots$$

where

$$X_1(0) = 1 \qquad (11\text{-}75a)$$

$$X_1^{(1)}(0) \triangleq \frac{d}{dz^{-1}}X_1(z^{-1})\Big|_{z^{-1}=0} = \frac{a}{(1 - az^{-1})^2}\Big|_{z^{-1}=0} = a \qquad (11\text{-}75b)$$

$$X_1^{(2)}(0) \triangleq \frac{d^2}{(dz^{-1})^2}X_1(z^{-1})\Big|_{z^{-1}=0} = \frac{2a^2}{(1 - az^{-1})^3}\Big|_{z^{-1}=0} = 2a^2 \qquad (11\text{-}75c)$$

$$X_1^{(k)}(0) \triangleq \frac{d^k}{(dz^{-1})^k}X_1(z^{-1})\Big|_{z^{-1}=0} = \frac{k!\,a^k}{(1 - az^{-1})^{k+1}}\Big|_{z^{-1}=0} = k!\,a^k \qquad (11\text{-}75d)$$

Substituting (11-75) into (11-74), we obtain

$$X(z) = 1 + az^{-1} + a^2z^{-2} + \ldots + a^kz^{-k} + \ldots$$

or

$$x(n) = a^n u(n) \qquad (11\text{-}76)$$

∎

Partial Fraction Expansion Method: When $X(z)$ is written in its factored form of (11-40), a partial fraction expansion of $X(z)$ gives

$$X(z) = \frac{\zeta_1}{1 - p_1 z^{-1}} + \frac{\zeta_2}{1 - p_2 z^{-1}} + \ldots + \frac{\zeta_N}{1 - p_N z^{-1}} \qquad (11\text{-}77)$$

where we have assumed that $N > M$ and the poles are distinct (i.e., $p_i \neq p_j$ whenever $i \neq j$). Note that ζ_i is the residue of $X(z)$ at the pole location $z = p_i$. Hence,

$$\zeta_i = (1 - p_i z^{-1})X(z)|_{z=p_i} \quad \text{for } i = 1, 2, \ldots, N \qquad (11\text{-}78)$$

Because the z-transform is a linear operation, the inverse z-transform is also a linear operation. Hence, $x(n)$ can be obtained by summing the inverse z-transform of each individual term in (11-77). That is,

$$x(n) = (\zeta_1 p_1^n + \zeta_2 p_2^n + \ldots + \zeta_N p_N^n)u(n)$$

$$= \left(\sum_{i=1}^{N} \zeta_i p_i^n\right)u(n) \qquad (11\text{-}79)$$

If all the poles are real, then (11-79) yields a comprehensive real $x(n)$. However, if some or all of the poles are complex, then it is not clear that the resulting sequence from (11-79) is a sequence with real numbers.

Suppose that all the coefficients of $X(z)$ are real. In this case, it is known that if a pole p_i is complex (including the purely imaginary case), then there is a pole p_k such that

$$p_k = \bar{p}_i \tag{11-80a}$$

where $\bar{a}$ denotes the complex conjugate of a. In addition, the residues corresponding to p_i and p_k are complex conjugates of each other. That is, we also have

$$\zeta_k = \bar{\zeta}_i \tag{11-80b}$$

Hence, the sum of the ith and kth terms in (11-77) is given by[13]

$$\zeta_i p_i^n + \zeta_k p_k^n = \zeta_i p_i^n + \overline{\zeta_i p_i^n}$$
$$= 2 \operatorname{Re} [\zeta_i p_i^n] \tag{11-81a}$$
$$= 2 |\zeta_i| |p_i|^n \cos (\underline{/\zeta_i} + n \underline{/p_i})$$

where

$$\zeta_i = |\zeta_i| \exp (j \underline{/\zeta_i}) \tag{11-81b}$$

and

$$p_i = |p_i| \exp (j \underline{/p_i}) \tag{11-81c}$$

Example 11-11   Let

$$X(z) = \frac{1}{(1 - az^{-1})(1 - bz^{-1})} \tag{11-82}$$

(a) Find the inverse z-transform of $X(z)$ via the partial fraction expansion method.
(b) If $a = 0.5 + j0.5$ and $b = \bar{a}$, find $x(n)$.

Solution: The partial fraction expansion of (11-82) is given by

$$X(z) = \frac{\zeta_1}{1 - az^{-1}} + \frac{\zeta_2}{1 - bz^{-1}} \tag{11-83a}$$

where the poles are at

$$p_1 = a \quad \text{and} \quad p_2 = b \tag{11-83b}$$

and their corresponding residues are

$$\zeta_1 = (1 - az^{-1})X(z)\Big|_{z=a} = \frac{1}{1 - bz^{-1}}\Big|_{z=a} = \frac{a}{a - b} \tag{11-83c}$$

and

$$\zeta_2 = (1 - bz^{-1})X(z)\Big|_{z=b} = \frac{1}{1 - az^{-1}}\Big|_{z=b} = -\frac{b}{a - b} \tag{11-83d}$$

Hence,

$$x(n) = (\zeta_1 a^n + \zeta_2 b^n)u(n)$$
$$= \left(\frac{a}{a - b} a^n - \frac{b}{a - b} b^n\right)u(n) \tag{11-84}$$
$$= \left(\frac{a^{n+1} - b^{n+1}}{a - b}\right)u(n)$$

---

[13]Let $\alpha = a + jb$ and $\bar{\alpha}$ be the complex conjugate of α. Then $\bar{\alpha} = a - jb$, and $\alpha + \bar{\alpha} = (a + jb) + (a - jb) = 2a = 2 \operatorname{Re} [\alpha]$.

If

$$a = 0.5 + j0.5 = \sqrt{(0.5)^2 + (0.5)^2} \exp (j45°)$$

$$= 0.707 \exp (j45°) \tag{11-85a}$$

then

$$p_1 = a = 0.707 \exp (j45°)$$

$$\zeta_1 = \frac{a}{a - \bar{a}} = 0.5 - j0.5 = 0.707 \exp (-j45°) \tag{11-85b}$$

and (11-81) yields

$$x(n) = (\zeta_1 a^n + \zeta_2 b^n)u(n)$$

$$= 2|\zeta_1||a|^n \cos (\underline{/\zeta_1} + n\underline{/a})u(n)$$

$$= 2(0.707)(0.707)^n \cos (-45° + 45n°)u(n) \tag{11-85c}$$

$$= (0.707)^{n-1} \cos [(n - 1)45°]u(n)$$

Note that we can also obtain (11-85c) directly from (11-84).   ∎

Example 11-12   Let S be a digital system represented by

$$y(n) - 3y(n - 1) + 2y(n - 2) = 2x(n - 1) - 2x(n - 2) \tag{11-86}$$

If the input $x(n)$ is given by

$$x(n) = 5\delta(n) \tag{11-87}$$

find the zero-state response $y(n)$.

Solution: By taking the z-transforms of (11-86), we obtain

$$Y(z)(1 - 3z^{-1} + 2z^{-2}) = (2z^{-1} - 2z^{-2})X(z)$$

or

$$Y(z) = \frac{2z^{-1} - 2z^{-2}}{1 - 3z^{-1} + 2z^{-2}} X(z) = \frac{10z^{-1} - 10z^{-2}}{1 - 3z^{-1} + 2z^{-2}}$$

$$= -5 + \frac{-5z^{-1} + 5}{1 - 3z^{-1} + 2z^{-2}}$$

$$= -5 + \frac{-5}{1 - 2z^{-1}}$$

From Table 11-1, we obtain

$$y(n) = -5\delta(n) + [5(2)^n]u(n) \tag{11-88}$$

Note that the system characterized by (11-86) is unstable.   ∎

11-3   FOURIER TRANSFORM

The Fourier transform $X_F(e^{j\theta})$ of a sequence $x(n)$ is defined to be[14]

$$X_F(e^{j\theta}) \triangleq \sum_{n=-\infty}^{\infty} x(n)e^{-jn\theta} \tag{11-89}$$

Comparing (11-25) and (11-89), we conclude that the Fourier transform of a

---

[14] θ is a real quantity.

sequence is the z-transform of the sequence evaluated along the unit circle in the z-plane, as shown in Fig. 11-7. That is,

$$X_F(e^{j\theta}) = X(z)|_{z=e^{j\theta}} \triangleq X(e^{j\theta}) \tag{11-90}$$

Hereafter, we use $X(e^{j\theta})$ to denote the Fourier transform of a sequence $x(n)$ where $X(z)$ is the z-transform of $x(n)$.

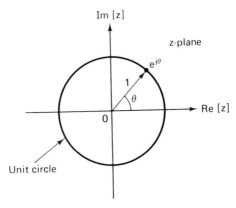

Fig. 11-7 Fourier transforms are z-transforms evaluated along the unit circle.

Note that for any integer k, we have

$$e^{j\theta} = e^{j(\theta+2\pi k)} \tag{11-91}$$

Hence,

$$X(e^{j\theta}) = X[e^{j(\theta+2\pi k)}] \tag{11-92}$$

This means that the Fourier transform of a sequence is a *periodic* function of θ.

Example 11-13 Find the Fourier transform of the sequence $h(n)$ given by

$$h(n) = a \quad \text{for } 0 \leq n \leq N-1$$
$$= 0 \quad \text{elsewhere} \tag{11-93}$$

Solution: By (11-89), the Fourier transform of $h(n)$ is given by

$$H(e^{j\theta}) = \sum_{n=-\infty}^{\infty} h(n)e^{-j\theta n} = \sum_{n=0}^{N-1} a e^{-j\theta n} \tag{11-94a}$$

$$= \frac{a[1 - e^{-j\theta N}]}{1 - e^{-j\theta}}$$

$$= \frac{a \exp\left(-j\frac{\theta N}{2}\right)\left[\exp\left(j\frac{\theta N}{2}\right) - \exp\left(-j\frac{\theta N}{2}\right)\right]\Big/2j}{\exp\left(-j\frac{\theta}{2}\right)\left[\exp\left(j\frac{\theta}{2}\right) - \exp\left(-j\frac{\theta}{2}\right)\right]\Big/2j} \tag{11-94b}$$

$$= a \exp\left[-j\frac{\theta(N-1)}{2}\right]\frac{\sin(N\theta/2)}{\sin(\theta/2)}$$

Because both the numerator and the denominator on the right-hand side of (11-94a) are periodic as

$$1 - e^{-j(\theta+2\pi k)N} = 1 - e^{-j\theta N}e^{-j2\pi kN} = 1 - e^{-j\theta N} \quad (11\text{-}95a)$$

and

$$1 - e^{-j(\theta+2\pi k)} = 1 - e^{-j\theta}e^{-j2\pi k} = 1 - e^{-j\theta} \quad (11\text{-}95b)$$

where k is an integer, we conclude that $H(e^{j\theta})$ of (11-94) is a periodic function of θ. ∎

Consider a linear time-invariant digital system characterized by an impulse response $h(n)$. Given the input sequence $x(n)$, the zero-state output sequence $y(n)$ can be obtained by a convolution sum, as indicated by (11-17). Suppose that $x(n)$ is given by

$$x(n) = e^{j\theta n} \quad -\infty < n < \infty \quad (11\text{-}96)$$

Then the output $y(n)$ is given by

$$
\begin{aligned}
y(n) &= \sum_{k=-\infty}^{\infty} h(k)x(n-k) \\
&= \sum_{k=-\infty}^{\infty} h(k)e^{j\theta(n-k)} \\
&= e^{j\theta n} \sum_{k=-\infty}^{\infty} h(k)e^{-j\theta k} \\
&= H(e^{j\theta})e^{j\theta n} \\
&= H(e^{j\theta})x(n)
\end{aligned}
\quad (11\text{-}97)
$$

where θ is the input exponential frequency.[15] From (11-97), $H(e^{j\theta})$ is the multiplier (independent of n) that converts the exponential input sequence $x(n)$ of (11-96) to the output sequence $y(n)$. Because the input sequence $x(n)$ of (11-96) is functionally equivalent to a sampled sinusoid with frequency θ, $H(e^{j\theta})$ in (11-97) is called the *frequency response* of the system. In other words, the frequency response $H(e^{j\theta})$ of a system S is the transfer function $H(z)$ of the system S evaluated along the unit circle—by letting $z = e^{j\theta}$ with $0 \leq \theta < 2\pi$—in the z-plane.[16] [Recall that $H(z)$ is the z-transform of $h(n)$, and, hence, $H(e^{j\theta})$ is the Fourier transform of $h(n)$, where $h(n)$ is the impulse response of the system.] From (11-97), we observe that if the input sequence is a sinusoid, then the output sequence can be obtained simply by multiplying the input sequence with the frequency response of the system.

---

[15] Let $\hat{x}(t) = e^{j\omega t}$ be the exponential sinusoidal continuous-time function. Then the corresponding sampled sequence $x(n)$ is given by $x(n) \triangleq \hat{x}(nT) = e^{j\omega nT} = e^{j\theta n}$, where $\theta \triangleq \omega T$ is the digital frequency of the sampled sequence $x(n)$, and T is the sampling period.

[16] This is analogous to the continuous-time case, where the frequency response $\hat{H}(j\omega)$ of a system is the transfer function $\hat{H}(s)$ of the system, with s evaluated along the imaginary axis in the s-plane—by letting $s = j\omega$ with $-\infty < \omega < \infty$. Here $\hat{H}(s)$ is the Laplace transform of the impulse response $\hat{h}(t)$ of the system.

Example 11-14 Let S be a system characterized by

$$y(n) - ay(n - 1) = x(n) \tag{11-98}$$

If the input sequence is given by

$$x(n) = \cos \theta n \tag{11-99}$$

find the output sequence $y(n)$.

Solution: Taking the z-transforms of (11-98), we obtain

$$(1 - az^{-1})Y(z) = X(z) \tag{11-100}$$

Hence, the transfer function of the system is[17]

$$H(z) \triangleq \frac{Y(z)}{X(z)} = \frac{1}{1 - az^{-1}} \tag{11-101}$$

The input $x(n)$ can be written as $H(e^{\pm j\theta}) = \dfrac{1}{1 - a e^{+j\theta}}$

$$x(n) = \cos n\theta = \tfrac{1}{2}e^{jn\theta} + \tfrac{1}{2}e^{-jn\theta} \tag{11-102}$$
$$\triangleq x_1(n) + x_2(n)$$

where

$$x_1(n) \triangleq \tfrac{1}{2}e^{j\theta n} \tag{11-103a}$$

and

$$x_2(n) \triangleq \tfrac{1}{2}e^{-j\theta n} \tag{11-103b}$$

From (11-97), the responses $y_1(n)$ and $y_2(n)$ due to $x_1(n)$ and $x_2(n)$, respectively, are given by

$$y_1(n) = \frac{1}{2}H(e^{j\theta})e^{j\theta n} = \frac{1}{2}\frac{e^{jn\theta}}{1 - ae^{-j\theta}} \tag{11-104a}$$

and

$$y_2(n) = \frac{1}{2}H(e^{-j\theta})e^{-j\theta n} = \frac{1}{2}\frac{e^{-jn\theta}}{1 - ae^{j\theta}} \tag{11-104b}$$

Consequently, the output $y(n)$ due to the input $x(n)$ can be obtained by the linearity property as

$$
\begin{aligned}
y(n) &= y_1(n) + y_2(n) \\
&= \frac{1}{2}\left(\frac{e^{jn\theta}}{1 - ae^{-j\theta}} + \frac{e^{-jn\theta}}{1 - ae^{j\theta}}\right) \\
&= \frac{1}{2}\left[\frac{e^{jn\theta}(1 - ae^{j\theta}) + e^{-jn\theta}(1 - ae^{-j\theta})}{(1 - ae^{-j\theta})(1 - ae^{j\theta})}\right] \\
&= \frac{1}{2}\left[\frac{e^{jn\theta} + e^{-jn\theta} - a[e^{j(n+1)\theta} + e^{-j(n+1)\theta}]}{1 - a[e^{j\theta} + e^{-j\theta}] + a^2}\right] \\
&= \frac{\cos n\theta - a\cos[(n+1)\theta]}{1 - 2a\cos(\theta) + a^2}
\end{aligned}
\tag{11-105}
$$

■

---

[17]Notice that in Example 11-1 the impulse response $h(n)$ of the system is given by (11-24) as $h(n) = a^n u(n)$. By Table 11-1, the transfer function of the system (which is the z-transform of this impulse response) is given by (11-101).

11-3-1. Sampling Theorem

Basic to digital filtering are the problems associated with the sampling of continuous signals to form digital signals and the construction of continuous signals from their digital counterparts. In this subsection, we deal with these problems via the Fourier transforms of continuous and digital signals.[18]

Let $\hat{x}(t)$ be a continuous-time signal that has a Fourier representation

$$\hat{x}(t) = \frac{1}{2\pi} \int_{-\infty}^{\infty} \hat{X}(j\omega)e^{j\omega t}\, d\omega \qquad (11\text{-}106a)$$

where

$$\hat{X}(j\omega) = \int_{-\infty}^{\infty} \hat{x}(t)e^{-j\omega t}\, dt \qquad (11\text{-}106b)$$

is called the Fourier transform of $\hat{x}(t)$. Let $x(n)$ be the sequence defined by

$$x(n) = \hat{x}(nT) \qquad (11\text{-}107a)$$

where T is the *sampling period*, and

$$f_s \triangleq \frac{1}{T} \qquad (11\text{-}107b)$$

is called the *sampling frequency*. The Fourier transform of the sequence $x(n)$ is given by (11-89) as

$$X(e^{j\theta}) = \sum_{n=-\infty}^{\infty} x(n)e^{-jn\theta} \qquad (11\text{-}108a)$$

Because $X(e^{j\theta})$ is a periodic function of θ with period 2π, (11-108a) represents the Fourier series expansion of $X(e^{j\theta})$ with the Fourier coefficients being $x(n)$. In terms of $X(e^{j\theta})$, $x(n)$ is given by

$$x(n) = \frac{1}{2\pi} \int_{-\pi}^{\pi} X(e^{j\theta})e^{j\theta n}\, d\theta \qquad (11\text{-}108b)$$

Because $x(n)$ is obtained by sampling the continuous signal $\hat{x}(t)$ as indicated by (11-107), it is possible to relate $\hat{X}(j\omega)$, the Fourier transform of $\hat{x}(t)$, and $X(e^{j\theta})$, the Fourier transform of $x(n)$. Substituting (11-106a) into (11-107a) and with $t = nT$, we obtain

$$x(n) = \hat{x}(nT) = \frac{1}{2\pi} \int_{-\infty}^{\infty} \hat{X}(j\omega)e^{j\omega nT}\, d\omega$$

$$= \frac{1}{2\pi} \sum_{k=-\infty}^{\infty} \int_{[(2k-1)\pi]/T}^{[(2k+1)\pi]/T} \hat{X}(j\omega)e^{j\omega nT}\, d\omega \qquad (11\text{-}109)$$

---

[18]Except for the analog frequency ω, we use the symbol "$^\wedge$" to denote variables associated with the continuous-time case. For examples, $\hat{x}(t)$ is a continuous-time function, and $\hat{H}(s)$ is a transfer function of an analog system.

By a change of the integration variable with

$$\omega' \triangleq \omega - \frac{2\pi k}{T} \tag{11-110}$$

and noting that

$$e^{j\omega nT} = e^{j[\omega' + (2\pi k/T)]nT}$$

$$= e^{j\omega' nT} e^{j2\pi kn} = e^{j\omega' nT} \tag{11-111}$$

(11-109) can be written as

$$x(n) = \frac{1}{2\pi} \sum_{k=-\infty}^{\infty} \int_{-\pi/T}^{\pi/T} \hat{X}\left[j\left(\omega' + \frac{2\pi k}{T}\right)\right] e^{j\omega' nT} \, d\omega'$$

$$= \frac{1}{2\pi} \int_{-\pi/T}^{\pi/T} \sum_{k=-\infty}^{\infty} \hat{X}\left[j\left(\omega + \frac{2\pi k}{T}\right)\right] e^{j\omega nT} \, d\omega \tag{11-112}$$

where the dummy variable ω' is replaced by another dummy integration variable ω. With another change of variable

$$\theta = \omega T \tag{11-113}$$

we can write (11-112) as

$$x(n) = \frac{1}{2\pi} \int_{-\pi}^{\pi} \frac{1}{T} \sum_{k=-\infty}^{\infty} \hat{X}\left[j\left(\frac{\theta}{T} + \frac{2\pi k}{T}\right)\right] e^{jn\theta} \, d\theta \tag{11-114}$$

By comparing (11-108b) and (11-114), we obtain

$$X(e^{j\theta}) = \frac{1}{T} \sum_{k=-\infty}^{\infty} \hat{X}\left[j\left(\frac{\theta}{T} + \frac{2\pi k}{T}\right)\right] \tag{11-115a}$$

or

$$X(e^{j\omega T}) = \frac{1}{T} \sum_{k=-\infty}^{\infty} \hat{X}\left[j\left(\omega + \frac{2\pi k}{T}\right)\right] \tag{11-115b}$$

Observe that $\hat{X}[j(\omega + p)]$ is a frequency-shifted version of $\hat{X}(j\omega)$. For example, if $\hat{X}(j\omega)$ is given by Fig. 11-8(a), then $\hat{X}[j(\omega + p)]$ is shown in Fig. 11-8(b), where we have assumed that p is a positive real number. Hence, (11-115) says that the frequency characteristic of the sampled sequence $x(n)$ is a scaled sum of an infinite number of frequency-shifted copies of the frequency characteristic of the corresponding continuous-time signal $\hat{x}(t)$. In the case when a continuous-time signal is bandlimited with a bandwidth ω_0; i.e.,

$$\hat{X}(j\omega) = 0 \quad \text{for } |\omega| \geq \frac{\omega_0}{2} \tag{11-116}$$

as shown in Fig. 11-9(a), then (11-115) yields various possible $X(e^{j\theta})$, as shown in Figs. 11-9(b), (c), or (d), depending on the sampling period T being

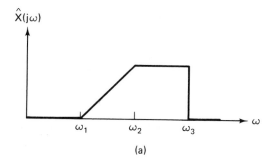

(a)

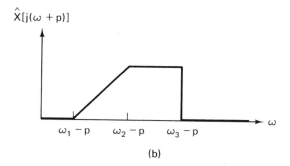

(b)

Fig. 11-8 An illustration of the relationship between (a) $\hat{X}(j\omega)$ and (b) $\hat{X}[j(\omega + p)]$.

greater, smaller, or equal to $2\pi/\omega_0$. When[19]

$$T \leq \frac{2\pi}{\omega_0} \tag{11-117}$$

(11-115) reduces to

$$X(e^{j\theta}) = \frac{1}{T}\hat{X}\left(j\frac{\theta}{T}\right) \quad \text{for } |\theta| = \omega T \leq \pi \tag{11-118}$$

That is, the frequency characteristics of the continuous-time signal and its sampled sequence are identical in shape and differ only by a scale factor for $|\theta| \leq \pi$. This fact can also be observed from Fig. 11-9.

Because (11-118) implies that the frequency characteristics of both the continuous-time signal and its corresponding sampled sequence are identical up to a constant scaling factor, it is reasonable to expect that given $x(n)$ and the sampling period T, we can construct a bandlimited continuous-time signal $\hat{x}(t)$ such that $\omega_0 T \leq 2\pi$, where ω_0 is the bandwidth of the constructed signal $\hat{x}(t)$. In other words, when both (11-116) and (11-117) hold, we expect

---

[19]The relationship between the sampling period T and the signal bandwidth ω_0 in (11-117) is called the *Nyquist condition*. The sampling rate or frequency f_s such that $f_s \triangleq 1/T = \omega_0/2\pi$ is called the *Nyquist rate*.

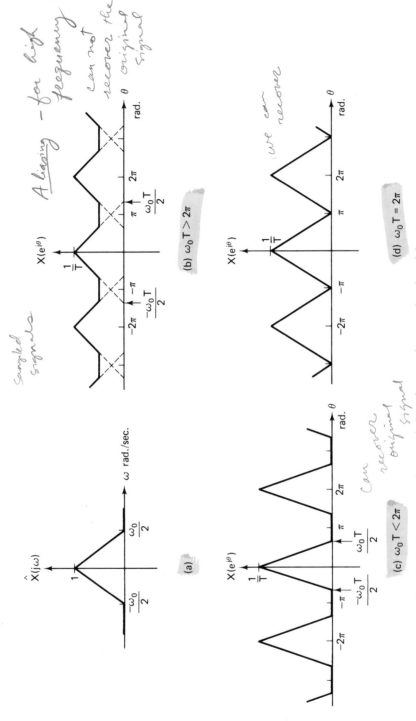

Fig. 11-9 Frequency characteristics of a continuous signal and its corresponding sampled sequence.

that it is possible to reconstruct the continuous signal $\hat{x}(t)$ from its sampled sequence $x(n)$.[20] To see this, let us substitute (11-116) into (11-106a) to obtain

$$\hat{x}(t) = \frac{1}{2\pi} \int_{-\infty}^{\infty} \hat{X}(j\omega) e^{j\omega t} \, d\omega$$

$$= \frac{1}{2\pi} \int_{-\omega_0/2}^{\omega_0/2} \hat{X}(j\omega) e^{j\omega t} \, d\omega \qquad (11\text{-}119)$$

By a change of variable with $\theta \triangleq \omega T$, we can write (11-119) as

$$\hat{x}(t) = \frac{1}{2\pi} \int_{-(\omega_0 T)/2}^{(\omega_0 T)/2} \hat{X}\left(j\frac{\theta}{T}\right) \exp\left(j\frac{\theta t}{T}\right) \frac{d\theta}{T} \qquad (11\text{-}120)$$

Substituting (11-118) into (11-120), we obtain

$$\hat{x}(t) = \frac{1}{2\pi} \int_{-(\omega_0 T)/2}^{(\omega_0 T)/2} X(e^{j\theta}) \exp\left(j\frac{\theta t}{T}\right) d\theta \qquad (11\text{-}121)$$

As can be observed from Fig. 11-9, when the sampling period satisfies the Nyquist condition of (11-117), we have

$$X(e^{j\theta}) = 0 \quad \text{for } \frac{\omega_0 T}{2} < |\theta| < \pi \qquad (11\text{-}122)$$

In view of (11-122), (11-121) can be written as

$$\hat{x}(t) = \frac{1}{2\pi} \int_{-\pi}^{\pi} X(e^{j\theta}) \exp\left(j\frac{\theta t}{T}\right) d\theta \qquad (11\text{-}123)$$

Substituting (11-108a) into (11-123), we obtain

$$\hat{x}(t) = \frac{1}{2\pi} \int_{-\pi}^{\pi} \sum_{n=-\infty}^{\infty} x(n) e^{-j\theta n} \exp\left(j\theta t/T\right) d\theta$$

$$= \frac{1}{2\pi} \sum_{n=-\infty}^{\infty} x(n) \int_{-\pi}^{\pi} \exp\left[-j\theta(n - t/T)\right] d\theta$$

$$= \frac{1}{2\pi} \sum_{n=-\infty}^{\infty} x(n) \frac{\exp\left[-j(n - t/T)\pi\right] - \exp\left[j(n - t/T)\pi\right]}{-j(n - t/T)} \qquad (11\text{-}124)$$

$$= \sum_{n=-\infty}^{\infty} x(n) \frac{-2j \sin\left[\pi(n - t/T)\right]}{-j(n - t/T)2\pi}$$

$$\boxed{\hat{x}(t) = \sum_{n=-\infty}^{\infty} x(n) \frac{\sin\left[\dfrac{\pi}{T}(nT - t)\right]}{\dfrac{\pi}{T}(nT - t)}}$$

Sampled sequence

Given a sampled sequence $x(n)$, (11-124) provides an interpolating formula

---

[20]Note that if the Nyquist condition is not satisfied, then the construction of a continuous-time signal from the sequence $x(n)$ will not yield the original signal $\hat{x}(t)$ but one with a bandwidth satisfying the Nyquist condition where the sampling period T is fixed.

for recovering the continuous signal $\hat{x}(t)$. In the frequency domain, (11-124) essentially states that the frequency characteristics of the continuous-time signal can be obtained by passing the sampled sequence through an ideal low-pass filter with a cutoff frequency at $\omega_c = \pi/T$, as illustrated in Fig. 11-10. For example, if we pass the sampled sequence associated with either Fig. 11-9(c) or (d) through the ideal filter of Fig. 11-10, then the continuous-time output signal will be $\hat{x}(t)$ associated with Fig. 11-9(a). Notice that (11-124) is derived under the conditions that the continuous signal is bandlimited as denoted by (11-116) and that the sampling rate satisfies the Nyquist condition of (11-117).

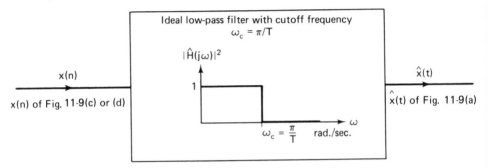

Fig. 11-10 The interpolation filter to construct a continuous-time signal from a sampled sequence.

If the Nyquist condition of (11-117) is not satisfied (the sampling rate is not fast enough), then the frequency characteristics $\hat{X}(j\omega)$ and $X(e^{j\theta})$ of the continuous signal $\hat{x}(t)$ and the sampled sequence $x(n)$ are no longer linearly related, as seen in Figs. 11-9(a) and (b). In this case, a portion of the high-frequency information in $\hat{X}(j\omega)$ is shifted into the lower frequencies in $X(e^{j\theta})$, as illustrated in Fig. 11-9(b) by the dotted lines. This shifting of information is called *aliasing* or the *folding effect*. In this case, one can *not* construct the continuous-time signal $\hat{x}(t)$ from its sampled sequence $x(n)$.

11-4 DISCRETE FOURIER TRANSFORM

In the previous two sections, we have discussed two representations, namely the z-transform and the Fourier transform of sequences. When a sequence $x(n)$ is either periodic or of finite duration, it is possible to have yet another representation, which is referred to as *discrete Fourier transform* or *DFT*. It is shown in Chapter 12 that one of the techniques used to design digital filters with a finite impulse response is via DFT.

Let $x_p(n)$ be a periodic sequence with period N.[21] Then

$$x_p(n) = x_p(n + mN) \qquad (11\text{-}125)$$

where m is any integer. In general, $x_p(n)$ does not admit a z-transform representation, because there is no finite value of z such that

$$X_p(z) = \sum_{n=-\infty}^{\infty} x_p(n) z^{-n} \qquad (11\text{-}126)$$

will converge. Consequently, $x_p(n)$ will not have a Fourier transform representation either. However, because $x_p(n)$ is periodic, it has a discrete Fourier series representation as[22]

$$x_p(n) = \sum_{k=-\infty}^{\infty} \tilde{X}_p(k) e^{j(2\pi/N)kn} \qquad (11\text{-}127)$$

where the $\tilde{X}_p(k)$'s are the Fourier series coefficients. Note that for any integer m, we have

$$e^{j(2\pi/N)(k+mN)n} = e^{j[(2\pi/N)kn + 2\pi mn]}$$
$$= e^{j(2\pi/N)kn} e^{j2\pi mn} = e^{j(2\pi/N)kn} \qquad (11\text{-}128)$$

This means that (11-127) contains redundant information. In view of (11-128), there are only N distinct exponential frequencies in (11-127), namely,

$$\frac{2\pi}{N}k \quad \text{for } k = 0, 1, 2, \ldots, N-1 \qquad (11\text{-}129)$$

Hence, (11-127) can be expressed as

$$x_p(n) = \frac{1}{N} \sum_{k=0}^{N-1} \tilde{X}_p(k) e^{j(2\pi/N)kn} \qquad (11\text{-}130)$$

where $1/N$ is a normalization factor.

Multiplying (11-130) by $\exp[-j2\pi mn/N]$ and summing n over one period, we obtain

$$\sum_{n=0}^{N-1} x_p(n) e^{-j(2\pi/N)mn} = \frac{1}{N} \sum_{n=0}^{N-1} \sum_{k=0}^{N-1} \tilde{X}_p(k) e^{j(2\pi/N)n(k-m)}$$
$$= \frac{1}{N} \sum_{k=0}^{N-1} \tilde{X}_p(k) \sum_{n=0}^{N-1} e^{j(2\pi/N)n(k-m)} \qquad (11\text{-}131a)$$
$$= \sum_{k=0}^{N-1} \tilde{X}_p(k)\, \delta(k-m)$$

---

[21]A sequence with a subscript p denotes a periodic sequence.

[22]Recall that in the continuous-time case, a periodic signal $\hat{x}_p(t)$ with period T has a Fourier series representation $\hat{x}_p(t) = \sum_{k=-\infty}^{\infty} \tilde{\hat{X}}_p(k) e^{jk\omega t}$, where $\omega = 2\pi/T$. If we let $t = n$ and $T = N$, we obtain the Fourier series representation of a periodic sequence in (11-127).

where we have used the relation

$$\sum_{n=0}^{N-1} e^{j(2\pi/N)n(k-m)} = N \quad \text{if } k = m \tag{11-131b}$$

$$= 0 \quad \text{otherwise}$$

From (11-131a), the Fourier coefficients of (11-130) are given by

$$\tilde{X}_p(k) = \sum_{n=0}^{N-1} x_p(n)e^{-j(2\pi/N)kn} \tag{11-132}$$

Observe that (11-132) is similar in form to (11-130). Hence, we can conclude that the sequence $\tilde{X}_p(k)$ is periodic with period N. The discrete Fourier series representation of $\tilde{X}_p(k)$ is given by (11-132), where $x_p(n)$ are the Fourier series coefficients. Equation (11-132) is called the *discrete Fourier transform* (DFT) of the sequence $x_p(n)$, and (11-130) is called the *inverse discrete Fourier transform* (IDFT) of the sequence $\tilde{X}_p(k)$.[23]

Example 11-15   Let $x_p(n)$ be a periodic sequence given by

$$x_p(n) = a^n \quad \text{for } 0 \le n \le N - 1$$

and

$$x_p(n + mN) = x_p(n) \tag{11-133}$$

where m is an integer. Find the DFT of $x_p(n)$.

Solution: By (11-132),

$$\tilde{X}_p(k) = \sum_{n=0}^{N-1} a^n e^{-j(2\pi k/N)n}$$

$$= \frac{1 - a^N e^{-j(2\pi k/N)N}}{1 - ae^{-j(2\pi k/N)}} = \frac{1 - a^N}{1 - ae^{-j(2\pi k/N)}} \tag{11-134}$$

Notice that $\tilde{X}_p(k)$ is indeed periodic with period N, because

$$\tilde{X}_p(k + mN) = \frac{1 - a^N}{1 - a \exp[-j2\pi(k + mN)/N]}$$

$$= \frac{1 - a^N}{1 - a \exp(-j2\pi k/N) \exp(-j2\pi m)}$$

$$= \frac{1 - a^N}{1 - a \exp(-j2\pi k/N)} = \tilde{X}_p(k) \qquad \blacksquare$$

Note that in both (11-130) and (11-132), the DFT and IDFT of a periodic sequence can be determined by just one period of the periodic sequence. Let us consider a finite duration sequence[24] $x(n)$ given by

$$x(n) = x_p(n) \quad \text{for } 0 \le n \le N - 1$$

$$= 0 \quad \text{elsewhere} \tag{11-135}$$

---

[23]We use the symbol "~" to denote DFT variables.

[24]A sequence $x(n)$ is said to be of finite duration if $x(n) = 0$ for $n \le N_1$ and $n \ge N_2$, where N_1 and N_2 are integers such that $-\infty < N_1 < N_2 < \infty$.

That is, $x(n)$ is a single period of $x_p(n)$. In this case, the z-transform $X(z)$ of $x(n)$ exists, and

$$X(z) = \sum_{n=-\infty}^{\infty} x(n)z^{-n} = \sum_{n=0}^{N-1} x_p(n)z^{-n} \qquad (11\text{-}136)$$

A comparison of (11-136) and (11-132) shows that the relationship between the z-transform of $x(n)$, which is the first period of $x_p(n)$, and the DFT of $x_p(n)$ is given by

$$\tilde{X}_p(k) = X(z)|_{z=\exp\,[j2\pi k/N]} = X(e^{j2\pi k/N}) \qquad (11\text{-}137)$$

From another point of view, the DFT of $x_p(n)$ is an N-point sampled sequence of the Fourier transform function $X(e^{j\theta})$, with a uniform spacing of θ for $0 < \theta < 2\pi$. This is because (11-137) can be written as

$$\tilde{X}_p(k) = X(e^{j\theta})|_{\theta=2\pi k/N} \quad k = 0, 1, 2, \ldots, N-1 \qquad (11\text{-}138)$$

Example 11-16 Let $x(n)$ be a finite sequence given by

$$x(n) = a^n \quad \text{for } 0 \le n \le N-1$$
$$= 0 \quad \text{elsewhere} \qquad (11\text{-}139)$$

Find the DFT of the periodic sequence $x_p(n)$ defined as

$$x_p(n) = a^n \quad \text{for } 0 \le n \le N-1$$

and

$$x_p(n + mN) = x_p(n) \qquad (11\text{-}140)$$

where m is an integer.

Solution: The z-transform and the Fourier transform of the sequence $x(n)$ are given by

$$X(z) = \sum_{n=0}^{N-1} a^n z^{-n} = \frac{1 - a^N z^{-N}}{1 - az^{-1}} \qquad (11\text{-}141\text{a})$$

$$X(e^{j\theta}) = \frac{1 - a^N e^{-jN\theta}}{1 - ae^{-j\theta}} \qquad (11\text{-}141\text{b})$$

By (11-138), we obtain the DFT of $x_p(n)$ as

$$\begin{aligned}
\tilde{X}_p(k) &= X(e^{j\theta})|_{\theta=2\pi k/N} \\
&= \frac{1 - a^N \exp(-j2\pi k)}{1 - a \exp(-j2\pi k/N)} \qquad (11\text{-}142) \\
&= \frac{1 - a^N}{1 - a \exp(-j2\pi k/N)}
\end{aligned}$$

Where $k = 0, 1, 2, \ldots, N-1$. ∎

Example 11-17 Find the DFT of the periodic sequence $x_p(n)$ defined by

$$x_p(n) = (\tfrac{1}{2})^n \quad \text{for } 0 \le n \le 3$$

and

$$x_p(n + 4m) = x_p(n) \qquad (11\text{-}143)$$

for all integer m.

Solution: Let us define a finite sequence $x(n)$ as

$$x(n) = (\tfrac{1}{2})^n \quad \text{for } 0 \leq n \leq 3$$
$$= 0 \quad \text{elsewhere} \tag{11-144}$$

Using results of Example 11-16 with $a = 1/2$ and $N = 4$, we obtain

$$X(e^{j\theta}) = \frac{1 - (1/2)^4 e^{-j4\theta}}{1 - (1/2)e^{-j\theta}} \tag{11-145}$$

and

$$\tilde{X}_p(k) = \frac{1 - (1/2)^4}{1 - \tfrac{1}{2}\exp(-j\pi k/2)} \tag{11-146}$$

With $k = 0, 1, 2,$ and 3, (11-146) yields

$$\tilde{X}_p(0) = \frac{15/16}{1 - (1/2)(1)} = \frac{15}{16}(2) = \frac{15}{8} \tag{11-147a}$$

$$\tilde{X}_p(1) = \frac{15/16}{1 - (1/2)(-j)} = \frac{15/16}{1 + (j/2)} = \frac{(15/16)[1 - (j/2)]}{5/4}$$
$$= \frac{3}{4}\left(1 - \frac{j}{2}\right) = \frac{3}{8}(2 - j) \tag{11-147b}$$

$$\tilde{X}_p(2) = \frac{15/16}{1 - (1/2)(-1)} = \frac{15}{16}\left(\frac{2}{3}\right) = \frac{5}{8} \tag{11-147c}$$

$$\tilde{X}_p(3) = \frac{15/16}{1 - (1/2)(j)} = \frac{15/16}{1 - (j/2)} = \frac{3}{8}(2 + j) \tag{11-147d}$$

$$\tilde{X}_p(4) = \tilde{X}_p(8) = \ldots = \tilde{X}_p(4m) = \tilde{X}_p(0) = \frac{15}{8} \tag{11-147e}$$

$$\tilde{X}_p(5) = \tilde{X}_p(9) = \ldots = \tilde{X}_p(4m + 1) = \tilde{X}_p(1) = \frac{3}{8}(2 - j) \tag{11-147f}$$

$$\tilde{X}_p(6) = \tilde{X}_p(10) = \ldots = \tilde{X}_p(4m + 2) = \tilde{X}_p(2) = \frac{5}{8} \tag{11-147g}$$

$$\tilde{X}_p(7) = \tilde{X}_p(11) = \ldots = \tilde{X}_p(4m + 3) = \tilde{X}_p(3) = \frac{3}{8}(2 + j) \tag{11-147h}$$

where m is an integer. ∎

In view of (11-137) and (11-138), we define the DFT $\tilde{X}(k)$ of a finite sequence $x(n)$ of length N, where

$$x(n) = 0 \quad \text{for } n < 0 \quad \text{and} \quad \text{for } n \geq N \tag{11-148}$$

as

$$\tilde{X}(k) = \sum_{n=0}^{N-1} x(n)e^{-j2\pi kn/N} \quad \text{for } 0 \leq k \leq N - 1$$
$$= 0 \quad \text{elsewhere} \tag{11-149}$$

Conversely the IDFT of $\tilde{X}(k)$ of (11-149) is defined to be

$$x(n) = \frac{1}{N}\sum_{k=0}^{N-1} \tilde{X}(k)e^{j2\pi kn/N} \quad \text{for } 0 \leq n \leq N - 1$$
$$= 0 \quad \text{elsewhere} \tag{11-150}$$

Note that (11-149) and (11-150) are the truncated versions of (11-137) and

(11-138), respectively. Hence, it can be shown that the DFT of a finite sequence is unique, and so is the IDFT of a finite sequence. In addition, the operations of (11-149) and (11-150) are the inverses of each other. Based on (11-137) and (11-138), (11-149) yields

$$
\begin{aligned}
\tilde{X}(k) &= X(z)\big|_{z=\exp\,[j(2\pi k/N)]} \\
&= X(e^{j\theta})\big|_{\theta=2\pi k/N} \quad \text{for } 0 \le k \le N-1 \\
&= 0 \quad \text{elsewhere}
\end{aligned}
\tag{11-151}
$$

Example 11-18   Find $\tilde{X}(k)$ the DFT of the sequence

$$
\begin{aligned}
x(n) &= a^n \quad \text{for } 0 \le n \le N-1 \\
&= 0 \quad \text{elsewhere}
\end{aligned}
\tag{11-152}
$$

where $a = 1/2$ and $N = 4$.

Solution: From (11-141) and (11-151), we obtain

$$
\begin{aligned}
\tilde{X}(k) &= \frac{1-a^N}{1 - a\exp\,(-j2\pi k/N)} \quad \text{for } 0 \le k \le N-1 \\
&= 0 \quad \text{elsewhere}
\end{aligned}
\tag{11-153}
$$

With $a = 1/2$ and $N = 4$, (11-153) gives

$$
\tilde{X}(1) = \frac{15}{8}, \quad \tilde{X}(2) = \frac{3}{8}(2-j),
$$

$$
\tilde{X}(3) = \frac{5}{8}, \quad \tilde{X}(4) = \frac{3}{8}(2+j),
$$

and

$$
\tilde{X}(k) = 0 \quad \text{for } k < 0 \quad \text{and} \quad \text{for } k \ge 4.
\tag{11-154}
$$

∎

Given the z-transform of a finite sequence, we can use (11-151) to find its DFT.[25] In most design situations where the DFT $\tilde{H}(k)$ of a finite impulse response $h(n)$ of length N is given in some manner as specifications, the problem is to construct a transfer function $H(z)$ such that $\tilde{H}(k)$ satisfies (11-151) —$\tilde{H}(k)$ is a sampled sequence of the frequency response $H(e^{j\theta})$ of the desired filter. To this end, let us substitute (11-150) into the z-transform of $h(n)$ as

$$
\begin{aligned}
H(z) &= \sum_{n=0}^{N-1} h(n)z^{-n} \\
&= \sum_{n=0}^{N-1} \frac{1}{N} \sum_{k=0}^{N-1} \tilde{H}(k)e^{j(2\pi/N)kn}z^{-n} \\
&= \sum_{k=0}^{N-1} \frac{\tilde{H}(k)}{N} \sum_{n=0}^{N-1} e^{j(2\pi k/N)n}z^{-n} \\
&= \sum_{k=0}^{N-1} \frac{\tilde{H}(k)}{N} \frac{1-z^{-N}}{1 - z^{-1}\exp\left(j\dfrac{2\pi k}{N}\right)}
\end{aligned}
\tag{11-155}
$$

---

[25]An efficient procedure to compute DFT and IDFT is called the fast Fourier transform or FFT. See Reference [22] for details.

That is, given $\tilde{H}(k)$ a set of N desired frequency response points uniformly spaced along the unit circle in the z-plane, (11-155) can be used to find a desired transfer function of the digital filter. This technique is called the *frequency-sampling method*. Evaluating $H(z)$ along the unit circle in the z-plane, we obtain a relationship between the frequency response and the DFT of a finite sequence as

$$H(e^{j\theta}) = \sum_{k=0}^{N-1} \frac{\tilde{H}(k)}{N} \frac{1 - \exp(-j\theta N)}{1 - \exp\left[-j\left(\theta - \frac{2\pi k}{N}\right)\right]}$$

$$= \sum_{k=0}^{N-1} \frac{\tilde{H}(k)}{N} \frac{\exp\left(-\frac{j\theta N}{2}\right)\left[\exp\left(\frac{j\theta N}{2}\right) - \exp\left(-\frac{j\theta N}{2}\right)\right]}{\exp\left[-j\left(\frac{\theta}{2} - \frac{\pi k}{N}\right)\right]\left\{\exp\left[j\left(\frac{\theta}{2} - \frac{\pi k}{N}\right)\right] - \exp\left[-j\left(\frac{\theta}{2} - \frac{\pi k}{N}\right)\right]\right\}}$$

$$= \sum_{k=0}^{N-1} \frac{\tilde{H}(k)}{N} \frac{\exp\left[-j\frac{\theta}{2}(N-1)\right]}{\exp\left[j\frac{\pi k}{N}\right]} \frac{\sin\frac{\theta N}{2}}{\sin\left[\frac{\theta}{2} - \frac{\pi k}{N}\right]} \tag{11-156}$$

The interrelationships of the z-transform $H(z)$, the frequency response $H(e^{j\theta})$, and the DFT $\tilde{H}(k)$ of an impulse response sequence $h(n)$ with a finite duration are summarized in (11-151), (11-155), and (11-156). We will show that (11-155) and (11-156) play a key role in the development of the frequency-sampling method for the design and realization of finite impulse response digital filters in Secs. 12-2 and 13-2.

11-5 BASIC BUILDING BLOCK CONSIDERATIONS

As stated before, a digital filter can be implemented either as software on a general- or special-purpose computer or as hardware. Either way, the basic concepts of digital filter implementation involve the following two steps:

1. to convert the input–output relationship of a digital filter into an algorithm.
2. to implement or to realize the algorithm in terms of a set of basic operations or digital hardware.

As an illustration, consider a digital filter with a transfer function given by

$$H(z) \triangleq \frac{Y(z)}{X(z)} = \frac{1 + az^{-1}}{1 + bz^{-1}} \tag{11-157}$$

where $X(z)$ and $Y(z)$ are, respectively, the z-transforms of the input and the output sequences. To realize this transfer function, we convert it into a difference equation as

$$y(n) + by(n-1) = x(n) + ax(n-1)$$

or

$$y(n) = x(n) + ax(n-1) - by(n-1) \quad (11\text{-}158)$$

From (11-158), the present output $y(n)$ is an algebraically weighted sum of past output values and the past and present input values. To realize the transfer function of (11-157) is equivalent to implementing the algorithm of (11-158), which requires the following:

(a) delay units or shift registers to store past output and past input values;

(b) multipliers or multiplication operations to provide the necessary scaling or weighting factors to sampled values; and

(c) summers or addition operations (which include subtractions as well) to add up the various quantities indicated on the right-hand side of (11-158) to give the present output values.

Both the software and the hardware implementations of (11-157) require the availability of the aforementioned three basic components, namely, delays or shift registers, summers or addition operations, and multipliers or multiplication operations whose symbols are shown in Fig. 11-11(a), (b), and (c),

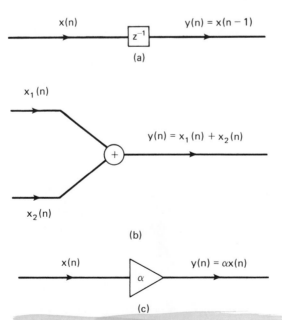

Fig. 11-11   Basic building blocks for digital filters:
(a) delays, (b) summers, and (c) multipliers.

respectively. Figure 11-11 also shows the input–output relationship of these three basic digital components. Hereafter, for simplicity, we call them *delays*, *summers*, and *multipliers*.

Note that in Fig. 11-11, every input or output line associated with a digital element contains an arrow that indicates the direction of signal flow. For convenience, we assume that a summer exists at every junction to sum up all the signals approaching the junction. This is illustrated in Fig. 11-12(a),

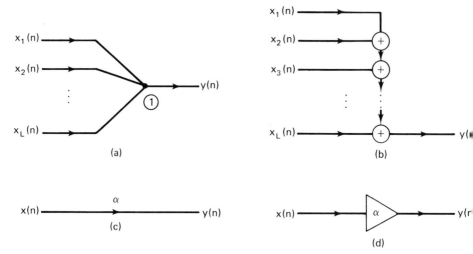

Fig. 11-12 Simplified schematics for (a) and (b) summers, and (c) and (d) multipliers.

where the output $y(n)$ is a sum of all the inputs converging at the junction of node ① as

$$y(n) = x_1(n) + x_2(n) + \ldots + x_L(n) \qquad (11\text{-}159)$$

In fact, Fig. 11-12(a) represents the detailed digital circuit of Fig. 11-12(b). In addition, a multiplier has a simplified notation, as shown in Fig. 11-12(c), where the output is given by

$$y(n) = \alpha x(n) \qquad (11\text{-}160)$$

Figure 11-12(c) is equivalent to the digital circuit in Fig. 11-12(d). When no multiplying constant is associated with an arrow, it simply means that the multiplying constant α is 1.

Example 11-19 Find the transfer function of the digital circuit shown in Fig. 11-13(a).

Solution: Note that the circuit in Fig. 11-13(a) represents the digital circuit of Fig. 11-13(b). As shown in Fig. 11-13(a), the difference equation and its corre-

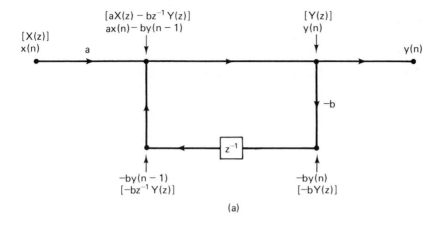

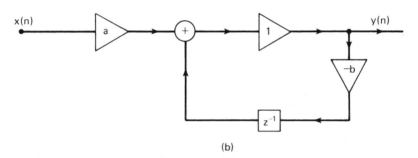

Fig. 11-13   A digital circuit (a) with simplified notations, and (b) with explicitly drawn components.

sponding z-transform equation are given, respectively, by

$$y(n) + by(n - 1) = ax(n) \qquad (11\text{-}161\text{a})$$

and

$$(1 + bz^{-1}) Y(z) = aX(z) \qquad (11\text{-}161\text{b})$$

Hence, the transfer function of the digital circuit in Fig. 11-13 is

$$H(z) = \frac{Y(z)}{X(z)} = \frac{a}{1 + bz^{-1}} \qquad (11\text{-}162)$$

∎

Contrary to the analog filter case, where the basic passive components of $R, L,$ and C are required to have positive and real values, the multiplying constants here are not restricted at all. However, some simple structures of digital filter may cause inconsistencies and/or computational impossibilities. Consider the circuit in Fig. 11-14. Let $x_1(n), x_2(n), x_3(n),$ and $x_4(n)$ be the outputs of the summers at nodes 1, 2, 3, and 4, respectively. From Fig. 11-14,

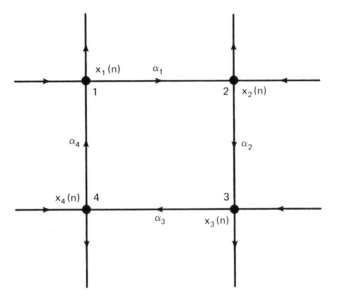

Fig. 11-14 An illegal structure for digital filters.

we observe that:

1. to compute $x_1(n)$, we need to know $x_4(n)$.
2. to compute $x_4(n)$, we need to know $x_3(n)$.
3. to compute $x_3(n)$, we need to know $x_2(n)$.
4. to compute $x_2(n)$, we need to know $x_1(n)$.

This going-around-the-circle type of procedure imposes a computational impossibility for computing $x_1(n)$, $x_2(n)$, $x_3(n)$, and $x_4(n)$. Notice that this computational impossibility arises because there is a loop without delay elements.[26] Hence, it is necessary to check that there are no delay-free loops in the final realizations of digital transfer functions.[27]

11-6 STABILITY CONSIDERATIONS

In the time domain, a digital filter is stable if its impulse response satisfies (11-18). Here we examine the stability conditions of digital filters in the z-domain.

---

[26] A loop in a digital filter always means a *directed* loop.

[27] A technique to transform a digital filter circuit with delay-free loops into one without delay-free loops is presented in Chapter 13.

Consider a general transfer function given by (11-40), which is reproduced here for convenience.

$$H(z) = \frac{\alpha \prod_{i=1}^{M} (1 - z_i z^{-1})}{\prod_{k=1}^{N} (1 - p_k z^{-1})} \tag{11-163}$$

Any filter whose transfer functions are given by (11-163) with $N \geq 1$ is called an *infinite impulse response* (IIR) digital filter, because there does *not* exist a finite integer L such that

$$h(n) = 0 \quad \text{for } n > L \tag{11-164}$$

where $h(n)$ is the impulse response of the filter. For IIR digital filters, let us assume that

$$M \leq N \tag{11-165}$$

This assumption holds true for almost all cases of practical interest. A partial fraction expansion of (11-163) gives

$$H(z) = \xi_0 + \frac{\xi_1}{1 - p_1 z^{-1}} + \frac{\xi_2}{1 - p_2 z^{-1}} + \cdots + \frac{\xi_N}{1 - p_N z^{-1}} \tag{11-166a}$$

where

$$\xi_0 = \alpha \quad \text{if } N = M$$
$$= 0 \quad \text{if } N > M \tag{11-166b}$$

and

$$\xi_i = (1 - p_i z^{-1}) H(z)|_{z = p_i} \quad \text{for } i = 1, 2, \ldots, N \tag{11-166c}$$

Hence, the corresponding impulse response of (11-163) is given by

$$h(n) = [\xi_1 p_1^n + \xi_2 p_2^n + \cdots + \xi_N p_N^n] u(n) + \xi_0 \delta(n) \tag{11-167}$$

Clearly, the necessary and sufficient conditions for the impulse response of (11-167) to satisfy the stability criteria of

$$\sum_{n=-\infty}^{\infty} |h(n)| < \infty \tag{11-168}$$

is that

$$|p_i| < 1 \quad \text{for } i = 1, 2, \ldots, N \tag{11-169}$$

That is, all the pole locations of the digital filter are *within* the unit circle in the z-plane.

Example 11-20   Show that the circuit in Fig. 11-15 is stable.

Solution: The difference equation representing the circuit is given by

$$y(n) = a_0 x(n) + y(n - 1) - 0.5 y(n - 2) \tag{11-170}$$

The transfer function of the circuit can be obtained by taking the z-transforms of (11-170) as

$$(1 - z^{-1} + 0.5 z^{-2}) Y(z) = a_0 X(z)$$

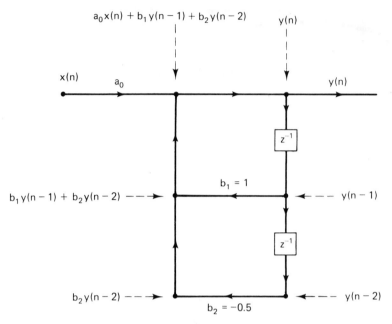

Fig. 11-15 A stable digital circuit for Example 11-20.

or

$$H(z) \triangleq \frac{Y(z)}{X(z)} = \frac{a_0}{1 - z^{-1} + 0.5z^{-2}}$$

$$= \frac{a_0 z^2}{z^2 - z + 0.5} \tag{11-171}$$

Hence, the pole locations of the filter are at

$$p_{1,2} = \frac{1 \pm \sqrt{1 - 4(0.5)}}{2}$$

$$= \frac{1 \pm j1}{2} = 0.5 \pm j0.5 \tag{11-172}$$

That is, $H(z)$ can be written as

$$H(z) = \frac{a_0}{[1 - (0.5 + j0.5)z^{-1}][1 - (0.5 - j0.5)z^{-1}]} \tag{11-173}$$

Because

$$|p_1| = |p_2| = 0.71 \tag{11-174}$$

the circuit in Fig. 11-15 is stable. ∎

When the transfer function of a digital filter is given by

$$H(z) = a_0 + a_1 z^{-1} + \ldots + a_M z^{-M} \tag{11-175}$$

which is equivalent to the case when $N = 0$ in (11-163), the digital filter is said to be of *finite impulse response* (FIR) type. This name is used because the impulse response of (11-175) has the property that

$$h(n) = 0 \quad \text{for } n > M \quad \text{and} \quad \text{for } n < 0 \qquad (11\text{-}176)$$

That is, the corresponding impulse response is of *finite* duration. In this case, there are no poles. Hence, this type of filter is always stable.

11-7   A SIMPLE DIGITAL FILTER EXAMPLE

Consider the RC circuit in Fig. 11-16, where the initial capacitor voltage is zero. With $\hat{v}_i(t) = 0$ for $t < 0$, the output $\hat{v}_o(t)$ is given by

$$\hat{v}_o(t) = \int_0^t \frac{1}{RC} e^{-(1/RC)(t-\tau)} \hat{v}_i(\tau) \, d\tau \qquad (11\text{-}177\text{a})$$

$$= \hat{h}(t) * \hat{v}_i(t)$$

where

$$\hat{h}(t) = \frac{1}{RC} e^{-(1/RC)t} \qquad (11\text{-}177\text{b})$$

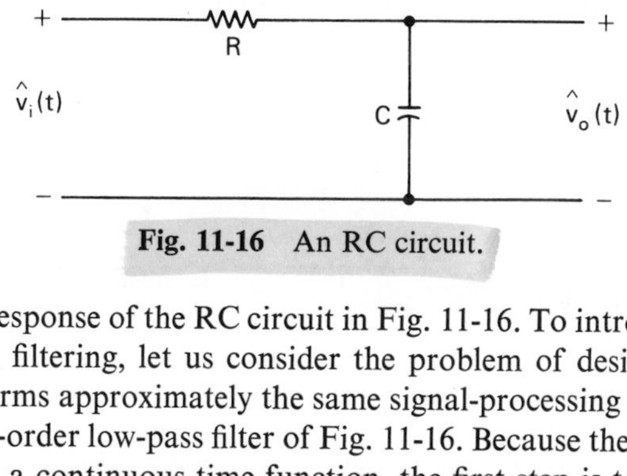

Fig. 11-16   An RC circuit.

is the impulse response of the RC circuit in Fig. 11-16. To introduce the basic ideas of digital filtering, let us consider the problem of designing a digital filter that performs approximately the same signal-processing function as the simple RC first-order low-pass filter of Fig. 11-16. Because the input signal in the RC filter is a continuous-time function, the first step is to have an A/D converter at the input end to convert the input voltage $\hat{v}_i(t)$ into an input sequence $v_i(n)$. In a reverse manner, a D/A converter is placed at the output end of the digital filter to convert the output sequence $v_o(n)$ into a continuous output signal $\hat{v}_o(t)$, as shown in Fig. 11-17, where the box labeled digital filter is the heart of this design problem.

Fig. 11-17   A general setting for digital filters.

Because the RC circuit in Fig. 11-16 is described by a first-order differential equation

$$\frac{d\hat{v}_o}{dt} + \frac{1}{RC}\hat{v}_o(t) = \frac{1}{RC}\hat{v}_i(t)$$ (11-178a)

with

$$\hat{v}_o(0-) = 0$$ (11-178b)

let us assume that the digital filter in Fig. 11-17 is characterized by a first-order difference equation

$$v_o(n) = av_o(n-1) + bv_i(n)$$ (11-179)

with

$$v_o(-1) = 0$$

Taking z-transforms of (11-179), we obtain

$$(1 - az^{-1})V_o(z) = bV_i(z)$$

or

$$H(z) \triangleq \frac{V_o(z)}{V_i(z)} = \frac{b}{1 - az^{-1}}$$ (11-180)

Hence, the impulse response is given by

$$h(n) = ba^n u(n)$$ (11-181)

By (11-17), the output $v_o(n)$ of the digital filter is given by

$$v_o(n) = h(n) * v_i(n)$$

$$= \sum_{k=-\infty}^{\infty} h(n-k)v_i(k)$$ (11-182)

$$= \sum_{k=0}^{n} ba^{n-k}v_i(k)$$

If a rectangular sum approximation is used to integrate (11-177) with time spacing T seconds apart, we obtain

$$\hat{v}_o(nT) = \sum_{k=0}^{n} \frac{T}{RC} e^{-(n-k)(T/RC)}\hat{v}_i(kT)$$ (11-183)

By comparing (11-182) and (11-183), we observe that if

1. the sampling period in the A/D and D/A converters is T seconds,
2. the constants a and b in the assumed digital-filter characterization equation of (11-179) take on the values

$$b = \frac{T}{RC}$$ (11-184a)

$$a = e^{-(T/RC)}$$ (11-184b)

then the output $v_o(n)$ of the digital filter is a sampled sequence of $\hat{v}_o(t)$ of the RC low-pass filter of Fig. 11-16. A digital filter implementing the difference

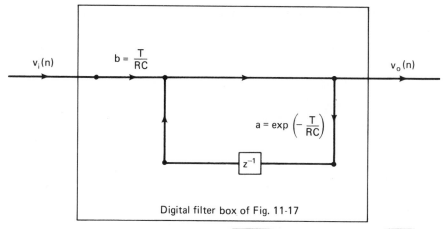

Fig. 11-18   A digital filter simulation of the RC circuit in Fig. 11-16.

equation of (11-179) with the parameters given by (11-184) is shown in Fig. 11-18. By substituting Fig. 11-18 into Fig. 11-17, we obtain a simulation of the RC circuit in Fig. 11-16. Clearly, a different numerical integration method applied to (11-177) will give rise to a different digital filter in Fig. 11-18.

11-8   ANALYSIS OF DIGITAL FILTERS

In this section, we present a simple technique to analyze digital-filter circuits. The method introduced here is similar to the nodal analysis of analog circuits. Indeed, it retains many desirable properties of nodal analysis including simple formulation, easy machine implementation, and efficient computation due to the applicability of sparse matrix techniques.

Consider a single-input single-output digital circuit S with $N + 2$ nodes and b branches. Let node 0 be the input (or the *source*) node and node $N + 1$ be the output (or the *sink*) node. For $\alpha = 1, 2, \ldots, N$, let $x_\alpha(n)$ be the variable associated with the output of the summer at node α. Let $x_{in}(n)$ be the input sequence and $x_{out}(n)$ be the output sequence. Finally, let $X_i(z)$ be the z-transform of $x_i(n)$ for $i = 1, 2, \ldots, N$, in and out.

At each node α, let us write a node equation describing the signal interactions among the branches incident at node α, where $\alpha = 1, 2, \ldots, N$. The result will be a system of N algebraic complex equations

$$\mathbf{A}(z)\mathbf{X}(z) = \mathbf{B}(z)\,X_{in}(z) \qquad (11\text{-}185)$$

where $\mathbf{A}(z)$ is an $N \times N$ matrix involving the branch characteristics, $\mathbf{B}(z)$ is an $N \times 1$ vector, $X_{in}(z)$ is the input, and $\mathbf{X}(z)$ is an $N \times 1$ vector containing the N nodal variables

$$\mathbf{X}(z) = \begin{bmatrix} X_1(z) \\ X_2(z) \\ \cdot \\ \cdot \\ \cdot \\ X_N(z) \end{bmatrix}$$

Solving for $\mathbf{X}(z)$, (11-185) yields

$$\mathbf{X}(z) = \mathbf{A}^{-1}(z)\mathbf{B}(z)X_{\text{in}}(z) \tag{11-186}$$

With an additional equation at node $N + 1$, we obtain the output equation

$$X_{\text{out}}(z) = \mathbf{C}(z)\mathbf{X}(z) + D(z)X_{\text{in}}(z) \tag{11-187}$$

where $\mathbf{C}(z)$ is a $1 \times N$ row vector and $D(z)$ is a scalar. Substituting (11-186) into (11-187) gives

$$\begin{aligned} X_{\text{out}}(z) &= (\mathbf{C}\mathbf{A}^{-1}\mathbf{B} + D)X_{\text{in}}(z) \\ &\triangleq H(z)X_{\text{in}}(z) \end{aligned} \tag{11-188a}$$

where

$$H(z) = \mathbf{C}(z)\mathbf{A}^{-1}(z)\,\mathbf{B}(z) + D(z) \tag{11-188b}$$

is the transfer function of the circuit. Notice that the transfer function $H(z)$ {or the frequency response $H(e^{j\theta})$} of the circuit can be obtained by solving for $X_{\text{out}}(z)$ {or $X_{\text{out}}(e^{j\theta})$} with the input being set to $X_{\text{in}}(z) = 1$ {or $X_{\text{in}}(e^{j\theta}) = 1$ for all θ}.

Example 11-21 Find the frequency response and the transfer function of the circuit in Fig. 11-19.

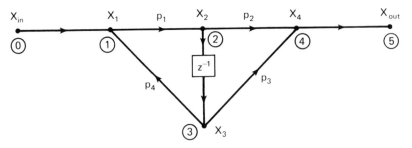

Fig. 11-19 A digital filter circuit.

Solution: Because we are asked to find the frequency response and the transfer function of the circuit, we may assume that all initial conditions of the circuit are zero. Let $X_k(z)$ be the z-transform of the nodal sequence at node k for $k = 1, 2, 3$, and 4. The node equations are:

$$X_1(z) = X_{in}(z) + p_4 X_3(z)$$

$$X_2(z) = p_1 X_1(z)$$

$$X_3(z) = z^{-1} X_2(z)$$

$$X_4(z) = p_2 X_2(z) + p_3 X_3(z)$$

or

$$\begin{bmatrix} 1 & 0 & -p_4 & 0 \\ -p_1 & 1 & 0 & 0 \\ 0 & -z^{-1} & 1 & 0 \\ 0 & -p_2 & -p_3 & 1 \end{bmatrix} \begin{bmatrix} X_1(z) \\ X_2(z) \\ X_3(z) \\ X_4(z) \end{bmatrix} = \begin{bmatrix} 1 \\ 0 \\ 0 \\ 0 \end{bmatrix} X_{in}(z) \qquad (11\text{-}189)$$

The output equation is given by

$$X_{out}(z) = X_4(z) \qquad (11\text{-}190)$$

Solving for $X_4(z)$ from (11-189) and substituting the result into (11-190), we obtain

$$X_{out}(z) = \frac{p_1(p_2 + p_3 z^{-1})}{1 - p_1 p_4 z^{-1}} X_{in}(z) \qquad (11\text{-}191)$$

Hence, the transfer function and the frequency response of the circuit in Fig. 11-19 are given by

$$H(z) = \frac{X_{out}(z)}{X_{in}(z)} = \frac{p_1 p_2 \left(1 + \frac{p_3}{p_2} z^{-1}\right)}{1 - p_1 p_4 z^{-1}} \qquad (11\text{-}192a)$$

and

$$H(e^{j\theta}) = \frac{p_1 p_2 \left[1 + \frac{p_3}{p_2} \exp(-j\theta)\right]}{1 - p_1 p_4 \exp(-j\theta)} \qquad (11\text{-}192b)$$

■

REFERENCES AND FURTHER READING

[1] RABINER, L. R., and RADER, C. M. *Digital Signal Processing*. New York: IEEE Press, 1972.

[2] STEIGLITZ, K. *An Introduction to Discrete Systems*, New York: John Wiley, 1974.

[3] BOGNER, R. E., and CONSTANTINIDES, A. G. *Introduction to Digital Filtering*. New York: John Wiley, 1975.

[4] Digital Signal Processing Committee of IEEE Acoustics, Speech and Signal Processing Society, ed. *Digital Signal Processing II*. New York: IEEE Press, 1975.

[5] OPPENHEIM, A. V., and SCHAFER, R. W. *Digital Signal Processing*. Englewood Cliffs, N.J.: Prentice-Hall, Inc., 1975.

[6] RABINER, L. R., and GOLD, B. *Theory and Application of Digital Signal Processing*. Englewood Cliffs, N.J.: Prentice-Hall, Inc., 1975.

[7] PELED, A., and LIU, B. *Digital Signal Processing.* New York: John Wiley, 1976.

[8] LEON, B. J., and BASS, S. C. "Designer's Guide to Digital Filter Parts 1–6," *EDN* (Jan. 1974): 30–36; (Feb. 1974): 65–72; (Mar. 1974): 51–59; (Apr. 1974): 57–62; (May 1974): 61–68; and (June 1974): 69–75.

[9] KUO, F. F., and KAISER, J. F. *System Analysis by Digital Computer.* New York: John Wiley, 1966.

[10] GIBBS, A. J. "An Introduction to Digital Filters," *Australian Telecommunications Research* 3 (1969): 3–14.

[11] ROSENFELD, A. *Picture Processing by Computer.* New York: Academic Press, 1969.

[12] FLANAGAN, J. L., and RABINER, L. R. *Speech Synthesis.* New York: Dowden, Huchington and Ross, 1973.

[13] CADZOW, J. A. *Discrete Time Systems.* Englewood Cliffs, N.J.: Prentice-Hall, Inc., 1973.

[14] PELED, A., and LIU, B. "A New Hardware Realization of Digital Filters." *IEEE Trans. Acoustics, Speech, Signal Processing* ASSP-22 (1974): 456–62.

[15] LIU, B. "Effect of Finite World Length on Accuracy of Digital Filters—A Review." *IEEE Trans. Circuit Theory* CT-18 (1971): 670–77.

[16] FETTWEIS, A. "On the Connection Between Multiplier Word Length Limitation and Roundoff Noise in Digital Filters." *IEEE Trans. Circuit Theory* CT-19 (1972): 486–91.

[17] YAKOWITZ, S., and PARKER, S. R. "Computation of Bounds for Digital Filter Quantization Errors." *IEEE Trans. Circuit Theory* CT-20 (1973): 391–96.

[18] CROCHIERE, R. E. "A New Statistical Approach to the Coefficient Word Length Problem for Digital Filters." *IEEE Trans. Circuit and Systems* CAS-22 (1975): 190–96.

[19] MITRA, S. K., and SHERWOOD, R. J. "Estimation of Pole-Zero Displacements of Digital Filter due to Coefficient Quantization." *IEEE Trans. Circuit and Systems* CAS-21 (1974): 116–24.

[20] CORSINI, P., and FROSINI, G. "Structures for Evaluating the Discrete Fourier Transform on Staggered Blocks." *IEEE Trans. Acoustics, Speech, Signal Processing* ASSP-24 (1976): 128–31.

[21] BONGIOVANNI, G., CORSINI, P., and FROSINI, G. "Procedure for Computing the Discrete Fourier Transform on Staggered Blocks." *IEEE Trans. Acoustics, Signal Processing* ASSP-24 (1976): 132–37.

[22] BRIGHAM, E. O. *The Fast Fourier Transform.* Englewood Cliffs, N.J.: Prentice-Hall, Inc., 1974.

[23] JURY, E. I. *Theory and Application of the Z-Transform Method.* New York: John Wiley, 1964.

PROBLEMS

11-1. Find the unit step and the unit impulse responses of the following systems:

(a) $y(n) - 0.5y(n - 1) = x(n)$
(b) $y(n) + 0.5y(n - 1) = x(n)$
(c) $y(n) + 2y(n - 1) = x(n)$
(d) $y(n) - 2y(n - 1) = x(n)$
(e) $y(n) - 0.5y(n - 1) - 0.5y(n - 2) = x(n)$
(f) $y(n) + 0.5y(n - 1) - y(n - 2) = x(n) + x(n - 1)$

11-2. Suppose that a system S is characterized by the difference equation

$$y(n) + y(n - 1) + \tfrac{1}{2}y(n - 2) = 2x(n) - x(n - 1)$$

where $y(n)$ is the output and $x(n)$ is the input.

(a) Find the transfer function of S.
(b) Determine if S is stable.
(c) Determine if S is causal.

Assuming that $y(-1) = y(-2) = 0$, find $y(n)$ if

(d) $x(n) = u(n) =$ the unit step sequence
(e) $x(n) = \delta(n) =$ the unit impulse sequence
(f) $x(n) = 2u(n) + 5\delta(n)$

11-3. Find the inverse z-transforms of the following $X(z)$:

(a) $X(z) = \dfrac{1}{1 - 0.75z^{-1} + 0.125z^{-2}}$

(b) $X(z) = \dfrac{2z^{-1}}{1 - 0.25z^{-2}}$

(c) $X(z) = \dfrac{1 + 2z^{-1}}{1 + 0.5z^{-1} + 0.5z^{-2}}$

(d) $X(z) = \dfrac{2 + z^{-1} + z^{-2}}{1 + z^{-1} + 0.5z^{-2}}$

(e) $X(z) = \dfrac{1 - z^{-1}}{(1 + z^{-1})(1 + 0.4z^{-1} - 0.1z^{-2})}$

(f) $X(z) = \dfrac{1 - 3z^{-1} + 2z^{-2}}{(1 + 0.5z^{-1})(1 + 0.1z^{-1} + z^{-2})}$

(g) $X(z) = \dfrac{1}{(1 + 0.5z^{-1} + 0.5z^{-2})(1 - 0.75z^{-1} + 0.125z^{-2})}$

(h) $X(z) = \dfrac{(1 - z^{-1})(1 + 0.75z^{-1} + z^{-2})}{(1 + 0.1z^{-1} + z^{-2})(1 + z^{-1} + 0.5z^{-2})}$

(i) $X(z) = \dfrac{1 - z^{-1}}{1 + 0.1z^{-1} + z^{-2}} + \dfrac{1 + 0.75z^{-1} + z^{-2}}{1 + z^{-1} + 0.5z^{-2}}$

(j) $X(z) = \dfrac{1 + z^{-1}}{1 + 0.5z^{-1} + 0.5z^{-2}} + \dfrac{1 - z^{-1}}{1 - 0.75z^{-1} + 0.125z^{-2}}$

11-4. Suppose that a digital filter is characterized by

$$y(n) + \tfrac{1}{4}y(n - 1) - \tfrac{1}{8}y(n - 2) = x(n)$$

where $y(n)$ is the output and $x(n)$ is the input.

(a) Find the transfer function of the digital filter.

(b) Find $y(n)$ if $x(n) = \exp(-n)u(n)$ and $y(-1) = y(-2) = 0$.

(c) Find $y(n)$ if $x(n) = nu(n)$ and $y(-1) = y(-2) = 0$.

(d) Repeat (b) and (c) if $y(-1) = 1$ and $y(-2) = 0$.

11-5. Compute the convolution sum of the following two sequences:

$$x_1(n) = n + 1 \quad \text{for } 0 \leq n \leq 1$$
$$= 0 \qquad \text{otherwise}$$
$$x_2(n) = n^2 \qquad \text{for } 0 \leq n \leq 2$$
$$= 0 \qquad \text{otherwise}$$

(a) by using the convolution sum formula.

(b) by using z-transforms and inverse z-transforms.

11-6. Suppose that a digital filter is characterized by

$$y(n) + b_1 y(n - 1) + b_2 y(n - 2) = x(n)$$

(a) Find the transfer function $H(z) = Y(z)/X(z)$ of the filter.

(b) Let $b_1 = 0.5$ and $b_2 = 0.4$; find $h(n)$, the unit impulse response of the filter.

(c) Let $b_1 = 0.3$ and $b_2 = 0.4$; find $s(n)$, the unit step response of the filter.

(d) Let $b_1 = 0.2$ and $b_2 = 0.5$. If $y(-1) = y(-2) = 0$ and

$$x(n) = n \quad \text{for } -1 \leq n \leq 1$$
$$= 0 \quad \text{otherwise}$$

find $y(n)$.

11-7. Suppose that a digital filter is characterized by

$$y(n) - \tfrac{1}{2}y(n - 1) + \tfrac{1}{8}y(n - 2) = x(n - 1) + \tfrac{1}{2}x(n)$$

(a) Find the unit impulse response $h(n)$.

If the input sequence is given by

$$x(n) = n \quad \text{for } -1 \leq n \leq 1$$
$$= 0 \quad \text{otherwise}$$

(b) find $y(n)$ by convolution.

(c) find $y(n)$ by z-transforms and inverse z-transforms.

11-8. Consider the analog circuit shown in Fig. P11-8.

(a) Find the impulse response $\hat{h}(t)$.

(b) Let the sampling period $T = 0.1$ sec., and let us define the sequence $h(n) \triangleq \hat{h}(nT)$. Find the z-transform of $h(n)$.

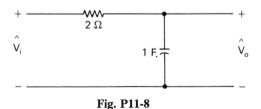

Fig. P11-8

(c) Find the frequency response of the sequence $h(n)$.

(d) Sketch the magnitude function of the frequency response of $h(n)$.

11-9. Consider the analog circuit shown in Fig. P11-9.

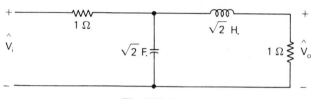

Fig. P11-9

(a) Find the impulse response $\hat{h}(t)$.

(b) Define $h(n) \triangleq \hat{h}(nT)$, where $T = 0.1$ sec. Find the z-transform of $h(n)$.

(c) Find the frequency response of $h(n)$.

(d) Find the difference equation corresponding to the results obtained in (b).

(e) If the input $\hat{v}_i(t) = \cos t$, find the steady-state response $\hat{v}_o(t)$ of the circuit in Fig. P11-9.

(f) If $v_i(n) \triangleq \hat{v}_i(nT)$ is the input to the discretized system of (d), find the corresponding steady-state output $v_o(n)$.

11-10. Suppose that a digital filter is characterized by the transfer function

$$H(z) = \frac{Y(z)}{X(z)} = \frac{1}{1 - 0.5z^{-1} + 0.5z^{-2}}$$

(a) Find the frequency response of the filter.

(b) If the input $x(n) = \exp(jn)$, find the steady-state output $y(n)$.

(c) If the input $x(n) = \exp(-jn)$, find the steady-state output $y(n)$.

(d) If the input $x(n) = \cos n$, find the steady-state output $y(n)$.

(e) If the input $x(n) = \cos \pi n/2$, find the steady-state output $y(n)$.

(f) If the input $x(n) = \cos 0.1n$, find the steady-state output $y(n)$.

(g) Sketch the magnitude function of the frequency response of the filter.

(h) Comment on the results obtained in (d), (e), and (f) with respect to the plot obtained in (g).

11-11. Let $\hat{x}_1(t) = \cos \omega t$ and $\hat{x}_2(t) = \cos[\omega + (2\pi/T)]t$, where $\omega = 1$ and $T = 1$. Define $x_1(n) \triangleq \hat{x}_1(nT)$ and $x_2(n) \triangleq \hat{x}_2(nT)$.

(a) Construct a table (with 3 columns) giving the corresponding values of n, $x_1(n)$, and $x_2(n)$, and comment on the results obtained.

(b) Let $x(n) = x_2(n)$, and let $\hat{x}(t)$ be the analog signal obtained from $x(n)$ via the sampling theorem. Determine if $\hat{x}(t) = \hat{x}_1(t)$ or $\hat{x}(t) = \hat{x}_2(t)$. Give reasons.

(c) Repeat (a) and (b) if $\omega = 0.1$.

(d) What happens to the results of (a) and (b) if $\omega = 10$? Give reasons.

11-12. Find the largest and yet appropriate sampling period T for the signal $x(t)$, which has a Fourier transform magnitude curve shown in

(a) Fig. P11-12(a).

(b) Fig. P11-12(b).

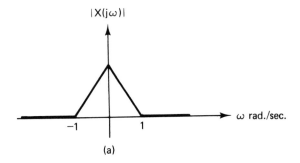

(a)

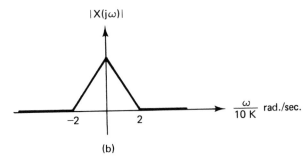

(b)

Fig. P11-12

11-13. Suppose that a signal is characterized by a Laplace transform

$$\hat{X}(s) = \frac{10^8}{s^2 + \sqrt{2} \times 10^4 s + 10^8}$$

Find the maximum sampling period T such that the aliasing effect is less than

(a) 10% (b) 5% (c) 1%
(d) 0.5% (e) 0.1%

11-14. Consider the sequence

$$x(0) = x(2) = 0.5$$
$$x(1) = 1$$
$$x(n) = 0 \quad \text{for } n < 0 \text{ and } n > 2$$

(a) Find the z-transform of the sequence.
(b) Find the Fourier transform of the sequence.
(c) Find the DFT of the sequence.
(d) Verify (11-151), (11-155), and (11-156) for this case.

11-15. Consider the sequence

$$x(0) = x(5) = 2$$
$$x(1) = x(4) = 1$$
$$x(2) = x(3) = 2$$
$$x(n) = 0 \quad \text{for } n < 0 \quad \text{and} \quad \text{for } n > 5$$

(a) Find the z-transform $X(z)$ of the sequence.

(b) Find the DFT $\tilde{X}(k)$ of the sequence.

Define the periodic sequence

$$x_p(n) = x(n) \quad \text{for } 0 \leq n \leq 5$$
$$x_p(6m + n) = x(n) \quad \text{for all integer } m$$

(c) Find the DFT $\tilde{X}_p(k)$ of the periodic sequence $x_p(n)$.

11-16. Consider the sequence

$$h(n) = n + 1 \quad \text{for } n = 0, 1, 2, 3$$
$$= 0 \qquad \text{otherwise}$$

(a) Find the z-transform $H_1(z)$ of the sequence.

(b) Find the DFT $\tilde{H}(k)$ of the sequence.

(c) Based on the results obtained in (b), find the z-transform $H_2(z)$ of the sequence $h(n)$.

(d) Compare $H_1(z)$ and $H_2(z)$, and comment.

11-17. Find the transfer function and the frequency response of each circuit shown in Fig. P11-17.

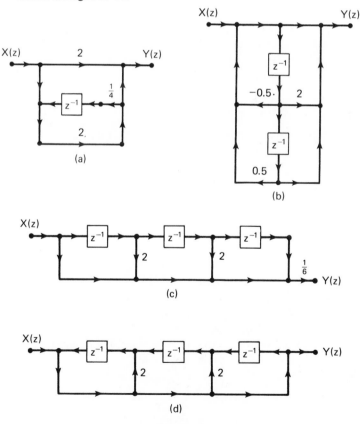

(a)

(b)

(c)

(d)

Fig. P11-17

12

DESIGN
OF DIGITAL FILTERS

As is in the case of analog filters, the design of digital filters involves the process of finding appropriate transfer functions to meet the required specifications. Specifications for digital filters are often given in the frequency domain. It has been shown in (11-92) that the frequency response $H(e^{j\theta})$ of a digital filter is a continuous function of θ with period 2π as

$$H(e^{j\theta}) = H[e^{j(\theta+m2\pi)}] \tag{12-1}$$

where m is an integer. The period is normally taken from $-\pi$ to π. This implies that if $H(e^{j\theta})$ is specified for θ from $-\pi$ to π, then $H(e^{j\theta})$ is specified for all θ. Writing $H(e^{j\theta})$ in the polar form, we have

$$H(e^{j\theta}) = |H(e^{j\theta})| e^{-j\phi(\theta)} \tag{12-2a}$$

where $|H(e^{j\theta})|$ is called the *magnitude function* and $\phi(\theta)$ defined by

$$\phi(\theta) \triangleq - \underline{/H(e^{j\theta})} \tag{12-2b}$$

is called the *phase (lag) angle* of the filter. Because magnitude functions are even functions,

$$|H(e^{j\theta})| = |H(e^{-j\theta})| \tag{12-3a}$$

and phase functions are odd,

$$\phi(\theta) = -\phi(-\theta) \tag{12-3b}$$

it suffices to specify the frequency response $H(e^{j\theta})$ of a digital filter for θ from $\theta = 0$ to $\theta = \pi$—along the top half of the unit circle in the z-plane, as shown in Fig. 12-1. To illustrate these repetitive patterns, the frequency selective filters of ideal low-pass, bandpass, high-pass, band-reject, and all-pass[1] filters

---

[1]Strictly speaking, an all-pass digital filter is a phase filter rather than a frequency-selective filter.

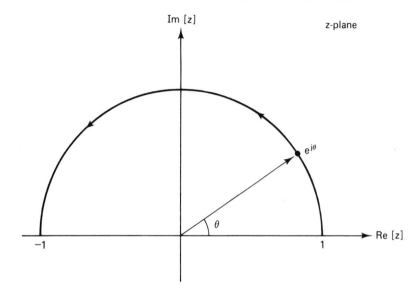

Fig. 12-1   Frequency response of a digital filter is specified along the top half of the unit circle.

have the magnitude functions shown in Fig. 12-2, and linear phase filters have the phase characteristics shown in Fig. 12-3.

In designing filters, it is more convenient to discuss the magnitude squared function and the group delay function rather than the magnitude and phase functions. The magnitude squared function is given by[2]

$$|H(e^{j\theta})|^2 = H(z)\,H(z^{-1})|_{z=e^{j\theta}} \tag{12-4}$$

From (12-4), we observe that if

$$z_k\{p_k\} = r_k \exp[j\theta_k] \tag{12-5a}$$

is a zero {pole} of $H(z)H(z^{-1})$, then

$$z_k^{-1}\{p_k^{-1}\} = \frac{1}{r_k} \exp[-j\theta_k] \tag{12-5b}$$

is also a zero {pole} of $H(z)H(z^{-1})$. Because complex zeros {poles} must occur in conjugate pairs, we conclude that

$$\bar{z}_k\{\bar{p}_k\} = r_k \exp[-j\theta_k] \tag{12-5c}$$

and

$$\overline{z_k^{-1}}\,\overline{\{p_k^{-1}\}} = \frac{1}{r_k} \exp[j\theta_k] \tag{12-5d}$$

are zeros {poles} of $H(z)H(z^{-1})$. From (12-5), we have the following conclusions:

---

[2]We assume that $H(z)$ has real coefficients only.

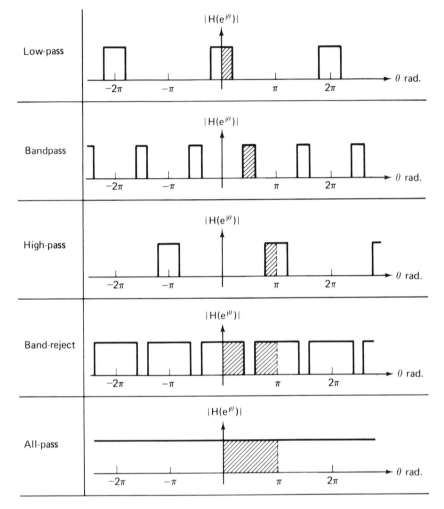

Fig. 12-2 Magnitude characteristics of ideal low-pass, bandpass, high-pass, band-reject, and all-pass filters.

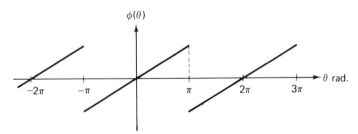

Fig. 12-3 Phase characteristics of linear phase filters.

1. If $z_k = a$ is a real zero {pole} of $H(z)H(z^{-1})$, then $z_k^{-1} = a^{-1}$ is also a real zero {pole} of $H(z)H(z^{-1})$. In the particular case when $a = \pm 1$, the zero {pole} is of even multiplicity.

2. If $z_k = \exp[j\theta_k]$ is a zero {pole} of $H(z)H(z^{-1})$, then $z_k^{-1} = \exp[-j\theta_k]$ is also a zero {pole} of $H(z)H(z^{-1})$. In addition, both z_k and z_k^{-1} are zeros {poles} of $H(z)H(z^{-1})$ with even multiplicities.

3. If $z_k = r_k \exp[j\theta_k]$, where $r_k \neq 1$ and $\theta_k \neq 0$ or π, is a zero {pole} of $H(z)H(z^{-1})$, then $r_k \exp[-j\theta_k]$, $(1/r_k) \exp[j\theta_k]$, and $(1/r_k) \exp[-j\theta_k]$ are also zeros {poles} of $H(z)H(z^{-1})$.

These pole-zero properties of the magnitude squared function of $H(z)H(z^{-1})$ are illustrated in Fig. 12-4.

The group delay function $\tau(\theta)$ is a measure of the delay of the filter response and is defined by

$$\tau(\theta) \triangleq \frac{d\phi(\theta)}{d\theta} \qquad (12\text{-}6)$$

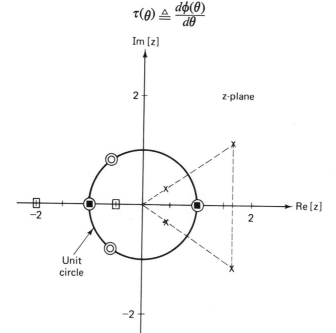

Legend: X   Occur in quadruples

◎   Occur in conjugate pairs with even multiplicities

☐   Occur in pairs

◉   Occur with even multiplicities

Fig. 12-4   Pole-zero properties of $H(z)H(z^{-1})$.

A desirable group delay characteristic of a filter in general is one that approximates a constant over the passband frequencies of the filter.

The problem of designing filters is to find a frequency response or transfer function such that some aspects of the filter's response meet the desired specifications. As such, the filter design problem is basically a mathematical approximation problem. In order to progress systematically, a mathematical approximation problem is conveniently handled with a set of basis functions. This set of basis functions provides a family of functions, one or more of which is a solution of the approximation problem. In the analog filter case discussed in Chapter 8, the families of functions such as those associated with the Butterworth, Chebyshev, inverse Chebyshev, elliptic, and Bessel filters are rational functions of the complex frequency s. These families are chosen because in the analog filter case, both passive and active circuits can only realize transfer functions in the form of a rational function. In the digital filter case, the realizable functions are polynomials of z^{-1} as well as rational functions of z^{-1}. Digital filters characterized by transfer functions in the form of a polynomial,

$$H(z) = a_0 + a_1 z^{-1} + \ldots + a_M z^{-M} \tag{12-7}$$

are called *finite impulse response* (FIR) digital filters. On the other hand, digital filters characterized by transfer functions in the form of a rational function,[3]

$$H(z) = \frac{\sum_{i=0}^{M} a_i z^{-i}}{\sum_{k=0}^{N} b_k z^{-k}} \triangleq \frac{A(z^{-1})}{B(z^{-1})} \tag{12-8}$$

where $B(z^{-1})$ is not a constant, are called *infinite impulse response* (IIR) digital filters.[4] In the FIR case, there is no problem concerning stability and causality, because all FIR filters are stable and causal. In the IIR case, the digital filter is stable if all the poles of $H(z)$ of (12-8) are within the unit circle in the z-plane and causal if b_L is the first nonzero coefficient in the denominator (i.e., $b_0 = b_1 = \ldots b_{L-1} = 0$), then $a_0 = a_1 = \ldots = a_{L-1} = 0$ in the numerator. Because we are concerned with causal filters only, it is convenient to assume that $b_0 = 1$. Hence, the general transfer functions of IIR digital filters are in the form of

$$H(z) = \frac{\sum_{i=0}^{M} a_i z^{-i}}{1 + \sum_{k=1}^{N} b_k z^{-k}} \tag{12-9}$$

---

[3]For simplicity, we assume hereafter that there are no nontrivial common factors between the numerator and the denominator of the transfer function of an IIR digital filter. In other words, the greatest common divisor of $A(z^{-1})$ and $B(z^{-1})$ in (12-8) is a constant.

[4]The rationale behind these names is that the impulse response sequence of (12-7) is a *finite* sequence, $h(n) = 0$ for $n > M$ and $n < 0$, where M is a finite integer; the impulse response of (12-8) is an *infinite* sequence.

In this chapter, we discuss filter design techniques for both the IIR and the FIR digital filters.

12-1   DESIGN OF IIR DIGITAL FILTERS

In the case of IIR digital filters, the transfer functions are in the form of (12-9). Observe that with z replaced by s, (12-9) is a transfer function of an analog filter. Because of the similarities between the transfer functions of IIR digital filters and those of analog filters, the most popular techniques for designing IIR digital filters are, in some manner, digital versions of analog filter designs. These techniques require the construction of simple mapping procedures to map analog filter designs into IIR digital filter designs.[5] This means that the design of an IIR digital filter involves the following two steps:

STEP 1. Design an analog filter by obtaining an appropriate transfer function $\hat{H}(s)$ to meet the signal-processing requirements.[6]

STEP 2. Construct a mapping procedure to transform $\hat{H}(s)$ into an appropriate transfer function $H(z)$, thus resulting in an IIR digital filter design that will meet the specifications.

This two-step procedure for designing IIR digital filters is illustrated in Fig. 12-5. This procedure is most useful for designing standard filters such as low-pass, bandpass, high-pass and band-reject filters, for which a considerable body of knowledge on analog filtering is available. Design techniques for analog filters have been discussed at length in Chapter 8. To complete the design procedure of Fig. 12-5, in this section we discuss various methods to implement Step 2.

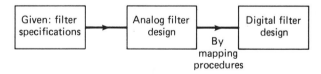

Fig. 12-5   A two-step procedure for designing IIR digital filters.

Because the analog filters in Step 1 are designed to meet the signal-processing requirements, we must make sure that the resulting digital filters retain the desirable properties of the analog filters, including the frequency characteristics, the magnitude and phase behavior of the analog filters. As

---

[5]See Chapter 8 for some design techniques for analog filters.

[6]In this chapter, we use the symbol "^" to denote variables associated with analog filters and continuous-time signals.

a consequence, it is desirable that the mapping procedures in Step 2 satisfy the following two conditions:[7]

CONDITION 1. The imaginary axis of the s-plane ($s = j\omega$ for $-\infty < \omega < \infty$) is mapped into the unit circle of the z-plane ($z = e^{j\theta}$ for $-\pi < \theta \leq \pi$), as shown in Fig. 12-6(a). Notationally, this condition is repre-

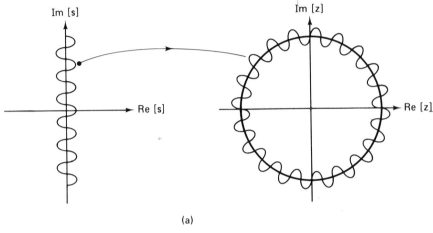

(a)

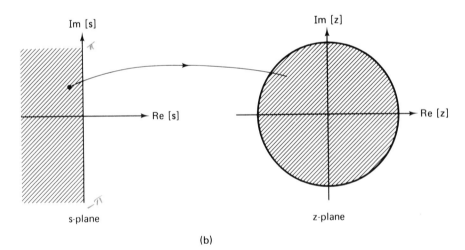

(b)

Fig. 12-6   Two desirable requirements for the mapping procedures in Fig. 12-5.

---

[7]Note that it is desirable that every mapping procedure in Step 2 satisfy these two conditions. Condition 2 is an absolutely necessary requirement. However, Condition 1 is not a mandatory requirement for a mapping procedure to be useful. Very often, a useful mapping procedure can only satisfy Condition 1 over portions of the unit circle in the z-plane.

sented by[8]

$$\{s = j\omega \,|-\infty < \omega < \infty\} \longrightarrow \{z = e^{j\theta} \,|-\pi < \theta \leq \pi\} \qquad (12\text{-}10a)$$

This condition is needed to preserve the frequency characteristics of the analog filters.

CONDITION 2. The LH s-plane (Re $[s] < 0$) is mapped into the interior of the unit circle of the z-plane ($|z| < 1$), as shown in Fig. 12-6(b). Notationally, this condition is represented by

$$\{s \,|\, \text{Re}\,[s] < 0\} \longrightarrow \{z \,|\, |z| < 1\} \qquad (12\text{-}10b)$$

This condition is needed to preserve the stability properties of analog filters. In other words, we require the mapping procedures to map stable analog filters to stable digital filters.

12-1-1. Numerical Integration Techniques *(limited to low freq. signals only)*

One method to obtain a digital filter design from an analog filter design is via numerical integration techniques, where a derivative is approximated by some finite differences. The resulting effect is to replace a differential equation (characterizing an analog filter) with a difference equation (characterizing a digital filter). This action gives rise to a mapping of the complex variable s in the transfer function of an analog filter to the complex variable z in the transfer function of a digital filter

$$s = f(z) \qquad (12\text{-}11)$$

Clearly, different numerical integration methods will give rise to different mapping functions of (12-11), and, hence, the resulting digital filters will be different. In this section, we discuss the simplest case—the *Euler approximation*.

The Euler's method approximates the time derivative of a continuous-time function $d\hat{y}(t)/dt$ by a finite difference as

$$\left. \frac{d\hat{y}(t)}{dt} \right|_{t=nT} = \frac{y(n) - y(n-1)}{T} \qquad (12\text{-}12a)$$

where T is the sampling period and

$$y(k) \triangleq \hat{y}(t)|_{t=kT} \qquad (12\text{-}12b)$$

for all integers k. In terms of operators, (12-12) gives

$$s = \frac{1 - z^{-1}}{T} \triangleq f(z) \qquad \textit{Euler's approximation} \qquad (12\text{-}13)$$

Conversely, (12-13) implies that

$$z = \frac{1}{1 - sT} \qquad (12\text{-}14)$$

---

[8]The symbol "$\longrightarrow$" represents the phrase "is mapped to."

Example 12-1   Consider a low-pass Bessel filter with a transfer function

$$\hat{H}(s) = \frac{K}{s^2 + 3s + 3} \tag{12-15}$$

Find the corresponding digital filter by the Euler approximation method.

Solution: From (12-13), the corresponding digital filter has a transfer function given by

$$H(z) = \hat{H}(s)\big|_{s=f(z)=(1-z^{-1})/T}$$

$$= \frac{K}{\left(\dfrac{1-z^{-1}}{T}\right)^2 + 3\left(\dfrac{1-z^{-1}}{T}\right) + 3}$$

$$= \frac{KT^2}{(1 - 2z^{-1} + z^{-2}) + 3T(1 - z^{-1}) + 3T^2} \tag{12-16}$$

$$= \frac{KT^2}{z^{-2} - (2 + 3T)z^{-1} + (1 + 3T + 3T^2)}$$

Notice that we can also arrive at (12-16) by performing the basic Euler approximation of derivatives as follows:

Let $\hat{Y}(s)$ and $\hat{X}(s)$ be, respectively, the output and the input of the Bessel filter. Then (12-15) yields

$$(s^2 + 3s + 3)\hat{Y}(s) = K\hat{X}(s) \tag{12-17a}$$

Hence, the differential equation characterizing the analog Bessel filter is given by

$$\frac{d^2\hat{y}(t)}{dt^2} + 3\frac{d\hat{y}(t)}{dt} + 3\hat{y}(t) = K\hat{x}(t) \tag{12-17b}$$

With

$$y(n) \triangleq \hat{y}(t)\big|_{t=nT} \tag{12-18a}$$

and

$$x(n) \triangleq \hat{x}(t)\big|_{t=nT} \tag{12-18b}$$

the Euler approximation of derivatives gives

$$\frac{d\hat{y}}{dt}\bigg|_{t=nT} = \frac{y(n) - y(n-1)}{T} \tag{12-18c}$$

$$\frac{d\hat{y}}{dt}\bigg|_{t=(n-1)T} = \frac{y(n-1) - y(n-2)}{T} \tag{12-18d}$$

and

$$\frac{d^2\hat{y}}{dt}\bigg|_{t=nT} = \frac{\dfrac{d\hat{y}}{dt}\Big|_{t=nT} - \dfrac{d\hat{y}}{dt}\Big|_{t=(n-1)T}}{T}$$

$$= \frac{\dfrac{y(n) - y(n-1)}{T} - \dfrac{y(n-1) - y(n-2)}{T}}{T} \tag{12-18e}$$

$$= \frac{y(n) - 2y(n-1) + y(n-2)}{T^2}$$

Substituting (12-18) into (12-17b), we obtain

$$\frac{1}{T^2}[y(n) - 2y(n-1) + y(n-2)] + \frac{3}{T}[y(n) - y(n-1)] + 3y(n) = Kx(n)$$

or

$$(1 + 3T + 3T^2)y(n) - (2 + 3T)y(n-1) + y(n-2) = KT^2x(n) \quad (12\text{-}19)$$

Taking the z-transforms of (12-19), we obtain the transfer function of the resulting digital filter as

$$[(1 + 3T + 3T^2) - (2 + 3T)z^{-1} + z^{-2}]Y(z) = KT^2X(z)$$

or

$$H(z) \triangleq \frac{Y(z)}{X(z)} = \frac{KT^2}{z^{-2} - (2 + 3T)z^{-1} + (1 + 3T + 3T^2)} \quad (12\text{-}20)$$

At dc when $\theta = 0$, we have

$$z^{-1} = e^{-j\theta} = 1 \quad (12\text{-}21\text{a})$$

and (12-20) yields

$$H(e^{-j\theta}) = \frac{K}{3} \quad (12\text{-}21\text{b})$$

That is, the dc gain of the resulting digital filter of (12-20) is identical to the dc gain of the original analog filter of (12-15). ∎

Observe that the digital filter of (12-20) is only an approximation to the analog filter of (12-15). To consider the quality of this approximation, let us examine the two conditions of (12-10) for the Euler mapping procedure. According to (12-14), the imaginary axis of the s-plane is mapped to

$$z = \frac{1}{1 - j\omega T} = \frac{\frac{1}{2} - \frac{1}{2}(j\omega T) + \frac{1}{2} + \frac{1}{2}(j\omega T)}{1 - j\omega T}$$

$$= \frac{1}{2} + \frac{1}{2}\left(\frac{1 + j\omega T}{1 - j\omega T}\right)$$

or

$$z - \frac{1}{2} = \frac{1}{2}\left(\frac{1 + j\omega T}{1 - j\omega T}\right)\left(\frac{1 + j\omega T}{1 + j\omega T}\right)$$

$$= \frac{1}{2}\left[\frac{1 - (\omega T)^2 + 2j\omega T}{1 + (\omega T)^2}\right]$$

$$= \frac{1}{2}\frac{\sqrt{[1 - (\omega T)^2]^2 + [2\omega T]^2}}{1 + (\omega T)^2}\exp\left[j\tan^{-1}\frac{2\omega T}{1 - (\omega T)^2}\right] \quad (12\text{-}22)$$

$$= \frac{1}{2}\exp\left[j\tan^{-1}\frac{2\omega T}{1 - (\omega T)^2}\right]$$

From (12-22), we conclude that

$$|z - \tfrac{1}{2}| = \tfrac{1}{2} \quad \text{for all } \omega \quad (12\text{-}23\text{a})$$

and the phase angle $\gamma(\omega)$ of $[z - (1/2)]$ is given by

$$\gamma(\omega) \triangleq \tan^{-1} \frac{2\omega T}{1 - (\omega T)^2} \qquad \text{(12-23b)}$$

As shown in Fig. 12-7, $\gamma(\omega)$ goes from $-\pi$ to π as ω goes from $-\infty$ to ∞.

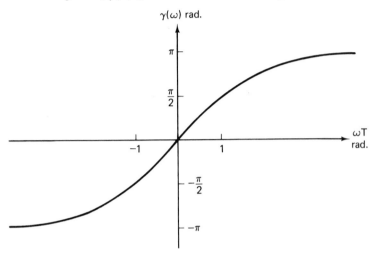

Fig. 12-7 The phase characteristics of $\gamma(\omega)$ of (12-23b).

This implies that the image of the imaginary axis of the s-plane is a circle in the z-plane with radius $1/2$ and centered at $z = 1/2$, as shown in Fig. 12-8. When

$$\text{Re}\,[s] = \text{Re}\,[\sigma + j\omega] = \sigma < 0 \qquad \text{(12-24)}$$

the mapping procedure of (12-14) gives

$$z = \frac{1}{1 - \sigma T + j\omega T}$$

and, hence,

$$|z| = \frac{1}{\sqrt{(1 - \sigma T)^2 + (\omega T)^2}} \leq \frac{1}{|1 - \sigma T|} \leq 1 \qquad \text{(12-25)}$$

This means that the LH s-plane is mapped into the unit circle of the z-plane.[9] Thus Condition 2 of (12-10b) is satisfied.

From Fig. 12-8, Condition 2 of (12-10b) is satisfied, but Condition 1 of (12-10a) is not satisfied completely. However, for $|\theta|$ small, such as $|\theta| \leq \Delta\theta$ in Fig. 12-8, the mapping procedure of (12-13) meets Condition 1 rather closely. Hence, the Euler mapping procedure of (12-13) will give satisfactory results for low-frequency operations and low-pass filters. In other words,

---

[9]It can be shown that the LH s-plane is mapped into a circle Γ with radius $1/2$ and centered at $z = 1/2$, as shown in Fig. 12-8.

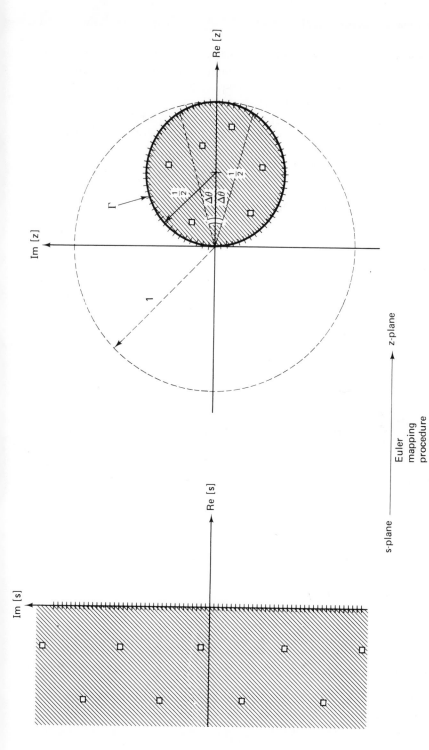

Fig. 12-8 Results of Euler mapping procedure between the *s*-plane and the *z*-plane.

the resulting low-pass digital filter obtained by the Euler mapping procedure from a low-pass analog filter will have about the same passband frequency characteristics as that of the original low-pass analog filter, provided that the sampling period T is sufficiently small.

If, instead of the simple Euler approximation of (12-12), a time derivative is approximated by a weighted sum of finite differences of higher order, such as[10]

$$\frac{d\hat{y}(t)}{dt}\bigg|_{t=nT} = \frac{1}{T} \sum_{k=0}^{L} \alpha_k y(n-k) \tag{12-26}$$

where L is a positive integer, then the mapping procedure is given by

$$s = \frac{1}{T} \sum_{k=0}^{L} \alpha_k z^{-k} \tag{12-27}$$

In this case, it can be shown that the mapping procedure of (12-27) will satisfy Condition 2 of (12-10b) but not Condition 1 of (12-10a). In fact, the region or the range of values of θ where Condition 1 is approximately satisfied decreases as L, the order of approximation, increases.[11] This means that any approximation of time derivatives with an order higher than that of Euler's is not practical and will not produce good results in general, except at extremely low digital frequencies.

12-1-2. Impulse Invariant Transformation (Band limited)

A mapping procedure to obtain digital filters from analog filters is called the *impulse invariant transformation*. This procedure ensures that the impulse response $h(n)$ of the resulting digital filter is the sampled version of the impulse response $\hat{h}(t)$ of its corresponding analog filter by defining

$$h(n) \triangleq \hat{h}(t)|_{t=nT} \tag{12-28}$$

where T is the sample period. A design procedure for this method is shown in Fig. 12-9.

To see how the impulse invariant transformation method operates, let us perform a partial fraction expansion of the transfer function $\hat{H}(s)$ of the desired analog filter as

$$\hat{H}(s) = \frac{\sum_{i=0}^{M} \hat{a}_i s^i}{\sum_{i=0}^{N} \hat{b}_i s^i} = \sum_{i=1}^{N} \frac{\xi_i}{s - \hat{p}_i} \tag{12-29}$$

where we have assumed that $N > M \geq 0$, $b_N \neq 0$, $b_0 \neq 0$ and that all poles

---

[10]With $L = 1$, $\alpha_0 = \alpha_1 = 1$, and $\alpha_k = 0$ for $k > 1$, we obtain the Euler approximation.

[11]See Reference [12].

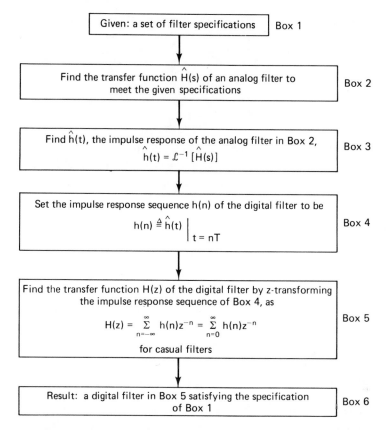

Fig. 12-9 A design procedure for the impulse invariant transformation method.

are distinct. In addition, for each $i = 1, 2, \ldots, N$, $\hat{p}_i$ is the ith pole of the analog filter and ξ_i is the residue of $\hat{H}(s)$ at the pole $\hat{p}_i$. The impulse response $\hat{h}(t)$ of the analog filter can be obtained by taking the inverse Laplace transform of (12-29). The result is

$$\hat{h}(t) = \sum_{i=1}^{N} \xi_i e^{\hat{p}_i t} \hat{u}(t) \tag{12-30}$$

where $\hat{u}(t)$ represents the unit step function. Substituting (12-30) into (12-28) yields the impulse response sequence $h(n)$ of the corresponding digital filter

$$h(n) \triangleq \hat{h}(t)|_{t=nT} = \sum_{i=1}^{N} \xi_i e^{\hat{p}_i nT} u(n) \tag{12-31}$$

where $u(n)$ represents the unit step sequence. The transfer function $H(z)$ of the resulting digital filter can be obtained by finding the z-transform of the impulse response sequence of (12-31) as

$$H(z) = \sum_{n=0}^{\infty} h(n) z^{-n} = \sum_{n=0}^{\infty} \sum_{i=1}^{N} \xi_i e^{\hat{p}_i n T} z^{-n}$$

$$= \sum_{i=1}^{N} \xi_i \sum_{n=0}^{\infty} (e^{\hat{p}_i T} z^{-1})^n \qquad (12\text{-}32)$$

$$= \sum_{i=1}^{N} \frac{\xi_i}{1 - z^{-1} \exp[\hat{p}_i T]}$$

By comparing (12-29) and (12-32), the mapping relation between analog and digital filters in the impulse invariant transformation method is given by

$$\frac{\xi_i}{s - \hat{p}_i} \longrightarrow \frac{\xi_i}{1 - z^{-1} \exp[\hat{p}_i T]} \triangleq \frac{\xi_i}{1 - p_i z^{-1}} \qquad (12\text{-}33a)$$

where

$$p_i \triangleq \exp[\hat{p}_i T] \qquad (12\text{-}33b)$$

is the digital filter pole corresponding to the analog filter pole at $\hat{p}_i$.

Example 12-2   Suppose that the desired analog filter has a transfer function given by

$$\hat{H}(s) = \frac{2s}{(s + 1)(s + 2)} \qquad (12\text{-}34)$$

Find $H(z)$, the transfer function of the corresponding digital filter, by the impulse invariance method.

Solution: Writing $\hat{H}(s)$ of (12-34) in partial fraction form, we have

$$\hat{H}(s) = \frac{-2}{s + 1} + \frac{4}{s + 2} \qquad (12\text{-}35a)$$

where

$$\hat{p}_1 = -1 \quad \text{and} \quad \hat{p}_2 = -2 \qquad (12\text{-}35b)$$

By (12-33), $H(z)$ is given by

$$H(z) = \frac{-2}{1 - z^{-1} \exp[-T]} + \frac{4}{1 - z^{-1} \exp[-2T]} \qquad (12\text{-}36a)$$

where T is the sample period. Simplifying (12-36a), we obtain

$$H(z) = \frac{-2(1 - z^{-1} e^{-2T}) + 4(1 - z^{-1} e^{-T})}{(1 - z^{-1} e^{-T})(1 - z^{-1} e^{-2T})}$$

$$= \frac{2 + (2e^{-2T} - 4e^{-T}) z^{-1}}{1 - (e^{-T} + e^{-2T}) z^{-1} + e^{-3T} z^{-2}} \qquad (12\text{-}36b)$$ ∎

Example 12-3   A normalized second-order Chebyshev low-pass filter with a 3 dB passband ripple has a transfer function given by

$$\hat{H}(s) = \frac{0.5011887}{s^2 + 0.6448996 s + 0.7079478} \qquad (12\text{-}37)$$

Find $H(z)$, the transfer function of the corresponding digital filter, via the impulse invariance method.

Solution: Writing $\hat{H}(s)$ of (12-37) in factored form, we have

$$\hat{H}(s) = \frac{0.5011887}{(s + 0.3224498 + j0.7771576)(s + 0.3224498 - j0.7771576)}$$

$$= \frac{-j0.3224498}{s + 0.3224498 + j0.7771576} + \frac{j0.3224498}{s + 0.3224498 - j0.7771576} \tag{12-38}$$

By applying (12-33) to (12-38), we obtain

$$H(z) = \frac{-j0.3224498}{1 - z^{-1} \exp\left[(-0.3224498 - j0.7771576)T\right]}$$

$$+ \frac{j0.3224498}{1 - z^{-1} \exp\left[(-0.3224498 + j0.7771576)T\right]} \tag{12-39}$$

$$= \frac{[-2e^{-0.3224498T}0.3224498 \sin(0.7771576T)]z^{-1}}{1 - 2z^{-1}e^{-0.3224498T}\cos(0.7771576T) + e^{-0.6448996T}z^{-2}}$$

When $T = 1$ sec., (12-39) becomes

$$H_1(z) = \frac{-0.3275899z^{-1}}{1 - 1.0328240z^{-1} + 0.5247152z^{-2}} \tag{12-40}$$

and when $T = 0.1$ sec., (12-39) becomes

$$H_{0.1}(z) = \frac{-0.0484797z^{-1}}{1 - 1.9306935z^{-1} + 0.9375455z^{-2}} \tag{12-41}$$

The magnitude characteristics of (12-40) and (12-41) are shown in Fig. 12-10.

Recall that $|H(e^{j\theta})|$ is a periodic function of θ with period 2π and that $|\hat{H}(j\omega)|$ is not a periodic function. The effect of these basic distinct properties of digital and analog filters is that the magnitude characteristics of the resulting digital filter will depart from those of the original analog filter by the time the curves reach $\theta = \pi$ or $\omega = \pi/T$, where T is the sampling period. If the sampling period is small enough, then the departure will start at a point close to $\theta = \pi$. Otherwise, the deviation will begin long before the curves reach the point $\theta = \pi$. A case in point is shown in Fig. 12-10. Observe that the digital filter's cutoff frequencies are at

$$\theta_{c1,2} = \pm\omega_c T = \pm T \text{ rad.} \tag{12-42a}$$

where we have used the information that the analog cutoff frequency is at $\omega_c = 1$ rad./sec. These cutoff frequencies will repeat thereafter at

$$\theta_{c1,2} \pm k2\pi \text{ rad.} \tag{12-42b}$$

where k is any integer. ∎

Because the impulse response sequence $h(n)$ of the digital filter obtained by the impulse invariance technique is actually a sampled version of the impulse response $\hat{h}(t)$ of the analog filter, the frequency response of the digital filter is an aliased version of the frequency response of the analog filter, as stated by (11-115) and repeated here for convenience:

$$H(e^{j\theta}) = \frac{1}{T}\sum_{k=-\infty}^{\infty} \hat{H}\left[j\left(\frac{\theta}{T} + \frac{2\pi k}{T}\right)\right] \tag{12-43a}$$

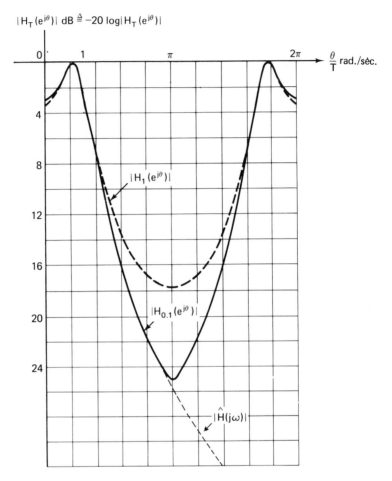

Legend: — — Analog case
          ——— Digital case with T = 0.1 sec.
          — — Digital case with T = 1 sec.

Fig. 12-10 Magnitude characteristics of a second-order Chebyshev filter with a 3 dB ripple.

or

$$H(e^{j\omega T}) = \frac{1}{T} \sum_{k=-\infty}^{\infty} \hat{H}\left[j\left(\omega + \frac{2\pi k}{T} \right) \right] \qquad (12\text{-}43\text{b})$$

If the sampling rate is fast enough, the aliasing effect is minimal. As illustrated in Fig. 12-10, when $T = 0.1$ sec., the aliasing effect represented by the difference between the frequency responses of the analog and the digital filters for $0 < \theta < \pi$ is hardly noticeable. However, when the sampling rate is not fast enough, such as the $T = 1$ sec. case in Fig. 12-10, the aliasing effect comes into play as we observe that $|H_1(e^{j\theta})|$ is markedly different from that of $|\hat{H}(j\omega)|$. By letting $s = j\omega$ in (12-43), we obtain[12]

$$H(e^{sT}) = \frac{1}{T} \sum_{k=-\infty}^{\infty} \hat{H}\left(s + j\frac{2\pi k}{T}\right)$$

or

$$H(z)|_{z=e^{sT}} = \frac{1}{T} \sum_{k=-\infty}^{\infty} \hat{H}\left(s + j\frac{2\pi k}{T}\right) \tag{12-44}$$

Observe that (12-44) gives the relationship between the transfer functions of the digital filter and its corresponding analog filter under the impulse invariance transformation.

To examine the performance of the impulse invariance method with regard to the two desired conditions for mapping procedures in (12-10), we consider the relationship[13]

$$z = e^{sT} \tag{12-45a}$$

and hence

$$\theta = \omega T \tag{12-45b}$$

Fig. 12-11 shows that a horizontal strip of height $2\pi/T$ in the s-plane is mapped into the entire z-plane, with the left-half of the strip mapped into the interior of the unit circle, the right-half of the strip into the exterior of the unit circle, and the imaginary axis of the strip onto the unit circle. From Fig. 12-11 we can see that the source of the aliasing effect is that the mapping of (12-45) is not one-to-one.[14] For example, the points $s = 0$, $s = j(2\pi/T)$, and $s = j(4\pi/T)$ are mapped to the single point $z = 1$. In fact, (12-45) says that the analog transfer function of each $2\pi/T$ strip is overlayed onto the complete z-plane to form the digital transfer function. Thus, the impulse invariance method is not a simple linear or affine mapping from the s-plane onto the z-plane.[15] Because of this aliasing effect, the impulse invariance method is applicable only to filters with an essentially bandlimited analog frequency

---

[12]When the sampling rate is very high ($1/T$ is very large), the resulting digital filter will have a very high gain. This gives rise to many undesirable problems such as overflow. For this reason, the transfer function of the resulting digital filter obtained by the impulse invariant transformation method of (12-33) is multiplied by a factor of T to reduce the gain level of the digital filter to that of the analog filter.

[13]As indicated by (12-44), (12-45) is *not* the mapping relationship between the frequency variables s and z under the impulse invariance transformation. This fact will be expounded upon later. However, the relationship in (12-45) does bring out the essential properties of the impulse invariant transformation mapping procedure in a simple manner.

[14]A function $f(x)$ is said to be one-to-one if $f(x_1) \neq f(x_2)$ whenever $x_1 \neq x_2$.

[15]A *linear* map has the form $y = Ax$, and an *affine* map is characterized by $y = Ax + b$.

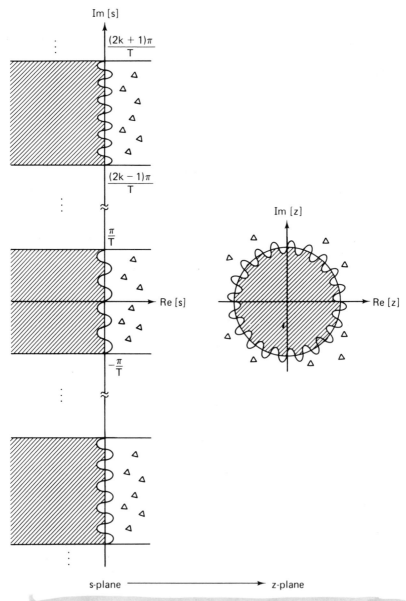

Fig. 12-11 Properties of the impulse invariant-transformation mapping procedure.

response satisfying the condition

$$|\hat{H}(j\omega)| \simeq 0 \quad \text{for } |\omega| > \omega_B \tag{12-46}$$

such as in the cases of low-pass and bandpass filters.

As we have shown, the mapping procedure of the impulse invariance method is given by (12-33), which states that the pole locations $\hat{p}_i$ of the analog filter are transformed to the pole locations

$$p_i \triangleq e^{\hat{p}_i T} \qquad i = 1, 2, \ldots, N \tag{12-47}$$

Thus, (12-45) relates the pole locations of the digital and analog filters. However, it is absolutely not true that (12-45) relates the zero locations of the digital and analog filters under impulse invariant transformation. A case in point is as follows:

Example 12-4 We are given the transfer function of an analog filter as[16]

$$\hat{H}(s) = \frac{s + a}{(s + a)^2 + b^2} \tag{12-48}$$

where $a \neq 0$ and $b \neq 0$. Find the zero and pole locations of the digital filter obtained by the impulse invariant transformation.

Solution: A partial fraction expansion of $\hat{H}(s)$ of (12-48) gives

$$\hat{H}(s) = \frac{1/2}{s + a + jb} + \frac{1/2}{s + a - jb} \tag{12-49}$$

The transfer function of the corresponding digital filter is given by (12-33) as

$$\begin{aligned} H(z) &= \frac{1/2}{1 - e^{-(a+jb)T}z^{-1}} + \frac{1/2}{1 - e^{-(a-jb)T}z^{-1}} \\ &= \frac{1 - (e^{-aT}\cos bT)z^{-1}}{1 - (2e^{-aT}\cos bT)z^{-1} + e^{-2aT}z^{-2}} \end{aligned} \tag{12-50}$$

From (12-50), the finite zero position of the digital filter is

$$z_1 = e^{-aT}\cos bT \neq e^{\hat{z}_1 T} = e^{-aT} \tag{12-51}$$

where $\hat{z}_1 = -a$ is the zero location of the analog filter. However, the pole locations of the digital filter are at

$$p_1 = e^{-(a+jb)T} = e^{\hat{p}_1 T} \tag{12-52a}$$

$$p_2 = e^{-(a-jb)T} = e^{\hat{p}_2 T} \tag{12-52b}$$

where $\hat{p}_1 = -(a + jb)$ and $\hat{p}_2 = -(a - jb)$ are the pole locations of the analog filter. The pole-zero diagrams of the analog filter and its associated digital filter are shown in Fig. 12-12. ∎

As we have seen, (12-33) applies to both real and complex poles $\hat{p}_i$. However, when $\hat{p}_i$ is complex, it is more convenient to consider the pair of poles $\hat{p}_i$ and $\bar{\hat{p}}_i$ together, where the bar above a variable indicates its complex conjugate. By applying (12-33) appropriately, we obtain the transformation pairs for the following two second-order cases:

1. If the transfer function of an analog filter is given by

$$\hat{H}(s) = \frac{s + \sigma_1}{(s + \sigma_1)^2 + \omega_1^2} \tag{12-53a}$$

---

[16]Filters characterized by (12-48) are called *Lerner* filters. It has been shown that Lerner filters have a high degree of phase linearity and reasonably selective passbands. For more details, consult Reference [16].

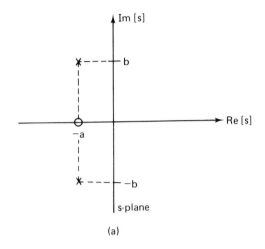

(a)

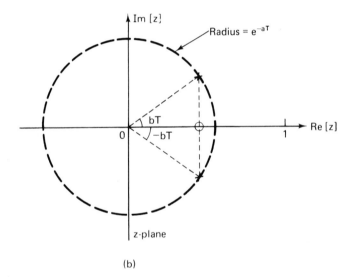

(b)

Fig. 12-12 Pole-zero diagrams of a second order Lerner filter.
(a) Analog filter version. (b) Digital filter version obtained by
the impulse invariance method.

where the poles are at

$$\hat{p}_{1,2} = -\sigma_1 \pm j\omega_1 \qquad (12\text{-}53\text{b})$$

then the transfer function of the corresponding digital filter is given by

$$H(z) = \frac{1 - z^{-1}e^{-\sigma_1 T}\cos\omega_1 T}{1 - 2z^{-1}e^{-\sigma_1 T}\cos\omega_1 T + z^{-2}e^{-2\sigma_1 T}} \qquad (12\text{-}54)$$

2. If $\hat{H}(s)$ is given by

$$\hat{H}(s) = \frac{\omega_1}{(s + \sigma_1)^2 + \omega_1^2} \qquad (12\text{-}55)$$

then, under the mapping procedure of (12-33), $H(z)$ is given by

$$H(z) = \frac{z^{-1}e^{-\sigma_1 T} \sin \omega_1 T}{1 - 2z^{-1}e^{-\sigma_1 T} \cos \omega_1 T + z^{-2}e^{-2\sigma_1 T}} \qquad (12\text{-}56)$$

Example 12-5 A third-order low-pass Butterworth analog filter has a transfer function given by

$$\hat{H}(s) = \frac{\omega_c^3}{(s + \omega_c)\left[s + \left(\frac{1}{2} + j\frac{\sqrt{3}}{2}\right)\omega_c\right]\left[s + \left(\frac{1}{2} - j\frac{\sqrt{3}}{2}\right)\omega_c\right]} \qquad (12\text{-}57)$$

Find the transfer function of the corresponding third-order Butterworth digital filter by the impulse invariant transformation method.

Solution: $\hat{H}(s)$ can be written as

$$\hat{H}(s) = \frac{\omega_c}{s + \omega_c} + \frac{-\omega_c s}{\left(s + \frac{\omega_c}{2}\right)^2 + \left(\frac{\sqrt{3}}{2}\omega_c\right)^2}$$

$$= \frac{\omega_c}{s + \omega_c} + \frac{-\omega_c\left(s + \frac{\omega_c}{2}\right)}{\left(s + \frac{\omega_c}{2}\right)^2 + \left(\frac{\sqrt{3}}{2}\omega_c\right)^2} \qquad (12\text{-}58)$$

$$+ \frac{\frac{\omega_c}{\sqrt{3}}\left(\frac{\sqrt{3}}{2}\omega_c\right)}{\left(s + \frac{\omega_c}{2}\right)^2 + \left(\frac{\sqrt{3}}{2}\omega_c\right)^2}$$

By (12-33) and (12-53) through (12-56), the desired digital filter has a transfer function given by

$$H(z) = \frac{\omega_c}{1 - z^{-1}\exp\left(-\omega_c T\right)}$$

$$- \frac{\omega_c\left[1 - z^{-1}\exp\left(-\frac{\omega_c T}{2}\right)\cos\left(\frac{\sqrt{3}}{2}\omega_c T\right)\right]}{1 - 2z^{-1}\exp\left(-\frac{\omega_c T}{2}\right)\cos\left(\frac{\sqrt{3}}{2}\omega_c T\right) + z^{-2}\exp\left(-\omega_c T\right)}$$

$$+ \frac{\omega_c}{\sqrt{3}}\frac{z^{-1}\exp\left(-\frac{\omega_c T}{2}\right)\sin\left(\frac{\sqrt{3}}{2}\omega_c T\right)}{1 - 2z^{-1}\exp\left(-\frac{\omega_c T}{2}\right)\cos\left(\frac{\sqrt{3}}{2}\omega_c T\right) + z^{-2}\exp\left(-\omega_c T\right)}$$

$$= \frac{\omega_c\left\{-1 + \exp\left(-\frac{\omega_c T}{2}\right)\left[\cos\left(\frac{\sqrt{3}}{2}\omega_c T\right) + \frac{1}{\sqrt{3}}\sin\left(\frac{\sqrt{3}}{2}\omega_c T\right)\right]z^{-1}\right\}}{1 - 2z^{-1}\exp\left(-\frac{\omega_c T}{2}\right)\cos\left(\frac{\sqrt{3}}{2}\omega_c T\right) + z^{-2}\exp\left(-\omega_c T\right)}$$

$$+ \frac{\omega_c}{1 - z^{-1}\exp\left(-\omega_c T\right)} \qquad (12\text{-}59)$$

∎

Example 12-6 Suppose that a low-pass digital filter is desired to satisfy the following conditions:

(a) The 3 dB cutoff point is at 0.2π rad.
(b) The passband magnitude is within 0.1 dB of its maximum value for $0 < \theta < 0.1\pi$ rad.
(c) The stopband attenuation is greater than 30 dB for $0.5\pi < \theta < \pi$.
(d) A monotonically decreasing magnitude curve is desired for $0 < \theta < \pi$.
(e) The sampling period $T = 10\pi$ μsec.

Find a transfer function for the desired digital filter.

Solution: The first step is to translate these digital criteria to analog criteria. This is done by noting that when T satisfies the Nyquist criteria, (12-43) approximately reduces to

$$H(e^{j\theta}) = \frac{1}{T}\hat{H}\left(j\frac{\theta}{T}\right) \tag{12-60a}$$

and, hence,

$$\omega = \frac{\theta}{T} \tag{12-60b}$$

With (12-60b), the desired analog filter should meet the following specifications:

(a') The 3 dB cutoff frequency is at

$$\omega_C = \frac{0.2\pi}{10\pi \times 10^{-6}} = 20 \text{ K rad./sec.} \tag{12-61a}$$

(b') The passband magnitude is within 0.1 dB for

$$0 < \omega < \frac{0.1\pi}{10\pi \times 10^{-6}} = 10 \text{ K rad./sec.} \tag{12-61b}$$

(c') The stopband attenuation is greater than 30 dB for

$$\omega > \frac{0.5\pi}{10\pi \times 10^{-6}} = 50 \text{ K rad./sec.} \tag{12-61c}$$

(d') A monotonically decreasing magnitude curve is desired for $\omega \geq 0$.

Criterion (d') indicates that a Butterworth filter is needed. Hence, the magnitude function is of the form

$$|\hat{H}(j\omega)|^2 = \frac{1}{1 + \left(\dfrac{\omega}{\omega_C}\right)^{2n}} \tag{12-62}$$

This Butterworth filter must satisfy the following two conditions:

$$-10 \log|\hat{H}(j10^4)|^2 \leq 0.1 \tag{12-63a}$$

and

$$-10 \log|\hat{H}(j5 \times 10^4)|^2 > 30 \tag{12-63b}$$

Condition (12-63a) implies that

$$-\log\left|\frac{1}{1 + \left(\dfrac{10^4}{2 \times 10^4}\right)^{2n}}\right| \leq 0.01$$

or

$$n \geq 3 \tag{12-64a}$$

and (12-63b) requires that

$$-10 \log \left| \frac{1}{1 + \left(\frac{5 \times 10^4}{2 \times 10^4}\right)^{2n}} \right| > 30$$

or

$$n \geq 4 \qquad (12\text{-}64\text{b})$$

Hence, the minimal order of Butterworth filter needed to meet the specifications is $n = 4$. For $n = 4$, the pole locations of the analog Butterworth filter with a unity bandwidth, or a cutoff frequency at $\omega = 1$ rad./sec., can be found from (8-34) and (8-35) to be

$$\hat{s}_{1,4} = -0.38268 \pm j0.92388$$
$$\hat{s}_{2,3} = -0.92388 \pm j0.38268 \qquad (12\text{-}65)$$

This means that the transfer function of the normalized fourth-order Butterworth filter is given by

$$\hat{H}_N(s) = \frac{1}{(s - \hat{s}_1)(s - \hat{s}_4)(s - \hat{s}_2)(s - \hat{s}_3)}$$

$$= \frac{1}{(s^2 + 0.76537s + 1)(s^2 + 1.84776s + 1)}$$

$$\hat{H}_N(s) = -\frac{0.92388s + 0.70711}{s^2 + 0.76537s + 1} + \frac{0.92388s + 1.70711}{s^2 + 1.84776s + 1} \qquad (12\text{-}66)$$

Hence, the transfer function of the desired analog filter—one that satisfies criteria (a′) to (d′)—is given by

$$\hat{H}(s) = \hat{H}_N\left(\frac{s}{\omega_C}\right) = H_N\left(\frac{s}{2 \times 10^4}\right)$$

$$= -\frac{0.92388\omega_C s + 0.70711\omega_C^2}{s^2 + 0.76537\omega_C s + \omega_C^2} + \frac{0.92388\omega_C s + 1.70711\omega_C^2}{s^2 + 1.84776\omega_C s + \omega_C^2}$$

or

$$\hat{H}(s) = -\frac{(1.84776 \times 10^4)s + (2.82844 \times 10^8)}{s^2 + (1.53074 \times 10^4)s + (4 \times 10^8)}$$

$$+ \frac{(1.84776 \times 10^4)s + (6.82844 \times 10^8)}{s^2 + 3.69552s + (4 \times 10^8)} \qquad (12\text{-}67)$$

where the poles are at

$$\hat{p}_{1,2} = \omega_C \hat{s}_{1,4} = -0.76537 \times 10^4 \pm j1.84776 \times 10^4$$
$$\hat{p}_{3,4} = \omega_C \hat{s}_{2,3} = -1.84776 \times 10^4 \pm j0.76537 \times 10^4 \qquad (12\text{-}68)$$

To fit into the forms of (12-53) and (12-55), (12-68) is written as

$$\hat{H}(s) = -\frac{(1.84776 \times 10^4)[s + (0.76537 \times 10^4)]}{s^2 + (1.53074 \times 10^4)s + (4 \times 10^8)}$$

$$- \frac{(0.76537 \times 10^4)(1.84776 \times 10^4)}{s^2 + (1.53074 \times 10^4)s + (4 \times 10^8)}$$

$$+ \frac{(1.84776 \times 10^4)[s + (1.84776 \times 10^4)]}{s^2 + 3.69552s + (4 \times 10^8)} \qquad (12\text{-}69)$$

$$+ \frac{(4.46087 \times 10^4)(0.76537 \times 10^4)}{s^2 + 3.69552s + (4 \times 10^8)}$$

By (12-53) through (12-56), the transfer function of the desired digital filter—one that satisfies all the specifications of (a) through (e)—is given by

$$H(z) =$$

$$10^4\left\{\frac{-1.84776 + z^{-1}e^{-0.076537\pi}[(1.84776\cos 0.184776\pi)-(0.76537\sin 0.184776\pi)]}{1 - 2z^{-1}e^{-0.076537\pi}\cos 0.184776\pi + z^{-2}e^{-0.153073\pi}}\right.$$

$$\left. + \frac{1.84776 + z^{-1}e^{-0.184776\pi}[(-1.84776\cos 0.076537\pi) + (4.46087\sin 0.076537\pi)]}{1 - 2z^{-1}e^{-0.184776\pi}\cos 0.076537\pi + z^{-2}e^{-0.369552\pi}}\right\}$$

$$= \frac{10^4[-1.84776 + 0.88482z^{-1}]}{1 - 1.314958z^{-1} + 0.61823z^{-2}} + \frac{10^4[1.84776 - 0.409815z^{-1}]}{1 - 1.087049z^{-1} + 0.313179z^{-2}} \qquad (12\text{-}70)$$

Notice that the cutoff frequency of the analog low-pass filter is at 20 K rad./ sec. This means that the analog filter is effectively bandlimited at about $\omega_0/2 \triangleq 80$ K rad./sec., as shown in Fig. 12-13(a). Because the sampling rate of 200 K rad./sec. is above the Nyquist rate,[17] we expect almost no aliasing effect.[18] Hence, we have

$$H(e^{j\theta}) \simeq \frac{1}{T}\hat{H}\left(j\frac{\theta}{T}\right) \qquad (12\text{-}71a)$$

and

$$\theta = \omega T \qquad (12\text{-}71b)$$

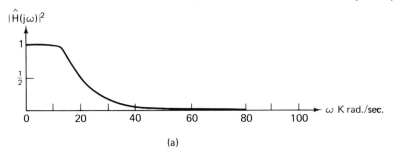

(a)

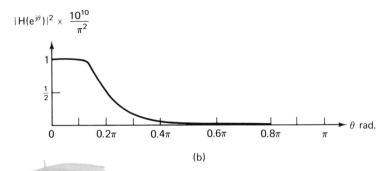

(b)

Fig. 12-13   Magnitude characteristics of a fourth-order Butterworth low-pass filter. (a) Analog filter of (12-69). (b) Digital filter of (12-70).

[17]Nyquist rate means that the sampling period $T_N = 2\pi/\omega_0$, or $1/T_N = \omega_0/2\pi$.

[18]In this case, the error due to aliasing effect is roughly 0.02% at dc.

for $-\pi < \theta < \pi$. In view of (12-71), the magnitude curve of the digital filter is similar to that of the corresponding analog filter, as shown in Fig. 12-13(b).

Notice that the gain of the digital filter at $\theta = 0$ is exactly $1/T$, whereas the gain of the analog filter at $\omega = 0$ is 1. To eliminate this high gain effect, the final design is to let the transfer function of the digital filter be

$$H_F(z) \triangleq TH(z)$$

$$= \frac{(\pi/10)(-1.84776 + 0.88482z^{-1})}{1 - 1.314958z^{-1} + 0.61823z^{-2}} + \frac{(\pi/10)(1.84776 - 0.409815z^{-1})}{1 - 1.087049z^{-1} + 0.313179z^{-2}}$$

(12-72)

Observe that the dc gain of $H_F(z)$ has been normalized to unity. ∎

12-1-3. Bilinear Transformation

It has been shown that the aliasing effect in the impulse invariant transformation method is caused by a mapping that is not a one-to-one function from the s-plane onto the z-plane. To eliminate this undesirable aliasing effect, we need to find a one-to-one continuous mapping from the s-plane onto the z-plane. One such transformation is called the *bilinear transformation*, defined by[19]

$$s = f(z) \triangleq \frac{2}{T} \frac{1 - z^{-1}}{1 + z^{-1}}$$

(12-73)

With some algebraic manipulations, we obtain the inverse relationship

$$z^{-1} = \frac{1 - \dfrac{sT}{2}}{1 + \dfrac{sT}{2}} = \frac{2 - sT}{2 + sT}$$

(12-74a)

or

$$z = \frac{2 + sT}{2 - sT}$$

(12-74b)

We now examine the properties of the bilinear transformation mapping procedure with due regard given to the two conditions in (12-10). Let us first consider the imaginary axis of the s-plane. With $s = j\omega$, (12-74) becomes

$$z = \frac{2 + j\omega T}{2 - j\omega T}$$

$$= \frac{(2 + j\omega T)^2}{4 + (\omega T)^2} = \frac{4 - (\omega T)^2 + 4j\omega T}{4 + (\omega T)^2}$$

$$= \frac{\sqrt{[4 - (\omega T)^2]^2 + (4\omega T)^2}}{4 + (\omega T)^2} \exp\left\{ j \tan^{-1}\left[\frac{4\omega T}{4 - (\omega T)^2} \right] \right\}$$

(12-75a)

$$= \exp\left\{ j \tan^{-1}\left[\frac{4\omega T}{4 - (\omega T)^2} \right] \right\} \triangleq e^{j\theta(\omega)}$$

---

[19]It has been shown in Reference [13] that the bilinear transformation of (12-73) provides a one-to-one mapping between analog and digital systems.

where

$$\theta(\omega) = \tan^{-1}\left[\frac{4\omega T}{4 - (\omega T)^2}\right] \tag{12-75b}$$

From (12-75a), we observe that the imaginary axis of the s-plane is mapped to the unit circle (where $|z| = 1$) in the z-plane. In particular, a point $0 + j\omega$ in the s-plane is mapped to the corresponding point $\exp[j\theta(\omega)]$ in the z-plane. As in the case of (12-23b) and as illustrated by Fig. 12-7, the phase angle $\theta(\omega)$ varies from $-\pi$ to π as ω varies from $-\infty$ to ∞. Hence, we conclude that the imaginary axis of the s-plane is mapped *onto* the unit circle of the z-plane, as shown in Fig. 12-14. In other words, Condition 1 of (12-10)

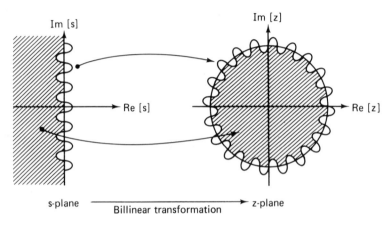

Fig. 12-14 Properties of the bilinear transformation mapping procedure.

is satisfied by the bilinear transformation of (12-73). To check Condition 2 of (12-10), we let

$$s = \sigma + j\omega \tag{12-76a}$$

where

$$\sigma < 0 \tag{12-76b}$$

Then (12-74) gives

$$z = \frac{2 + sT}{2 - sT}\bigg|_{s=\sigma+j\omega} = \frac{2 + \sigma T + j\omega T}{2 - \sigma T - j\omega T}$$

or

$$|z|^2 = \frac{(2 + \sigma T)^2 + (\omega T)^2}{(2 - \sigma T)^2 + (\omega T)^2} \tag{12-77}$$

If $\sigma < 0$, the denominator of (12-77) is always greater than its numerator. We conclude that

$$|z| < 1 \tag{12-78}$$

whenever Re $[s] = \sigma < 0$. Hence, Condition 2 of (12-10b) is also satisfied, as shown in Fig. 12-14. In addition, it can be shown that the bilinear transformation of (12-73) is a one-to-one onto function. This means that each point in the z-plane corresponds to exactly one point in the s-plane and *vice versa*. As a result of this uniqueness property, there is no aliasing effect in the bilinear mapping procedure.

The design procedure for digital filters under the bilinear transformation method involves the finding of an appropriate transfer function $\hat{H}(s)$ of an analog filter and the application of the bilinear transformation of (12-73) or (12-74) to obtain the transfer function $H(z)$ of the desired digital filter,

$$H(z) = \hat{H}(s)\big|_{s=(2/T)(1-z^{-1})/(1+z^{-1})} \tag{12-79}$$

where T is the sampling period. This transformation will preserve both the frequency characteristics and the stability properties of the analog filter. However, this does not mean that the frequency characteristics of the digital filters and that of the analog filter are identical. It simply means that the "shapes" are identical. For example, if the magnitude function of an analog filter is monotonically decreasing for $0 < \omega < \infty$, then its corresponding digital filter obtained by (12-79) will have a monotonically decreasing magnitude function from 0 to π; or if the magnitude function of an analog filter has k ups and downs for $0 < \omega < \infty$, then the magnitude function of the corresponding digital filter under (12-79) will also have k ups and downs.

Example 12-7   Suppose that an analog filter has a transfer function given by

$$\hat{H}(s) = \frac{K}{s - \hat{p}} \tag{12-80}$$

Find the transfer function of the corresponding digital filter by the bilinear transformation method.

Solution: By (12-79), the transfer function $H(z)$ of the desired digital filter is given by

$$H(z) = \hat{H}(s)\big|_{s=(2/T)(1-z^{-1})/(1+z^{-1})}$$

$$= \frac{K}{\dfrac{2}{T}\left(\dfrac{1-z^{-1}}{1+z^{-1}}\right) - \hat{p}} = \frac{KT(1+z^{-1})}{2(1-z^{-1}) - \hat{p}T(1+z^{-1})} \tag{12-81}$$

$$= \frac{KT(1+z^{-1})}{(2-\hat{p}T) - (2+\hat{p}T)z^{-1}} = \frac{\dfrac{KT}{2-\hat{p}T}(1+z^{-1})}{1 - \dfrac{2+\hat{p}T}{2-\hat{p}T}z^{-1}} \qquad\blacksquare$$

Figure 12-15 shows the magnitude function of the analog filter represented by (12-80), with $K = 1$ and $\hat{p} = -1$, and the magnitude function of the corresponding digital filter of (12-81), with $T = 1$ sec. These curves in Fig. 12-15 are considered to have the same "shape." If we imagine that the curve $|H(e^{j\theta})|$ versus θ is plotted with a *nonuniform* θ scale (if the scale for θ is com-

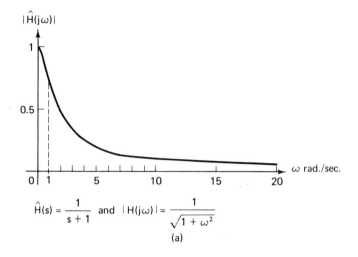

$$\hat{H}(s) = \frac{1}{s+1} \quad \text{and} \quad |H(j\omega)| = \frac{1}{\sqrt{1+\omega^2}}$$

(a)

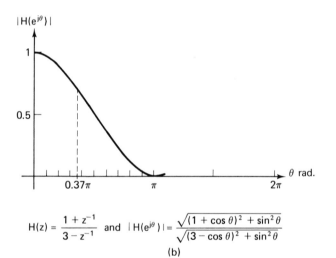

$$H(z) = \frac{1+z^{-1}}{3-z^{-1}} \quad \text{and} \quad |H(e^{j\theta})| = \frac{\sqrt{(1+\cos\theta)^2 + \sin^2\theta}}{\sqrt{(3-\cos\theta)^2 + \sin^2\theta}}$$

(b)

Fig. 12-15   Magnitude characteristics of an analog filter and its corresponding digital filter obtained by the bilinear transformation method.

pressed for $0 < \theta < 0.5\pi$ and is stretched for $0.5\pi < \theta < \pi$), then the curve in Fig. 12-15(b) will look more like the one in Fig. 12-15(a). This is because the relationship between the digital frequency variable θ and the analog frequency variable ω is nonlinear, as indicated by (12-75b). To fully examine this nonlinear relationship between θ and ω, we need to find an expression for ω in terms of θ. Theoretically, we can invert (12-75b) to obtain such an expression. On the other hand, we can also let $z = \exp[j\theta]$ and find the image of such a z point in the s-plane. Taking the latter route, (12-73) yields

$$s = \sigma + j\omega = \frac{2}{T}\left(\frac{1 - e^{-j\theta}}{1 + e^{-j\theta}}\right) = \frac{2}{T}\frac{\exp(j\theta/2) - \exp(-j\theta/2)}{\exp(j\theta/2) + \exp(-j\theta/2)}$$

$$= \frac{2}{T}\left[\frac{j\sin(\theta/2)}{\cos(\theta/2)}\right] = j\left(\frac{2}{T}\tan\frac{\theta}{2}\right) \tag{12-82}$$

By comparing the real and the imaginary parts of both sides of (12-82), we obtain

$$\sigma = 0 \tag{12-83a}$$

and

$$\omega = \frac{2}{T}\tan\frac{\theta}{2} \tag{12-83b}$$

Note that the relationships of (12-75b) and (12-83b) between the digital frequency variable θ and the analog frequency variable ω are the inverses of each other. These relationships are plotted in Fig. 12-16.

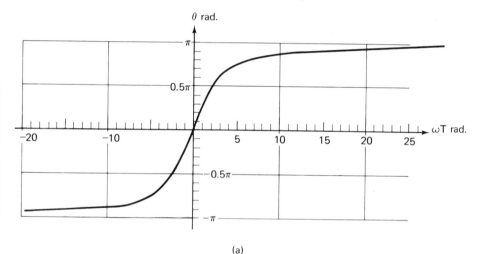

(a)

θ	ωT
0	0
0.1π	0.31677
0.2π	0.64984
0.3π	1.01905
0.4π	1.45309
0.5π	2
0.6π	2.75276
0.7π	3.92522
0.8π	6.15537
0.9π	12.62750
0.95π	25.41241
π	∞

(b)

Fig. 12-16 Relationships between θ and ω. (a) A plot. (b) A table of correspondence.

From Fig. 12-16, we observe that the sampling period T can be used to stretch or compress the curve along the ωT axis. Of course, given a sampling period T, the curve of θ versus ω will be fixed. If the frequency characteristics [the magnitude function $|\hat{H}(j\omega)|$ and/or the phase function $\hat{\phi}(\omega) \triangleq -\underline{/\hat{H}(j\omega)}$] of an analog filter are given, then (12-83b) can be used to obtain the frequency characteristics of the corresponding digital filter as

$$|H(e^{j\theta})| = |\hat{H}(j\omega)||_{\omega=(2/T)\,\tan\,(\theta/2)} \tag{12-84a}$$

and

$$\phi(\theta) \triangleq -\underline{/H(e^{j\theta})} = \hat{\phi}(\omega)|_{\omega=(2/T)\,\tan\,(\theta/2)} \tag{12-84b}$$

In view of (12-84), given any frequency characteristics of an analog filter, we can graphically construct the frequency characteristics of the digital filter by a quadruple diagram as shown in Fig. 12-17, where the arrows indicate the directions of construction lines. Specifically, a point $(\omega_1, \hat{x}_1)$ in the analog characteristic, where $\hat{x}_1$ can be either the magnitude $|\hat{H}(j\omega_1)|$ or the phase angle $\hat{\phi}(\omega_1) \triangleq -\underline{/\hat{H}(j\omega_1)}$ at the point ω_1, is reflected in two directions. First, the value of ω_1 is reflected down to the θ-ω curve to give its corresponding θ_1 value. The θ_1 value is reflected by the 45° line to provide the θ_1 value in the digital characteristic plot. Second, the value of $\hat{x}_1$ is reflected horizontally to provide the ordinate value x_1 for the digital characteristic plot, where x_1 can be either the magnitude value $|H(e^{j\theta_1})|$ or the phase value $\phi(\theta_1) \triangleq$

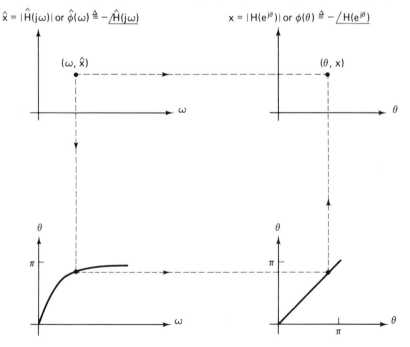

Fig. 12-17 Construction procedure to obtain frequency characteristics of a digital filter under bilinear transformation mapping.

$-\underline{/H(e^{j\theta_1})}$ depending on the nature of $\hat{x}_1$. By constructing a number of points $(\omega_1, \hat{x}_1), (\omega_2, \hat{x}_2), \ldots, (\omega_N, \hat{x}_N)$ to produce $(\theta_1, x_1), (\theta_2, x_2), \ldots, (\theta_N, x_N)$, we can join the points together and form the digital-frequency characteristic plots. Notice that this method will produce the digital frequency characteristics for $0 < \theta < \pi$. By the symmetry (even for magnitude functions and odd for phase functions) and periodicity properties of digital-frequency responses, we can construct the frequency characteristics for all θ.

Example 12-8   Given the magnitude curve of an analog filter in Fig. 12-18(a),[20] find the magnitude curve of its corresponding digital filter under a bilinear transformation.

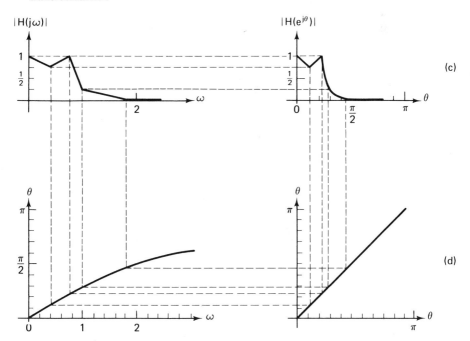

Fig. 12-18   Construction diagrams for Example 12-8.

Solution: Using the construction procedure of Fig. 12-17, we obtain the magnitude curve $|H(e^{j\theta})|$ versus θ in Fig. 12-18(d), where we have assumed $T = 1$ sec.   ∎

From Example 12-7, we observe that under the bilinear transformation, a pole location $\hat{p}$ of an analog filter is transformed to the pole location

$$p \triangleq \frac{2 + \hat{p}T}{2 - \hat{p}T} \qquad (12\text{-}85)$$

---

[20]Figure 12-18(a) is a piecewise linear approximation of a third-order Chebyshev low-pass filter.

of the digital filter. In addition, based on (12-81) of Example 12-7, if the transfer function $\hat{H}(s)$ of an analog filter is given in a partial fraction form

$$\hat{H}(s) = \sum_{k=1}^{N} \frac{\xi_i}{s - \hat{p}_i} \tag{12-86}$$

then the corresponding digital filter, under the bilinear transformation, will have a transfer function given by

$$H(z) = \sum_{k=1}^{N} \frac{\dfrac{\xi_i T}{2 - \hat{p}_i T}(1 + z^{-1})}{1 - \dfrac{2 + \hat{p}_i T}{2 - \hat{p}_i T} z^{-1}} \tag{12-87}$$

Example 12-9   Suppose that the desired filter has an analog transfer function given by

$$\hat{H}(s) = \frac{2s}{(s + 1)(s + 2)} \tag{12-88}$$

Find $H(z)$, the transfer function of the corresponding digital filter, by the bilinear transformation method.

Solution: Writing $\hat{H}(s)$ of (12-88) in partial fraction form, we obtain

$$\hat{H}(s) = \frac{-2}{s + 1} + \frac{4}{s + 2} \tag{12-89a}$$

where

$$\hat{p}_1 = -1 \quad \text{and} \quad \hat{p}_2 = -2 \tag{12-89b}$$

By (12-87), the desired digital transfer function $H(z)$ is given by

$$H(z) = \frac{\dfrac{-2T}{2 + T}(1 + z^{-1})}{1 - \dfrac{2 - T}{2 + T} z^{-1}} + \frac{\dfrac{4T}{2 + 2T}(1 + z^{-1})}{1 - \dfrac{2 - 2T}{2 + 2T} z^{-1}} \tag{12-90}$$

$$= \frac{2T}{(2 + T)(1 + T)} \frac{(1 - z^{-2})}{\left[1 - \dfrac{2 - T}{2 + T} z^{-1}\right]\left[1 - \dfrac{1 - T}{1 + T} z^{-1}\right]}$$

Observe that in Example 12-9, the number of finite zeros in the analog filter is different from that of the associated digital filter. This is the case in general for the bilinear transformation.

Example 12-10   Suppose that a low-pass digital filter is desired to satisfy the following conditions:

(a) The 3 dB cutoff point θ_C is at 0.5π rad.
(b) The passband magnitude is within 0.1 dB of its maximum value for $0 < \theta < 0.295\pi$.
(c) The stopband magnitude is at least 30 dB down for $0.75\pi < \theta < \pi$.
(d) A monotonically decreasing magnitude curve is desired.
(e) The sampling period $T = 100 \ \mu\text{sec}$.

Find the transfer function for the desired digital filter.

Solution: The first step is to translate the digital criteria to their analog equivalence. The specifications ask for a Butterworth filter where:

(a′) The cutoff frequency

$$\omega_C = \frac{2}{T} \tan \frac{\theta_C}{2} = \frac{2}{T} \tan \frac{0.5\pi}{2} = 20 \text{ K rad./sec.}$$

(b′) The passband magnitude is within 0.1 dB for

$$0 < \omega < \frac{2}{T} \tan \frac{0.295\pi}{2} \simeq 10 \text{ K rad./sec.}$$

(c′) The stopband magnitude is at least 30 dB down for

$$\omega > \frac{2}{T} \tan \frac{0.75\pi}{2} \simeq 50 \text{ K rad./sec.}$$

As in the case of Example 12-6, the transfer function of the desired analog filter is given by (12-67) as

$$\hat{H}(s) = -\frac{(1.84776 \times 10^4)s + (2.82844 \times 10^8)}{s^2 + 1.53074 \times 10^4)s + (4 \times 10^8)}$$
$$+ \frac{(1.84776 \times 10^4)s + (6.82844 \times 10^8)}{s^2 + 3.69552s + (4 \times 10^8)} \tag{12-91a}$$

where the poles are

$$\hat{p}_{1,2} = -0.76537 \times 10^4 \pm j1.84776 \times 10^4$$
$$\hat{p}_{3,4} = -1.84776 \times 10^4 \pm j0.76537 \times 10^4 \tag{12-91b}$$

To fit $\hat{H}(s)$ of (12-91) into the form of (12-86), we perform a further partial fraction expansion on $\hat{H}(s)$ to obtain

$$\hat{H}(s) = \frac{(0.92388 \times 10^4) + j(2.23044 \times 10^4)}{s + [(0.76537 \times 10^4) - j(1.84776 \times 10^4)]}$$
$$+ \frac{(0.92388 \times 10^4) - j(2.23044 \times 10^4)}{s + [(0.76537 \times 10^4) + j(1.84776 \times 10^4)]}$$
$$+ \frac{(0.92388 \times 10^4) + j(0.38268 \times 10^4)}{s + [(1.84776 \times 10^4) - j(0.76537 \times 10)^4]}$$
$$+ \frac{(0.92388 \times 10^4) - j(0.38268 \times 10^4)}{s + [(1.84776 \times 10^4) + j(0.76537 \times 10^4)]} \tag{12-92}$$

By (12-87), the transfer function of the desired digital filter, which satisfies conditions (a) through (e), is given by

$$H(z) = \frac{(-0.14161 + j0.71194)(1 + z^{-1})}{1 - j0.66818z^{-1}}$$
$$+ \frac{(-0.14161 - j0.71194)(1 + z^{-1})}{1 + j0.66818z^{-1}}$$
$$+ \frac{(0.21194 + j0.14161)(1 + z^{-1})}{1 - j0.19891z^{-1}}$$
$$+ \frac{(0.21194 - j0.14161)(1 + z^{-1})}{1 + j0.19891z^{-1}} \tag{12-93a}$$

where the pole locations of the digital filter are

$$p_{1,2} = \pm j0.66818$$
$$p_{3,4} = \pm j0.19891$$

(12-93b)

By combining the conjugate pairs in (12-93a), we obtain

$$H(z) = -\frac{(1 + z)(0.28322 + 0.95140z^{-1})}{1 + 0.44646z^{-2}}$$

$$-\frac{(1 + z)(0.42388 + 0.05634z^{-1})}{1 + 0.03957z^{-2}}$$ $\blacksquare$

(12-94)

The bilinear transformation provides a simple mapping procedure between analog and digital filters such that frequency characteristics are preserved under this transformation. This means that wideband sharp-cutoff analog filters can be mapped to wideband sharp-cutoff digital filters without aliasing effect. This is an advantage over the impulse invariant transformation. On the negative side, the nonlinear relationship between the digital frequency θ and the analog frequency ω under the bilinear transformation distorts the frequency characteristics of the analog filters. In addition, the impulse response is not preserved under this transformation.

12-1-4. Frequency Transformations

In the preceding subsections, we have discussed three methods for designing digital filters. All these methods involve first finding a suitable analog filter to meet the specifications. As discussed in Chapter 8, the design of an analog filter relies on first finding an appropriate low-pass prototype analog filter. A suitable analog frequency transformation is then used to transform this low-pass prototype to the desired analog filter. Finally, a mapping procedure is used to map this analog filter to a desired IIR digital filter that meets the specifications. This overall design procedure is summarized in Fig. 12-19(a).

From the previous subsections, we know that the mapping procedures of the impulse invariance transformation and Euler's methods will not give good digital filter designs unless the analog filter is essentially bandlimited to low frequencies. Because of the nonlinear relationship between the digital frequency θ and the analog frequency ω, bilinear transformation will produce best results only when the frequency characteristics of the analog filter are piecewise constant. This means that the design procedure of Fig. 12-19(a) will not yield good designs for high-pass, band-reject, and some bandpass filters. To eliminate these shortcomings, there is another approach to the design of IIR digital filters via analog filter design. This approach is outlined in Fig. 12-19(b). In this approach, the mapping procedure will always deal with a normalized low-pass prototype. Hence, the three mapping procedures discussed in the previous subsections will yield good results. Basically, this

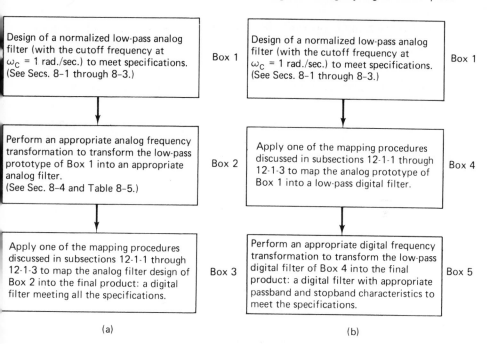

Design of a normalized low-pass analog filter (with the cutoff frequency at $\omega_C = 1$ rad./sec.) to meet specifications. (See Secs. 8-1 through 8-3.)	Box 1
Perform an appropriate analog frequency transformation to transform the low-pass prototype of Box 1 into an appropriate analog filter. (See Sec. 8-4 and Table 8-5.)	Box 2
Apply one of the mapping procedures discussed in subsections 12-1-1 through 12-1-3 to map the analog filter design of Box 2 into the final product: a digital filter meeting all the specifications.	Box 3

(a)

Design of a normalized low-pass analog filter (with the cutoff frequency at $\omega_C = 1$ rad./sec.) to meet specifications. (See Secs. 8-1 through 8-3.)	Box 1
Apply one of the mapping procedures discussed in subsections 12-1-1 through 12-1-3 to map the analog prototype of Box 1 into a low-pass digital filter.	Box 4
Perform an appropriate digital frequency transformation to transform the low-pass digital filter of Box 4 into the final product: a digital filter with appropriate passband and stopband characteristics to meet the specifications.	Box 5

(b)

Fig. 12-19 Overall design procedures for digital filters.

approach involves finding an appropriate normalized low-pass analog filter. This analog prototype will be mapped into a low-pass digital filter prototype. Finally, a *digital* frequency transformation is used to transform the low-pass digital prototype into the final design, a digital filter with appropriate pass- and stopband characteristics to meet the specifications. In this subsection, we discuss the various digital frequency transformations needed to complete the design tool required in Fig. 12-19(b).

For all the digital frequency transformations to be discussed in this sub-section, we assume that the low-pass digital filter prototype has a cutoff frequency at θ_p. For example, consider the transfer function of the second-order normalized low-pass Butterworth analog filter

$$\hat{H}(s) = \frac{1}{s^2 + \sqrt{2}\,s + 1} \tag{12-95a}$$

where the poles are

$$\hat{p}_{1,2} = -\frac{1}{\sqrt{2}} \pm j\frac{1}{\sqrt{2}} \tag{12-95b}$$

By (12-56), the impulse invariance transformation maps the analog filter design of (12-95) into a digital filter with the transfer function given by

$$H_p(z) = \frac{\sqrt{2}\,z^{-1} \exp(-T/\sqrt{2}) \sin(T/\sqrt{2})}{1 - 2z^{-1} \exp(-T/\sqrt{2}) \cos(T/\sqrt{2}) + z^{-2} \exp(-\sqrt{2}\,T)} \tag{12-96}$$

where T is the sampling period. Because the cutoff frequency ω_C of the normalized low-pass Butterworth filter is at

$$\omega_C = 1 \text{ rad./sec.} \tag{12-97}$$

the analog low-pass prototype is effectively bandlimited to, say, $\omega_0/2 = 6$ rad./sec.,

$$|\hat{H}(j\omega)| \simeq 0 \quad \text{for} \quad |\omega| > \frac{\omega_0}{2} = 6 \tag{12-98}$$

as shown in Fig. 12-20(a). Any sampling period T satisfying the Nyquist condition of

$$\omega_0 T \leq 2\pi \tag{12-99}$$

will not cause much aliasing. For simplicity, we let $T = 0.5$ sec. Clearly,

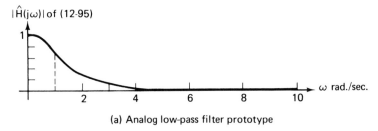

(a) Analog low-pass filter prototype

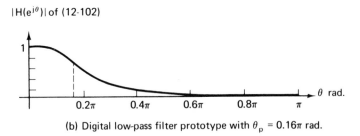

(b) Digital low-pass filter prototype with $\theta_p = 0.16\pi$ rad.

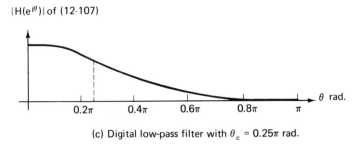

(c) Digital low-pass filter with $\theta_c = 0.25\pi$ rad.

Fig. 12-20 Illustrations of digital frequency transformations.

$|H(e^{i\theta})|$ of (12-112)

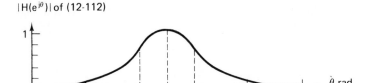

(d) Digital band pass filter with $\theta_0 = 0.5\pi$, $\theta_u = 0.6\pi$ and $\theta_\ell = 0.4\pi$ rad.

$|H(e^{i\theta})|$ of (12-116)

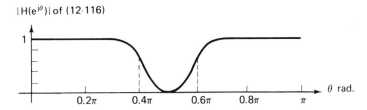

(e) Digital band reject filter with $\theta_0 = 0.5\pi$, $\theta_u = 0.6\pi$ and $\theta_\ell = 0.4\pi$ rad.

$|H(e^{i\theta})|$ of (12-120)

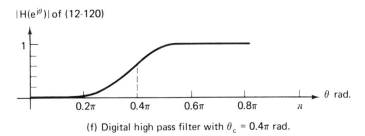

(f) Digital high pass filter with $\theta_c = 0.4\pi$ rad.

Fig. 12-20 (Continued)

$T = 0.5$ sec. satisfies (12-99). Hence, (12-96) becomes

$$H_p(z) = \frac{0.344z^{-1}}{1 - 1.318z^{-1} + 0.493z^{-2}} \tag{12-100}$$

Notice that the digital filter of (12-100) has a "dc" gain of[21]

$$|H_p(e^{j0})| = \frac{0.344}{1 - 1.318 + 0.493}$$

$$= 1.966 \simeq \frac{1}{T}|\hat{H}(j0)| = \frac{1}{T} = 2 \tag{12-101}$$

---

[21]The small discrepancy is due partly to the roundoff arithmetic errors in calculating the coefficients of (12-100) and partly due to the small but unavoidable aliasing.

To get rid of this undesired gain due to the sampling period, the digital filter of (12-100) is multiplied by the value of the sampling period. Hence, the transfer function of the low-pass digital filter prototype is given by[22]

$$H_p(z) = \frac{0.175z^{-1}}{1 - 1.318z^{-1} + 0.493z^{-2}} \tag{12-102}$$

Because T is smaller than the Nyquist sampling period, aliasing is almost nonexistent in this case. Hence, by (12-60), the digital frequency θ and the analog frequency ω are effectively related by

$$\theta = \omega T \tag{12-103}$$

This means that θ_p, the cutoff frequency of the digital filter prototype of (12-102), is given by

$$\theta_p = \omega_c T = 0.5 = 0.16\pi \tag{12-104}$$

We use the low-pass digital filter prototype of (12-102) to illustrate the effect of various digital frequency transformations in this subsection. For reference purposes, the magnitude characteristics of the low-pass digital filter prototype are shown in Fig. 12-20(b).

12-1-4-1. Low-Pass to Low-Pass Transformation. Suppose that we like to obtain a low-pass digital filter with a cutoff frequency at θ_C from a low-pass prototype with a cutoff frequency at θ_p. Then the digital frequency transformation needed is given by

$$z^{-1} \longrightarrow \frac{z^{-1} - \alpha}{1 - \alpha z^{-1}} \tag{12-105a}$$

where

$$\alpha \triangleq \frac{\sin[(\theta_p - \theta_C)/2]}{\sin[(\theta_p + \theta_C)/2]} \tag{12-105b}$$

Example 12-11   Suppose that we have to design a second-order low-pass Butterworth filter with a cutoff frequency at 0.25π rad. Find the transfer function of the desired digital filter based on (12-102).

Solution: By (12-105), the parameter α is given by

$$\alpha = \frac{\sin[(0.16\pi - 0.25\pi)/2]}{\sin[(0.16\pi + 0.25\pi)/2]} = -0.235 \tag{12-106}$$

---

[22]Actually the transfer function of (12-102) is obtained by dividing the transfer function of (12-100) with the "dc" gain of (12-101) to compensate for the computation roundoff errors that already occurred and for the small distortion due to aliasing.

and the desired digital filter has a transfer function

$$H(z) = H_p\left[\left(\frac{z^{-1} + 0.235}{1 + 0.235z^{-1}}\right)^{-1}\right]$$

$$= \frac{0.175\left(\dfrac{z^{-1} + 0.235}{1 + 0.235z^{-1}}\right)}{1 - 1.318\left(\dfrac{z^{-1} + 0.235}{1 + 0.235z^{-1}}\right) + 0.493\left(\dfrac{z^{-1} + 0.235}{1 + 0.235z^{-1}}\right)^2}$$

$$= \frac{0.175(z^{-1} + 0.235)(1 + 0.235z^{-1})}{(1 + 0.225z^{-1})^2 - 1.318(z^{-1} + 0.235)(1 + 0.235z^{-1}) + 0.493(z^{-1} + 0.235)^2}$$

$$= \frac{0.041 + 0.185z^{-1} + 0.041z^{-2}}{0.718 - 0.691z^{-1} + 0.239z^{-2}} \tag{12-107}$$

As in (12-102), the "dc" gain of the digital filter of (12-107) is[23]

$$|H(e^{j0})| = \frac{0.041 + 0.185 + 0.041}{0.718 - 0.691 + 0.239}$$

$$= \frac{0.267}{0.266} = 1.003 \simeq 1 \tag{12-108}$$

The magnitude function of (12-107) is plotted in Fig. 12-20(c). ∎

12-1-4-2. Low-Pass to Bandpass Transformation. Suppose that we have to convert a low-pass digital filter prototype with a cutoff frequency at θ_p to a bandpass filter with center frequency θ_0, upper passband frequency limit θ_u, and lower passband frequency limit θ_l, where θ_0, θ_u, and θ_l are constrained by[24]

$$\cos\theta_0 = \frac{\cos[(\theta_u + \theta_l)/2]}{\cos[(\theta_u - \theta_l)/2]} \tag{12-109}$$

The digital frequency transformation needed is given by

$$z^{-1} \longrightarrow -\frac{z^{-2} - \left(\dfrac{2\alpha\beta}{\beta + 1}\right)z^{-1} + \left(\dfrac{\beta - 1}{\beta + 1}\right)}{\left(\dfrac{\beta - 1}{\beta + 1}\right)z^{-2} - \left(\dfrac{2\alpha\beta}{\beta + 1}\right)z^{-1} + 1} \tag{12-110a}$$

where

$$\alpha = \cos\theta_0 \tag{12-110b}$$

$$\beta = \cot[(\theta_u - \theta_l)/2]\tan(\theta_p/2) \tag{12-110c}$$

---

[23]Notice that the "dc" gain should be exactly 1. The small discrepancy is due to the roundoff errors in computation.

[24]This means that two of the three parameters θ_0, θ_u, and θ_l are free and the third one is not.

Example 12-12 Suppose that we have to convert the low-pass filter of (12-102) to a bandpass filter with center frequency $\theta_0 = 0.5\pi$, $\theta_u = 0.6\pi$, and $\theta_l = 0.4\pi$.[25] Find the transfer function of the desired digital filter.

Solution: Before we proceed, let us calculate the parameters needed for the frequency transformation

$$\alpha = \cos 0.5\pi = 0 \tag{12-111a}$$

$$\beta = (\cot 0.1\pi)(\tan 0.08\pi) = 0.786 \tag{12-111b}$$

$$\frac{\beta - 1}{\beta + 1} = -0.120 \tag{12-111c}$$

$$\frac{2\alpha\beta}{\beta + 1} = 0 \tag{12-111d}$$

Substituting (12-111) and (12-110) into (12-102), we obtain the transfer function of the desired digital filter[26]

$$H(z) = H_p\left[\left(-\frac{z^{-2} - 0.12}{-0.12z^{-2} + 1}\right)^{-1}\right]$$

$$= \frac{-0.175\left(\dfrac{z^{-2} - 0.12}{-0.12z^{-2} + 1}\right)}{1 + 1.318\left(\dfrac{z^{-2} - 0.12}{-0.12z^{-2} + 1}\right) + 0.493\left(\dfrac{z^{-2} - 0.12}{-0.12z^{-2} + 1}\right)^2}$$

$$= \frac{-0.175(z^{-2} - 0.12)(-0.12z^{-2} + 1)}{(-0.12z^{-2} + 1)^2 + 1.318(z^{-2} - 0.12)(-0.12z^{-2} + 1) + 0.493(z^{-2} - 0.12)^2}$$

$$= \frac{0.021z^{-4} - 0.178z^{-2} + 0.021}{0.349z^{-4} + 0.979z^{-2} + 0.849} \tag{12-112}$$

The midband gain of the resulting digital filter can be obtained by substituting

$$z = \exp[j0.5\pi] = j$$

into (12-112) as

$$H(e^{j0.5\pi}) = \frac{0.220}{0.219} = 1.004 \simeq 1$$

The magnitude function of the desired bandpass filter of (12-112) is shown in Fig. 12-20(d). ∎

12-1-4-3. Low-Pass to Band-Reject Transformation. Suppose that we have to transform a low-pass digital filter prototype with a cutoff frequency at θ_p to a band-reject filter with θ_0 as the center frequency of the rejection band, and with θ_u and θ_l as the upper and lower frequency limits of the rejection band, where θ_0, θ_u, and θ_l are constrained by

$$\cos \theta_0 = \frac{\cos[(\theta_u - \theta_l)/2]}{\cos[(\theta_u + \theta_l)/2]} \tag{12-113}$$

---

[25]Clearly, (12-109) is satisfied here.

[26]In general, the transfer function $H(z)$ of a bandpass filter is not an even rational function as in (12-112).

The digital frequency transformation required is given by

$$z^{-1} \longrightarrow \frac{z^{-2} - \left(\dfrac{2\alpha}{1 + \beta}\right)z^{-1} + \left(\dfrac{1 - \beta}{1 + \beta}\right)}{\left(\dfrac{1 - \beta}{1 + \beta}\right)z^{-2} - \left(\dfrac{2\alpha}{1 + \beta}\right)z^{-1} + 1} \qquad \text{(12-114a)}$$

where

$$\alpha \triangleq \cos \theta_0 \qquad \text{(12-114b)}$$

$$\beta \triangleq \tan [(\theta_u - \theta_l)/2] \tan (\theta_p/2) \qquad \text{(12-114c)}$$

Example 12-13 Suppose that we have to convert the low-pass digital filter prototype of (12-102) to a band-reject filter with $\theta_0 = 0.5\pi$ rad., $\theta_u = 0.6\pi$ rad., and $\theta_l = 0.4\pi$ rad.[27] Find the transfer function of the desired digital filter.

Solution: From (12-114), we have

$$\alpha = \cos 0.5\pi = 0 \qquad \text{(12-115a)}$$

$$\beta = (\tan 0.1\pi)(\tan 0.08\pi) = 0.083 \qquad \text{(12-115b)}$$

$$\frac{2\alpha}{1 + \beta} = 0 \qquad \text{(12-115c)}$$

$$\frac{1 - \beta}{1 + \beta} = 0.847 \qquad \text{(12-115d)}$$

Substituting (12-114) and (12-115) into (12-102), the desired transfer function is given by

$$H(z)$$

$$= H_p\left[\left(\frac{z^{-2} + 0.847}{0.847z^{-2} + 1}\right)^{-1}\right]$$

$$= \frac{0.175\dfrac{z^{-2} + 0.847}{0.847z^{-2} + 1}}{1 - 1.318\left(\dfrac{z^{-2} + 0.847}{0.847z^{-2} + 1}\right) + 0.493\left(\dfrac{z^{-2} + 0.847}{0.847z^{-2} + 1}\right)^2} \qquad \text{(12-116)}$$

$$= \frac{0.175(z^{-2} + 0.847)(0.847z^{-2} + 1)}{(0.847z^{-2} + 1)^2 - 1.318\,(z^{-2} + 0.847)(0.847z^{-2} + 1) + 0.493(z^{-2} + 0.847)^2}$$

$$= \frac{0.148z^{-4} + 0.300z^{-2} + 0.148}{0.094z^{-4} + 0.266z^{-2} + 0.237}$$

Notice that the "dc" gain of this band-reject filter is given by

$$H(e^{j0}) = \frac{0.596}{0.597} = 0.998 \simeq 1 \qquad \text{(12-117)}$$

The small error is due to computation error. The magnitude characteristic of the band-reject filter is shown in Fig. 12-20(e). ∎

12-1-4-4. Low-Pass to High-Pass Transformation. The digital frequency transformation needed to convert a low-pass digital filter with cutoff fre-

---

[27]Observe that (12-113) is satisfied here.

quency θ_p to a high-pass digital filter with a cutoff frequency at θ_c is given by

$$z^{-1} \longrightarrow -\frac{z^{-1} + \alpha}{1 + \alpha z^{-1}} \qquad (12\text{-}118a)$$

where

$$\alpha \triangleq -\frac{\cos\left[(\theta_p - \theta_c)/2\right]}{\cos\left[(\theta_p + \theta_c)/2\right]} \qquad (12\text{-}118b)$$

Example 12-14 Suppose that we have to convert the low-pass digital filter prototype of (12-102) into a high-pass digital filter with cutoff frequency at $\theta_c = 0.4\pi$ rad. Find the desired transfer function.

Solution: From (12-118b), we obtain

$$\alpha = -\frac{\cos 0.12\pi}{\cos 0.28\pi} = -0.687 \qquad (12\text{-}119)$$

Substituting (12-118) and (12-119) into (12-102), the desired transfer function is found to be

$$H(z)$$

$$= H_p\left[\left(-\frac{z^{-1} - 0.687}{1 - 0.687z^{-1}}\right)^{-1}\right]$$

$$= \frac{-0.175\left(\dfrac{z^{-1} - 0.687}{1 - 0.687z^{-1}}\right)}{1 + 1.318\left(\dfrac{z^{-1} - 0.687}{1 - 0.687z^{-1}}\right) + 0.493\left(\dfrac{z^{-1} - 0.687}{1 - 0.687z^{-1}}\right)^2} \qquad (12\text{-}120)$$

$$= \frac{-0.175(z^{-1} - 0.687)(1 - 0.687z^{-1})}{(1 - 0.687z^{-1})^2 + 1.318(z^{-1} - 0.687)(1 - 0.687z^{-1}) + 0.493(z^{-1} - 0.687)^2}$$

$$= \frac{0.120z^{-2} - 0.258z^{-1} + 0.120}{0.059z^{-2} - 0.111z^{-1} + 0.327}$$

Observe that the "dc" gain and the high-frequency gain of the resulting digital filter are given, respectively, by

$$H(e^{j0}) = -\frac{0.018}{0.275} = -0.065 \qquad (12\text{-}121a)$$

and

$$H(e^{j\pi}) = \frac{0.498}{0.497} = 1.002 \simeq 1 \qquad (12\text{-}121b)$$

Ideally, $H(e^{j0})$ should be zero and $H(e^{j\pi})$ should be unity. Observe that the nonideal result in (12-120) is primarily due to computation errors that occurred at (12-102) rather than to aliasing. This is because the impulse invariance method was applied to a low-pass filter with effective bandlimited characteristics rather than to a high-pass filter. The resulting high-pass filter was obtained by digital frequency transformation. The magnitude curve of this high-pass filter is shown in Fig. 12-20(f). ∎

To close this subsection, we would like to point out that the overall digital filter design procedure of Fig. 12-19(b) can be used to design high-pass, bandpass, and band-reject filters as well as low-pass filters. There is not much aliasing distortion in the final design. However, this procedure requires more accurate coefficient representations and needs more significant digits in computation leading to higher cost than their corresponding counterparts in the design procedure of Fig. 12-19(a). This economic drawback often overshadows some of the technical advantages this method has over the procedure presented in Fig. 12-19(a).

12-1-5. Design of All-pass Digital Filters

In all the design procedures discussed so far in Sec. 12-1, we have avoided discussing all-pass digital filters. This is partly because all-pass filters operate quite differently and partly because it is extremely difficult to work out the phase characteristics of all-pass digital filters. In this subsection, we discuss some basic characteristics of all-pass digital filters.

An all-pass digital filter is an IIR digital filter with a constant magnitude function for all digital frequency values. The necessary condition for a transfer function $H(z)$ to represent an all-pass filter is that for every pole $p_k = r_k \exp(j\theta_k)$, there is a corresponding zero $z_k = (1/r_k) \exp(j\theta_k)$. If $\theta_k \neq 0$ or π, then the pole p_k and zero z_k will occur in conjugate pairs.

A typical first-order section of an all-pass digital filter has a transfer function

$$H_1(z) = \frac{z^{-1} - a}{1 - az^{-1}} \tag{12-122}$$

where a is real. The all-pass filter of (12-122) has a pole at $z = a$ and a zero at $z = 1/a$, as shown in Fig. 12-21(a). To be stable, we must have

$$|a| < 1 \tag{12-123}$$

To see that (12-122) is indeed an all-pass filter, we calculate its magnitude function as

$$
\begin{aligned}
|H_1(e^{j\theta})|^2 &= \left| \frac{e^{-j\theta} - a}{1 - ae^{-j\theta}} \right|^2 \\
&= \left| \frac{\cos\theta - a - j\sin\theta}{1 - a\cos\theta + aj\sin\theta} \right|^2 \\
&= \frac{(\cos\theta - a)^2 + \sin^2\theta}{(1 - a\cos\theta)^2 + (a\sin\theta)^2} \\
&= \frac{\cos^2\theta - 2a\cos\theta + a^2 + \sin^2\theta}{1 - 2a\cos\theta + a^2\cos^2\theta + a^2\sin^2\theta} \\
&= \frac{1 - 2a\cos\theta + a^2}{1 - 2a\cos\theta + a^2} = 1
\end{aligned}
\tag{12-124}
$$

which means that the filter defined by (12-122) is indeed an all-pass filter.

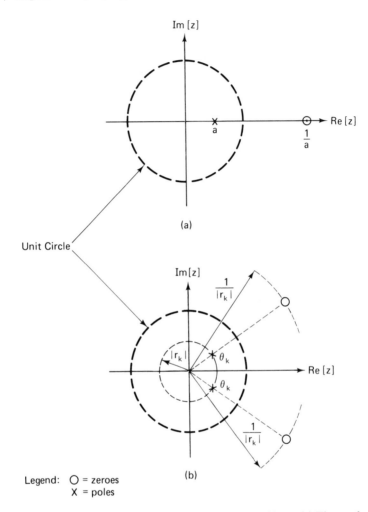

Legend: ○ = zeroes
        X = poles

Fig. 12-21   Pole-zero patterns of all-pass digital filters. (a) First-order case. (b) Second-order case.

A typical second-order section of an all-pass filter has a transfer function given by[28]

$$H_2(z) = \frac{1 - (2/r_k)\cos\theta_k z^{-1} + (1/r_k^2)z^{-2}}{1 - 2r_k\cos\theta_k z^{-1} + r_k^2 z^{-2}}$$

$$= \frac{[1 - (1/r_k)z^{-1}\exp(j\theta_k)][1 - (1/r_k)z^{-1}\exp(-j\theta_k)]}{[1 - r_k z^{-1}\exp(j\theta_k)][1 - r_k z^{-1}\exp(-j\theta_k)]} \tag{12-125a}$$

where the poles are at

$$p_{1,2} = r_k \exp(\pm j\theta_k) \tag{12-125b}$$

---

[28]Here, we assume that $\theta_k \neq l\pi$ for any integer l.

and the zeros are at

$$z_{1,2} = (1/r_k) \exp(\pm j\theta_k) \tag{12-125c}$$

as shown in Fig. 12-21(b). For the filter to be stable, we require that

$$|r_k| < 1 \tag{12-126}$$

If we let $z = e^{j\theta}$, we find the magnitude function of (12-125) to be

$$|H_2(e^{j\theta})|^2 = \left| \frac{\exp(j\theta) - (1/r_k)\exp(j\theta_k)}{\exp(j\theta) - r_k\exp(j\theta_k)} \right|^2 \left| \frac{\exp(j\theta) - (1/r_k)\exp(-j\theta_k)}{\exp(j\theta) - r_k\exp(-j\theta_k)} \right|^2 \tag{12-127}$$

Let us consider the first term in the expression for $|H_2(e^{j\theta})|^2$.

$$
\begin{aligned}
& \left| \frac{\exp(j\theta) - (1/r_k)\exp(j\theta_k)}{\exp(j\theta) - r_k\exp(j\theta_k)} \right|^2 \\
&= \frac{|[\cos\theta - (1/r_k)\cos\theta_k] + j[\sin\theta - (1/r_k)\sin\theta_k]|^2}{|(\cos\theta - r_k\cos\theta_k) + j(\sin\theta - r_k\sin\theta_k)|^2} \\
&= \frac{[\cos\theta - (1/r_k)\cos\theta_k]^2 + [\sin\theta - (1/r_k)\sin\theta_k]^2}{(\cos\theta - r_k\cos\theta_k)^2 + (\sin\theta - r_k\sin\theta_k)^2} \\
&= \frac{1 + (1/r_k^2) - (2/r_k)\cos(\theta - \theta_k)}{1 + r_k^2 - 2r_k\cos(\theta - \theta_k)} = r_k^{-2}
\end{aligned}
\tag{12-128a}
$$

In a similar manner, we can show that

$$\left| \frac{\exp(j\theta) - (1/r_k)\exp(-j\theta_k)}{\exp(j\theta) - r_k\exp(-j\theta_k)} \right|^2 = r_k^{-2} \tag{12-128b}$$

Substituting (12-128) into (12-127), we have

$$|H_2(e^{j\theta})|^2 = r_k^{-4} = \text{constant for all } \theta \tag{12-129}$$

This implies that the digital filter of (12-125) is indeed an all-pass digital filter.

One important property concerning all-pass filters is that a digital filter, obtained by a cascade connection of all-pass filter sections, is an all-pass filter. Mathematically speaking, this means that if $H_1(z), H_2(z), \ldots, H_N(z)$ are transfer functions representing all-pass filters, then the transfer function

$$H(z) \triangleq H_1(z)H_2(z)\ldots H_N(z) \tag{12-130}$$

represents an all-pass filter.

Example 12-15   Show that the digital filter represented by

$$H(z) = \left(\frac{z^{-1} - a}{1 - az^{-1}} \right)\left(\frac{r_k^2 - 2r_k z^{-1}\cos\theta_k + z^{-2}}{1 - 2r_k z^{-1}\cos\theta + r_k^2 z^{-2}} \right) \tag{12-131}$$

is an all-pass filter.

Solution: Observe that

$$H(z) = H_1(z)H_2(z)r_k^2 \tag{12-132}$$

where $H_1(z)$ is given by (12-122) and $H_2(z)$ by (12-125). By (12-124) and (12-129), the magnitude function

$$|H(e^{j\theta})|^2 = |H_1(e^{j\theta})|^2 |H_2(e^{j\theta})|^2 r_k^4$$

is given by

$$|H(e^{j\theta})|^2 = (1)(r_k^{-4})(r_k^4) = 1 \quad \text{for all } \theta \tag{12-133}$$

Hence (12-131) represents an all-pass digital filter. ∎

12-2 DESIGN OF FIR DIGITAL FILTERS

The transfer function of an FIR digital filter is in the form of

$$H(z) = \sum_{n=0}^{N-1} h(n)z^{-n} \tag{12-134}$$

where the impulse response is of length N or has a duration of N samples. If the impulse response of an FIR digital filter satisfies

$$h(n) = h(N - 1 - n) \tag{12-135}$$

for $n = 0, 1, \ldots, (N/2) - 1$ if N is even, and for $n = 0, 1, \ldots, (N - 1)/2$ if N is odd, then it can be shown that the digital filter will have a linear phase characteristic. Indeed, when N is odd, (12-134) and (12-135) give

$$
\begin{aligned}
H(e^{j\theta}) &= \sum_{n=0}^{N-1} h(n)e^{-jn\theta} \\
&= \sum_{n=0}^{(N-3)/2} [h(n)e^{-jn\theta} + h(N-1-n)e^{-j(N-1-n)\theta}] + h\left(\frac{N-1}{2}\right)e^{-j[(N-1)/2]\theta} \\
&= \sum_{n=0}^{(N-3)/2} h(n)[e^{-jn\theta} + e^{-j(N-1-n)\theta}] + h\left(\frac{N-1}{2}\right)e^{-j[(N-1)/2]\theta} \quad \text{(12-136a)} \\
&= e^{-j[(N-1)/2]\theta}\left\{h\left(\frac{N-1}{2}\right) + \sum_{n=0}^{(N-3)/2} h(n)[e^{-j\{n-[(N-1)/2]\}\theta} + e^{j\{n-[(N-1)/2]\}\theta}]\right\} \\
&= e^{-j[(N-1)/2]\theta}\left\{h\left(\frac{N-1}{2}\right) + \sum_{n=0}^{(N-3)/2} 2h(n)\cos\left[\left(n - \frac{N-1}{2}\right)\theta\right]\right\}
\end{aligned}
$$

In the same manner, when N is even, the frequency response is given by

$$H(e^{j\theta}) = e^{-j[(N-1)/2]\theta}\left\{\sum_{n=0}^{(N/2)-1} 2h(n)\cos\left[\left(n - \frac{N-1}{2}\right)\theta\right]\right\} \tag{12-136b}$$

In both cases, the phase $\phi(\theta)$ of the FIR digital filter is given by

$$\phi(\theta) = -\underline{/H(e^{j\theta})} = \frac{N-1}{2}\theta \tag{12-137}$$

which is linear for $-\pi < \theta \leq \pi$. The group delay function

$$\tau(\theta) \triangleq \frac{d\phi(\theta)}{d\theta} = \frac{N-1}{2} \tag{12-138}$$

is constant for $-\pi < \theta \leq \pi$.

In most situations, it is the demand of a linear phase or a constant group delay requirement that prompts one to use FIR digital filters. Because of the constraint imposed by (12-135), the zero locations of a linear phase FIR digital filter are restricted to meet certain symmetry requirements. To see this, we write (12-134) as

$$H(z) = \sum_{n=0}^{N-1} h(n)z^{-n}$$

$$= z^{-(N-1)} \sum_{n=0}^{N-1} h(n)z^{(N-n-1)} \tag{12-139}$$

Let us define a new independent variable

$$m \triangleq N - n - 1 \tag{12-140}$$

With (12-135), (12-139) can be written in terms of the new dummy variable m as

$$H(z) = z^{-(N-1)} \sum_{m=0}^{N-1} h(N-m-1)z^{m}$$

$$= z^{-(N-1)} \sum_{m=0}^{N-1} h(m)(z^{-1})^{-m} \tag{12-141}$$

$$= z^{-(N-1)} H(z^{-1})$$

This means that the zeros of $H(z)$ are the zeros of $H(z^{-1})$ except, perhaps, for the "phantom" zeros at the origin. Based on this observation, the zeros of a linear phase FIR digital filter have the following symmetry properties:

(a) If $z_i = a$ is a real zero of $H(z)$, then $z_i^{-1} = a^{-1}$ is also a zero of $H(z)$.
(b) If $z_i = \exp(j\theta_i)$ is a zero of $H(z)$, where $\theta_i \neq 0$ and $\theta_i \neq \pi$, then $z_i^{-1} = \overline{z}_i = \exp(-j\theta_i)$ is also a zero of $H(z)$.
(c) If $z_i = r_i \exp(j\theta_i)$ is a zero of $H(z)$, where $r_i \neq 1$, $\theta_i \neq 0$, and $\theta_i \neq \pi$, then $\overline{z}_i = r_i \exp(-j\theta_i)$, $z_i^{-1} = (1/r_i)\exp(-j\theta_i)$ and $\overline{z_i^{-1}} = (1/r_i)\exp(j\theta_i)$ are also zeros of $H(z)$.

These symmetric properties of zero locations are illustrated in Fig. 12-22. As a consequence, the transfer function of a linear phase FIR digital filter can be written as a product of elementary factors as

$$H(z) = \prod_{i=1}^{K} H_i(z) \tag{12-142}$$

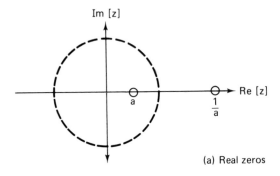

(a) Real zeros

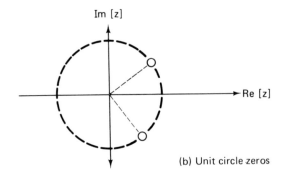

(b) Unit circle zeros

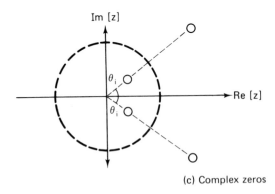

(c) Complex zeros

Fig. 12-22 Symmetry properties of zero locations of linear phase FIR digital filters.

where each $H_i(z)$ can take on one of the following three formats:

$$H_A(z) = (1 - az^{-1})\left[1 - \left(\frac{1}{a}\right)z^{-1}\right]$$

$$= 1 - \left(a + \frac{1}{a}\right)z^{-1} + z^{-2}$$

(12-143a)

$$H_B(z) = (1 - e^{j\theta_i}z^{-1})(1 - e^{-j\theta_i}z^{-1})$$
$$= 1 - (2\cos\theta_i)z^{-1} + z^{-2}$$

(12-143b)

$$H_C(z) = [1 - r_i e^{j\theta_i}z^{-1}][1 - r_i e^{-j\theta_i}z^{-1}][1 - (1/r_i)e^{j\theta_i}z^{-1}][1 - (1/r_i)e^{-j\theta_i}z^{-1}]$$

$$= 1 - 2\left[\frac{r_i^2 + 1}{r_i}\right](\cos\theta_i)z^{-1} + \left[r_i^2 + \frac{1}{r_i^2} + 4\cos\theta_i\right]z^{-2}$$

$$- 2\left[\frac{r_i^2 + 1}{r_i}\right](\cos\theta_i)z^{-3} + z^{-4}$$

(12-143c)

12-2-1. Frequency Sampling Method

As discussed in Sec. 11-4, an FIR digital filter characterized by (12-134) has an equivalent DFT representation

$$\tilde{H}(k) = \sum_{n=0}^{N-1} h(n) \exp\left[-\frac{j2\pi nk}{N}\right]$$

(12-144)

where $\tilde{H}(k)$ is actually the uniformly spaced N-point sample sequence of the frequency response of the digital filter. As a consequence, the impulse response sequence $h(n)$ and the transfer function $H(z)$ of the FIR digital filter, in terms of the DFT of (12-144), are given by

$$h(n) = \frac{1}{N} \sum_{k=0}^{N-1} \tilde{H}(k) \exp\left[\frac{j2\pi nk}{N}\right]$$

(12-145)

and

$$H(z) = \frac{1}{N} \sum_{k=0}^{N-1} \tilde{H}(k) \frac{1 - z^{-N}}{1 - z^{-1}\exp[j2\pi k/N]}$$

(12-146)

Equation (12-146) is a key to the design of an FIR digital filter.

Suppose that a desired frequency response $H_d(e^{j\theta})$ is given for $-\pi \leq \theta \leq \pi$. This means that $H_d(e^{j\theta})$ is defined for all θ. A design procedure is to let $\tilde{H}(k)$ be the uniformly spaced N-point sample sequence of the desired frequency response,

$$\tilde{H}(k) \triangleq H_d(e^{j\theta})|_{\theta=2\pi k/N}$$

(12-147)

where $k = 0, 1, 2, \ldots, N - 1$. Using the raw data of (12-147), we can obtain an appropriate FIR transfer function by (12-146). This procedure ensures that the resulting frequency response coincides with the desired characteristics at the sampled points

$$\theta = \frac{2\pi k}{N} \quad \text{for } k = 0, 1, 2, \ldots, N - 1$$

(12-148)

Example 12-16 Suppose that we are to design a low-pass digital filter whose magnitude characteristics are shown in Fig. 12-23. Find an appropriate transfer function via a 16-point frequency sampling method.

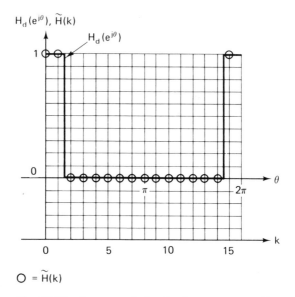

$H_d(e^{i\theta}), \tilde{H}(k)$

$O = \tilde{H}(k)$

Fig. 12-23 An example for the frequency-sampling method.

Solution: In this case the DFT sequence is given by

$$\tilde{H}(0) = \tilde{H}(1) = \tilde{H}(15) = 1$$
$$\tilde{H}(k) = 0 \quad \text{for } k = 2, 3, 4, \ldots, 14 \qquad (12\text{-}149)$$

By using (12-146), we obtain the desired transfer function

$$
\begin{aligned}
H(z) &= \frac{1}{16}\left[\sum_{k=0}^{15} \frac{(1 - z^{-16})\tilde{H}(k)}{1 - z^{-1} \exp{(j\pi k/8)}}\right] \\
&= \frac{1 - z^{-16}}{16}\left[\frac{1}{1 - z^{-1} \exp{(j\pi 0/4)}} + \frac{1}{1 - z^{-1} \exp{(j\pi/8)}}\right. \\
&\quad \left. + \frac{1}{1 - z^{-1} \exp{(j\pi 15/8)}}\right] \qquad (12\text{-}150) \\
&= \frac{1 - z^{-16}}{16}\left[\frac{1}{1 - z^{-1}} + \frac{1}{1 - z^{-1} \cos{(\pi/8)} - jz^{-1} \sin{(\pi/8)}}\right. \\
&\quad \left. + \frac{1}{1 - z^{-1} \cos{(\pi/8)} + jz^{-1} \sin{(\pi/8)}}\right] \\
&= \frac{1 - z^{-16}}{16}\left[\frac{1}{1 - z^{-1}} + \frac{2(1 - z^{-1} \cos{(\pi/8)})}{1 - 2z^{-1} \cos{(\pi/8)} + z^{-2}}\right] \quad \blacksquare
\end{aligned}
$$

It can be shown that the frequency response of (12-150) will be equal to the specifications of (12-149) at the sampling digital frequencies

$$\theta = \frac{k\pi}{8} \quad \text{for } k = 0, 1, 2, \ldots, 15 \qquad (12\text{-}151)$$

However, the resulting frequency response of (12-150) may not behave well in-between the sampling frequencies. This behavior is related to the Gibbs phenomenon, which describes the overshoot of a step function represented by a truncated Fourier series.

12-2-2. The Method of Windowing

Because the frequency response $H(e^{j\theta})$ of any digital filter is a periodic function of θ, it has a Fourier series expansion as

$$H(e^{j\theta}) = \sum_{n=-\infty}^{\infty} h(n)e^{-j\theta n} \qquad (12\text{-}152a)$$

where

$$h(n) = \frac{1}{2\pi} \int_{-\pi}^{\pi} H(e^{j\theta})e^{j\theta n} \, d\theta \qquad (12\text{-}152b)$$

Obviously, the Fourier series coefficients $h(n)$ are, in fact, the impulse response sequence of the digital filter.

One possible way of obtaining an FIR digital filter that approximates $H(e^{j\theta})$ is to truncate the infinite series of (12-152a) into a finite series. However, the well-known *Gibbs phenomenon* states that the truncation of the infinite series of (12-152a) will cause overshoots and ripples before and after any point of discontinuity in the desired frequency response. In addition, these overshoot and ripple sizes will not decrease no matter how long the sequence is, provided only that it is of finite length. This, in essence, implies that the direct truncation of (12-152a) to obtain an FIR digital filter approximation is not a satisfactory method.

The method of windowing is to use *finite* weighting sequences $w(n)$, called *windows*, to modify the Fourier coefficients of (12-152a) to a desirable finite impulse response sequence $h_D(n)$, where

$$h_D(n) = h(n)w(n) \qquad (12\text{-}153a)$$

and $w(n)$ is a sequence of finite length with

$$w(n) = 0 \quad \text{for} \quad n > N \quad \text{and} \quad n < 0 \qquad (12\text{-}153b)$$

From (12-153), we observe that the resulting impulse response $h_D(n)$ is also of duration N. That is

$$h_D(n) = 0 \quad \text{for} \quad n > N \quad \text{and} \quad n < 0 \qquad (12\text{-}154)$$

We now summarize the design procedure for the windowing method as follows:

1. Given the desired frequency response function $H(e^{j\theta})$, which may be the result obtained by the frequency sampling method.

2. Find its associated impulse response sequence $h(n)$ by either (12-152) or by finding the inverse z-transform of $H(z)$, where $H(z)$ is obtained from $H(e^{j\theta})$ by replacing $e^{j\theta}$ with z.

3. Employ an appropriate window function $w(n)$ to modify the sequence $h(n)$ to obtain the FIR digital filter's impulse response sequence $h_D(n)$ by (12-153). *multiply the h(n) found with chosen w(n) to get $h_D(n)$*

Because multiplication of two sequences in the time domain is equivalent to the convolution of two frequency responses in the frequency domain, the windowing method has the effect of smoothing out the rough points—moderating the overshoots and the ripples—in the original frequency response. For example, consider the frequency response of the FIR digital filter shown in Fig. 12-24(a).[29] With the simple window function

$$w(n) = 1 + \cos\frac{2\pi n}{N} \quad \text{for } 0 \le n \le N - 1 \tag{12-155}$$
$$= 0 \qquad\qquad \text{otherwise}$$

applied to Fig. 10-24(a), we obtain the frequency response of Fig. 10-24(b). It is apparent that the original response of Fig. 10-24(a) has been smoothed in such a manner that the sidelobe ripples are considerably reduced. The drawback is that the transition band has been widened.

To close this subsection, we list some established window functions as follows:

RECTANGULAR WINDOW:

$$w(n) = 1 \quad \text{for } 0 \le n \le N - 1$$
$$= 0 \quad \text{elsewhere} \tag{12-156}$$

BARTLETT WINDOW OR TRIANGULAR WINDOW:

$$w(n) = \frac{2n}{N-1} \qquad \text{for } 0 \le n \le \frac{N-1}{2}$$
$$= 2 - \frac{2n}{N-1} \quad \text{for } \frac{N-2}{2} \le n \le N - 1 \tag{12-157}$$
$$= 0 \qquad\qquad \text{elsewhere}$$

where N is even.

HANN WINDOW:

$$w(n) = \frac{1}{2}\left[1 - \cos\left(\frac{2\pi n}{N-1}\right)\right] \quad \text{for } 0 \le n \le N - 1$$
$$= 0 \qquad\qquad\qquad\qquad \text{elsewhere} \tag{12-158}$$

---

[29]Figure 12-24(a) shows the frequency response of an FIR digital filter designed to implement a low-pass filter via the frequency sampling technique.

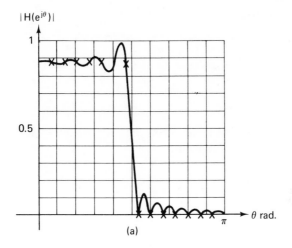

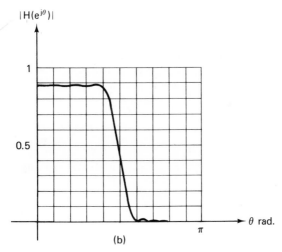

Fig. 12-24 Magnitude characteristics of a low-pass filter (a) before windowing, and (b) after windowing with (12-155).

HAMMING WINDOW:

$$w(n) = 0.54 - 0.46 \cos\left(\frac{2\pi n}{N-1}\right) \quad \text{for } 0 \le n \le N-1$$

$$= 0 \qquad\qquad\qquad \text{elsewhere} \tag{12-159}$$

BLACKMAN WINDOW:

$$w(n) = 0.42 - 0.5 \cos\left(\frac{2\pi n}{N-1}\right) + 0.08 \cos\left(\frac{4\pi n}{N-1}\right) \quad \text{for } 0 \le n \le N-1$$

$$= 0 \quad \text{elsewhere} \tag{12-160}$$

KAISER WINDOW:

$$w(n) = \frac{I_0\left[\omega_a\sqrt{\left(\frac{N-1}{2}\right)^2 - \left(n - \frac{N-1}{2}\right)^2}\right]}{I_0\left[\omega_a\left(\frac{N-1}{2}\right)\right]} \quad \text{for } 0 \leq n \leq N-1$$

$$= 0 \quad \text{elsewhere} \tag{12-161}$$

where $I_0(\cdot)$ is a modified zeroth-order Bessel function of the first kind and ω_a is a window shape parameter.

12-2-3. Some Comments On FIR Digital Filters

As in the case of analog filters, IIR digital filters can not have perfect linear phase characteristics. In contrast, FIR digital filters can be designed to have linear phase characteristics. In addition, FIR digital filters are always stable. These are the good points of FIR digital filters. On the negative side, implementation of an FIR digital filter requires more computations and more digital components; hence, FIR digital filters are more expensive than IIR digital filters.[30] For example, the FIR digital filter

$$H(z) = 1 + z^{-1} + z^{-2} + \ldots + z^{-L} \tag{12-162a}$$

or

$$y(n) = x(n) + x(n-1) + x(n-2) + \ldots + x(n-L) \tag{12-162b}$$

can be implemented by summing $(L+1)$ numbers. Taking the IIR digital filter approach, we obtain

$$H(z) = \frac{1 - z^{-(L+1)}}{1 - z^{-1}} \tag{12-163a}$$

or

$$y(n) = y(n-1) + x(n) - x(n-L-1) \tag{12-163b}$$

That is, we can implement the same filtering function by summing three numbers. There is a tremendous amount of saving in computation and hardware requirements.

The amount of computation and hardware needed to perform a filtering process is usually an important practical consideration. In general, IIR digital filters require lesser computations and/or hardware to achieve a particular filtering function than those required by the corresponding FIR digital filters. Hence, in most situations, FIR digital filters are called for to

---

[30]For more information on the comparisons between FIR and IIR digital filters, consult Reference [19].

perform tasks not possible and/or not practical by IIR digital filters such as linear phase filters, and multirate filters where the input signals and the corresponding output signals are sampled at different rates.

REFERENCES AND FURTHER READING

[1]   RABINER, L. R., and RADER, C. M. *Digital Signal Processing*. New York: IEEE Press, 1972.

[2]   OPPENHEIM, A. V., and SCHAFER, R. W. *Digital Signal Processing*. Englewood Cliffs, N.J.: Prentice-Hall, Inc., 1975.

[3]   RABINER, L. R., and GOLD, B. *Theory and Application of Digital Signal Processing*. Englewood Cliffs, N.J.: Prentice-Hall, Inc., 1975.

[4]   DANIELS, R. W. *Approximation Methods for Electronic Filter Design with Applications to Passive, Active and Digital Networks*. New York: McGraw-Hill, 1974.

[5]   RHODES, J. D. *Theory of Electrical Filters*. New York: John Wiley, 1976.

[6]   BLINCHIKOFF, H. J., and ZVEREV, A. I. *Filtering in the Time and Frequency Domains*. New York: Wiley Interscience, 1976.

[7]   BOGNER, R. E., and CONSTANTINIDES, A. G. *Introduction to Digital Filtering*. New York: John Wiley, 1975.

[8]   LEON, B. J., and BASS, S. C. "Designer's Guide to Digital Filter Parts 1–6." *EDN* 30–36, Jan., 1974; pp. 65–72, Feb., 1974; pp. 51–59, Mar., 1974; pp. 57–62, Apr., 1974; pp. 61–68, May, 1974; and pp. 69–75, June, 1974.

[9]   KUO, F. F., and KAISER, J. F. *System Analysis by Digital Computer*. New York: John Wiley, 1966.

[10]   GIBBS, A. J. "An Introduction to Digital Filters," *Australian Telecommunications Research* 3 (1969): 3–14.

[11]   BRIGHAM, E. O. *The Fast Fourier Transform*. Englewood Cliffs, N.J.: Prentice-Hall, Inc., 1974.

[12]   GEAR, C. W. *Numerical Initial Value Problems in Ordinary Differential Equations*. Englewood Cliffs, N.J.: Prentice-Hall, Inc., 1971.

[13]   STEIGLITZ, K. "The Equivalence of Digital and Analog Signal Processing." *Information and Control* 8 (1965): 455–67.

[14]   GIBBS, A. J. "The Design of Digital Filters." *Australian Telecommunication Research* 4 (1970): 29–34.

[15]   RADER, C. M., and GOLD, B. "Digital Filter Design Techniques in the Frequency Domain." *Proc. IEEE* 55 (1967): 149–71.

[16] LERNER, R. M. "Band Pass Filters with Linear Phase." *Proc. IEEE* 52 (1964): 249–68.

[17] CONSTANTINIDES, A. G. "Spectral Transformations for Digital Filters." *Proc. IEEE* 117 (1970): 1585–90.

[18] RABINER, L. R. "Techniques for Designing Finite-Duration Impulse-Response Digital Filters." *IEEE Trans. Communication Technology* COM-19 (1971): 188–95.

[19] RABINER, L. R., KAISER, J. F., HERRMANN, O., and DOLAN, M. T. "Some Comparisons Between FIR and IIR Digital Filters." *Bell System Tech. J.* 53 (1974): 305–31.

[20] McCLELLAN, J. H., and PARKS, T. W. "A Unified Approach to the Design of Optimum FIR Linear Phase Digital Filters." *IEEE Trans. Circuit Theory* CT-20 (1973): 697–701.

[21] KAISER, J. F. "Nonrecursive Digital Filter Design Using I_0-sinh Window Function." *Proc. 1974 IEEE International Symposium on Circuit and Systems*, pp. 20–23.

PROBLEMS

12-1. **(a)** Find the magnitude squared function of

$$H(z) = \frac{1 + z^{-1}}{1 + 0.5z^{-1} + 0.5z^{-2}}$$

(b) Construct the pole-zero diagram of $H(z)$.

(c) Construct the pole-zero diagram of the magnitude squared function of $H(z)$.

12-2. Repeat Problem 12-1 for the transfer function

$$H(z) = \frac{1 + z^{-2}}{(1 + 0.5z^{-1})(1 + 0.2z^{-1} + 0.2z^{-2})}$$

12-3. Consider the transfer function of an analog filter

$$\hat{H}(s) = \frac{1}{s^2 + \sqrt{2}\,s + 1}$$

Let the sampling period $T = 0.1$ sec. Find the corresponding digital transfer function by:

(a) Euler's approximation method;

(b) the impulse invariance method; and

(c) the bilinear transformation method.

For each case of (a), (b), and (c),

(d) find the pole-zero diagram of the resultant transfer function.

(e) sketch the magnitude characteristics.

12-4. Repeat Problem 12-3 for the analog transfer function

$$\hat{H}(s) = \frac{3}{s^2 + 3s + 3}$$

12-5. Consider the analog transfer function

$$\hat{H}(s) = \frac{10^8}{s^2 + 10^4 s + 10^8}$$

Let the sampling period $T = 10^{-5}$ sec. Find the corresponding digital transfer function by:

(a) the impulse invariance method; and

(b) the bilinear transformation method.

(c) Sketch the magnitude characteristics of the resultant transfer functions obtained in (a) and (b).

12-6. Suppose that a low-pass Butterworth filter is desired to satisfy the following requirements:

  (i) The 3 dB cutoff point is at $\theta_c = 0.1\pi$ rad.

  (ii) The passband attenuation is at most 0.2 dB for $0 \leq \theta \leq 0.05\pi$ rad.

  (iii) The stopband attenuation is at least 40 dB for 0.5π rad. $\leq \theta \leq \pi$ rad.

  (iv) The sampling period T is 10π μsec.

Using the procedure of Fig. 12-19(a), find the desired transfer function:

(a) by the impulse invariance method; and

(b) by the bilinear transformation method.

(c) Sketch the magnitude characteristics of (a) and (b).

12-7. Repeat Problem 12-6 by using the digital frequency transformation procedure of Fig. 12-19(b).

12-8. Suppose that an equiripple low-pass digital filter is desired to meet the following requirements:

  (i) The passband ripples are 0.5 dB for $0 \leq \theta \leq 0.2\pi$ rad.

  (ii) The stopband loss is at least 19 dB for 0.366π rad. $\leq \theta \leq \pi$ rad.

  (iii) The sampling frequency is 1 KHz.

Find the desired transfer function by:

(a) the impulse invariance method via Fig. 12-19(a); and

(b) the bilinear transformation method via Fig. 12-19(b).

12-9. Suppose that we need to implement a third-order Butterworth low-pass filter with the 3 dB cutoff frequency at $\omega_c = 100$ K rad./sec. in terms of a digital filter.

(a) Use the impulse invariance method to find the transfer function of the desired digital filter with the 3 dB cutoff frequency at $\theta_c = 0.2\pi$ rad.

(b) Suppose that the frequency characteristics of the *normalized* third-order Butterworth filter are given by Fig. P12-9. Sketch the frequency characteristics of the digital filter in (a) for $0 \leq \theta \leq 4\pi$ rad.

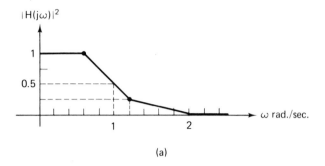

(a)

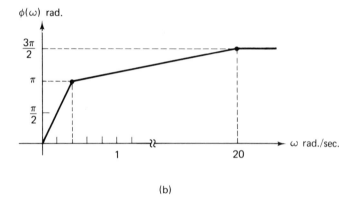

(b)

Fig. P12-9

12-10. A normalized low-pass second-order Butterworth filter has a transfer function

$$\hat{H}(s) = \frac{1}{s^2 + \sqrt{2}s + 1}$$

(a) Find the transfer function of the corresponding low-pass digital filter by the bilinear transformation method with sample period $T = 0.1$ sec.

(b) Find the digital cutoff frequency of the filter obtained in (a).

(c) Sketch the magnitude characteristics of the filter in (a).

12-11. Suppose that a low-pass equiripple digital filter is desired to meet the following requirements:

(i) The passband ripples are 0.1 dB with ripple bandwidth $B = 0.1\pi$ rad.

(ii) The stopband attenuation is greater than 20 dB for 0.6π rad. $\leq \theta < \pi$ rad.

(iii) The sampling period $T = 10\pi$ μsec.

Find the desired digital transfer function by the impulse invariance method via the procedure of:

(a) Fig. 12-19(a); and

(b) Fig. 12-19(b).

12-12. Repeat Problem 12-11 by using the bilinear transformation method.

12-13. Suppose that a fourth-order Butterworth bandpass digital filter is desired with the center frequency at $\theta_0 = 0.4\pi$ rad. and the lower passband frequency at 0.3π rad. If the sampling period $T = 0.1$ sec., find the desired transfer function by the impulse invariance method via the procedure of:

(a) Fig. 12-19(a); and

(b) Fig. 12-19(b).

Sketch the magnitude characteristics of the filter:

(c) obtained in (a); and

(d) obtained in (b).

12-14. Repeat Problem 12-13 by using the bilinear transformation method.

12-15. The second-order normalized low-pass Butterworth filter has the analog transfer function

$$\hat{H}(s) = \frac{1}{s^2 + \sqrt{2}\,s + 1}$$

(a) Using the procedure of impulse invariance method and digital frequency transformation, find the transfer function of the corresponding digital bandpass filter with:

    (i) the passband center frequency $\theta_0 = 0.5\pi$ rad. corresponding to the analog frequency $\omega_0 = 120\pi$ rad./sec.; and

    (ii) the lower passband frequency $\theta_l = 0.4\pi$ rad.

(b) Sketch the magnitude function of (a) for $0 \leq \theta \leq 4\pi$ rad.

(c) Assuming that there is no aliasing and a set of perfect A/D and D/A converters are connected to the digital filter in (a), as shown in Fig. P12-15, sketch the magnitude function of the resultant analog filter in Fig. P12-15. Indicate all important frequency points explicitly.

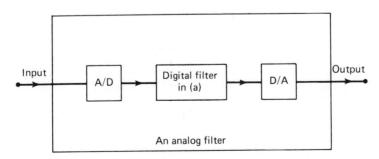

Fig. P12-15

12-16. Suppose that a fourth-order Butterworth band-reject filter is desired with the center frequency $\theta_0 = 0.4\pi$ rad. and the lower band-rejection frequency $\theta_l = 0.35\pi$ rad. If the sampling period $T = 1$ μsec., find the desired digital transfer function by using the procedures of:

(a) the analog frequency transformation and the bilinear transformation method;

(b) the bilinear transformation method and the digital frequency transformation; and

(c) the impulse invariance method and the digital frequency transformation.

12-17. The second-order normalized low-pass Butterworth filter has the transfer function

$$\hat{H}(s) = \frac{1}{s^2 + \sqrt{2}s + 1}$$

(a) Using the procedure of the impulse invariance method and digital frequency transformation, find the transfer function of the corresponding digital high-pass filter with the 3 dB cutoff frequency $\theta_c = 0.8\pi$ rad. corresponding to the analog cutoff frequency $\omega_c = 192\pi$ rad./sec.

(b) Assuming no aliasing effect, sketch the magnitude characteristics for $0 \leq \theta \leq 4\pi$ rad.

12-18. The second-order Bessel filter has a transfer function

$$\hat{H}(s) = \frac{1}{s^2 + 3s + 3}$$

(a) Using the impulse invariance method and the digital frequency transformation procedure, find the transfer function of the corresponding digital high-pass Bessel filter with the 3 dB cutoff frequency $\theta_c = 0.8\pi$ rad. corresponding to the analog 3 dB cutoff frequency $\omega_c = 192\pi$ rad./sec.

(b) Assuming no aliasing effect, sketch the group delay function for -4π rad. $\leq \theta \leq 4\pi$ rad.

12-19. Suppose that a high-pass Chebyshev digital filter is desired to meet the following requirements:

(i) The passband ripples are 0.1 dB for 0.4π rad. $\leq \theta \leq \pi$ rad.

(ii) The stopband loss is at least 40 dB for $0 \leq \theta \leq 0.1\pi$ rad.

Find the desired digital transfer function by:

(a) using the procedure of Fig. 12-19(b) and the impulse invariance method;

(b) using the procedure of Fig. 12-19(a) and the bilinear transformation method; and

(c) using the procedure of Fig. 12-19(b) and the bilinear transformation method.

12-20. Find the group delay functions of the following FIR digital filters:

(a) $h(n) = 1$ for $0 \leq n \leq 4$
   $= 0$ otherwise

(b) $h(0) = h(4) = 2$
   $h(1) = h(3) = 1$
   $h(2) = 0.5$
   $h(n) = 0$ for $n < 0$ and for $n > 4$.

(c) $h(n) = 2$ for $0 \leq n \leq 5$
   $= 0$ otherwise

(d) $h(0) = h(5) = 2$
   $h(1) = h(4) = 1$
   $h(2) = h(3) = 0.5$
   $h(n) = 0$ for $n < 0$ and for $n > 5$.

(e) $h(n) = 1$ for $0 \leq n \leq 6$
   $= 0$ otherwise

12-21. Suppose that it is desired to design digital filters whose magnitude characteristics are shown in Fig. P12-21. For each magnitude characteristic, find an appropriate transfer function via an eight-point frequency-sampling method.

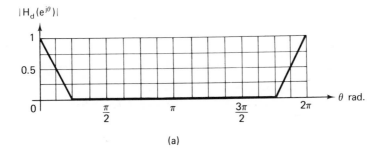

(a)

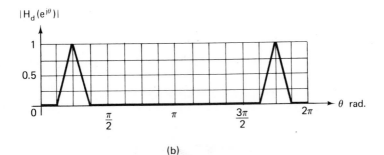

(b)

Fig. P12-21(a), (b)

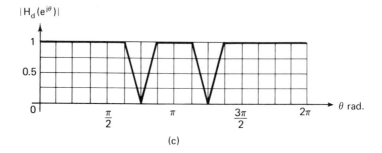

(c)

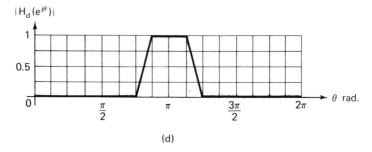

(d)

Fig. P12-21(c), (d)

12-22. For each magnitude characteristic shown in Fig. P12-21, find an appropriate digital transfer function via a 16-point frequency-sampling method.

12-23. Write a computer program to implement:

   (a) the impulse invariance mapping procedure; and
   (b) the bilinear transformation mapping procedure.

12-24. Write a computer program to implement the:

   (a) low-pass to low-pass
   (b) low-pass to bandpass
   (c) low-pass to band-reject
   (d) low-pass to high-pass

   digital frequency transformations.

12-25. Write a computer program to implement the two procedures outlined in Fig. 12-19:

   (a) for the impulse invariance method; and
   (b) for the bilinear transformation method.

13

REALIZATION
OF DIGITAL FILTERS

After obtaining a transfer function to meet the signal-processing requirements, the remaining problem is to implement or to realize the desired
transfer function. This chapter deals with the problem of realizing digital
transfer functions.

The standard components for the implementation of digital filters are
delay units, adders, and multipliers, as discussed in Sec. 11-5. It is basically
as easy to process negative numbers as positive numbers. Hence, the coefficients in the transfer functions are not restricted to positive numbers. By
examining some examples in Chapter 12, we see that some coefficients of
digital transfer functions are indeed negative numbers.

Because the transfer functions of infinite impulse response (IIR) digital
filters differ from those of finite impulse response (FIR) digital filters, we
shall, for the sake of clarity, discuss their realization techniques separately
even though the underlying principles are the same.

13-1 REALIZATION OF IIR DIGITAL FILTERS

The transfer function of an IIR digital filter is in the form

$$H(z) = \frac{\sum\limits_{i=0}^{M} a_i z^{-i}}{1 + \sum\limits_{i=1}^{N} b_i z^{-i}} \triangleq \frac{A(z)}{B(z)} \tag{13-1}$$

There are two approaches to realize (13-1). They are the *direct approach* and the *indirect approach*. In the direct approach, the transfer function $H(z)$ of (13-1) is realized in one piece. In the indirect approach, the transfer function of (13-1) is decomposed into a number of first- and second-order sections. The realization of (13-1) is then completed by realizing all the associated first- and second-order sections and interconnecting them together in some manner. As far as quantization errors are concerned, it has been found that the indirect approach gives results superior to those obtained by the direct approach.

13-1-1. Direct Realization

There are many techniques in the direct approach to realize digital transfer functions. Among the well-known techniques are the direct forms, ladder and lattice structures, multiplier-extraction techniques, and the modular forms of wave digital filters. The direct forms are realization techniques that implement the difference equations of the filters in various ways. The multiplying constants are the coefficients of the transfer functions. For low-order transfer functions, the direct forms are very competitive in performance and cost.[1] The ladder and lattice forms[2] have the inherent low structural sensitivity property. Their multiplying constants are computed via a series of arithmetic operations. This causes some degradation in the performance of the resulting digital filters. The multiplier-extraction technique[3] has the advantage that the resulting digital filters will always contain the minimum number of multipliers,[4] a property shared by some other realization techniques also. The modular forms of wave digital-filter realization[5] often take the route of converting a passive RLC circuit directly into a digital filter circuit via the scattering representations of analog circuit elements. In an informal study, we find that wave digital filters and regular digital filters require approximately the same amount of digital hardware to perform the same filtering requirements.

A digital transfer function can be realized by many methods including the ones mentioned in the previous paragraph. Attempts have been made[6] to identify structures and techniques to yield the best digital circuits in terms of cost (hardware requirements, word-length representations) and performance (end result sensitivities, resulting frequency responses). No overall

---

[1]In the indirect approach, the overall transfer function is decomposed into first- and second-order filter sections. The direct forms are very popular techniques to realize each individual section.

[2]See References [6 through 8].

[3]See Reference [9].

[4]A multiplier costs much more than an adder or a delay unit. Hence, it is economical to realize a digital transfer function with the minimum number of multipliers.

[5]See References [10, 11].

[6]See References [12 through 14].

best technique has yet been found; the choice of technique depends on the problem at hand.

In this subsection, we concentrate on the direct form and the ladder form realizations of digital filters. Direct form realizations are very popular, and they perform very well for low-order transfer functions, whereas ladder forms have the desirable low structural sensitivity property. Both techniques lead to the realizations of digital filters with the minimum number of multipliers.

13-1-1-1. Direct Forms. Recall that the transfer function of (13-1) defines a difference equation relating the input sequence $x(n)$ and the output sequence $y(n)$ as[7]

$$y(n) = \sum_{i=0}^{M} a_i x(n-i) + \sum_{i=1}^{N} (-b_i) y(n-i) \qquad (13\text{-}2)$$

Hence, a realization of the transfer function of (13-1) can be obtained by implementing a computation procedure for (13-2). Figure 13-1(a) shows a digital network implementation of (13-2).[8] This configuration is called the

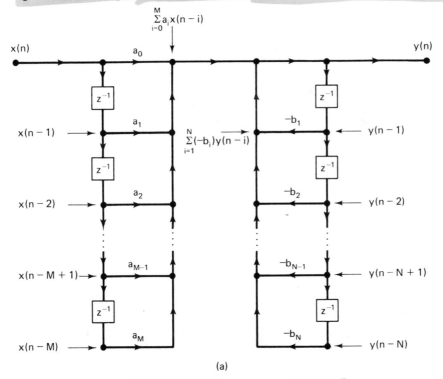

(a)

Fig. 13-1   Direct form I realization.

---

[7]See (11-53).

[8]In Figs. 13-1 through 13-3, we have assumed that $N < M$ in (13-1). Clearly, as can be seen from the context, this assumption is not necessary.

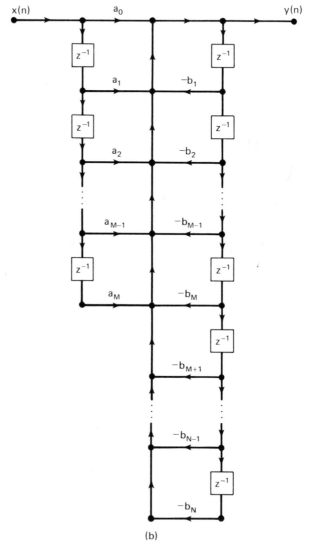

(b)

Fig. 13-1   (Continued)

direct form I realization of the transfer function of (13-1). In Fig. 13-1(a), each summer is used to sum two signals. A simplified diagram for direct form I is shown in Fig. 13-1(b), where certain summers are required to sum more than two signals.

Let $W(z)$ be defined by

$$\frac{W(z)}{X(z)} \triangleq \frac{1}{B(z)} \tag{13-3a}$$

Then (13-1) can be used to obtain

$$\frac{Y(z)}{W(z)} = \frac{Y(z)}{X(z)} \frac{X(z)}{W(z)} = \frac{A(z)}{B(z)} B(z) = A(z) \tag{13-3b}$$

From (13-3), we observe that one can realize the transfer function $H(z)$ of (13-1) by realizing two simpler transfer functions given by (13-3a) and (13-3b). This implementation is shown in Fig. 13-2(a). A simplified schematic of Fig. 13-2(a) is given in Fig. 13-2(b). Figure 13-2 illustrates the *direct form II* realization of (13-1). Notice that the direct form II realization requires only N delay elements. This is the smallest number of delay units required to realize an Nth-order digital filter such as the one specified by (13-1).[9] Both

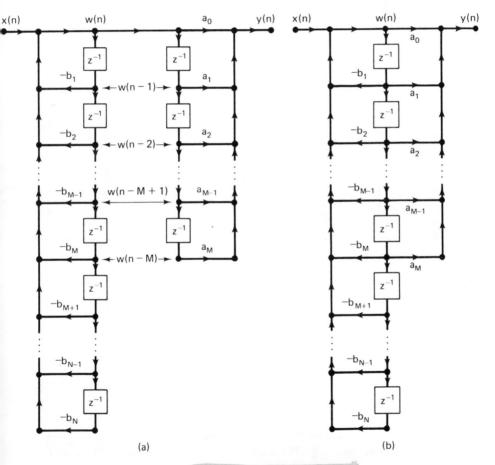

(a)   (b)

Fig. 13-2   Direct form II realization

---

[9]The order of an IIR digital filter characterized by (13-1) is equal to max $\{M, N\}$.

direct forms require $(N + M + 1)$ multipliers, which is the minimum number of multipliers needed to realize (13-1).

Based on the theory of signal flow graphs, both the transposition of a digital circuit and the original digital circuit have identical transfer functions. Specifically, the transposed digital circuit is obtained by reversing the directions of every branch in the circuit and by exchanging the input and output terminals. For examples, the transposed circuits of direct forms I and II of Figs. 13-1(b) and 2(b) are shown in Figs. 13-3(a) and (b), respectively. It can be shown that the transfer functions of Figs. 13-3(a) and (b) are given by (13-1).

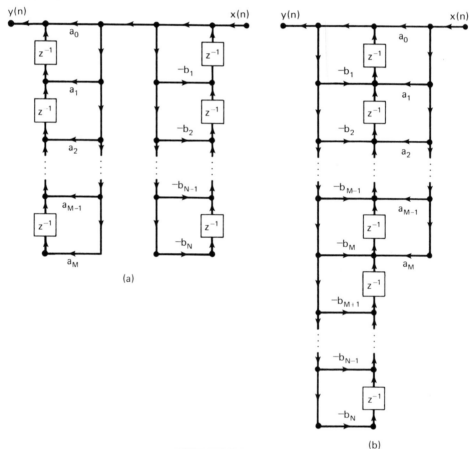

Fig. 13-3 Transposed direct forms. (a) Transposed direct form I. (b) Transposed direct form II.

Example 13-1 Realize the transfer function

$$H(z) = \frac{1 + 0.2z^{-1} - 0.2z^{-2}}{1 - 0.2z^{-1} + 0.3z^{-2} + z^{-3}} \qquad (13\text{-}4)$$

Solution: Identifying the corresponding terms between (13-4) and (13-1), we obtain

$$M = 2, \quad N = 3, a_0 = 1, \quad a_1 = 0.2, \quad a_2 = -0.2,$$
$$b_0 = 1, \quad b_1 = -0.2, \quad b_2 = 0.3, \quad \text{and} \quad b_3 = 1 \tag{13-5}$$

Figure 13-4(a), (b), (c), and (d), respectively, give the direct form I and II and the transposed direct form I and II realizations of (13-4). ∎

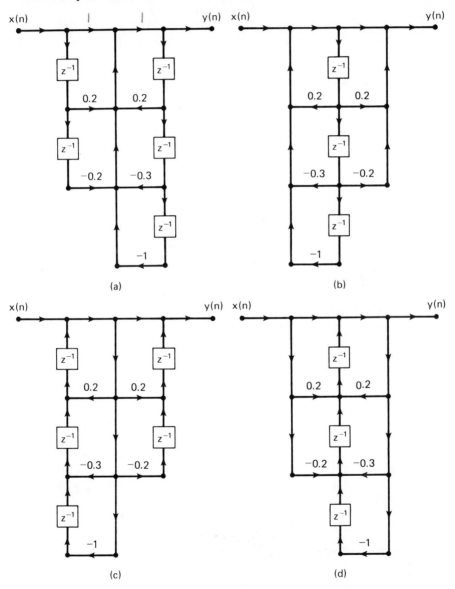

Fig. 13-4 Direct form and transposed direct form realizations of (13-4).

13-1-1-2. Ladder Forms. Suppose that the transfer function of the desired IIR digital filter is given by

$$H(z) = \frac{a_0 + a_1 z^{-1} + \ldots + a_M z^{-M}}{b_0 + b_1 z^{-1} + \ldots + b_N z^{-N}} \qquad (13\text{-}6a)$$

where

$$|N - M| \leq 1 \qquad (13\text{-}6b)$$

Then $H(z)$ may admit various equivalent representations in the form of continued fraction expansions. It will be shown later in this section that the realizations of these continued fraction expansions of $H(z)$ yield ladder network configurations. We now consider some specific situations.

CASE 1   Suppose that $H(z)$ of (13-6) admits a continued fraction expansion at $z^{-1} = \infty$ or $z = 0$:[10]

$$H_1(z) = A_0 + \cfrac{1}{B_1 z^{-1} + \cfrac{1}{A_1 + \cfrac{1}{\ddots}}} \qquad (13\text{-}7)$$

$$+ \cfrac{1}{B_N z^{-1} + \cfrac{1}{A_N}}$$

or

$$H_2(z) = B_0 z^{-1} + \cfrac{1}{A_0 + \cfrac{1}{B_1 z^{-1} + \cfrac{1}{A_1 + \ddots}}} \qquad (13\text{-}8)$$

$$+ \cfrac{1}{B_N z^{-1} + \cfrac{1}{A_N}}$$

By examining (13-7) and (13-8) closely, we conclude that the realizations of the continued fractions (13-7) and (13-8) can easily be accomplished if we can realize two building blocks characterized by the following two transfer functions:

$$H_{B1}(z) = \frac{1}{A + T(z)} \qquad (13\text{-}9)$$

---

[10]One simple sufficient condition is that the function $F(s) \triangleq H(1/s)$ has only simple, real, and alternating poles and zeros. This type of $F(s)$ is realizable as a DP impedance or admittance function of a 1-port containing passive capacitors and both passive and active resistors.

and

$$H_{B2}(z) = \frac{1}{Bz^{-1} + T(z)} \qquad (13\text{-}10)$$

where $T(z)$ is arbitrary. This is because the continued fractions (13-7) and (13-8) can be written in the forms (13-9) and (13-10) repeatedly. Figure 13-5(a) and (b) give a set of digital circuit realizations of $H_{B1}(z)$ and $H_{B2}(z)$ of (13-9) and (13-10), respectively.

With Fig. 13-5 providing the basic digital-circuit building blocks, we can now proceed to the realizations of (13-7) and (13-8). Specifically, let us consider the case of (13-7) first. Writing $H_1(z)$ as

$$\frac{1}{T_{A0}^1(z)} \triangleq H_1(z) = A_0 + T_{B1}^1(z) \qquad (13\text{-}11a)$$

where

$$T_{B1}^1(z) = \cfrac{1}{B_1 z^{-1} + \cfrac{1}{A_1 + \cfrac{1}{\ddots \quad + \cfrac{1}{A_N}}}} \qquad (13\text{-}11b)$$

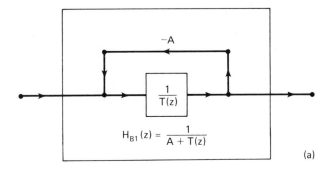

(a)

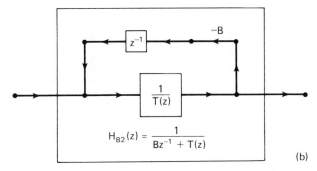

(b)

Fig. 13-5   Two basic building blocks for ladder realizations.

we can realize $H_1(z)$ by summing two transfer functions A_0 and $T_{B1}^1(z)$, as shown in Fig. 13-6(a). To realize $T_{B1}^1(z)$, we write

$$T_{B1}^1(z) = \frac{1}{B_1 z^{-1} + T_{A1}^1(z)} \qquad (13\text{-}12a)$$

where

$$\frac{1}{T_{A1}^1(z)} = A_1 + \cfrac{1}{B_2 z^{-1} + \begin{matrix} \cdot \\ \cdot \\ \cdot \end{matrix}} \qquad (13\text{-}12b)$$

$$+ \frac{1}{A_N}$$

By using Fig. 13-5(b), we can implement (13-12) by the circuit shown in Fig. 13-6(b). Observe that the transfer function of $T_{A1}^1(z)$ of (13-12b) is in the same form as that of $T_{A0}^1(z)$ of (13-11a) except simpler. Hence, we can use the pro-

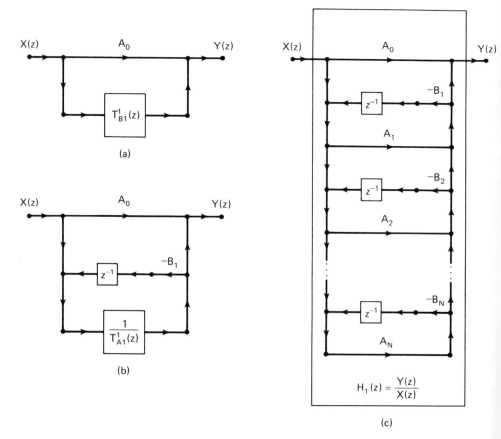

(a)

(b)

(c)

$$H_1(z) = \frac{Y(z)}{X(z)}$$

Fig. 13-6   A ladder circuit realization of $H_1(z)$ of (13-7). (a) and (b) Steps involved. (c) A final circuit realization.

cedures of (13-11) and (13-12) repeatedly until $H_1(z)$ is realized. A realization of $H_1(z)$ using the alternating procedure of (13-11) and (13-12) is shown in Fig. 13-6(c).

In a similar manner, the transfer function $H_2(z)$ of (13-8) can be realized by applying Fig. 13-5(a) repetitively. The corresponding steps and the final circuit realization are shown in Fig. 13-7, where

$$T^2_{A0}(z) = \frac{1}{A_0 + T^2_{B1}(z)} \tag{13-13a}$$

and

$$T^2_{B1}(z) = \cfrac{1}{B_1 z^{-1} + \cfrac{1}{A_1 + \cfrac{}{_{\displaystyle \cdot}}}} \tag{13-13b}$$

$$+ \frac{1}{A_N}$$

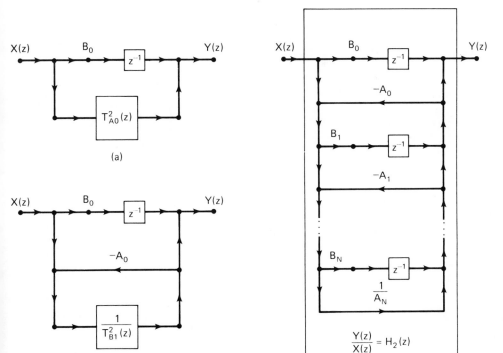

$$\frac{Y(z)}{X(z)} = H_2(z)$$

Fig. 13-7   A ladder circuit realization of $H_2(z)$ of (13-8). (a) and (b) Steps involved. (c) A final circuit realization.

Observe that in Fig. 13-7(c) there are loops without delay elements. As discussed in Sec. 11-5, delay-free loops are not allowed in digital filter circuits. In subsection 13-1-1-3, we will present a method to eliminate delay-free loops without altering the intended transfer functions. Note that if $1/A_N = 0$ (the continued fraction expansion terminates with $B_N z^{-1}$), then this process will yield valid realization circuits.

Example 13-2 Realize the transfer function

$$H(z) = \frac{-1 + z^{-1} + \left(\frac{3}{16}\right)z^{-2}}{1 - \left(\frac{1}{4}\right)z^{-1} - \left(\frac{1}{8}\right)z^{-2}} \tag{13-14}$$

by a ladder circuit.

Solution: By a long division process:

$$
\begin{array}{r}
\left(-\dfrac{3}{2}\right) \\
-\dfrac{1}{8}z^{-2} - \dfrac{1}{4}z^{-1} + 1 \overline{\smash{)}\ \dfrac{3}{16}z^{-2} + z^{-1} - 1} \\
\dfrac{3}{16}z^{-2} - \dfrac{3}{8}z^{-1} - \dfrac{3}{2} \qquad \left(-\dfrac{1}{5}z^{-1}\right) \\
\dfrac{5}{8}z^{-1} + \dfrac{1}{2}\ \overline{\smash{)}\ -\dfrac{1}{8}z^{-1} - \dfrac{1}{4}z^{-1} + 1} \\
-\dfrac{1}{8}z^{-1} - \dfrac{1}{10}z^{-1} \qquad \left(-\dfrac{25}{6}\right) \\
-\dfrac{3}{20}z^{-1} + 1\ \overline{\smash{)}\ \dfrac{5}{8}z^{-1} + \dfrac{1}{2}} \\
\dfrac{5}{8}z^{-1} - \dfrac{25}{6} \qquad \left(-\dfrac{9}{280}z^{-1}\right) \\
\dfrac{14}{3}\ \overline{\smash{)}\ -\dfrac{3}{20}z^{-1} + 1} \\
-\dfrac{3}{20}z^{-1} \qquad \left(\dfrac{14}{3}\right) \\
1\ \overline{\smash{)}\ \dfrac{14}{3}} \\
\dfrac{14}{3} \\
0
\end{array}
$$

a continued fraction expansion of $H(z)$ of (13-14) is given by

$$H(z) = -\frac{3}{2} + \cfrac{1}{-\left(\frac{1}{5}\right)z^{-1} + \cfrac{1}{-\frac{25}{6} + \cfrac{1}{-\left(\frac{9}{280}\right)z^{-1} + \cfrac{1}{\frac{14}{3}}}}} \tag{13-15}$$

The realization of the transfer function of (13-14) by a digital ladder circuit via (13-15) and Fig. 13-6 is given in Fig. 13-8. ∎

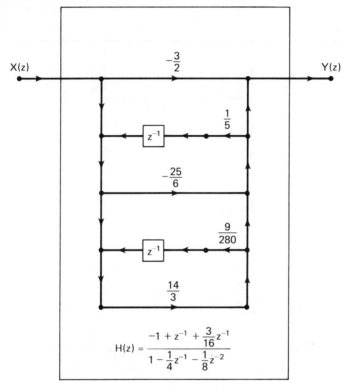

$$H(z) = \frac{-1 + z^{-1} + \frac{3}{16}z^{-1}}{1 - \frac{1}{4}z^{-1} - \frac{1}{8}z^{-2}}$$

Fig. 13-8   A ladder circuit realization of (13-14).

Example 13-3   Realize the transfer function

$$H(z) = \frac{z^{-2} + z^{-1}}{1 - \left(\frac{1}{4}\right)z^{-1} - \left(\frac{1}{8}\right)z^{-2}} \tag{13-16}$$

by a ladder network.

Solution: A continued fraction expansion of $H(z)$ of (13-16) gives

$$(Hz) = \cfrac{1}{-\frac{1}{8} + \cfrac{1}{-8z^{-1} + \cfrac{1}{-\frac{1}{72} + \frac{1}{9z^{-1}}}}} \tag{13-17}$$

A realization of (13-16) via (13-17) and Fig. 13-7 is shown in Fig. 13-9. ∎

CASE 2   Suppose that $H(z)$ of (13-6) admits a continued fraction expansion at $z^{-1} = 0$ or $z = \infty$:[11]

---

[11]Here we have assumed that $a_0 \neq 0$ and $b_0 \neq 0$ in (13-6).

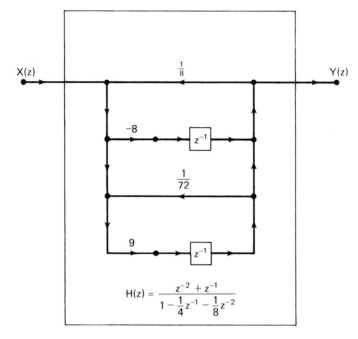

Fig. 13-9   A ladder circuit realization of (13-16).

$$H_3(z) = A_0 + \cfrac{1}{B_1 z + \cfrac{1}{A_1 + \cfrac{1}{\begin{matrix}\cdot\\\cdot\\\cdot\\ \quad + \cfrac{1}{B_N z + \cfrac{1}{A_N}}\end{matrix}}}} \tag{13-18}$$

or

$$H_4(z) = \cfrac{1}{A_0 + \cfrac{1}{B_1 z + \cfrac{1}{A_1 + \cfrac{1}{\begin{matrix}\cdot\\\cdot\\\cdot\\ \quad + \cfrac{1}{B_N z + \cfrac{1}{A_N}}\end{matrix}}}}} \tag{13-19}$$

In order to implement (13-18) or (13-19), we need building blocks that realize the two functions

$$H_{B3}(z) = \frac{1}{Bz + T(z)} \tag{13-20}$$

and

$$H_{B4}(z) = \frac{1}{A + T(z)} \tag{13-21}$$

Figure 13-10 gives a set of realizations of $H_{B3}(z)$ and $H_{B4}(z)$.

To realize the transfer function of (13-18), we write $H_3(z)$ as

$$H_3(z) = A_0 + T_{B1}^3(z) = A_0 + \frac{1}{B_1 z + T_{A1}^3(z)} \tag{13-22}$$

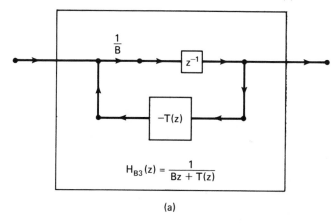

(a)

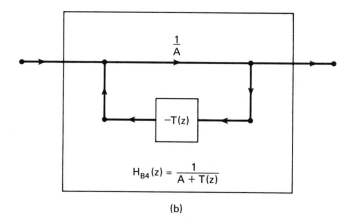

(b)

Fig. 13-10   Two basic building blocks for ladder realizations.

where

$$T_{B1}^3(z) = \frac{1}{B_1 z + T_{A1}^3(z)} \tag{13-23a}$$

and

$$T_{A1}^3(z) = \cfrac{1}{A_1 + \cfrac{1}{B_2 z + \cfrac{1}{\ddots \\ + \cfrac{1}{A_N}}}} \tag{13-23b}$$

By applying Fig. 13-10(a), the actions of (13-22) and (13-23) are implemented in Fig. 13-11(a) and (b). Notice that $-T_{A1}^3(z)$ in Fig. 13-11(b) can be written as

$$-T_{A1}^3(z) = \frac{1}{-A_1 - T_{B2}(z)} \tag{13-24a}$$

where

$$T_{B2}^3(z) = \cfrac{1}{B_2 z + \cfrac{1}{A_2 + \cfrac{1}{\ddots \\ + \cfrac{1}{B_N z + \cfrac{1}{A_N}}}}} \tag{13-24b}$$

With the aid of Fig. 13-10(b), Fig. 13-11(c) illustrates the step involved in (13-24). Observe that $T_{B2}^3(z)$ is similar to $T_{B1}^3(z)$ except simpler. By repeating the process of (13-23) and (13-24), we can realize $H_3(z)$ as shown in Fig. 13-11(d).

Similarly, by applying Figs. 13-10(a) and (b) repeatedly, we obtain the circuit realization of $H_4(z)$ of (13-19) as illustrated in Fig. 13-12, where

$$-T_{B1}^4(z) = \frac{1}{-B_1 z - T_{A1}^4(z)} \tag{13-25a}$$

and

$$T_{A1}^4(z) = \cfrac{1}{A_1 + \cfrac{1}{B_2 z + \cfrac{1}{\ddots \\ + \cfrac{1}{A_N}}}} \tag{13-25b}$$

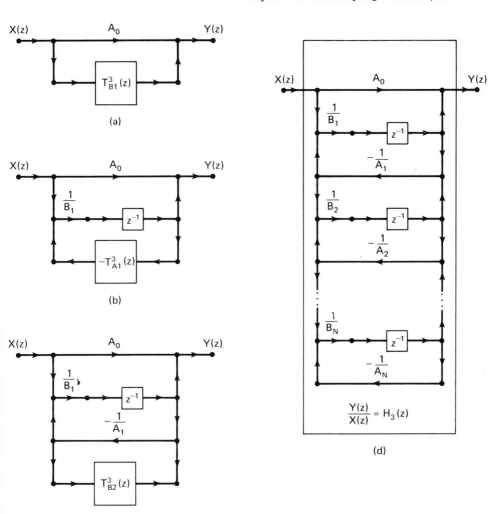

Fig. 13-11 A ladder circuit realization of $H_3(z)$ of (13-18). (a), (b), and (c) Steps involved. (d) A final circuit realization.

Example 13-4 Realize the transfer function

$$H(z) = \frac{z^{-1}}{1 - \left(\frac{1}{4}\right)z^{-1} - \left(\frac{1}{8}\right)z^{-2}} \qquad (13\text{-}26)$$

by the ladder circuit of Fig. 13-11.

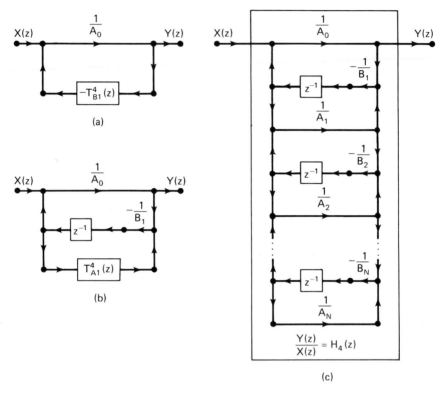

Fig. 13-12 A ladder circuit realization of $H_4(z)$ of (13-19). (a) and (b) Steps involved. (c) A final circuit realization.

Solution: Multiplying both the numerator and the denominator of $H(z)$ of (13-26) by z^2, we obtain

$$H(z) = \frac{z}{z^2 - \left(\dfrac{1}{4}\right)z - \dfrac{1}{8}}$$

A partial fraction expansion of $H(z)$ at $z = \infty$ (or equivalently at $z^{-1} = 0$) gives

$$H(z) = \cfrac{1}{z + \cfrac{1}{-4 + \cfrac{1}{\left(\dfrac{1}{2}\right)z + \dfrac{1}{4}}}} \tag{13-27}$$

A ladder circuit realization of (13-26) via (13-27) is shown in Fig. 13-13. ∎

Example 13-5 Realize the transfer function

$$H(z) = \frac{1 + z^{-1} + z^{-2}}{1 - \left(\dfrac{1}{4}\right)z^{-1} - \left(\dfrac{1}{8}\right)z^{-2}} \tag{13-28}$$

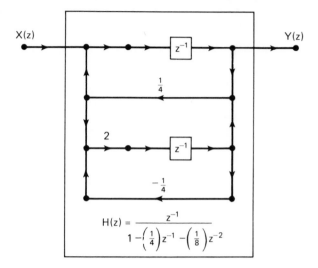

Fig. 13-13   A ladder circuit realization of (13-26).

by the ladder structure shown in Fig. 13-12.

Solution: With $H(z)$ of (13-28) written as

$$H(z) = \frac{z^2 + z + 1}{z^2 - \left(\frac{1}{4}\right)z - \frac{1}{8}}$$

a partial fraction expansion of $H(z)$ at $z = \infty$ yields

$$H(z) = \cfrac{1}{1 + \cfrac{1}{-\left(\frac{4}{5}\right)z + \cfrac{1}{-\frac{25}{2} + \cfrac{1}{\left(\frac{4}{455}\right)z + \cfrac{1}{\frac{91}{8}}}}}} \qquad (13\text{-}29)$$

A realization of (13-28) via (13-29) is given in Fig. 13-14. ∎

From Examples 13-2 through 13-5, we observe that an important draw-back of ladder realizations is that the multiplying constants in the final digital-circuit realizations are obtained after a series of computations. Consequently, the resulting circuit realizations may not realize the original transfer functions exactly. In addition, we do not have much control over the size (the magnitude) of the multiplying constants. For example, the number 455/4 in Fig. 13-14 is a very large number compared to other multiplying constants in the same circuit. This causes real difficulties in hardware designs.

As in the case of passive analog ladder circuits, a digital transfer function can be realized by a combination of various forms of digital ladder-realiza-

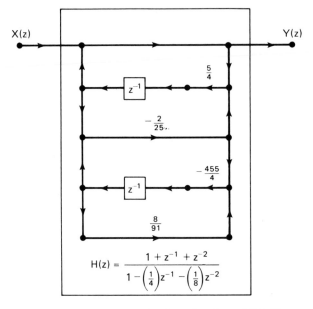

Fig. 13-14   A ladder circuit realization of (13-28).

tion procedures. Very often this process will yield better multiplying constants. A case in point is given by Example 13-6.

Example 13-6   Realize the transfer function $H(z)$ of (13-28) in Example 13-5 by first expanding $H(z)$ at $z^{-1} = 0$ and then at $z^{-1} = \infty$.

Solution: Expanding $H(z)$ at $z^{-1} = 0$ until the first delay element is extracted means that we write $H(z)$ as

$$H(z) = \frac{1 + z^{-1} + z^{-2}}{1 - \left(\dfrac{1}{4}\right)z^{-1} - \left(\dfrac{1}{8}\right)z^{-2}} = \frac{z^2 + z + 1}{z^2 - \left(\dfrac{1}{4}\right)z - \dfrac{1}{8}}$$

$$= \frac{1}{1 + \cfrac{1}{-\left(\dfrac{4}{5}\right)z + H_R(z)}} \tag{13-30}$$

where the remainder function

$$H_R(z) = \frac{\left(\dfrac{4}{5}\right)z + 8}{-10z - 9} = \frac{\dfrac{4}{5} + 8z^{-1}}{-10 - 9z^{-1}}$$

is expanded at $z^{-1} = \infty$ as

$$H_R(z) = \cfrac{1}{-\dfrac{9}{8} + \cfrac{1}{-8z^{-1} + \cfrac{1}{-\dfrac{5}{4}}}} \tag{13-31}$$

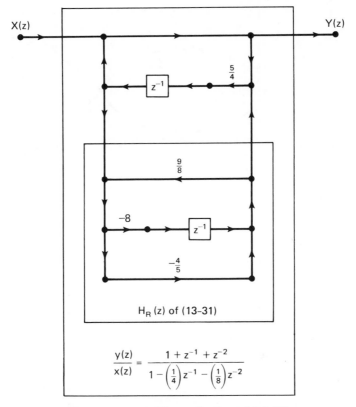

$$\frac{y(z)}{x(z)} = \frac{1 + z^{-1} + z^{-2}}{1 - \left(\frac{1}{4}\right)z^{-1} - \left(\frac{1}{8}\right)z^{-2}}$$

Fig. 13-15   A ladder realization of (13-28).

A circuit realization of (13-28) based on the expansion of $H(z)$ given by (13-30) and (13-31) is shown in Fig. 13-15.[12]   ∎

Before we conclude this subsection on ladder form realizations, we point out that the transposition of a ladder digital circuit is the original ladder circuit itself. In other words, they are self-transposed circuits.

13-1-1-3. Elimination of Delay-Free Loops. In Sec. 11-5, we discussed the impossibility of computing digital circuits with delay-free loops. In the previous subsection, we found that some ladder-realization techniques yield digital circuits with delay-free loops. Consequently, those circuits cannot be implemented without modifications. In this subsection, we introduce a procedure to eliminate delay-free loops in digital circuits without altering the intended overall transfer functions.

---

[12]Here we use a combination of Figs. 13-12 and 13-7 to perform the realization of (13-28). Note that Fig. 13-15 contains a delay-free loop. Techniques to transform a circuit with delay-free loops into one without is presented in the following subsection.

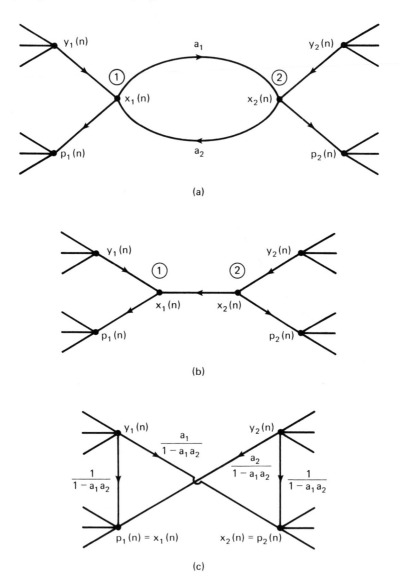

Fig. 13-16 Elimination of a two-node delay-free loop. (a) Original circuit. (b) Simplified circuit when $y_1(n) = y_2(n) = 0$ and $a_1 a_2 = 1$. (c) An equivalent circuit with the delay-free loop eliminated.

Consider first the partial circuit shown in Fig. 13-16(a), where the delay-free loop consists of two branches connecting between nodes 1 and 2. The equations describing this portion of the circuit are

$$x_1(n) = a_2 x_2(n) + y_1(n) \tag{13-32a}$$

$$x_2(n) = a_1 x_1(n) + y_2(n) \qquad \text{(13-32b)}$$

$$p_1(n) = x_1(n) \qquad \text{(13-32c)}$$

$$p_2(n) = x_2(n) \qquad \text{(13-32d)}$$

where $y_1(n)$ and $y_2(n)$, respectively, represent the aggregates of all signals going into nodes 1 and 2, and $p_1(n)$ and $p_2(n)$, respectively, represent the aggregates of signals going out of nodes 1 and 2. Solving the first two equations in (13-32), we obtain

$$x_1(n) = \frac{1}{1 - a_1 a_2} y_1(n) + \frac{a^2}{1 - a_1 a_2} y_2(n) \qquad \text{(13-33a)}$$

$$x_2(n) = \frac{a_1}{1 - a_1 a_2} y_1(n) + \frac{1}{1 - a_1 a_2} y_2(n) \qquad \text{(13-33b)}$$

If there is no signal going into nodes 1 and 2, then $y_1(n) = y_2(n) = 0$. In this case, if $a_1 a_2 \neq 1$, then (13-32) implies that $x_1(n) = x_2(n) = p_1(n) = p_2(n) = 0$. Thus, we can eliminate the partial circuit in Fig. 13-16(a) completely without altering the overall transfer function. If, when $y_1(n) = y_2(n) = 0$, we have $a_1 a_2 = 1$, then there are many solutions to (13-33). In the absence of better criteria, we can simply let $x_1(n) = x_2(n)$, and the circuit in Fig. 13-16(a) reduces to the one shown in Fig. 13-16(b).

Assume now that $y_1(n)$ and $y_2(n)$ are not simultaneously zero. That is, there is at least one nonzero signal going into either node 1 or node 2. If $a_1 a_2 = 1$, the original circuit is not proper, and there is no way to improve it without altering the intended transfer function. If $a_1 a_2 \neq 1$, then (13-33) yields proper results with

$$p_1(n) = \frac{1}{1 - a_1 a_2} y_1(n) + \frac{a_2}{1 - a_1 a_2} y_2(n) \qquad \text{(13-34a)}$$

$$p_2(n) = \frac{a_1}{1 - a_1 a_2} y_1(n) + \frac{1}{1 - a_1 a_2} y_2(n) \qquad \text{(13-34b)}$$

That is, we can eliminate nodes 1 and 2 completely. The resulting circuit is shown in Fig. 13-16(c). Notice that the delay-free loop of Fig. 13-16(a) is eliminated. Observe also that the overall transfer function remains unchanged because (13-34) is derived directly from (13-32).

For delay-free loops involving more than two nodes, a simple strategy is to reduce a k-node delay-free loop to a $(k - 1)$-node delay-free loop. By repeating this node reduction procedure a sufficient number of times, we arrive at the case where the delay-free loop involves two nodes only. Hence, the procedure illustrated in Fig. 13-16 can be applied to eliminate the delay-free loop completely. For the remainder of this subsection, we present a procedure to eliminate a node from a delay-free loop involving more than two nodes.

Consider the partial circuit shown in Fig. 13-17(a), where nodes 1, 2, 3, and 4 form a delay-free loop. Except for the signals within the delay-free loop, y_i and p_i, respectively, represent the aggregate signals going into and out of node i, where $i = 1, 2, 3$, and 4. The equations describing the circuit are

$$x_1(n) = a_4 x_4(n) + y_1(n) \tag{13-35}$$

$$x_i(n) = a_{i-1} x_{i-1}(n) + y_i(n) \quad \text{for } i = 2, 3, 4 \tag{13-36a}$$

$$p_k(n) = x_k(n) \quad \text{for } k = 1, 2, 3, 4 \tag{13-36b}$$

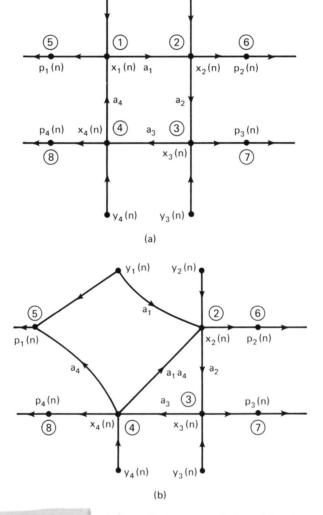

(a)

(b)

Fig. 13-17 Procedure to eliminate a node in a delay-free loop. (a) The original circuit with a four-node delay-free loop. (b) An equivalent circuit with a three-node delay-free loop.

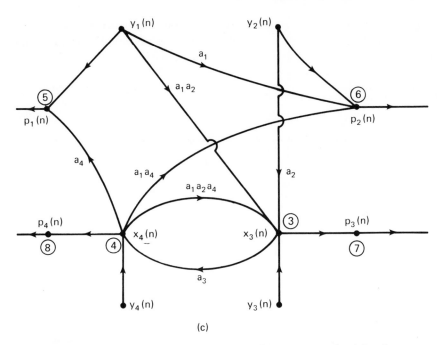

(c)

Fig. 13-17 (c) An equivalent circuit with a two-node delay-free loop.

By substituting (13-35) into (13-36), we obtain

$$x_2(n) = a_1a_4x_4(n) + a_1y_1(n) + y_2(n) \qquad (13\text{-}37a)$$

$$x_3(n) = a_2x_2(n) + y_3(n) \qquad (13\text{-}37b)$$

$$x_4(n) = a_3x_3(n) + y_4(n) \qquad (13\text{-}37c)$$

$$p_1(n) = a_4x_4(n) + y_1(n) \qquad (13\text{-}37d)$$

$$p_k(n) = x_k(n) \quad \text{for } k = 2, 3, 4 \qquad (13\text{-}37e)$$

A digital circuit implementing (13-37) is shown in Fig. 13-17(b). Observe that the delay-free loop in Fig. 13-17(b) consists of three nodes compared to the 4-node delay-free loop in Fig. 13-17(a).

Carrying this procedure one step further, we write (13-37) as

$$x_3(n) = a_1a_2a_4x_4(n) + a_1a_2y_1(n) + a_2y_2(n) + y_3(n) \qquad (13\text{-}38a)$$

$$x_4(n) = a_3x_3(n) + y_4(n) \qquad (13\text{-}38b)$$

$$p_1(n) = a_4x_4(n) + y_1(n) \qquad (13\text{-}38c)$$

$$p_2(n) = a_1a_4x_4(n) + a_1y_1(n) + y_2(n) \qquad (13\text{-}38d)$$

$$p_3(n) = x_3(n) \qquad (13\text{-}38e)$$

$$p_4(n) = x_4(n) \qquad (13\text{-}38f)$$

The circuit diagram for (13-38) is shown in Fig. 13-17(c). Note that the delay-free loop contains only two nodes now. That is, we can use the technique in

Fig. 13-16 to eliminate the final delay-free loop. Observe that the process of eliminating a node from a delay-free loop does not involve solving a set of simultaneous equations. It merely requires equation substitutions.

Example 13-7 Consider the circuit in Fig. 13-18(a). Find an equivalent circuit without delay-free loops.

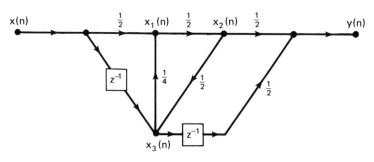

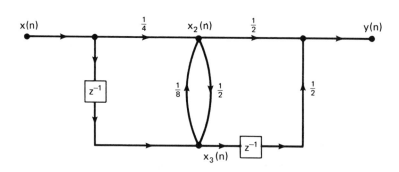

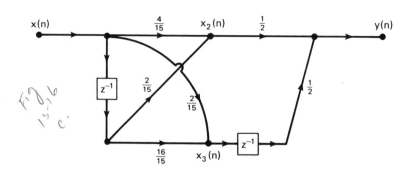

Fig. 13-18 A step-by-step procedure to eliminate a three-node delay-free loop in Example 13-7.

Solution: The equations describing the circuit are

$$x_1(n) = \left(\frac{1}{4}\right)x_3(n) + \left(\frac{1}{2}\right)x(n) \tag{13-39}$$

$$x_2(n) = \left(\frac{1}{2}\right)x_1(n) \tag{13-40a}$$

$$x_3(n) = \left(\frac{1}{2}\right)x_2(n) + x(n-1) \tag{13-40b}$$

$$y(n) = \left(\frac{1}{2}\right)x_2(n) + \left(\frac{1}{2}\right)x_3(n-1) \tag{13-40c}$$

By substituting (13-39) into (13-40), we obtain

$$x_2(n) = \left(\frac{1}{8}\right)x_3(n) + \left(\frac{1}{4}\right)x(n) \tag{13-41a}$$

$$x_3(n) = \left(\frac{1}{2}\right)x_2(n) + x(n-1) \tag{13-41b}$$

$$y(n) = \left(\frac{1}{2}\right)x_2(n) + \left(\frac{1}{2}\right)x_3(n-1) \tag{13-42}$$

Thus, the circuit in Fig. 13-18(a) can be replaced by its equivalent circuit in Fig. 13-18(b). Solving $x_2(n)$ and $x_3(n)$ from (13-41) yields

$$x_2(n) = \left(\frac{4}{15}\right)x(n) + \left(\frac{2}{15}\right)x(n-1) \tag{13-43a}$$

$$x_3(n) = \left(\frac{2}{15}\right)x(n) + \left(\frac{16}{15}\right)x(n-1) \tag{13-43b}$$

The resulting equivalent circuit characterized by (13-42) and (13-43) contains no delay-free loop and is shown in Fig. 13-18(c). ∎

13-1-2. Indirect Realization

To minimize the effect of quantization error or finite word-length effect, digital filters are often realized by interconnecting together first- and second-order sections. In this subsection, we first present some realizations of first- and second-order digital filters, and then we discuss two indirect realization methods.

A first-order digital filter is characterized by a transfer function of the form

$$H_1(z) = \frac{a_0 + a_1 z^{-1}}{1 + b_1 z^{-1}} \tag{13-44}$$

There are many distinct circuit realizations of (13-44). Figure 13-19 shows realizations of (13-44) by direct form I, direct form II, transposed direct form I, transposed direct form II, and two ladder form methods. Observe that every first-order circuit in Fig. 13-19 requires three multipliers, which is the minimum number of multipliers required to realize (13-44).

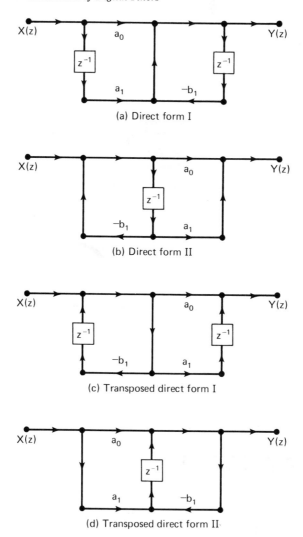

Fig. 13-19   Six first-order digital filter sections.

A general second-order digital filter is characterized by a transfer function in the form of

$$H_2(z) = \frac{a_0 + a_1 z^{-1} + a_2 z^{-2}}{1 + b_1 z^{-1} + b_2 z^{-2}} \tag{13-45}$$

As in the first-order case, there are many realizations of (13-45) including direct forms I and II, transposed direct forms I and II, and ladder forms. Figure 13-20 gives the direct form realizations and their transposed digital circuit realizations of (13-45).

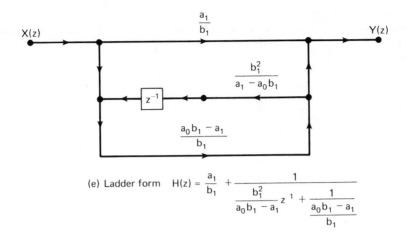

(e) Ladder form $H(z) = \dfrac{a_1}{b_1} + \dfrac{1}{\dfrac{b_1^2}{a_0 b_1 - a_1} z^{-1} + \dfrac{1}{\dfrac{a_0 b_1 - a_1}{b_1}}}$

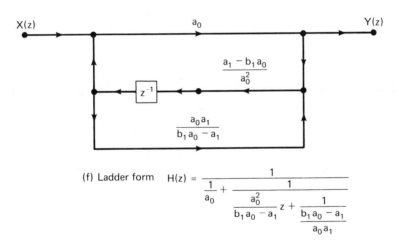

(f) Ladder form $H(z) = \dfrac{1}{\dfrac{1}{a_0} + \dfrac{1}{\dfrac{a_0^2}{b_1 a_0 - a_1} z + \dfrac{1}{\dfrac{b_1 a_0 - a_1}{a_0 a_1}}}}$

Fig. 13-19   (Continued)

With the basic building blocks of first- and second-order digital filter sections on hand, we now proceed to discuss two techniques among the indirect realizations of IIR digital filters of (13-1). In the following, we assume that

$$M \le N \qquad (13\text{-}46)$$

in (13-1). If (13-46) is not the case [i.e., if $M > N$ in (13-1)], then the transfer function is not a proper rational function, and we can write $H(z)$ of (13-1) as

$$H(z) = H_{\text{FIR}}(z) + H_{\text{IIR}}(z) \qquad (13\text{-}47a)$$

where

$$H_{\text{FIR}}(z) = c_0 + c_1 z^{-1} + \ldots + c_{M-N} z^{-(M-N)} \qquad (13\text{-}47b)$$

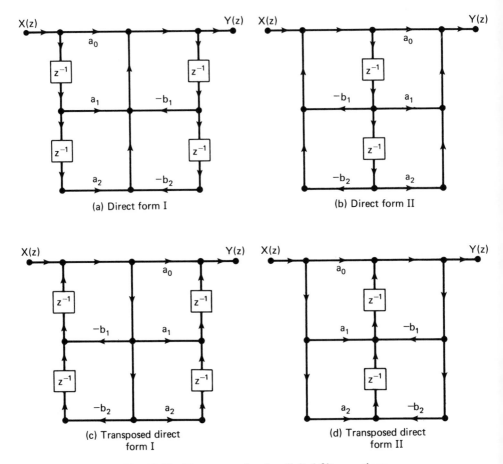

Fig. 13-20 Four second-order digital filter sections.

and

$$H_{\text{IIR}} = \frac{\displaystyle\sum_{i=0}^{N-1} d_i z^{-i}}{1 + \displaystyle\sum_{i=1}^{N} b_i z^{-i}} \qquad (13\text{-}47\text{c})$$

In this case, the realization of the transfer function can be obtained by realizing an FIR digital filter of (13-47b) and an IIR digital filter of (13-47c) and then by connecting these two digital filters together in parallel, as shown in Fig. 13-21. We discuss the realization of FIR digital filters in Sec. 13-2. Hence, it suffices here to consider the problem of realizing IIR digital filters characterized by the transfer function of (13-1) with $M \le N$.

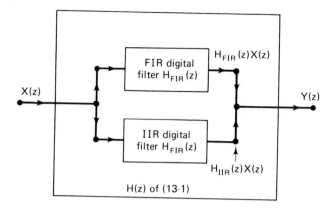

Fig. 13-21 Block diagram for improper digital transfer functions.

13-1-2-1. Cascade Realizations. Given a digital transfer function $H(z)$ of (13-1) with $M \leq N$, we can write $H(z)$ as

$$H(z) = H_1(z)H_2(z) \ldots H_K(z) \tag{13-48}$$

where $H_i(z)$ is either a first-order or second-order digital filter and $i = 1, 2, \ldots, K$. Based on (13-48), we can realize $H(z)$ by first realizing each individual $H_i(z)$ and by then cascading them together, as shown in Fig. 13-22.

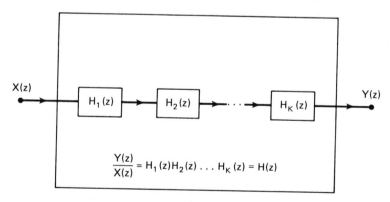

Fig. 13-22 Block diagram for cascade realization of digital filters.

Example 13-8 Realize the transfer function

$$H(z) = \frac{1 + z + z^{-2}}{\left[1 - \left(\frac{1}{4}\right)z^{-1} - \left(\frac{1}{8}\right)z^{-2}\right]\left[1 - \left(\frac{1}{3}\right)z^{-1}\right]\left[1 + \left(\frac{1}{2}\right)z^{-1} + \left(\frac{1}{2}\right)z^{-2}\right]} \tag{13-49}$$

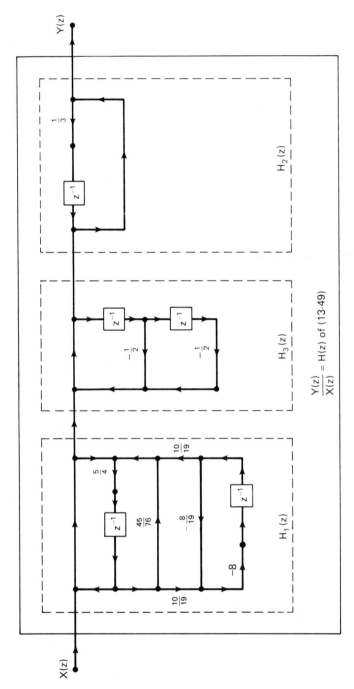

Fig. 13-23 A cascade realization of (13-49).

$$\frac{Y(z)}{X(z)} = H(z) \text{ of (13-49)}$$

612

Solution: We can decompose the overall transfer function into three sections as

$$H(z) = H_1(z)H_2(z)H_3(z) \tag{13-50a}$$

where

$$H_1(z) \triangleq \frac{1 + z + z^{-2}}{1 - \left(\frac{1}{4}\right)z^{-1} - \left(\frac{1}{8}\right)z^{-2}}$$

$$H_2(z) = \frac{1}{1 - \left(\frac{1}{3}\right)z^{-1}} \tag{13-50b}$$

$$H_3(z) = \frac{1}{1 + \left(\frac{1}{2}\right)z^{-1} + \left(\frac{1}{2}\right)z^{-2}}$$

By realizing $H_1(z)$, $H_2(z)$, and $H_3(z)$ separately and then cascading them together, we obtain a realization of $H(z)$, as shown in Fig. 13-23, where $H_1(z)$ is realized by Fig. 13-15 as in Example 13-6, $H_2(z)$ is realized by a ladder form (Case 1), and $H_3(z)$ is realized by direct form II. Note that the delay-free loop of $H_1(z)$ in Fig. 13-15 has been eliminated by the technique introduced in Section 13-1-1-3.

■

13-1-2-2. Parallel Realization. Given a digital transfer function $H(z)$ of (13-1) with $M < N$, we can perform a partial fraction expansion of $H(z)$ into the form

$$\begin{aligned}
H(z) &= \sum_{i=1}^{N_1} \frac{A_i}{1 - c_i z^{-1}} + \sum_{i=N_1+1}^{N_2} \frac{B_i - C_i z^{-1}}{(1 - d_i z^{-1})(1 - \bar{d}_i z^{-1})} \\
&= H_1(z) + H_2(z) + \ldots + H_{N_1}(z) + H_{N_1+1}(z) \\
&\quad + \ldots + H_{N_2}(z)
\end{aligned} \tag{13-51}$$

where $\bar{d}_i$ is the complex conjugate of d_i, all c_i, A_i, B_i, and C_i are real, $H_1(z)$, $\ldots, H_{N_1}(z)$ are transfer functions of first-order digital filters, and $H_{N_1+1}(z)$, $\ldots, H_{N_2}(z)$ are transfer functions of second-order digital filters. The interpretation of (13-51) is that a general nth order digital transfer function can be realized by realizing first- and second-order digital transfer functions of $H_1(z), \ldots, H_{N_2}(z)$ and then connecting them in parallel, as shown in Fig. 13-24.

Example 13-9   Realize the transfer function

$$H(z) = \frac{3 + \left(\frac{5}{3}\right)z^{-1} + \left(\frac{2}{3}\right)z^{-2}}{\left[1 - \left(\frac{1}{3}\right)z^{-1}\right]\left[1 + \left(\frac{1}{2}\right)z^{-1} + \left(\frac{1}{2}\right)z^{-2}\right]} \tag{13-52}$$

by the parallel method.

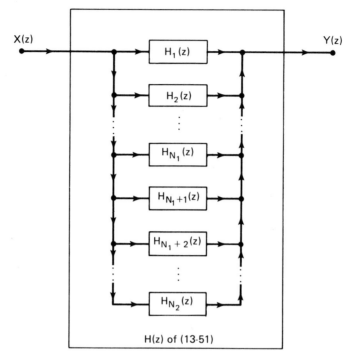

X(z)

Y(z)

$H_1(z)$

$H_2(z)$

$H_{N_1}(z)$

$H_{N_1+1}(z)$

$H_{N_1+2}(z)$

$H_{N_2}(z)$

H(z) of (13-51)

Fig. 13-24   Block diagram for parallel realization of digital filters.

Solution: A partial fraction expansion of $H(z)$ of (13-52) is given by

$$H(z) = \frac{2}{1 - \left(\frac{1}{3}\right)z^{-1}} + \frac{1 + z^{-1}}{1 + \left(\frac{1}{2}\right)z^{-1} + \left(\frac{1}{2}\right)z^{-2}} \qquad (13\text{-}53\text{a})$$

$$\triangleq H_1(z) + H_2(z)$$

where

$$H_1(z) \triangleq \frac{2}{1 - \left(\frac{1}{3}\right)z^{-1}} \qquad (13\text{-}53\text{b})$$

and

$$H_2(z) \triangleq \frac{1 + z^{-1}}{1 + \left(\frac{1}{2}\right)z^{-1} + \left(\frac{1}{2}\right)z^{-2}} \qquad (13\text{-}53\text{c})$$

A realization of $H(z)$ of (13-52) can be obtained by realizing $H_1(z)$ and $H_2(z)$ individually and then by connecting them in parallel, as shown in Fig. 13-25, where $H_1(z)$ is realized by direct form I transposed and $H_2(z)$ is realized by direct form II.   ∎

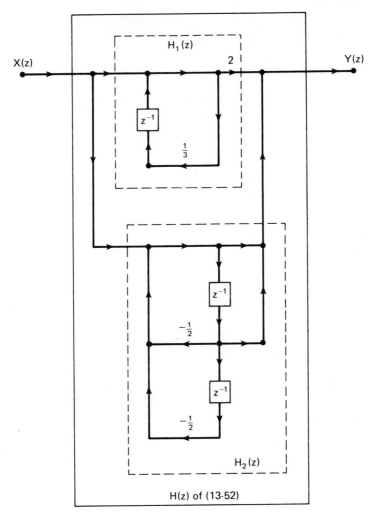

Fig. 13-25   A parallel realization of (13-52).

13-2 REALIZATION OF FIR DIGITAL FILTER

The transfer function of a FIR digital filter is given by

$$H(z) = \sum_{n=0}^{N-1} h(n)z^{-n} \qquad (13\text{-}54)$$

The realization of (13-54) is much simpler than the realization of IIR digital filters. A direct realization of (13-54) is shown in Fig. 13-26(a). Writing (13-54)

$$= \sum_{n=0}^{\frac{N}{2}-1} h(n)z^{-n} + \sum_{n=\frac{N}{2}}^{N-1} h(n)z^{-n}$$

$$= \sum_{n=0}^{\frac{N}{2}-1} h(n)z^{-n} + \sum_{n=0}^{\frac{N}{2}-1} h(N-1-n)z^{-(N-1-n)}$$

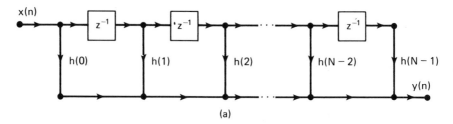

(a)

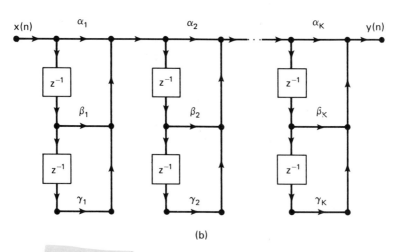

(b)

Fig. 13-26 Realizations of FIR digital filters. (a) Direct approach. (b) Cascade approach.

as a product of first- and second-order polynomials as

$$H(z) = H_1(z)H_2(z) \ldots H_K(z) \qquad (13\text{-}55a)$$

where

$$H_i(z) = \alpha_i + \beta_i z^{-1} + \gamma_i z^{-2} \qquad (13\text{-}55b)$$

an FIR digital filter can be realized in the cascaded form, as shown in Fig. 13-26(b).

In the particular case when the FIR digital filter is a linear phase filter, then[13]

$$h(n) = h(N - 1 - n) \qquad (13\text{-}56)$$

The number of multipliers in Fig. 13-26(a) can be halved as shown in Fig. 13-27(a) when N is even and as in Fig. 13-27(b) when N is odd. Finally, when

---

[13]See (12-135) through (12-137).

when $N =$ even

$$H(z) = \sum_{n=0}^{\frac{N}{2}-1} h(n) \left[z^{-n} + z^{-(N-1-n)} \right] \qquad \boxed{z = e^{j\omega}}$$

$$H(e^{j\omega}) = e^{j\omega \left[-\left(\frac{N-1}{2}\right) \right]} \left\{ \sum_{n=0}^{\frac{N}{2}-1} 2 h(n) \cos \left[\omega \left(n - \frac{N-1}{2} \right) \right] \right\}$$

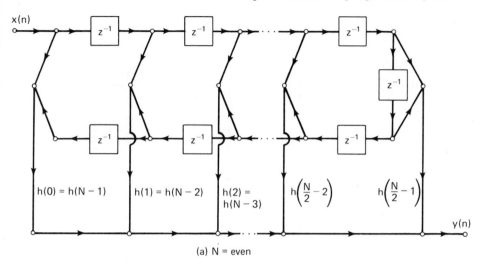

(a) N = even

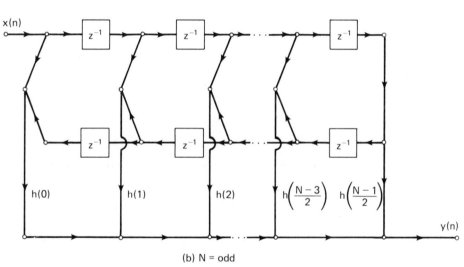

(b) N = odd

Fig. 13-27   Realization of linear phase FIR digital filters.

an FIR digital filter is obtained via the frequency-sampling method, the transfer function is given by[14]

$$H(z) = [1 - z^{-N}] \sum_{k=0}^{N-1} \frac{\tilde{H}(k)/N}{1 - z^{-1} \exp\left[j\dfrac{2\pi k}{N}\right]} \qquad (13\text{-}57)$$

A realization of (13-57) with complex multipliers is shown in Fig. 13-28.

---

[14]See (12-146).

when $N =$ odd

$$H(z) = \sum_{n=0}^{\frac{N-1}{2}-1} h(n)\left\{z^{-n} + z^{-(N-1-n)}\right\} + h\left(\frac{N-1}{2}\right)z^{-\left[\frac{N-1}{2}\right]}$$

$$h(e^{j\omega}) = e^{j\omega\left[\frac{N-1}{2}\right]}\left\{h\left(\frac{N-1}{2}\right) + \sum_{n=0}^{\frac{N-3}{2}} 2h(n)\cos\left\{\omega\left(n - \frac{N-1}{2}\right)\right\}\right\} \qquad \left(z = e^{j\omega}\right)$$

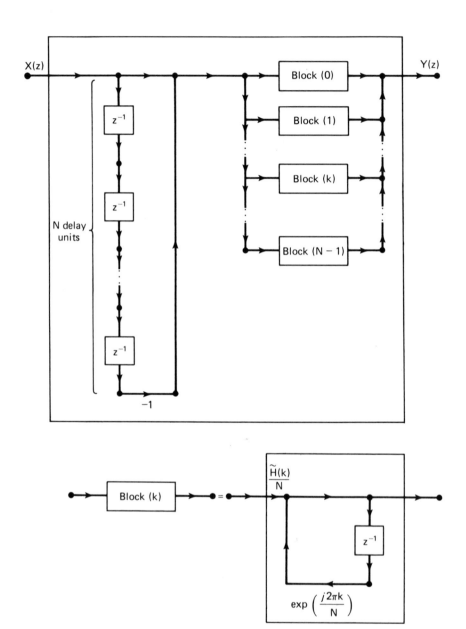

Fig. 13-28 Realization of FIR digital filters by the frequency-sampling technique.

REFERENCES AND FURTHER READING

[1] RABINER, L. R., and RADER, C. M. *Digital Signal Processing.* New York: IEEE Press, 1972.

[2] Digital Signal Processing Committee of IEEE Acoustics, Speech and Signal Processing Society, ed. *Digital Signal Processing II.* New York: IEEE Press, 1975.

[3] OPPENHEIM, A. V., and SCHAFER, R. W. *Digital Signal Processing.* Englewood Cliffs, N.J.: Prentice-Hall, Inc., 1975.

[4] RABINER, L. R., and GOLD, B. *Theory and Application of Digital Signal Processing.* Englewood Cliffs, N.J.: Prentice-Hall, Inc., 1975.

[5] JACKSON, L. B. "An Analysis of Roundoff Noise in Digital Filter." Sc. D. Thesis, Stevens Institute of Technology, 1967.

[6] MITRA, S. K., and SHERWOOD, R. J. "Canonic Realizations of Digital Filters Using Continued Fraction Expansion." *IEEE Trans. Audio Electroacoustics* AU-20 (1972): 185–94.

[7] MITRA, S. K., and SAGAR, A. D. "Additional Canonic Realization of Digital Filters Using the Continued Fraction Expansion." *IEEE Trans. Circuit and Systems* CAS-21 (1974): 135–36.

[8] GRAY, A. H., JR., and MARKEL, J. D. "Digital Lattice and Ladder Filter Synthesis." *IEEE Trans. Audio Electroacoustics* AU-21 (1973): 491–500.

[9] SZCZUPAK, J., and MITRA, S. K. "Digital Filter Realization Using Successive Multiplier-Extraction Approach." *IEEE Trans. Acoustics, Speech and Signal Processing* ASSP-23 (1975): 235–39.

[10] FETTWEIS, A. "Digital Filter Structures Related to Classical Filter Networks." *Arch. Elek. Ubertragung* 25 (1971): 79–89.

[11] SEDLMEYER, A., and FETTWEIS, A. "Digital Filters with True Ladder Configuration." *Intern. J. Circuit Theory Appl.* 1 (1973): 5–10.

[12] PARKER, S. R., and HESS, S. "Canonic Realization of Second Order Digital Filter due to Finite Precision Arithmetics." *IEEE Trans. Circuit Theory* CT-19 (1972): 410–13.

[13] HWANG, S. Y. "Realization of Canonical Digital Networks." *IEEE Trans. Acoustics, Speech, Signal Processing* ASSP-22 (1974): 27–38.

[14] SHIVA, S. G. "A Unified Approach to the Selection of Structures for Digital Filters." *IEEE Intern. Conf. Acoustics, Speech and Signal Processing*, May 9–11, 1977: 601–4.

[15] SZCZUPAK, J., and MITRA, S. K. "Detection, Location, and Removal of Delay-Free Loops in Digital Filter Configurations." *IEEE Trans. Acoustics, Speech and Signal Processing* ASSP-23 (1975): 558–62.

PROBLEMS

13-1. (a) Realize the difference equation

$$y(n) = \left(\frac{3}{4}\right)y(n-1) + \left(\frac{1}{8}\right)y(n-2) = x(n) + \left(\frac{1}{3}\right)x(n-1)$$

by direct forms I and II.

(b) Find the transposes of the circuits in (a).

(c) Show that the circuits in (b) are characterized by the difference equation given in (a).

13-2. Repeat Problem 13-1 for the difference equation

$$y(n) - \left(\frac{1}{2}\right)y(n-1) + \left(\frac{1}{4}\right)y(n-2) - \left(\frac{1}{8}\right)y(n-3) = x(n)$$

13-3. Realize each of the following transfer functions by direct forms I and II and transposed direct forms I and II:

(a) $H(z) = \dfrac{1 + z^{-1}}{1 + 0.5z^{-1} + 0.5z^{-2}}$

(b) $H(z) = \dfrac{1 + z^{-2}}{(1 + 0.5z^{-1})(1 + 0.2z^{-1} + 0.2z^{-2})}$

(c) $H(z) = \dfrac{(1 + z^{-1})(1 + z^{-2})}{(1 + 0.5z^{-1})(1 - 0.5z^{-1} + 0.5z^{-2})}$

(d) $H(z) = \dfrac{1 + z^{-1} - 0.5z^{-2}}{(1 - 0.5z^{-1})(1 + 0.2z^{-1} - 0.2z^{-2})}$

(e) $H(z) = \dfrac{(1 - z^{-1})^2}{1 + 0.1z^{-1} - 0.2z^{-2} + 0.3z^{-3} + 0.4z^{-4}}$

(f) $H(z) = \dfrac{0.1z^{-1} + z^{-3} + 0.9z^{-5}}{1 - 0.2z^{-2} + 0.4z^{-4} + 0.6z^{-6}}$

13-4. Realize each transfer function in Problem 13-3 by four ladder forms (if possible).

13-5. Realize each of the following difference equations by direct forms I and II and transposed direct forms I and II:

(a) $y(n) + \left(\frac{1}{2}\right)y(n-1) - \left(\frac{1}{4}\right)y(n-2) = x(n)$

(b) $y(n) + \left(\frac{1}{2}\right)y(n-1) - \left(\frac{1}{2}\right)y(n-2) + \left(\frac{1}{4}\right)y(n-3)$
$$= x(n) + \left(\frac{1}{3}\right)x(n-1)$$

(c) $y(n) + \left(\frac{1}{2}\right)y(n-1) - \left(\frac{1}{4}\right)y(n-2) + \left(\frac{1}{8}\right)y(n-3)$
$$- \left(\frac{1}{16}\right)y(n-4) = x(n) - \left(\frac{1}{4}\right)x(n-1) + \left(\frac{1}{4}\right)x(n-3)$$

(d) $y(n) + \left(\frac{1}{2}\right)y(n-1) = x(n) + \left(\frac{1}{2}\right)x(n-1) + x(n-4)$

(e) $y(n) - y(n-1) = x(n) - \left(\frac{1}{2}\right)x(n-1) + \left(\frac{1}{4}\right)x(n-2)$

$\qquad - \left(\frac{1}{8}\right)x(n-3)$

(f) $y(n) = \frac{1}{4}[x(n) + x(n-1) + x(n-2) + x(n-3)]$

13-6. Realize each difference equation in Problem 13-5 by four ladder forms (if possible).

13-7. Suppose that some realization procedures yield the digital circuits with delay-free loops, as shown in Fig. P13-7. For each circuit in Fig. P13-7,

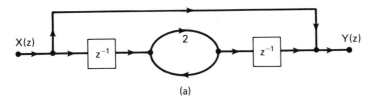

(a)

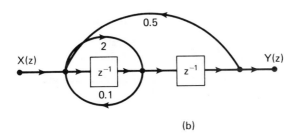

(b)

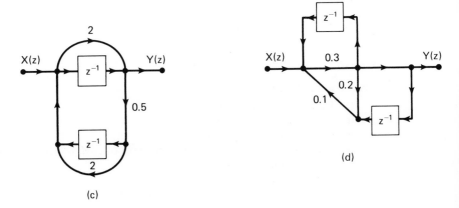

(c)

(d)

Fig. P13-7(a), (b), (c), (d)

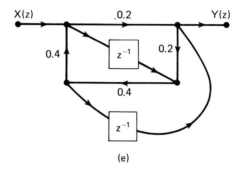

(e)

Fig. P13-7(e)

find an equivalent circuit (having the same overall transfer function) containing no delay-free loops.

13-8. Let

$$H_1(z) = \frac{1 + z^{-1}}{1 + z^{-1} + 0.5z^{-2}}$$

$$H_2(z) = \frac{1 - z^{-2}}{1 - 1.2z^{-1} + 0.5z^{-2}}$$

$$H_3(z) = \frac{1 - 2z^{-1} + 2z^{-2}}{1 + 0.5z^{-1} + 0.25z^{-2}}$$

Realize the following transfer functions by the cascade form:
(a) $H(z) = H_1(z)H_2(z)$
(b) $H(z) = H_1(z)H_3(z)$
(c) $H(z) = H_2(z)H_3(z)$
(d) $H(z) = H_1(z)H_2(z)H_3(z)$
(e) $H(z) = H_1(z) + H_2(z)$
(f) $H(z) = H_1(z) + H_3(z)$
(g) $H(z) = H_2(z) + H_3(z)$
(h) $H(z) = H_1(z) + H_2(z) + H_3(z)$

13-9. Realize the transfer functions in Problem 13-8 by the parallel form.

13-10. Consider the circuit in Fig. P13-10.
(a) Find the overall transfer function $H(z)$.
(b) If $H_B(z) = k_B$ and $H_A(z) = z^{-1}/(1 + 0.95z^{-2})$, find the overall transfer function $H(z)$.
(c) Based on the result of (b), find the range of values for k_B such that the overall circuit is stable.
(d) Repeat (b) and (c) if

$$H_A(z) = \frac{1 + z^{-1}}{1 + z^{-2}}$$

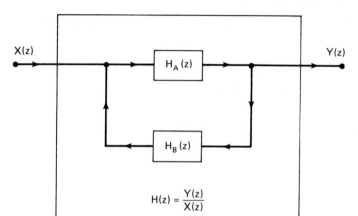

Fig. P13-10

13-11. Realize the following FIR digital filters:

    (a) $h(n) = 1$ for $0 \leq n \leq 4$
             $= 0$ otherwise

    (b) $h(0) = h(4) = 2$
        $h(1) = h(3) = 1$
        $h(2) = 0.5$
        $h(n) = 0$ for $n < 0$ and for $n > 4$

    (c) $h(n) = 2$ for $0 \leq n \leq 5$
             $= 0$ otherwise

    (d) $h(0) = h(5) = 2$
        $h(1) = h(4) = 1$
        $h(2) = h(3) = 0.5$
        $h(n) = 0$ for $n < 0$ and for $n > 5$

    (e) $h(n) = 1$ for $n = 0, 1, 2$
        $h(n) = 1.5$ for $n = 3, 4, 5$
        $h(n) = 2$ for $n = 6, 7, 8$
        $h(n) = 1$ for $n = 9$
        $h(n) = 0$ for $n < 0$ and for $n \geq 10$

    (f) $h(n) = n + 1$ for $n = 0, 1, 2, 3$
             $= 0$ otherwise

    (g) $h(n) = 1$ for $0 \leq n \leq 9$
           $= 0$ otherwise

    (h) $h(n) = n^2$ for $n = 0, 1, 2, 3$
          $= n + 6$ for $4 \leq n \leq 9$
          $= 0$ otherwise

13-12. Realize the transfer functions obtained by the frequency-sampling method in Problem 12-21.

13-13. Realize the transfer function obtained by the frequency-sampling method in Example 12-16.

13-14. Realize the transfer functions obtained by the frequency-sampling method in Problem 12-22.

13-15. Write a computer program to implement the four ladder-form realization methods.

13-16. Let S be a digital filter characterized by the transfer function

$$H(z) = \frac{Y(z)}{X(z)} = \frac{a_0 + a_1 z^{-1} + a_2 z^{-2} + \ldots + a_N z^{-N}}{1 + b_1 z^{-1} + b_2 z^{-2} + \ldots + b_N z^{-N}}$$

(a) Show that S can be described by the following set of first-order difference equations:

$$\begin{bmatrix} x_1(n+1) \\ x_2(n+1) \\ x_3(n+1) \\ \vdots \\ \vdots \\ x_N(n+1) \end{bmatrix} = \begin{bmatrix} -b_1 & -b_2 & -b_3 & \cdots & -b_{N-1} & -b_N \\ 1 & 0 & 0 & \cdots & 0 & 0 \\ 0 & 1 & 0 & \cdots & 0 & 0 \\ \vdots & & & \cdots & & \vdots \\ & & & \cdots & & \\ 0 & 0 & & \cdots & 1 & 0 \end{bmatrix} \begin{bmatrix} x_1(n) \\ x_2(n) \\ x_3(n) \\ \vdots \\ \vdots \\ x_N(n) \end{bmatrix} + \begin{bmatrix} 1 \\ 0 \\ 0 \\ \vdots \\ \vdots \\ 0 \end{bmatrix} x(n)$$

$$y(n) = \begin{bmatrix} c_1 & c_2 & c_3 & \cdots & c_N \end{bmatrix} \begin{bmatrix} x_1(n) \\ x_2(n) \\ x_3(n) \\ \vdots \\ \vdots \\ x_N(n) \end{bmatrix} + a_0 x(n)$$

where $x(n)$ and $y(n)$ are, respectively, the inverse z-transforms of $X(z)$ and $Y(z)$ and

$$c_i = a_i - b_i a_0 \quad \text{for } i = 1, 2, \ldots, N$$

(b) Find a realization of $H(z)$ via the difference equations in (a).
Note: This is called the *state-variable realization* of $H(z)$.

INDEX

INDEX

DHIREN SHAH